SEABIRD POPULATIONS OF BRITAIN AND IRELAND

SEABIRD 2000 STEERING GROUP

Dr Jim Reid	(Chair) Joint Nature Conservation Committee (JNCC)
Dr Ian Mitchell	(Seabird 2000 Co-ordinator) – JNCC
Dr Kate Thompson	JNCC
Tim Dunn	JNCC
Mark Tasker	Seabird Group & JNCC
Dr Sarah Wanless	Seabird Group
Prof. Mike Harris	Seabird Group
Dr Andy Douse	Scottish Natural Heritage (also representing English Nature, Countryside Commission for Wales and the Environment & Heritage Service, Northern Ireland)
Dr Norman Ratcliffe	Royal Society for the Protection of Birds (RSPB)
Julianne Evans	RSPB
Martin Heubeck	Shetland Oil Terminal Environmental Advisory Group
Dr Steve Newton	(Seabird 2000 Co-ordinator – Ireland) – BirdWatch Ireland
Oscar Merne	National Parks & Wildlife Service (Dept. of Environment, Heritage and Local Government)

SEABIRD 2000 PARTNERS

SEABIRD POPULATIONS OF BRITAIN AND IRELAND

RESULTS OF THE SEABIRD 2000

CENSUS (1998–2002)

P. IAN MITCHELL, STEPHEN F. NEWTON,
NORMAN RATCLIFFE & TIMOTHY E. DUNN

DATABASE DEVELOPMENT AND ANALYSIS BY
ANDREW COTTAM

T & A D POYSER
London

Dedicated to the memory of
Ann Waters (1955–2001)
Major Robin Ruttledge (1899–2001)

Published 2004 by Christopher Helm, an imprint of A & C Black Publishers Ltd.,
37 Soho Square, London W1D 3QZ

Copyright © 2004 text by P. Ian Mitchell, Stephen F. Newton, Norman Ratcliffe & Timothy E. Dunn
Copyright © 2004 illustrations by Ian Rendall

Northern Fulmar in flight by Tim Dunn on previous page

ISBN 0-7136-6901-2

A CIP catalogue record for this book is available from the British Library

A & C Black uses paper produced with elemental chlorine-free pulp, harvested from managed sustainable forests.

www.acblack.com

Typeset by J&L Composition, Filey, North Yorkshire

Printed and bound in China by Midas Printing International Ltd on behalf of compass Press Ltd

10 9 8 7 6 5 4 3 2 1

Contents

List of Figures 7
List of Tables 11
Acknowledgements 16

INTRODUCTION 23

CENSUS METHODS 28

DATA PROCESSING AND ANALYSIS 38

NORTHERN FULMAR *Fulmarus glacialis* 49
   Mark L. Tasker

MANX SHEARWATER *Puffinus puffinus* 63
   Stephen F. Newton, Kate Thompson and P. Ian Mitchell

EUROPEAN STORM-PETREL *Hydrobates pelagicus* 81
   P. Ian Mitchell and Stephen F. Newton

LEACH'S STORM-PETREL *Oceanodroma leucorhoa* 101
   P. Ian Mitchell

NORTHERN GANNET *Morus bassanus* 115
   Sarah Wanless and Mike P. Harris

GREAT CORMORANT *Phalacrocorax carbo* 128
   Robin Sellers

EUROPEAN SHAG *Phalacrocorax aristotelis* 146
   Sarah Wanless and Mike P. Harris

ARCTIC SKUA *Stercorarius parasiticus* 160
   Robert W. Furness and Norman Ratcliffe

GREAT SKUA *Stercorarius skua* 173
   Robert W. Furness and Norman Ratcliffe

MEDITERRANEAN GULL *Larus melanocephalus* 187
   Matthew Parsons

BLACK-HEADED GULL *Larus ridibundus* 196
   Timothy E. Dunn

COMMON GULL *Larus canus* 214
   Mark L. Tasker

LESSER BLACK-BACKED GULL *Larus fuscus* 226
   John Calladine

HERRING GULL (*Larus argentatus*) 242
  Brian Madden and Stephen F. Newton

GREAT BLACK-BACKED GULL *Larus marinus* 263
  James B. Reid

BLACK-LEGGED KITTIWAKE *Rissa tridactyla* 277
  Martin Heubeck

SANDWICH TERN *Sterna sandvicensis* 291
  Norman Ratcliffe

ROSEATE TERN *Sterna dougallii* 302
  Stephen F. Newton

COMMON TERN *Sterna hirundo* 315
  Norman Ratcliffe

ARCTIC TERN *Sterna paradisaea* 328
  Norman Ratcliffe

LITTLE TERN *Sterna albifrons* 339
  Georgina Pickerell

COMMON GUILLEMOT *Uria aalge* 350
  Mike P. Harris and Sarah Wanless

RAZORBILL *Alca torda* 364
  Oscar J. Merne and P. Ian Mitchell

BLACK GUILLEMOT *Cepphus grylle* 377
  P. Ian Mitchell

ATLANTIC PUFFIN *Fratercula arctica* 392
  Mike P. Harris

CAUSES OF SEABIRD POPULATION CHANGE 407
  Norman Ratcliffe

INTERNATIONAL IMPORTANCE OF THE SEABIRD POPULATION OF BRITAIN AND IRELAND 438
  James B. Reid

References 442

Appendices
I   Seabird 2000 Census Instructions and Recording Forms 481
II Techniques for estimating the response rates of storm-petrels and Manx Shearwaters to
    tape playback 504
III Common and scientific names of organisms referred to in the text 506
IV Numbers of seabirds breeding in Britain and Ireland in 1998–2002 507

Index 509

List of Figures

Census Methods   Figure 1: Example of Coastal Site Mapping.   35

Data Processing   Figure 1. The location tree in *Recorder 2000*.   39

& Analysis   Figure 2. The observations tree in *Recorder 2000*.   39

Figure 3: Geographical areas within a) Orkney and b) Shetland used to summarise data on maps showing distribution and abundance in each species' chapter.   42

Figure 4 Administrative boundaries used to summarise Seabird 2000 data.   44

Figure 5 Frequency histogram of the number of seabird colonies counted during Seabird 2000 and their distance from the coast (mean high-water mark).   46

Northern Fulmar   Figure 1a. Abundance and distribution of breeding Northern Fulmars in Britain and Ireland 1998–2002.   50

Figure 1b. Abundance and distribution of breeding Northern Fulmars in Orkney and Shetland 1998–2002.   51

Figure 2. Changes in the number of breeding Northern Fulmars (AOS) at major colonies in Britain and Ireland between the SCR Census (1985–88) and Seabird 2000 (1998–2002).   55

Manx Shearwater   Figure 1. Abundance and distribution of breeding Manx Shearwaters in Britain and Ireland 1998–2002.   69

European   Figure 1. Abundance and distribution of breeding European

Storm-petrel   Storm-petrels in Britain and Ireland 1998–2002.   87

Leach's   Figure 1. Abundance and distribution of breeding Leach's

Storm-petrel   Storm-petrels in Britain and Ireland 1999–2001.   106

Figure 2. Relationship between colony size (plotted on a log-scale axis) and proximity of deep oceanic water (1000 m isobath).   112

Northern Gannet   Figure 1. Abundance and distribution of breeding Northern Gannets in Britain and Ireland 1994–95.   118

Figure 2. Changes in the numbers of breeding Northern Gannets (AOS/AON) at all colonies in Britain and Ireland from 1984–85 to 1994–95.   119

Figure 3. Changes in the number of Northern Gannets (AOS/AON) at colonies in Britain and Ireland 1900–2000.   122

Figure 4. The world population of Northern Gannets 1900–99.   126

Great Cormorant   Figure 1. Abundance and distribution of breeding Great Cormorants in Britain and Ireland 1998–2002.   134

Figure 2. Changes in the number of breeding Great Cormorants (AON) at major coastal and inland colonies in Britain and Ireland between the SCR Census (1985–88) and Seabird 2000 (1999–2002).   135

European Shag   Figure 1. Abundance and distribution of breeding European Shags
                       in Britain and Ireland 1998–2002.   150
                       Figure 2. Changes in the number of breeding European Shags
                       (AON) at major colonies in Britain and Ireland between the SCR
                       Census (1985–88) and Seabird 2000 (1998–2002).   151
                       Figure 3. Number of breeding European Shags (AON) at colonies
                       in Britain and Ireland where repeated counts were conducted
                       1967–2002 (data from Seabird Colony Register Database,
                       JNCC/Seabird Group, Aberdeen; J.A.C. Craik pers. comm.).   155
                       Figure 4. Number of breeding European Shags (AON) on the Isle
                       of May 1918–2002.   156

Arctic Skua   Figure 1a. Abundance and distribution of breeding Arctic Skuas
                       (AOT) in Britain and Ireland 1998–2002.   162
                       Figure 1b. Abundance and distribution of breeding Arctic Skuas
                       in Orkney and Shetland 1998–2002.   163
                       Figure 2. Changes in the number of breeding Arctic Skuas (AOT)
                       at all colonies (except in Orkney and Shetland where change is
                       denoted for each count area—see Figure 1b and Tables 1b and 1c
                       for definitions) from 1979–88 to 1998–2002.   167
                       Figure 3. Numbers of breeding Arctic Skuas (AOT or pairs) at
                       colonies where repeated counts have been conducted during
                       1961–2002.   166

Great Skua   Figure 1a. Abundance and distribution of breeding Great Skuas in
                       Britain and Ireland 1998–2002.   178
                       Figure 1b. Abundance and distribution of breeding Great Skuas in
                       Orkney and Shetland 1998–2002.   179
                       Figure 2. Changes in the number of breeding Great Skuas (AOT)
                       at all colonies (except in Orkney and Shetland where change is
                       denoted for each count area—see Figure 1b and Tables 1c and 1c
                       for definitions) from 1979–88 to 1998–2002.   182
                       Figure 3. Numbers of nesting Great Skuas (AOT or pairs) at colonies
                       where repeated counts have been conducted during 1948–2001.   183

Mediterranean   Figure 1. Abundance and distribution of breeding Mediterranean
Gull   Gulls in Britain and Ireland 1999–2002.   190
                       Figure 2. Number of colonies and total number of breeding pairs
                       (AON) of Mediterranean Gull in Britain and Ireland, 1976–2001.   191

Black-headed   Figure 1. Abundance and distribution of breeding Black-headed
Gull   Gulls in Britain and Ireland 1998–2002.   202
                       Figure 2. Comparison of Black-headed Gull breeding occurrence
                       in OS 10-km squares in Britain and Ireland during Seabird 2000
                       (1998–2002) and the New Atlas of Breeding Birds (1989–1991;
                       Gibbons *et al.* 1993).   203
                       Figure 3. Number of Black-headed Gulls (pairs) breeding in coastal
                       and inland colonies in England and Wales during 1938–88.   208

Common Gull   Figure 1. Abundance and distribution of breeding Common Gulls
                       in Britain and Ireland 1998–2002.   218

Figure 2. Comparison of Common Gull breeding occurrence in
OS 10-km squares in Britain and Ireland during Seabird 2000
(1998–2002) and the New Atlas of Breeding Birds (1989–1991;
Gibbons *et al.* 1993).   219

Lesser Black-   Figure 1. Abundance and distribution of breeding Lesser Black-backed
backed Gull   Gulls in Britain and Ireland 1998–2002.   230

Figure 2. Changes in the number of breeding Lesser Black-backed
Gulls (AON) at major colonies in Britain and Ireland between SCR
Census (1985–88) and Seabird 2000 (1998–2002).   231

Herring Gull   Figure 1. Abundance and distribution of breeding Herring Gulls in
Britain and Ireland 1998–2002.   246

Figure 2. Changes in the number of breeding Herring Gulls (AON)
at major colonies in Britain and Ireland between SCR Census
(1985–88) and Seabird 2000 (1998–2002).   247

Figure 3. Numbers of breeding Herring Gulls (AON) at colonies
were repeated counts were conducted during 1970–2002.   253

Great Black-   Figure 1. Abundance and distribution of breeding Great Black-backed
backed Gull   Gulls in Britain and Ireland 1998–2002.   266

Figure 2. Changes in the number of breeding Great Black-backed
Gulls (AON) at major colonies in Britain and Ireland between SCR
Census (1985–88) and Seabird 2000 (1998–2002).   267

Black-legged   Figure 1. Abundance and distribution of breeding Black-legged
Kittiwake   Kittiwakes in Britain and Ireland 1998–2002.   282

Figure 2. Changes in the number of breeding Black-legged
Kittiwakes (AON) at major colonies in Britain and Ireland between
the SCR Census (1985–88) and Seabird 2000 (1999–2002).   283

Sandwich Tern   Figure 1. Abundance and distribution of breeding Sandwich Terns
in Britain and Ireland 1998–2002.   294

Figure 2. Population trends of breeding Sandwich Terns at key
colonies monitored in Britain and Ireland 1969–2001.   296

Roseate Tern   Figure 1. Abundance and distribution of breeding Roseate Terns in
Britain and Ireland 1999–2000.   306

Figure 2. Numbers of breeding Roseate Terns in Britain and Ireland
1969–2003.   308

Figure 3. Numbers of breeding Roseate Terns at colonies where
repeated counts have been conducted during 1969–2003.   308

Common Tern   Figure 1. Abundance and distribution of breeding Common Terns
in Britain and Ireland 1998–2002.   318

Figure 2. Comparison of Common Tern breeding occurrence in
OS 10-km squares in inland central England during Seabird 2000
(1998–2002) and the New Atlas of Breeding Birds (1989–1991;
Gibbons *et al.* 1993).   319

Arctic Tern   Figure 1. Abundance and distribution of breeding Arctic Terns in
Britain and Ireland 1998–2002.   331

Little Tern   Figure 1. Abundance and distribution of breeding Little Terns in
Britain and Ireland 1998–2002.   342

Figure 2. Numbers of breeding Little Terns in Great Britain and
Ireland 1969–1998.   344

Figure 3 The proportion of the population of Little Terns in Britain
and Ireland nesting in colonies of varying size during the SCR Census
(1988–85) and Seabird 2000 (1998–2002)   346

**Common
Guillemot**   Figure 1. Abundance and distribution of Common Guillemots in
Britain and Ireland 1998–2002.   354

Figure 2. Changes in the number of Common Guillemot (individual
adults) at major sites in Britain and Ireland between SCR census
(1985–88) and Seabird 2000 (1998–2002).   355

Figure 3. The relationship between the average annual proportional
change in numbers (1985–88 to 1999–2002) and colony size in
1985–88 (individual birds, log-scale) at 51 Common Guillemot
colonies.   357

Figure 4. Numbers of Common Guillemots at colonies in Britain
and Ireland where repeated counts have been conducted during
1968–2002 (Data from Seabird Colony Register Database.
JNCC/Seabird Group, Aberdeen).   358

Razorbill   Figure 1. Abundance and distribution of Razorbills in Britain and
Ireland 1998–2002.   370

Figure 2. Changes in the number of individual Razorbills at major
sites in Britain and Ireland between the SCR census (1985–88) and
Seabird 2000 (1998–2002).   371

Figure 3. Numbers of Razorbills at colonies in Britain and Ireland
where repeated counts have been conducted during 1963–2002
(Data from Seabird Colony Register Database. JNCC/Seabird Group,
Aberdeen).   372

Black Guillemot Figure 1. Abundance and distribution of pre-breeding Black
Guillemots in Britain and Ireland 1998–2003.   382

Figure 2. Changes in the number of adult Black Guillemots
(pre-breeding counts) in Britain and Northern Ireland between
the SCR Census (1982–91) and Seabird 2000 (1998–2003).   383

Atlantic Puffin Figure 1. Abundance and distribution of breeding Atlantic Puffins in
Britain and Ireland 1998–2002.   398

Figure 2. Changes in the number of Atlantic Puffins at colonies where
the same count units were used in the SCR Census and Seabird 2000.   399

Figure 3. Numbers of Atlantic Puffins (AOB) in east Britain,
1969–2000.   401

Figure 4. Estimated number of Atlantic Puffins (AOB) on Dun,
St Kilda derived from complete censuses in 1975 and 1999 and from
measurements of burrow density in fixed monitoring plots between
1976 and 1990.   401

Figure 5. Breeding success of Atlantic Puffin and Black-legged
Kittiwake on Fair Isle 1987–2002.   402

List of Tables

Census Methods Table 1: Summary of prescribed counting periods and units, used to assess count quality. — 34

Data Processing & Analysis Table 1: Administrative boundaries used to summarise Seabird 2000 data. — 41

Table 2: The criteria applied to SCR Census data (1985–88) to select a single count for each species at each site (from Lloyd *et al.* 1991). — 43

Table 3. Rounding convention applied to breeding population size estimates. — 48

Northern Fulmar Table 1. Numbers of breeding Northern Fulmars (AOS) in Britain and Ireland 1969–2002. — 53

Table 2. Changes in the number of breeding Northern Fulmars (AOS) at major colonies in Britain and Ireland between the SCR Census (1985–88) and Seabird 2000 (1998–2002). — 56

Table 3. International context. — 62

Manx Shearwater Table 1. Response rates to tape playback of male calls by Manx Shearwaters. — 66

Table 2. Numbers of Manx Shearwaters (AOS) at colonies in Britain and Ireland (1998–2002) compared to previous evidence of breeding given by Cramp *et al.* (1974) and Lloyd *et al.* (1991). — 70

Table 3. Numbers of breeding Manx Shearwaters (AOS) in Britain and Ireland 1999–2002. — 73

Table 4. International context. — 80

European Storm-petrel Table 1. Response rates to tape playback of purr calls by European Storm-petrels. — 85

Table 2. Numbers of European Storm-petrels (AOS) at colonies in Britain and Ireland (1999–2002) compared to previous evidence of breeding given by Cramp *et al.* (1974) and Lloyd *et al.* (1991). — 88

Table 3. Numbers of breeding European Storm-petrels (AOS) in Britain and Ireland 1999–2002. — 93

Table 4. International context. — 100

Leach's Storm-petrel Table 1. Response rates to tape playback of male chatter call by Leach's Storm-petrel. — 103

Table 2. Numbers of Leach's Storm-petrels (AOS) at colonies in Britain and Ireland (1999–2002) compared to previous evidence of breeding given by Cramp *et al.* (1974) and Lloyd *et al.* (1991). — 105

Table 3. Number of predators present (breeding pairs) at colonies of Leach's Storm-petrels. — 110

Table 4. International context. — 114

Northern Gannet	Table 1. Numbers of breeding Northern Gannets (AOS/AON) in Britain and Ireland 1968–2000.	121
	Table 2. International context.	127
Great Cormorant	Table 1. Numbers of breeding Great Cormorants (AON) in Britain and Ireland 1969–2002.	132
	Table 2. Changes in the number of breeding Great Cormorants (AON) at major coastal and inland colonies in Britain and Ireland between the SCR Census (1985–88) and Seabird 2000 (1999–2002).	136
	Table 3. International context.	144
European shag	Table 1. Numbers of breeding European Shags (AON) in Britain and Ireland 1969–2002.	152
	Table 2. Changes in the number of breeding European Shags (AON) at major colonies in Britain and Ireland between the SCR Census (1985–88) and Seabird 2000 (1999–2002).	154
	Table 3. International context.	159
Arctic Skua	Table 1a. Numbers of breeding Arctic Skuas (AOT) in Scotland 1969–2002.	164
	Table 1b. Numbers of breeding Arctic Skuas (AOT) in Orkney in 1982, 1992 and Seabird 2000 (1998–2002).	165
	Table 1c. Numbers of breeding Arctic Skuas (AOT) in Shetland in 1985–86, 1992 and Seabird 2000 (1998–2002).	166
	Table 2. Changes in the number of breeding Arctic Skuas (AOT) at major colonies or areas from 1969 to 2002.	168
	Table 3. International context.	172
Great Skua	Table 1a. Numbers of breeding Great Skuas (AOT) in Scotland and Ireland 1969–2002.	176
	Table 1b. Numbers of breeding Great Skuas (AOT) in Orkney in 1982, 1992 and Seabird 2000 (1998–2002).	177
	Table 1c. Numbers of breeding Great Skuas (AOT) in Shetland in 1985–86, 1992 and Seabird 2000 (1998–2002).	177
	Table 2. Changes in the number of breeding Great Skuas (AOT) at major colonies or areas from 1969 to 2002.	180
	Table 3. International context.	186
Mediterranean Gull	Table 1. Numbers of breeding Mediterranean Gulls (AON) in Britain and Ireland 1969–2002.	191
	Table 2. International context.	194
Black-headed Gull	Table 1a. Numbers of coastal-breeding Black-headed Gulls (AON) in Britain and Ireland 1969–2002.	200
	Table 1b. Numbers of inland and coastal-breeding Black-headed Gulls (AON) in Britain and Ireland 1985–2002.	204
	Table 2. Changes in the number of breeding Black-headed Gulls (AON) at major coastal and inland colonies in Britain and Ireland between the SCR Census (1985–88) and Seabird 2000 (1998–2002).	207

Table 3. Comparison of Black-headed Gull breeding occurrence within OS 10-km squares during Seabird 2000 (1998–2002) and the Atlas surveys in 1968–71 (Sharrock, 1976) and 1988–91 (Gibbons *et al.*, 1993). 208

Table 4. International context. 213

Common Gull Table 1. Numbers of coastal-breeding Common Gulls (AON) in Britain and Ireland 1969–2002. 220

Table 2. Numbers of roof-nesting Common Gulls (AON) in Scotland 1976–2002. 222

Table 3. Comparison of Common Gull breeding occurrence within OS 10-km squares during Seabird 2000 (1998–2002) and the Atlas surveys in 1968–71 (Sharrock, 1976) and 1988–91 (Gibbons *et al.*, 1993). 222

Table 4. International context. 225

Lesser Black-backed Gull Table 1. Numbers of coastal-breeding Lesser Black-backed Gulls (AON) in Britain and Ireland 1969–2002. 232

Table 2. Changes in the number of breeding Lesser Black-backed Gulls (AON) at major colonies in Britain and Ireland between the SCR Census (1985–88) and Seabird 2000 (1998–2002). 234

Table 3. Numbers of roof-nesting Lesser Black-backed Gulls (AON) in Britain and Ireland 1976–2002. 236

Table 4. International context. 241

Herring Gull Table 1. Numbers of coastal-breeding Herring Gulls (AON) in Britain and Ireland 1969–2002. 244

Table 2. Changes in the number of breeding Herring Gulls (AON) at major colonies in Britain and Ireland between the SCR Census (1985–88) and Seabird 2000 (1998–2002). 249

Table 3. Numbers of roof-nesting Herring Gulls (AON) in Britain and Ireland 1976–2002. 251

Table 4. International context. 262

Great Black-backed Gull Table 1. Numbers of coastal-breeding Great Black-backed Gulls (AON) in Britain and Ireland 1969–2002. 268

Table 2. Changes in the number of breeding Great Black-backed Gulls (AON) at major colonies in Britain and Ireland between the SCR Census (1985–88) and Seabird 2000 (1998–2002). 270

Table 3. Numbers of roof-nesting Great Black-backed Gulls (AON) in Britain 1976–2002. 271

Table 4. International context. 276

Black-legged Kittiwake Table 1. Numbers of breeding Black-legged Kittiwakes (AON) in Britain and Ireland 1969–2002. 280

Table 2. Changes in the number of breeding Black-legged Kittiwakes (AON) at major colonies in Britain and Ireland between the SCR Census (1985–88) and Seabird 2000 (1998–2002). 284

	Table 3. Comparison of regional trends in numbers of Kittiwakes estimated from monitoring plots at sample colonies in the Seabird Monitoring Programme (SMP) (Mavor *et al.*, 2002, 2003) and from changes in total counts between the SCR Census (1985–88) and Seabird 2000 (1998–2002).	284
	Table 4. International context.	289
Sandwich Tern	Table 1. Numbers of breeding Sandwich Terns (AON) in Britain and Ireland 1969–2002.	295
	Table 2. International context.	300
Roseate Tern	Table 1. Numbers of breeding Roseate Terns (AON) in Britain and Ireland 1969–2000.	305
	Table 2. International context.	313
Common Tern	Table 1. Numbers of breeding Common Terns (AON) in Britain and Ireland 1969–2002.	321
	Table 2. International context.	327
Arctic Tern	Table 1. Numbers of breeding Arctic Terns (AON) in Britain and Ireland 1969–2002.	332
	Table 2. Population status of Arctic Terns in the Northern Isles in 1980, 1989, 1994 and 2000	334
	Table 3. Productivity of Arctic Terns at a sample of colonies throughout Shetland and Orkney between 1990 and 1999.	336
	Table 4. International context.	338
Little Tern	Table 1. Numbers of breeding Little Terns (AON) in Britain and Ireland 1969–2002.	343
	Table 2. International context.	349
Common Guillemot	Table 1. Numbers of individual Common Guillemots in Britain and Ireland 1969–2002.	353
	Table 2. Changes in the number of individual Common Guillemots at major sites in Britain and Ireland between the SCR Census (1985–88) and Seabird 2000 (1998–2002).	356
	Table 3. International context.	363
Razorbill	Table 1. Numbers of individual Razorbills in Britain and Ireland 1969–2002.	368
	Table 2. Changes in the number of individual razorbills at major colonies in Britain and Ireland between the SCR Census (1985–88) and Seabird 2000 (1998–2002).	369
	Table 3. International context.	376
Black Guillemot	Table 1. Numbers of individual pre-breeding Black Guillemots in Britain and Ireland 1982–2003.	380
	Table 2. Numbers of individual pre-breeding Black Guillemots in Orkney and Shetland 1982–2002.	384
	Table 3. Numbers of individual Black Guillemots nesting in man-made structures 1983–2001.	385
	Table 4. International context.	391

Atlantic Puffin   Table 1. Numbers of breeding Atlantic Puffins (AOB) in Britain
                            and Ireland 1969–2002.   396
                            Table 2. Changes in the number of breeding Atlantic Puffins in
                            Britain and Ireland at colonies where the same count units were used
                            in the SCR Census (1985–88) and Seabird 2000 (1998–2002).   397
                            Table 3. International context.   406
International   Table 1. Biogeographical importance of breeding seabird populations
Importance   in Britain and Ireland.   439
of the Seabird   Table 2. Global importance of breeding seabird populations in
Population of   Britain and Ireland.   440
Britain and
Ireland

Acknowledgements

The following individuals kindly gave of their time to co-ordinate Seabird 2000 surveys in their region.

Chris Badenoch, Ian Barber, Roger Broad, Tom Cadwallender, Gail Churchill, Martin Cook, Bill Curtis, Mike Dennis, Michael Dryden, Dave Lesley Fairweather, Henry Fairweather, lamb, Simon Ford, Martin Heubeck, Angus Hogg, Geoff Holmes, Jamie Hooper, Stephen Hunter, Hugh Insley, Helene Jessop, Dave Jones, Rodney Key, Alan Leitch, Leigh Lock, Alison MacLennan, David MacLennan, Mike Nicoll, Matthew Parsons, Ken Partridge, David Rees, Peter Robinson, Hywel Roderick, Michael Rooney, Matthew Sennitt, Chris Sharpe, Andrew Stevenson, Steve Sutcliffe, Bob Swann, Fraser Symmonds, Carrie Temple, Derek Thomas, Matthew Tickner, Steve White, Sian Whitehead, Alan Wood, Mick Wright, Ron Youngman, Bernie Zonfrillo.

In the Republic of Ireland Brian Madden, Paul Galvin, Britta Gronewold and Hanjo Steinborn made significant contributions to the survey of Black Guillemots.

The following individuals took part in Seabird 2000 surveys:

John Adair, Sheila Adair, R.G. Adam, George Adams, Ian Addis, Gary Agar, D. Aiton, Peter Akers, John Allcock, Brian Allen, Dave Allen, Nigel Allen, David Allison, Gordon Allison, Peter Almond, Philip Amies, Bobby Anderson, Dave Anderson, D.J. Andrews, S. Anthony, Tim Appleton, Eugene Archer, Mike Archer, John Armitage, Ian Armstrong, M.A. Arnold, Elsie Ashworth, Jim Askins, Nik Aspey, Simon Avery, Chris Badenoch, John Badley, Tim Bagworth, Peter Baillie, Rachel Bain, Gordon Baker, J.A. Baker, Jillian Bale, Stuart Ball, David Ballance, Chris Balling, Simon Bament, R. Bamford, Chris Barfield, Ted Barker, Mike Barnett, Lucy Baron, A. J. Barrett, Jeff Barrett, Kate Barrett, Capt. M. K. Barritt RN, Colin Bartholomew, Christine Barton, Colin Barton, Dave Bateson, Paul Baxter, Chantal Beaudoin, Lynne Beckley, Rachel Beecham, M.V. Bell, Peter Bell, A. J. Bellamy, Stuart Benn, B.T. Bennet, Ian Bennet, Jo Bentley, Dominic Berridge, Simon Berrow, Loyd Berry, Dave Bickerton, Michael J. Bickmore, John Bird, Jason Bishop, Julie Bishop, K. Black, Marcel Blankers, M.A. Blick, Keith Blomerley, Phil Bone, Helen Booker, C.J. Booth, Sharon Bosley, Roy Bottomley, Alistair Boulton, Bruce Bower, Margaret Bower, Jonathon Bowley, Mark Bowyer, Paul Boyer, Jamie Boyle, Gareth Bradbury, S. Bradley, David Bray, B. Bree, Dermot Breen, Tom Bridge, P. Britten, Roger Broad, Keith Brockie, Simon Brogan, Mike Brooke, Colin Brooks, Paul Brooks, Andy Brown, Bob Brown, Davina Brown, Elsa Brown, Graham Brown, Jon Brown, Juan Brown, Mick Brown, Paul Brown, Bill Bruce, Boyd Bryce, K. Buck, John Bufton, Bob Bullock, Ian Bullock, Tim Burkitt, Adam Burrows, Gary Burrows, Colin Burt, D. Burt, Aleissey Burton, Paul Burton, Steve Bury, Simon Busuttil, Simon Butler, D. Butterfield, Trevor Buttle, Ian Buxton, Nigel Buxton, Carl Byrne, David Cabot, C.J. Cadbury, Martin Cade, Muriel Cadwallender, Tom Cadwallender, John Calladine, John Callion, Ed Cameron, Ray Cammack, Lennox Campbell, Phil Cannings, Mike Carrier, Andrew Carter, J. Carter, Sharon Casey, Maurice Cassidy, P. Catchpole, Steve Cawthray, Trish Chadwick, V. Chambers, Phil Charleton, Paul Charlton, Trevor Charlton, John Chester, Kenna Chisholm, David Chown, Gail Churchill, Hugh Clark, John Clark, David Clarke, John Clarke, W. Claydon, J. Clitheron, S. Cochrane, Chris Cockburn, Giles Cockburn, Mike Cockram, Robert Coleman, L. Colley, Bryan Collier, Paul Collin, Peter Collins, Steve Coney,

Martin Cook, Dave Cooke, Dick Coombes, Ronald Coombes, Tom Cooney, Dennis Cooper, Paul Copestake, Charles Copp, Gregg Corbett, John Corbett, P. Corbett, Frédérique Corrignan, Don Cotton, Martin Cotton, J.C. Coulson, Simon Cox, J.C.A. Craik, Stuart Croft, John Ciaran Cronin, Jason Crook, Jill Crosher, Fionbarr Cross, Simon Cross, John Crossby, Olivia Crowe, Kevin Crowley, Heather Croy, Steve Crummay, Janet Crummy, Fergus Crystal, Margery Curtis, Robin Curtis, Tom Curtis, W.F. Curtis, Derek Curtiss, Tom Curwen, Robert Cussen, Adrian Daly, Dave Daly, R. Daly, Tom Dargie, Maurice Davenport, Phil Davey, John Davies, Nicky Davies, A.J. Davis, P.E. Davis, Paul Daw, John C. Day, Anne de Potier, Ben Dean, Tim Dean, Janet Dedman, John Dedman, H. Delany, Brian Demby, Mike Dennis, Jan Densham, Hugh Delaney, P. Derbyshire, John Derwin, Stuart Devonald, J.R. Diamond, Hill Dick, D.E. Dickson, Wendy Dickson, I. Dillon, Tim Dingle, John Doherty, Anita Donaghy, A. Donald, Chris Donald, Sydney Donnell, Jack Donovan, Andy Douse, Pascal Dower, J. Dowrick, C. Drage, M. I. Driff, Michael Dryden, Stephen Duffield, Dave Duggan, Alison Duncan, Alistair Duncan, Keith Duncan, Raymond Duncan, Peter Dunlop, Stephen Dunstan, Maurice Durham, Peter Durnell, Jim Dustow, Andrew Easton, G.R. Ekins, T. Elborn, Norman Elkins, Pete Ellis, S. Ellis, Michael Ellison, Martin Elwell, Ian Enlander, Sarah Eno, Martin Enright, Brian Etheridge, Gwen Evans, Richard Evans, Sarah Evans, Simon Evans, Keith Fairclough, Dave Fairlamb, Jackie Fairweather, David Feast, Redmond Feat, Tony Fentier, Johanne Ferguson, Keith Ferry, James Finch, Suki Finney, Morag Fisher, Paul Fisher, S. Fisher, Andy Fitchett, Greg Fitchett, Martin Flack, Dave Fletcher, Kathy Fletcher, Mark Fletcher, Dave Flumm, Pat Foley, Martyn Ford, Pete Forrest, Simon Foster, Stephen Foster, Jim Fowler, Billy Fox, Derren Fox, Sinead Fox, I. Francis, Tom Francis, Alma C. Fraser, Robert Fraser, Rob Fray, Michael Freeman, Martin Furness, Mary Gade, David Galbraith, David Galloway, Paul Galvin, Sam Gamester, Lin Gander, Michael Gannon, Bill Gardner, Ian Gardner, Neil Gartshore, Joe Gatins, Sydney Gauld, Jim Gear, Sheila Gear, Simon Geary, Mike Gee, Brian Gibbs, Iain Gibson, Jack Gibson, Liz Giddings, Gillian Gilbert, Katie Gillham, Keith Gillon, Peter Giovannini, Tom Gittings, David Glaves, John Glazebrook, E. Glynn, Paul Goddard, Martin Godfrey, Bob Gomes, Catherine Goodenough, Emily Goodrum, Mike Goodwin, Peter Gordon, Ashley Gouch, Fred Gould, Andrew Graham, K. Graham, R. Graham, David Grant, Justin Grant, David Gray, Nick Gray, John Grearson, J. Green, Amy Greenwood, Julian Greenwood, Dan Grierson, David Grieve, Les Grisedale, Adrian Griffin, D.A. Griffiths, Britta Gronewold, Dixon Gunn, Valerie Gunn, Mervyn Guthrie, Liz Gynn, Keith Hague, Gregor Hall, B. Hamill, Liz Hammler, Nick Hamzij, Maurice Hanafin, Debbie Hanlon, Brian Haran, Richard Harbird, Andy Harding, Nigel Harding, Gordon Hardwicke, Andrew Harford, Paddy Harford, Mary Harman, F. Harmer, Ron Harold, Mike Harris, Rob Harris, Mick Hartnett, Paul Harvey, Robin Harvey, Veronica Harvey, E. Harwood, Les Hatton, P. Haworth, Bob Haycock, Simon Hayhow, Susan Haysom, Treleven Haysom, G. Heaney, Vickie Heaney, Clare Heardman, Jacquie Heaton, John Hedson, J. Heeney, Marie Louise Heffernan, Dave Helliar, Mike Helps, Darren Hemsley, D.S. Henderson, C.J. Henty, Martin Heubeck, James Hewitt, R.F Hewitt, Stephen Hewitt, Tim Hextell, Gary Hibberd, John Hillier, Paul Hillis, Katalin Himber, Tim Hodge, Don Hodgers, Mike Hodgson, John Hodson, Angus Hogg, Aisling Holling, Mark Holling, Geoff Holmes, Paul Holmes, Brayton Holt, Norman Holton, Jamie Hooper, David Hope, Ian Hopkins, Robin Hopper, Phillipa Hoskin, Dan Houghton, James How, N. How, Aaron Howe, R.J. Howell, Tom Hubbard, Julian Hudson, E. Humphreys, R. Humpidge, D. Hunnybun, M. Hunnybun, Geoff Hunt, Jackie Hunt, Stephen Hunter, Hugh Insley, Paul Irving, Justin Ivory, Digger Jackson, George Jackson, L. James, D. Jardine, Dave Jarvis, Malcolm Jennings, Pete Jennings, John Jerome, Mark Jinnah Hashim, Alan Johnson, Alison Johnson, Andrew Johnson, Ann Johnson, Torquil Johnson-Ferguson, Ben Jones, Dave Jones, Elvet Jones, F.C. Jones, Gillian Jones, Louise Jones, Michael Jones, Roger Jones, Trevor Jones, Vicky Jones, Helen Jowett, Graeme Joynt, John Judge, D. Julian, Kyran Kane, Stuart Keenan, Judit Kelemen, Tom Kelly, Ian Kendall, Rodney W. Key, Angus Keys, James

Kilroy, Brian Kingston, Pete Kinnear, J. Klitaeron, Andy Knight, Rex Knight, Dick Lambert, David Lambie, Rachel Lander, Ivan Lang, David Law, R. Lawie, Jean Lawman, R. Lawman, Jacqui Lawrance, A. Lawrence, Sue Lawrence, Neil Lawton, Stan Laybourne, Helen Laycock, Genevieve Leaper, Jim Lee, Mary Legg, Alan Leitch, Alan J Leitch, Douglas Leith, Kerry Leonard, Colin Leslie, Ian Lewington, Chris Lewis, Neil Lewis, Vicky Lewis, Rob Lidstone-Scott, R Liford, Martin Limbert, Danielle Linton, Ally Little, Brian Little, Kenny Little, Nick Littlewood, Iain Livingstone, Leigh Lock, Mike Lofthouse, Wendy Lofthouse, Alix Lord, Derek Lord, Michael Lord, Bob Lord, John Love, Phil Luffingham, Richard Luxmoore, Mark MacDonald, Alan MacDonnell, Frazer MacFarlane, Dave MacKay, Alan MacKenzie, J.D.H. Mackie, Rob Macklin, Alison MacLennan, David MacLennan, Murray MacLeod, Shirley MacLeod, Fiona MacNab, Brian Madden, Mike Madders, Grahame Madge, Steve Madge, Emer Magee, Congella Maguire, Michael Maher, Tony Mainwood, Colin Mair, Bill Makin, I. MacLean, Rob Malsom, Jake Manson, Sinclair Manson, Brian Maran, Mara Marchesan, Eilean Marsh, Mike Marsh, P.J. Marsh, Tony Martin, J.C. Martin, Jim Martin, Mike Martin, P.J. Martin, S.J. Martin, Alison Matheson, Barry Mathews, R. Matson, Boo Matthews, Ron Matthews, Wendy Mattingley, J. Mattocks, Ben Maughan, Eric Maughan, Roddy Mavor, Frank Mawby, David Mawer, Peter Mayhew, Russell McAndrew, Glenda McBeath, Heather McCallum, Peter McCarron, B. McCarthy, Dave McCormach, Bob McCurley, Larry McDaid, Cormac McDonnell, Patricia McDonnell, L. McDougall, Anthony McElheron, Graham McEwaine, Graham McElwaine, Peter McEwan, Liam McFaul, Anthony McGeehan, A.D. McGill, Seamus McGinty, Jim McGrady, Declan McGrath, Eoin McGreal, Angus McHattie, Clive McKay, Claire McKeever, John McKenzie, Dee McKeown, Anne McKillop, Dermot McLaughlan, Ian McLean, S. McMinn, Callum McNab, Chick McNally, Jim McNally, Claire McSorley, Christy Meehan, Eric Meek, Mick Mellor, Mal Meninga, Oscar Merne, D. Merrie, Alan Miller, Peter Miller, Robbie Miller, Adrian Mills, Gordon Mills, George Milne, Tim Milsom, Phil Milton, Andy Mitchell, Barbara Mitchell, Donald Mitchell, Owen Mitchell, Ronald Mitchell, Pat Monaghan, Helen Moncrieff, Sarah Money, Alastair Moralee, Dom Morgan, Paul Morris, Ronnie Morris, Sean Morris, Paul Morrison, N Morrison, Stephen Morrison, R. Morton, Martin Moss, S. Moyes, Diana Claire Mucklow, G. Mudge, Noreen Mullan, Richard Mundy, John Murphy, Paul Murphy, Alan Murray, Frances Murray, John Murray, Ray Murray, Stuart Murray, Tony Murray, Roger Musgrove, Tony Nagle, Richard Nairn, R. Nason, Miriam Neatherway, Peter Neatherway, Gordon Nelson, Mark Newell, Paul Newman, Stuart Newson, C. Nicholas, Mike Nicoll, Adam Nicolson, John Nisbet, David Norman, Tina Norris, John O' Connell-Davidson, Michael O' Donnell, Steven O'Donoghue, John O' Halloran, Dave O'Hara, Danny O' Keeffe, Barry O' Mahony, Sue O'Brien, Declan O'Donnell, Tim O'Donoghue, Damian Offer, Malcolm Ogilvie, Dave Okill, Mark Oksien, Sally Oldfield, Geoff Oliver, Joe Oliver, Peter Oliver, Eamonn Olley, Brian Orr, C.A. Osbourne, John Osbourne, David O'Sullivan, Michael O'Sullivan (Kerry), Michael O'Sullivan (Cork), Oran O'Sullivan, Heather Page, Dennis Paice, Tony Paintin, Alison Palmer, Mike Palmer, Ian Paradine, Alice Parfitt, Charles Park, Ken Parker, Ian Parkinson, Dave Parrott, Tom Parry, A. J. Parsons, Matt Parsons, S. Parsons, John Partridge, Julia Partridge, Ken Partridge, Pat Partridge, Scott Paterson, Abbie Patterson, David Patterson, Kevin Peace, Mike Peacock, Dave Pearson, Martin Peers, Mike Pennington, A.S. Pepper, Robin Pepper, Jez Perkins, Ken Perry, George Petrie, Andy Phillips, John Phillips, Roy Phillips, Polly Phillpot, Georgina Pickerell, S. Pickering, Sally Pidcock, Sean Pierce, Bryan Pinchen, Steve Piotrowski, Adrian Plant, James Plowman, Robin Plowman, A. Polkey, Claire Pollock, George Polwarth, Paddy Pomeroy, Jim Poole, Anne Porteous, Steven Portugal, Colin Potter, T. Prater, Richard Prentice, David Price, John Price, A. Prior, Rhion Pritchard, Bob Proctor, Gary Pullan, Richard Pulley, Theresa Purcell, Brian Rabbitts, Stan Radcliffe, Stuart Rae, Noel Raftery, E. Rainey, Craig Ralston, Mike Ramage, A.D.K. Ramsay, Eileen Randall, John Randall, Colin Raven, Susan Raven, John Reaney, Peter Reay, Kevin Redgrave, Graham Rebecca, Denise Reed, Joe Reed,

Peter Reed, David Rees, Stuart Reeves, Ailsa Reid, Jim Reid, Robin Reid, J. Ribbands, Dawn Richardson, Mike Richardson, Roger Riddington, Kevin Rideout, Gilbert Rimes, Janet Ritchie, I. A. Roberts, Nick Roberts, Pete Roberts, Rheon Roberts, Rob Robertson, Katy Robinson, Martin Robinson, Peter Robinson, Rob Robinson, Julia Robinson-Dean, Brad Robson, Shaun Robson, Peter Rock, Hywel Roderick, Chris Rollie, Michael Rooney, Julie Roper, Paul Roper, Jim Rose, Anja Rösler, A. Ross, Ben Ross, Nick Rossiter, A. Rothwell, Alison Rothwell, Fiona Rout, S. Rowland, Adam Rowlands, Peter Roworth, Martin Rule, Chris Ruse, David Russell, Norrie Russell, Graeme Ruthven, Colin Ryall, Kevin Rylands, W. Sandison, Bazil Sansom, Aron Sapsford, David Saunders, D. J. Scanlan, Donal Scannell, Sabine Schmitt, Debbie Scott, Derek Scott, Harry Scott, Joanna Scott, Malcolm Smith, Rod Scott-Smith, Nigel Scriven, Robert Seaton, C. Self, Andrew Selp, Paul Semmens, Mr & Mrs K. Senior, Ken Seward, Dave Shackleton, Ron Shanks, Joe Shannon, Chris Sharpe, Colin Shaw, Del Shaw, Ken Shaw, Stuart Shaw, Anne Shepherd, Mike Shepherd, Lee Shields, Mark Shorten, Allan Sillence, Dave Simmons, Fraser Simpson, Ken Simpson, M. Simpson, I. Sims, Fiona Sinclair, Kenny Sinclair, A. Skene, C. Slack, Peter Slater, Larry Slattery, Sue Sloggins, Mike Smedley, Pat Smiddy, A. Smith, Andy Smith, D.E. Smith, Gavin Smith, Grahame Smith, Julian Smith, Simon Smith, Stephen Smith, D. Sowter, Karen Carol Sparling, Andrew Speer, Kevin Spindloe, Richard Sprakes, Clair Spray, Stuart Spray, Stephen Srutt, Gareth Stamp, Donald Standing, Steve Stansfield, Hanjo Steinborn, Raymond Stephens, M. Stephenson, Andrew Stevenson, John Stewart, L. Stewart, Julie Stoneman, Uwe Stoneman, Pamela Strachan, Jeff Stratford, Graeme Stringer, Andy Summers, T. Sunderland, Anna Sutcliffe, Steve Sutcliffe, Alison Sutherland, Ian Suttie, B. Sutton, Phil Swainson, A. Swainston, Jonathan Swale, Tony Swandale, R L Swann, Fraser Symonds, R. Tapping, Mark Tasker, Carole Taylor, Colon Taylor, John Taylor, Natalie Taylor, Carrie Temple, Marjory Tharme, D.K. Thomas, Gareth Thomas, Mark Thomas, Graham Thompson, Kate Thompson, R R Thompson, D. A. Thompson, David Thomson, Ian Thomson, J. Thomson, Andy Thorpe, Hugh Thurgate, Matthew Tickner, David Tierney, Alex Tinlin, Barbara Tinlin, David Tipping, Peter Tithecott, Bruna Toldartzu, Bryony Tolhurst, Howard Towll, Simon Travis, Gordon Trenerry, John Trevor, Dave Tripplett, Paul Troake, Paul Trodd, Graham Tucker, Daniel Turner, Chris Tyas, Andy Upton, Ewan Urquhart, Brian Uttley, John Uttley, Denbeigh Vaughan, Pat Vaughan, J. Veal, Richard Vernon, Steve Votier, Bryan Wainwright, Kevin Waite, Mike Wakeman, J. Walder, Dylan Walker, Simon Walker, Ted Walker, Nick Wall, Sean Wall, Eugene Wallace, Chris Walpole, Alyn Walsh, Noel Walsh, Paul Walsh, Michael Walter, John Walton, Sarah Wanless, Jean Ward, Robin Ward, Patrick Warner, Andrew Warwick, Martin Watkins, George Watola, Dave Watson, Ian Watson, Les Watson, Philip Watson, Caroline Watt, David Watt, Hazel Weaver, Andy Webb, J. Webb, G. Webber, P. Webster, Simon Wellock, Chris Wernham, David West, Rob West, Steve Westcott, Janet Whelehan, Graham Whitby, Peter Whitcomb, Anna White, Graham White, Richard White, Steve White, Yvonne White, Jerry Whitman, Peter Whitmarsh, Malcolm Whitmore, D. Whitton, Chris. Whitworth, Craig Whyte, J. Widows, V. Widows, Tom Wigglesworth, Andy Wight, Steve Wignill, Steve Wilkinson, Brian Williams, Colin Williams, E. Williams, Jim Williams, Jacqui Savery, Williams, C. Willis, Steve Willis, Faith Wilson, Jared Wilson, Jim Wilson, John Wilson, Roger Wilson, Ruth Wilson, Tony Wilson, Val Wilson, Steve Wing, Pete Wolstenholme, Alan Wood, Hiliary Wood, Nigel Wood, Bill Woodall, S Woodman, Leon Woodrow, Andrew Wraithmel, D Wright, Mick Wright, Chris Wyeth, Russell Wynn, Barry Yates, Jane Yeomans, A. Young, Juliette Young, Simon Young, Fergus Younger, R.E. Youngman, Bernie Zonfrillo.

In addition to the Seabird 2000 partners, the following organizations took part in Seabird 2000 surveys:

AMEC, Chichester Harbour Conservancy, Clyde Bird Report, Cornwall County Council, Cotswold Water Park Society, Culzean Country Park, Cumbria Wildlife Trust, Durlston Marine

Project/Durlston Country Park, East Scotland Tern Conservation Group, Environmental Services Unit—Jersey, Essex Birdwatching Society, Fair Isle Bird Observatory, Farne Islands: National Trust Wardens, Fife Ranger Service, Fleetwood Museum, Forth Seabird Group, Glenveagh National Park, Highland Council Ranger Service, Highland Ringing Group, Just Ecology, Kent Ornithological Society, Kent Wildlife Trust, Landguard Bird Observatory, Lee Valley Park Ranger Service, Manx Bird Atlas, Mountains to Marine Bird Survey Team, National Parks & Wildlife Service, The National Trust, The National Trust for Scotland, North Cornwall District Council Heritage Coast & Countryside Service, North Ronaldsay Bird Observatory, North Sea Bird Club, Northamptonshire Bird Report, Northumberland and Tyneside Bird Club, Portland Bird Observatory and Field Centre, River Lee Country Park, Royal Air Force Ornithological Society, Rye Harbour Nature Reserve, Scottish Wildlife Trust, Severn Estuary Gull Group, Shetland Biological Records Centre, Shropshire Ornithological Society, Strangford Lough Wildlife Scheme, Sule Skerry Ringing Group, Teesmouth Bird Club, Treshnish Isles Auk Ringing Group, Ulster Wildlife Trust, Ulster Wildlife Trust, Wildlife Trust of South and West Wales.

Data was entered onto the Seabird 2000 database by:
   Tim Dunn, Heather McCallum, Shona MacKenzie, Roddy Mavor, Ian Mitchell, Matt Parsons and Ailsa Reid.

The following provided the editors with invaluable comments on earlier drafts of the various chapters in this book:
   Rob Barrett, Peter Becker, Tim Birkhead, Mike Brooke, Bernard Cadiou, John Calladine, Kees Camphuysen, Tony Diamond, Arend van Dijk, Jim Fowler, Bob Furness, Julian Greenwood, Mike Harris, Guido Keijl, Brian Madden, Peter Meininger, Pat Monaghan, Bill Montevecchi, Tycho Anker-Nilssen, Ian Nisbet, Richard Phillips, Jim Reid, Dave Shealer, Arie Spaans, Iain Stenhouse, Eric Stienen, Alberto Velando, Chris Wernham.

The authors and editors would also like to thank the following for providing data and information included in the species' chapters:
   Yuri Artukhin, Rob Barrett, Peter Becker, Bernard Cadiou, John Cortes, Gilles Chapdelaine, Clive Craik, Volker Dierschke, La Societe Gurnesiaise, Fair Isle Bird Observatory, Mauro Fasola, Bob Furness, Stefan Garthe, Maria Gavrilo, Steve Geelhoed, Isabel Guyot, Martti Hario, Måns Hjernquist, Jens-Kjeld Jensen, Yuri Krasnov, Stephen Kress, Xavier Lambin, Mattias Lif, Peter Lyngs, Tony Martin, Eric Meek, Oscar Merne, Liam McFaul, Alistair Moralee, Paul Morrison, Rab Morton, Stuart Murray, Mike Nicoll, Natalie Nikolaeva, Ian Nisbet, Malcolm Ogilvie, Burgur Olsen, Mark Oksien, Paul O'Neill, Daniel Oro, Ævar Petersen, David Price, Solway Ringing Group, John Ratcliffe, Dave Rees, Greg Robertsen, Sabine Schmitt, Chris Sharpe, Dave Shealer, Simon Smith, John Stewart, Eric Stienen, Henrik Skov, John-Claude Thibault, Tony Tree, Alberto Velando, Charlotte Webbon, Mick Wright, Bernie Zonfrillo.

The publicity for Seabird 2000 in the UK was co-ordinated by the JNCC's Communications Team, namely Trudi Harris, Cherry-Ann Vickery, the late Ann Waters; and the RSPB Public Relations Team and Press Office, namely Amanda Kelsall and Chris Harbard. We are very grateful to Elliot Morley MP for officially launching Seabird 2000 in the UK and to those who assisted during the launches in Scotland and England: George Anderson, Trevor Charlton, Jane Greg, Robert Oates, Jim Reid, Kevin Rideout, Mark Tasker, Malcolm Vincent. The Seabird 2000 Biannual Newsletter was edited by Ian Mitchell, Terressa Chambers, Carole McCormick, Kathleen Rosewarne and Georgina Sawford; and was designed, printed and distributed by RSPB.

In addition to the Seabird 2000 partners, the following organisations provided funding:

Atlantic Frontier Environmental Network (UK Offshore Operators Association), EU INTERREG IIC Atlantic Areas Programme (Project no. 414), Shetland Amenity Trust, Talisman Energy Ltd., The Heritage Council, The Sullom Voe Assoc. Ltd.

The co-ordinators of the UK and Republic of Ireland would like to thank the following for their assistance during Seabird 2000:

all the landowners who allowed Seabird 2000 surveyors to access their land; all the boatmen who enabled surveyors to reach otherwise inaccessible parts of the British Isles, the staff of SERCo. and QinetiQ on St Kilda; The Commissioners of Irish Lights; Catherine Brown, Tom Kirby and Faisal Khan of the INTERREG secretariat; Bob Harris and colleagues on Great Skellig; Padraig Comerford, Professor Richard Conway, Prof. Richard Conway, Roger Curran, Aidan Day, Johnny Fanning, Carl Ford, Bob Goodwin, Charles Haughey, Edward Horgan, Anthony Irwin, Des Lavelle, Liam Lysaght, Feicín Mulkerrin, Sean O'Shea, Paddy O'Sullivan, Grellan Rourke, the late R.F. Ruttledge, Neil Sharkey, Ralph Sheppard, Eoghan Slattery, Denis Strong, Bob Theakston, Norman Tenby, Eoin Walsh, Rev. Barry Wilson, Chris Wilson.

St Kilda (www.TinaNorris.co.uk)

Introduction

This book summarises the results of Seabird 2000, a census of all 25 seabird species that regularly breed in Britain and Ireland. Fieldwork commenced in 1998 and was completed in 2002. The project was a partnership between the Joint Nature Conservation Committee, the UK government's advisor on nature conservation, and other British and Irish government agencies and non-government organisations (NGOs): the Royal Society for the Protection of Birds (RSPB), Scottish Natural Heritage (SNH), English Nature (EN), the Countryside Council for Wales (CCW), the Environment and Heritage Service (EHS, Northern Ireland), the Seabird Group, Shetland Oil Terminal Environmental Advisory Group (SOTEAG), BirdWatch Ireland and National Parks and the National Parks and Wildlife Service (NPWS; Department of Environment, Heritage and Local Government—Republic of Ireland).

Seabird 2000 is the third complete seabird census to be conducted in Britain and Ireland. The first, Operation Seafarer, was conducted in 1969–70 by the then recently formed Seabird Group. More than 1,000 surveyors took part, coordinated by David Saunders and a specially convened Census Committee chaired by James Fisher. Funding for the census came mainly from the Torrey Canyon Appeal Fund, established by the RSPB, the Royal Society for Prevention of Cruelty to Animals and the World Wildlife Fund, following the infamous oil tanker disaster of 1967. The results of Operation Seafarer were summarised in Cramp *et al.* (1974) *The Seabirds of Britain and Ireland*. Operation Seafarer was a major achievement and provided the first comprehensive detailed account of the abundance and distribution of seabirds breeding around the coasts of Britain and Ireland. However, the work also highlighted major problems in accurately counting some species, particularly storm-petrels, Manx Shearwaters, Razorbills, Common Guillemots, Black Guillemots and Atlantic Puffins. Subsequent research addressed some of these problems and by the mid-1980s, the need to update the findings of Operation Seafarer became apparent.

In 1984, the Seabird Group joined forces with the Nature Conservancy Council (NCC, now split into JNCC, EN, CCW and SNH) to establish the Seabird Colony Register, a database that would serve as a single source of information on breeding seabirds in Britain and Ireland. The second census of breeding seabirds in Britain and Ireland was instigated by NCC and the Seabird Group as part of the establishment of the Seabird Colony Register. The census and the database are both known as the Seabird Colony Register or SCR; so to avoid confusion, we refer specifically to the SCR Database and the SCR Census throughout this book. Most fieldwork for the SCR Census was conducted in 1985–88, although some data were collected in previous or subsequent years as part of specialist surveys (e.g. of Black Guillemots, terns and skuas). NCC appointed Claire Lloyd to coordinate the survey work and to collate and analyse data, the results of which are summarised in Lloyd *et al.* (1991) *The Status of Seabirds in Britain and Ireland*. The SCR Census achieved several things. It provided the first assessment of nationwide trends in seabird numbers since Operation Seafarer. By deploying recently developed survey techniques it provided more reliable baseline population estimates for Common Guillemots, Razorbills and Black Guillemots, against which future surveys could be compared. It permitted the national importance of individual colonies to be assessed in both Britain and Ireland, thereby enabling classification of Special Protection Areas. It also served as the foundation for future monitoring of seabird populations. The SCR Database facilitated the collation and dissemination of information on seabird colonies collected not only during the SCR Census (1985–88), but subsequently, as well as from previous surveys including Operation Seafarer (1969–70). The SCR Database is currently held and maintained by JNCC's Seabird Colony Team in Aberdeen.

As well as a database, another legacy of the SCR is the Seabird Monitoring Programme (SMP). This began in 1986 and is coordinated by JNCC's Seabird Colony Team. It involves regular monitoring of various aspects of seabird demography such as population size and breeding success at colonies throughout Britain and Ireland. The SMP relies on contributions from the country conservation agencies and various conservation NGOs, as well as from dedicated, skilled volunteers. Data for colonies in Ireland are collated by JNCC and RSPB, in collaboration with NPWS and BirdWatch Ireland. The most detailed monitoring in the SMP is undertaken at several geographically dispersed 'key sites': the Isle of May (southeast Scotland), Fair Isle (Shetland), Canna (northwest Scotland), and Skomer (west Wales). Long-term monitoring of numbers and breeding success is also undertaken on Shetland, Orkney Mainland, St Kilda (northwest Scotland) and in Grampian (northeast Scotland). Monitoring of breeding success of cliff-nesting species is also encouraged by JNCC at many other colonies, partially by contributing to fieldwork costs of volunteers via the Seabird Group. The results of the SMP are published annually (e.g. Mavor *et al.*, 2003).

In light of the ongoing monitoring of seabird populations, why did we need another seabird census in the form of Seabird 2000? There are several good reasons. 1. Seabird 2000 has updated population estimates of each species of seabird breeding in Britain and Ireland against which national and international importance of individual colonies can be assessed and to ensure appropriate sites are protected under Article 4 of the EU's Directive on the Conservation of Wild Birds (EC/79/409). 2. Seabird 2000 will determine whether population trends recorded by the SMP at smaller scales (e.g. within regions or individual colonies) are representative of the wider population in Britain and Ireland. 3. Seabird 2000 will identify long-term (last 30 years) trends by comparison with the previous two censuses. 4. A comprehensive nationwide census can obtain more accurate population estimates of species such as terns and Great Cormorants that breed at different sites between years. 5. A large-scale project such as Seabird 2000 encourages the provision of resources required to census those species that require labour-intensive survey techniques (e.g. storm-petrels).

The main objective of Seabird 2000 was to obtain an accurate estimate of population sizes and distributions of the 25 species of seabird that regularly breed in Britain and Ireland. This meant: 1) maintaining good or better survey coverage of species well surveyed in the last complete census (e.g. cliff- nesters); and 2) obtaining accurate baseline figures of those species that were poorly surveyed in previous censuses (e.g. storm-petrels).

Ensuring the same survey coverage as during the SCR Census entailed counting over eight million breeding seabirds at 3,300 coastal colonies, distributed along 40,000 km of the British and Irish coastlines. However, increased coverage was achieved by extending the survey to some 900 inland colonies of terns, gulls and Great Cormorants. Obtaining accurate baseline estimates for populations of Leach's and European Storm-petrels and Manx Shearwaters involved visiting about 170 islands at times of the summer when other species were not being censused; most of these are remote and difficult to access.

In May 1998, the Joint Nature Conservation Committee (JNCC) appointed Ian Mitchell as Seabird 2000 Coordinator. He was responsible for the planning and completion of survey work, collation of data and final analysis, and production of this book. The Seabird 2000 coordinator implemented the recommendations of a steering group comprising members affiliated to each of the Seabird 2000 Partners. In the Republic of Ireland, Seabird 2000 was coordinated by Stephen Newton of BirdWatch Ireland.

The coordination of fieldwork in Britain, Northern Ireland, the Channel Islands and the Isle of Man was achieved through a team of 46 regional co-ordinators (see Acknowledgements). Of these, 18 were area staff of the Seabird 2000 partners, SNH, EN, CCW and the RSPB; the remainder were volunteer enthusiasts, often members of the Seabird Group, or County Bird Recorders or Regional Representatives for the British Trust for Ornithology. The role of regional coordinators was to i) recruit surveyors; ii) assign surveyors to colonies within their region; iii) ensure all colonies in the region were surveyed; and iv) issue surveyors with survey instructions, recording forms and guidelines on health and safety. In the Republic of Ireland virtually all fieldwork was centrally coordinated by Stephen Newton with assistance from Oscar Merne of NPWS. The fieldwork was conducted by BirdWatch Ireland volunteers and staff, and NPW Regional Management and Research staff.

More than 1,000 surveyors contributed to Seabird 2000 (see Acknowledgements). Most volunteers were recruited by the regional coordinators and by Ian Mitchell via the media, posters, leaflets and a biannual newsletter. Small grants were awarded to volunteers by the Seabird Group to cover incidental expenses (e.g. petrol, boat hire etc).

Funding to appoint the Seabird Coordinator and Data Handling Assistant to JNCC, and to provide other resources required for the everyday running of the project, were provided by the country conservation agencies and RSPB. These organizations, along with the other Seabird 2000 partners also greatly contributed to the fieldwork, by providing personnel and/or additional funds to contract specialist seabird surveyors. For surveys of more remote parts of Britain and Ireland, specialist teams were required and were funded by additional input from the Atlantic Frontier Environmental Network (UK Offshore Operators Association) EU INTERREG II-C Atlantic Areas Programme (project no. 414), The Heritage Council, Shetland Amenity Trust, The Sullom Voe Association Ltd. and Talisman Energy Ltd.

Seabird 2000 was officially launched on 12 April 1999 by Elliot Morley MP, the then Minister for Fisheries, Food and the Countryside. A press-release at the time promised 'once the survey is complete, the results will be published offering the most comprehensive and accurate picture of seabird conservation status in Britain and Ireland ever available'. This book aims to deliver that promise. It contains 25 species chapters, one for each species of seabird currently breeding in Britain and Ireland. Compared with published summaries of the previous two censuses, there is one additional species account; in the 15 years since the SCR Census, the Mediterranean Gull has become established as a breeding species in both England and Ireland. We have adopted the same species nomenclature as the British Ornithologists' Union (BOU) *British List*. However, in some cases this is at odds with more recent accounts (Clements, 2000; Malling Olsen & Larsson, 2003). For example, the BOU (and this book) does not recognise the speciation of the Yellow-legged Gull *Larus cachinnans*, which is referred to here as one of two subspecies of Herring Gull (*Larus argentatus michahellis* and *L. a. cachinnans*—see Herring Gull chapter).

Within each chapter, the current status of the species is described and compared with that in the previous two censuses and any other relevant surveys. The general presentation and treatment of data within each species chapter is described in the chapter on Data Processing and Analysis. The likely causes of population and distribution changes observed over the last 15–30 years are discussed and the main factors affecting abundance and distribution identified. For each species, the current sizes of the British and Irish populations are placed in their global contexts using the latest population estimates from elsewhere in the species' global range. Following the species accounts, there is a general overview of the main factors causing changes in seabird populations, discussing how external biotic and abiotic factors interact with seabird breeding biology. The final chapter of the book places the breeding seabird population of Britain and Ireland within the context of seabird populations elsewhere in the world, and highlights the most important aspects of Britain and Ireland's breeding seabird assemblage from an international perspective.

Marwick Head, Orkney (Tim Dunn)

Little Skellig (Skellig Michael), Co. Kerry holds Ireland's largest gannetry (Alyn Walsh)

In addition to the results summarised in this book, the information collected during Seabird 2000 will be made available on the worldwide web, (www.jncc.gov.uk/Seabird2000). A customised database has been created to host the data collected for Seabird 2000. This is compatible with the format used in The National Biodiversity Network, a UK government initiative to allow ready access to biological and environmental information by interested users online.

Census methods

DURATION

Most counts were conducted in 1998–2002. The original plan was to complete fieldwork in 2001, but in March 2001, foot and mouth disease broke out in England and soon spread throughout the country and into Wales, southern Scotland, Northern Ireland and Co. Louth, Republic of Ireland. Restrictions aimed at containing the disease and preventing its spread into northern Scotland and most of Ireland severely hindered Seabird 2000 fieldwork in 2001, and many surveys had to be postponed until 2002. Fieldwork in 1998 consisted of a Black Guillemot survey of eastern Ireland (Co. Louth to Co. Waterford), a Black Guillemot survey of Yell Sound (Shetland) and surveys of cliff-nesting seabirds on the Scottish islands of Sule Skerry, Sule Stack (both in Orkney), and Sula Sgeir, North Rona, Mingulay, Berneray and the Flannan Isles (all in the Western Isles). Counts conducted in 2003, of Black Guillemots in northwest Skye and of Atlantic Puffins on the Farne Islands (Northumberland), were also included. In each year counts were conducted between late March and late July, depending on the species (see below).

COVERAGE

Barton (1997) assessed the resources required to undertake a complete census of breeding seabirds in Britain and Ireland. Using data from the SCR Census (1985–88), he identified potential problems and the best strategy to obtain accurate population estimates for all 25 species of seabird breeding in Britain and Ireland. He suggested that strategies be deployed for groups of species with similar survey methodology. For certain species groups (e.g. storm-petrels, inland gulls) and certain geographical areas (northwest Scotland and western Ireland) where complete survey coverage would be difficult to achieve, he suggested sampling strategies that would provide an unbiased estimate of the total population of Britain and Ireland. The sampling strategies involved selecting at random and surveying a certain percentage of either colonies, or 20-km OS grid squares, or both (see Barton, 1997).

Given the various scenarios presented by Barton (1997), the Seabird 2000 Steering Group decided that Seabird 2000 should aim to count all colonies in Britain and Ireland. This presented two major challenges for the coordinators: 1) locating all existing colonies, and 2) ensuring that no major gaps were left. Hence, a sampling strategy based on some of the recommendations of Barton (1997) was prepared (see below) to ensure that any gaps in coverage remaining at the end of the census would not introduce any major bias into the resultant population estimates for Britain and Ireland.

To ensure that all colonies were located, a list of all known colonies was extracted from the Seabird Colony Register (SCR) Database, administered by JNCC. The SCR Database contains records of colonies throughout Britain and Ireland, including the results of the two preceding national censuses (see Introduction). Regional coordinators were sent a list of all colonies extracted from the SCR Database within their region, containing details of the most recent counts of each species at each site.

The list was divided into i) cliff-nesters (i.e. Northern Fulmar, European Shag, Black-legged Kittiwake, Great Black-backed Gull, Common Guillemot, Razorbill and Atlantic Puffin); ii) Great Cormorant; iii) inland/urban-nesting gulls; iv) Manx Shearwater, Leach's Storm-petrel and European Storm-petrel; and v) Black Guillemots. Regional coordinators were asked to provide information on additional sites that may not have been recorded in the SCR Database. They were also asked to survey stretches of coastline either side of the listed coastal colonies in order to take into account the expansion of colonies and the formation of new ones.

COVERAGE OF CLIFF-NESTERS

An aim of Seabird 2000 was to survey all cliff-nesting colonies in Britain and Ireland. To ensure that no major gaps were left, colonies were prioritised in terms of size (cf. Barton, 1997). In 1999, all colonies that contained 5% of the British or Irish population of one or more species were targeted. The remaining colonies of cliff-nesters were then divided into high and low priority, and coordinators were asked to ensure that all high-priority colonies at least were counted. For each species, colonies were listed in order of size. The high-priority colonies were those that contained the top of 95% of the remaining British or Irish population of one or more species, or the top 90% of the British or Irish population of European Shag.

All cliff-nesting colonies in Britain, Northern Ireland, Channel Islands and the Isle of Man were surveyed in Seabird 2000. The coastline of north and northwest Scotland is sparsely populated, remote and difficult to access in places other than by boat. As a result, surveys of this region were incomplete during both Operation Seafarer (1969–70) and the SCR Census (1985–88) (Barton 1997). Seabird 2000 deployed dedicated teams to the region and ensured all the coastline was surveyed between Helmsdale (east Sutherland) and Oban (north Argyll & Bute), including the Isle of Skye. In southwest and western Ireland, long stretches of coast containing low densities of Northern Fulmars, European Shags and gulls were not surveyed during the SCR Census (1985–88), due to a shortage of surveyors. During Seabird 2000 coverage of southwest and western Ireland was much improved, although gaps remained in west Cork and some other areas. Limited time and numbers of surveyors in Ireland also resulted in most Atlantic Puffin colonies not being censused using the preferred method of counting apparently occupied burrows Alternatively, the number of individuals attending colonies during the evening were counted, which offers a much less precise estimate of colony size (see Atlantic Puffin chapter). Details of survey coverage achieved for cliff-nesters are presented in the relevant species' chapters.

COVERAGE OF EUROPEAN AND LEACH'S STORM-PETRELS AND MANX SHEARWATERS

Storm-petrels and Manx Shearwaters nest underground, hidden from view in burrows or in rock cavities, and only appear above ground at colonies during hours of darkness. They nest almost exclusively on islands, most of which are remote, uninhabited and difficult to access. These factors combined make these three species the most difficult to census of all Britain and Ireland's seabirds. As a result, population estimates for Britain and Ireland were wide-ranging, particularly for European and Leach's Storm-petrels, which Lloyd *et al.* (1991) estimated at 70,000–250,000 pairs and 10,000–100,000 pairs respectively. Furthermore, we had only an incomplete understanding of

Surveying a large cliff-nesting colony at Marwick Head, Orkney (Matt Parsons)

Photographs can be used to identify predefined count sections in large cliff-nesting colonies (Matt Parsons)

Using the tape playback technique to survey a colony of European Storm-petrels nesting in stone walls on Inishglora, Co. Mayo (Steve Newton)

A video endoscope can be used to investigate burrows of nocturnal species such as Manx Shearwaters (Tim Dunn)

their distribution. The lack of quantitative information on storm-petrels was due to the absence of a reliable and accurate technique for counting them. However, the RSPB has recently developed such a technique called tape playback (see Ratcliffe *et al.* 1998e). This involves playing tape-recordings of the storm-petrels' calls during the day in suitable nesting habitat in order to elicit calls from adults incubating in nest cavities. Manx Shearwaters were also surveyed using tape playback. At some colonies their burrows are visibly conspicuous and can be counted directly, although tape playback is sometimes invaluable in distinguishing them from burrows of Atlantic Puffins and rabbits.

A major objective of Seabird 2000 was to use tape playback to improve our knowledge of the abundance and distribution of storm-petrels and Manx Shearwaters. This was most definitely achieved (see relevant species' chapters). However, the census of these species required a huge input of time and resources. Chartering boats to access their remote colonies and ensuring high levels of health and safety was expensive. JNCC and BirdWatch Ireland were awarded a grant from the EU INTERREG IIC Programme Atlantic Area (EA-D2IRE- No. 4.14) to survey the most remote colonies situated along the Atlantic Frontier of Scotland and the Republic of Ireland.

Coverage was targeted at islands where there had been previous records of confirmed or suspected breeding in either the SCR Database and in the literature (e.g. Cramp *et al.*, 1974; Lloyd *et al.*, 1991). Coverage was expanded to other nearby islands with suitable habitat, priority being given to those free of mammalian predators (e.g. rats and feral cats).

COVERAGE OF NORTHERN GANNETS

A complete census of Northern Gannets was not undertaken for Seabird 2000. A regular census of all British and Irish colonies takes place every ten years (see Murray & Wanless, 1997), the next being planned for 2004. Hence, in order to make optimal use of the available resources, the Seabird 2000 Steering Group decided to use the results of the last Northern Gannet survey in 1994–95 and afford priority to other species. However, some Northern Gannet colonies were counted during Seabird 2000 (see Northern Gannet chapter).

COVERAGE OF GREAT CORMORANTS

Great Cormorants show a low degree of site faithfulness between years and regional population estimates based on counts from different colonies spread over several years are prone to errors caused by the same birds breeding at different colonies in successive years. To overcome this problem, Seabird 2000 aimed to count all colonies in a single year within as large an area as possible. The extent to which this was achieved is described in the chapter on Great Cormorants.

Seabird 2000 surveyed all colonies in Britain, aided by contributions from the ongoing Cormorant Breeding Colony Survey coordinated by Robin Sellers. Coverage in Ireland was incomplete, particularly on some inland loughs. 'Best-guess' estimates were made for these sites and constituted 17% of the population estimate for Ireland (see Great Cormorant chapter for more details).

COVERAGE OF TERNS

Similar problems arise when censusing terns, as they do when censusing Great Cormorants. In areas where islands and other suitable habitat are plentiful, terns also show low site fidelity and may often move en masse between different colonies from one season to the next. This is such a significant problem that in order to gain an accurate national estimate of tern numbers, a simultaneous census was planned to cover all colonies in Britain within a single year (cf. Barton 1997). Hence, in 2000, the majority of British tern colonies were surveyed, including extensive surveys of Orkney and Shetland, coordinated by the RSPB and SNH. The main exception was in the Western Isles where most tern colonies in Lewis and Harris were surveyed in 1999, whilst those in the southern Sound of Harris to Barra Head were surveyed in 2002. In Ireland it was decided by the Seabird 2000 Steering Group to make the most of limited resources and utilise results from the All Ireland tern survey conducted in 1995 (Hannon *et al.*, 1997). More recent counts (with those from 2000 given priority) were included for some colonies, including all those along the entire east coast.

Colonies of inland terns were targeted using a combination of sources, including previous records held on the SCR Database and by local County Bird Recorders. Any sites that were previously unreported were either missed or reported on an ad hoc basis by surveyors that knew of their existence.

COVERAGE OF INLAND-BREEDING GULLS

Information on the size and location of inland gull colonies in Britain and Ireland held in the SCR Database was neither comprehensive or up to date. Neither Operation Seafarer (1969–70) or the SCR Census (1985–88) surveyed inland seabird colonies and there has been no other comprehensive survey of gulls breeding inland in Britain and Ireland. Prior to the start of Seabird 2000, in 1999, County Bird Recorders throughout Britain were asked to amend lists of inland gull colonies extracted from the SCR Database. The coverage of inland-breeding gulls was prioritised in the same manner used to prioritise coverage of cliff-nesting colonies (see above).

COVERAGE OF BLACK GUILLEMOTS

The optimum time of year to survey Black Guillemots is late March to mid-May, prior to the breeding season when other species are counted (see below). The aim of Seabird 2000 was to repeat the pre-breeding surveys of Black Guillemots conducted in 1982–91 (Lloyd *et al.*, 1991) throughout their range in Britain, Isle of Man and Northern Ireland, and to conduct the first complete pre-breeding survey in the Republic of Ireland. This meant the coastline of the Northern Isles, north and western Scotland and Ireland was surveyed twice; once for Black Guillemots and once for all other cliff-nesting species. Full coverage was achieved in Seabird 2000 apart from minor gaps in southeast Argyll & Bute and in Stewartry (see Black Guillemot chapter).

COUNT METHODS

The counting methods implemented in Seabird 2000 were identical to those outlined in the *Seabird Monitoring Handbook* (Walsh *et al.*, 1995) and to those of Gilbert *et al.* (1998a) for the two species of storm-petrel. A slimmed-down synopsis of the methods detailed in the Handbook was included in the counting instructions provided to all counters (see Appendix I).

ASSESSMENT OF COUNT QUALITY

Table 1 summarises the prescribed seasonal and diurnal timings and units for counting each species. Each species chapter gives an assessment of the overall count quality, i.e. the proportion of counts conducted as follows: 1) at the recommended date and time; 2) at the recommended date, but outside the recommended time period; 3) at the recommended date, but time not given; 4) date not given; and 5) outside the recommended date and time.

Table 1   Summary of prescribed counting periods and units, used to assess count quality.

Species	Time of year	Time of day (BST)	Count Unit
Northern Fulmar	15 May–5 July	09.00–17.30	AOS
Manx Shearwater	late May–early June	Daylight	AOS
European Storm-petrel	July	Daylight	AOS
Leach's Storm-petrel	Late June–early July	Daylight	AOS
Great Cormorant	1 May–25 June	Daylight	AON
European Shag	15 May–25 June	Daylight	AON
Skuas	15 May–15 July	Daylight	AOT
Gulls (*Larus* spp.)	15 May–5 June	(recommended 09.00–16.00 for flush counts of individuals)	AON
Black-legged Kittiwake	26 May–25 June	Daylight	AON
Terns	15 May–5 July	(recommended 08.00–16.00 or preferably 10.00–12.00 for flush counts of individuals)	AON
Common Guillemot and Razorbill	1–21 June	08.00–16.00	Individuals on suitable breeding ledges
Black Guillemot	26 March–15 May	05.00–09.00	Individuals on sea and/or land
Atlantic Puffin	25 April–5 June	Daylight	AOB

AON = Apparently Occupied Nest; AOT = Apparently Occupied Territory; AOS = Apparently Occupied Site, AOB = Apparently Occupied Burrow.

DEFINING SITES

The list of sites provided to regional coordinators at the beginning of the census was based on the definitions given by contributors to the SCR Database, including the previous two national censuses. Over the years, colonies had been counted on the same stretch of coastline by different observers who had divided the coast up quite differently and thus, direct comparisons between different years was

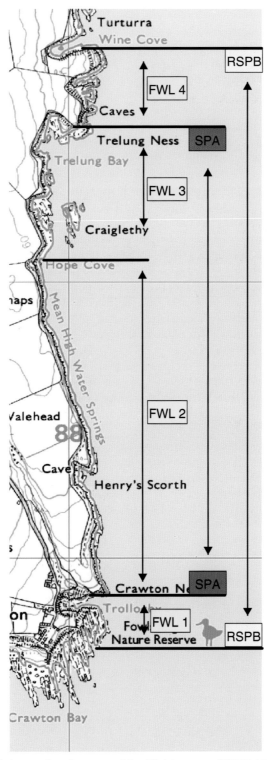

Figure 1   Example of coastal site mapping. Crown copyright. All rights reserved JNCC 100017955 (2004).

often not possible at the scale at which observers had collected the data. In view of this, the Seabird 2000 Steering Group recommended that a priority of Seabird 2000 should be to standardise the division of the coastline of Britain and Ireland, and produce a definitive list of colonies to provide a basis for future censuses and monitoring.

Stretches of coastline were divided into 'sites', which were usually based on previous count sections defined in the SCR Database. In the UK, the National Coordinator provided counters with 1:10,000 scale maps on which the boundaries of each site were clearly marked. Also marked on the maps of sites in the UK were the boundaries of areas designated for protection (e.g. SSSI, LNR and NNRs, SPAs), plus boundaries of independent nature reserves (e.g. RSPB, local Wildlife Trusts etc.) (see Fig. 1). In the Republic of Ireland, 1:50,000 Discovery series maps were used together with six inch to the mile or GIS produced maps that were available for some SPAs.

In coastal areas, surveyors were instructed to divide sites into easily defined count sections or 'sub-sites', around 1 km in length, and to provide separate counts for each sub-site. Surveyors were instructed that no sub-site should cross one of the existing boundaries marked on the field maps (e.g. SPA or RSPB reserve) and each sub-site should be chosen so that a different observer, visiting the area years later, could identify the section exactly, by using the above 1:10,000 or 1:50,000 maps. The aim of this mapping approach was to ensure that counts could be ascribed to a specific area along a stretch of coastline. This will be extremely useful to the end-users of the Seabird 2000 database, e.g. the UK Country Conservation Agencies, who may only be interested in obtaining data for stretches of coastline which fall within legislative boundaries, such as SPAs. Likewise, local Wildlife Trusts may require information relating solely to one of their nature reserves, which may lie within a larger seabird colony.

The six-figure OS grid references of the start and finish point of each sub-site were entered onto sheet A of the recording forms. Inland colonies of gulls, terns and Great Cormorants were defined by a single six-figure grid reference denoting the centre of the colony. A separate set of forms was completed for each site. The information collected on each visit to each sub-site was recorded separately on sheets B and C (see Appendix II).

Black Guillemots tend to occur in small groups, scattered along long stretches of coastline. In view of this, sub-sites of Black Guillemot surveys were defined on OS 1:50,000 or 1:25,000 scale maps. Sections of surveyed coastline were divided into sub-sections of 1 km or less only where Black Guillemots were actually present. Sections of coastline surveyed but not found to contain Black Guillemots were not sub-divided into 1 km-long sub-sites, and a zero count was entered.

RECORDING COUNTS

Surveyors were asked to enter their counts on recording forms (see Appendix I). The forms consisted of three separate sheets. Sheet A recorded information about the site (e.g. site name, six-figure OS grid reference, habitat type). Sheet B recorded information about each visit to the site (i.e. date, time, count method used, weather conditions). Sheet C recorded the counts obtained on each visit to the site (i.e. species name, count, count unit, count accuracy). The structure of the forms was designed to be compatible with the new system of data capture designed for Seabird 2000 (see Data Processing and Analysis).

WEATHER CONDITIONS

All surveyors were instructed to record weather conditions on Seabird 2000 recording forms (see Appendix I). They were instructed to conduct counts, when possible, during optimum weather conditions. Weather conditions can greatly affect the attendance of some cliff-nesting birds at colonies (e.g. Common Guillemots, Razorbills, Black Guillemots, Northern Fulmars), so counts should be conducted within the specified conditions to ensure comparability of counts made in different years and at different colonies. The species chapters give an assessment of the overall quality of weather conditions in which counts were conducted, i.e. the proportion of counts conducted in either 'ideal' and 'poor' weather conditions. Ideal weather conditions were defined as follows: 1) wind speed equal to or less than Beaufort force 4; 2) sea state less than or equal to force 4; 3) good visibility; and 4) either dry, or if rain is light and/or discontinuous.

Surveyors were instructed to avoid flush counts, or any other disturbance of colonies during wet weather, in order to prevent eggs and chicks becoming irreversibly chilled.

OTHER INFORMATION COLLECTED

Surveyors were also asked to record the presence of potential predators of seabirds and give details of the evidence of their presence (e.g. sightings, scats, prints, regurgitated pellets). Predation is an important factor driving changes in population size and distribution of certain seabirds (see chapter on Causes of Seabird Population Change). It is particularly important to determine the presence of mammalian predators introduced on islands that contain ground-nesting seabirds (e.g. Atlantic Puffins, storm-petrels, Manx Shearwaters), since these predators can have devastating effects on such populations.

Habitat classifications as used in the BTO's Breeding Bird Survey (Crick, 1992) were used to define habitat type for each sub-site (see Appendix I). Up to four habitat codes were permitted per sub-site.

DUPLICATE COUNTS

Any analysis that summarises count data at a spatial scale must have only one count for a species at a location. In practice, surveyors may have revisited a sub-site to recount a species if the previous count was not reliable, due to sub-optimal timing, weather conditions or some other factor. Surveyors were instructed to record on sheet B whether or not a count for a particular species on a particular visit should be added to previous counts or replace them.

Figure 1 shows a copy of a 1:10,000 scale map provided to a Seabird 2000 counter for the site 'Fowlsheugh'. Boundaries of the designated Special Protection Area (SPA) and the RSPB reserve are marked on the map. The arrows indicate the separate sub-sites that the counter divided the into and labelled 'Fowlsheugh 1, 2, 3 & 4'. The sub-sections were chosen so that: i) no sub-section is more than 1 km in length; ii) each sub-section is demarcated by a distinct geographical feature; iii) no sub-section crosses the desinated boundaries (i.e. RSPB, SPA) and thus, total counts can be obtained for both the SPA and the RSPB reserve, if counts from the relevant sub-sections are added together.

(Tim Dunn)

Data processing and analysis

DATA ENTRY

Once the completed Seabird 2000 recording forms had been collated, logged and checked they were ready for data entry. From very early in the project it was decided that the data would be collected and disseminated according to the principles and standards of the National Biodiversity Network (NBN). The NBN is a UK wide initiative to share information about wildlife via the internet (for more information see www.nbn.org.uk). For data entry, Recorder 2000 software was used and was customised to permit the data to be entered directly from the survey sheets into a relational database. In total, Seabird 2000 surveyors recorded over 25,000 individual species counts, which took the equivalent of one person two years to enter onto the database.

Validation and checking of the data were required to ensure that they had been accurately copied from the Seabird 2000 recording forms. The customised 'add-in' for Recorder 2000 provided validation routines during data entry to ensure that, for example, grid references were correct, dates were within the survey period specified etc. These validation routines were able to identify some but not all errors in data entry. Therefore, once the data had been entered and had satisfied the validation routines, data-entry personnel then checked and ticked off the entries presented in two data-trees in Recorder 2000. The Location Tree contains information about each site and its constituent sub-sites (Fig. 1). The Observations Tree contains information collected on each visit to a sub-site, including records of species present, counts, habitat types and predators present (Fig. 2).

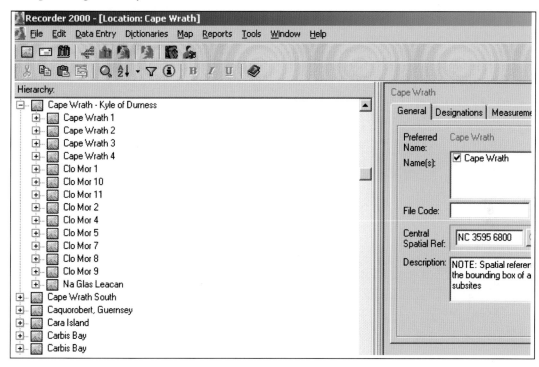

Figure 1   The Location Tree in Recorder 2000.

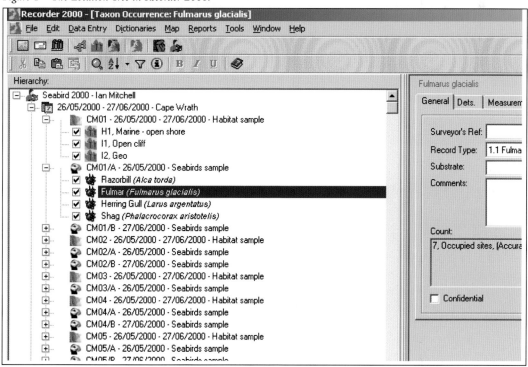

Figure 2   The Observations Tree in Recorder 2000.

A frequent source of error in the final analysis of the Seabird 2000 data was caused by duplicate counts of the same species at the same sub-site. The Seabird 2000 recording forms enabled surveyors to enter repeated counts of a species at a sub-site as 'recounts', if they superseded previous counts because they were of better quality (see previous chapter on Census Methods and Appendix I). However, some surveyors failed to flag recounts on the forms. Such errors were mostly identified at the data entry stage, but some duplicates were mistakenly entered on the database. All duplicate counts entered on the database for the same species at the same sub-site, that were not flagged as recounts, were individually checked to remove any errors.

Information in the Seabird 2000 database is held in 120 interrelated tables. Once all the data had been entered and were ready for analysis, an automatic routine moved the data into a single spreadsheet.

PRESENTATION OF SEABIRD 2000 COUNT DATA

Within each species chapter, the population size and distribution of each species is summarised at the following scales: colony, administrative area and country.

COLONY

Each species chapter presents a map of Britain and Ireland showing the position and size of each colony. In most cases, a 'colony' equates to a single Seabird 2000 sub-site. However, to improve clarity, counts from adjacent sub-sites in areas of high seabird density or in island groups, have been combined and presented as a single colony. Within all species chapters (except, Leach's and European Storm-petrels, Manx Shearwaters, Arctic and Great Skuas and Black Guillemots) the data for Shetland and Orkney presented on maps showing distribution and abundance have been summarised by the geographical areas shown in Figure 3. However, the inset maps of Orkney and Shetland on the same figures present data at the sub-site/colony level.

ADMINISTRATIVE AREA

Each chapter presents a table containing the total population size of the particular species in each administrative area within Great Britain, Northern Ireland and the Republic of Ireland, plus totals for each of the Isle of Man and the Channel Islands. The administrative boundaries used in this book to summarise Seabird 2000 data are shown Table 1 and Figure 4. However, these administrative areas no longer used by local and national governments within the UK and were replaced in 1996 by new county and unitary authority boundaries. We considered the old boundaries (Table 1) to be more appropriate for summarising seabird distribution in the UK since the new boundaries are based upon head of population and thus tend to be small in urban areas and large in rural areas. Furthermore, the boundaries used in this book are much more comparable to those used to summarise data from the previous two censuses (Cramp *et al.*, 1974; Lloyd *et al.*, 1991) and still provide a spatial scale that is relevant to conservation GOs and NGOs throughout the UK.

The administrative areas of Caithness, Sutherland and Ross & Cromarty in northern Scotland include coastlines adjacent to both the North Atlantic and the North Sea. In order to examine any

Table 1   Administrative boundaries used to summarise Seabird 2000 data.

Country	Administrative area type	Spatial data source
England	English County 1974–96	[1]OS Boundary-Line and [2]ESRI Data and Maps 2000
Wales	Welsh County 1974–96	[1]OS Boundary Line
Scotland	Scottish District 1974–96	[3]The Scottish Office
Northern Ireland	Northern Ireland District 1974–96	[2]ESRI Data and Maps 2000
Republic of Ireland	Irish Vice-county	[2]ESRI Data and Maps 2000

[1] OS Boundary-Line ™ © Crown copyright. All rights reserved JNCC 100017955 (2004).

[2] ESRI Data and Maps 2000 CD1 supplied as part of ArcView 8.2 (2001) © ESRI.

[3] 'Local Authority Districts (pre-1996) showing Regional and District extents at 1:625,000'. Geographic Information Group, Hope Terrace, Scottish Natural Heritage, © The Scottish Office.

differences in the seabird populations breeding along the two coastlines, coastal counts from the SCR Census and Seabird 2000 were divided into i) north coast Caithness and east coast Caithness, separated at Duncansby Head Lighthouse (OS grid ref. ND406733); ii) northwest coast Sutherland and east coast Sutherland; iii) west coast Ross & Cromarty and east coast Ross & Cromarty. (This division was not possible for Operation Seafarer counts).

COUNTRY

Separate population totals are given for Britain (including Isle of Man and the Channel Isles) and for Ireland (i.e. Northern Ireland and the Republic of Ireland combined). This division is relevant to the frames of the EU Birds Directive (1979) within which, the importance of bird populations are assessed in the contexts of Britain and Ireland.

COMPARISON WITH PREVIOUS SURVEYS

OPERATION SEAFARER

Most counts were conducted in 1969 and 1970, with some from 1968 and 1971. Coverage was confined to coastal colonies but was thought to be complete apart from gaps in Foula, Shetland, and in Caithness. The survey was initially summarised by Cramp *et al.* (1974). The data were then entered on the SCR database and summarised by Lloyd *et al.* (1991) in order to compare directly with the results of the SCR Census and to take account of changing administrative boundaries between the two censuses. They also applied more consistent criteria to select counts from locations where repeated counts had been conducted. Therefore the totals summarised in Lloyd *et al.* (1991) for Operation Seafarer are slightly different from those in Cramp *et al.* (1974). In this book we have used the totals for Operation Seafarer given in Lloyd *et al.* (1991). The Operation Seafarer totals for administrative areas and countries are tabulated alongside those from Seabird 2000 in each species chapter, except for Black Guillemot, storm-petrels and Manx Shearwater, as census methods for these species were not comparable between the two censuses (see chapter on Census Methods).

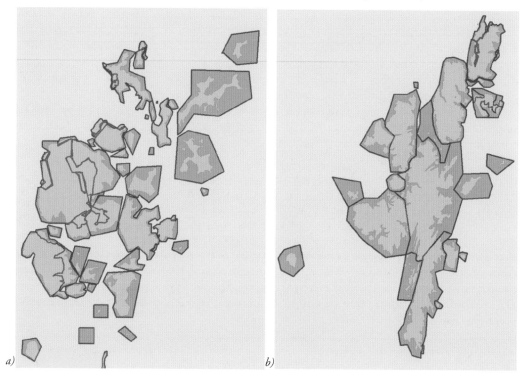

a)   *b)*

Figure 3   Geographical areas within a) Orkney and b) Shetland used to summarise data on maps showing distribution and abundance in each species' chapter (NB. Does not apply to inset maps).

SEABIRD COLONY REGISTER (SCR) CENSUS

Most counts were conducted in 1985–87, but counts were used from 1988 if no previous counts were available (see Lloyd *et al.* 1991). Some data on urban gulls, terns, skuas and Black Guillemots were collected outwith 1985–88 but were still included in the results of the SCR Census (Lloyd *et al.* 1991) and are detailed below. Data from the SCR Database for 1985–88 were imported into the Recorder 2000 database, so it could be viewed and analysed alongside the Seabird 2000 dataset and others (see below). The SCR data contained duplicate counts from the same sites but conducted in different years. A single count was selected for each site according to the criteria used by Lloyd *et al.* (1991) and listed in Table 2.

As in Operation Seafarer, the SCR Census did not attempt to survey storm-petrels and Manx Shearwaters. Some colonies were visited in one or both of the censuses and best guesses of the size of breeding populations, usually of orders of magnitude, were made. These were listed in Lloyd *et al.* (1991), along with a list of other known colonies based on information given in Cramp *et al.* (1974) gathered during Operation Seafarer and from historical records.

Apart from Black Guillemots and urban gulls (see below), the task of completing a comprehensive comparison of counts from the SCR and Seabird 2000 censuses for every colony of every species in Britain and Ireland proved beyond the scope and timetable for producing this book. During the SCR Census *c.*3,300 coastal and 700 inland sites in Britain and Ireland were recorded on the SCR database. The main problems with comparing these to sites surveyed during Seabird 2000 were four-fold. 1) Coastal sites in the SCR were of widely varying size from stretches of coastline of less than

1 km to single large islands or even groups of islands. 2) SCR sites did not necessarily take account of important boundaries such as SSSIs or SPAs (first designated in 1982). 3) 77% of coastal sites were defined by only a single, central OS grid reference, making it impossible to assess where the site actually started and ended. 4) Some stretches of coast, particularly those containing large numbers of seabirds were completely counted in more than one year during the SCR Census, but surveyors in each year, counted slightly different stretches of coast.

Hence, presentation of change at the colony level was restricted to the largest and most important colonies of each species. For most species, these colonies were selected on the basis of SCR Census counts and colony definitions. For a given species, the counts for each colony from the SCR were listed separately for Britain and for Ireland, in descending order of size, and those colonies containing a certain percentage (see individual species chapters) of the British or all-Ireland population were selected as 'top colonies'. For those species aggregated in fewer colonies (e.g. Atlantic Puffin), a higher percentage of the respective populations were represented by the 'top colonies' than for those species that are more dispersed (e.g. European Shag). Colonies of gulls tend to be more mobile between years, with some colonies disappearing whilst new ones form. In order to ensure that important new gull colonies were selected as 'top sites', large colonies of gulls were selected not just on the basis of their size during the SCR, but also of their size during Seabird 2000. Top sites of Great Cormorants were selected in a similar way. Within each species chapter, the size of each top colony during Seabird 2000 and the SCR Census are tabulated and their location marked on a map, which also denotes the percentage change in numbers between the two censuses.

Table 2   The criteria applied to SCR Census data (1985–88) to select a single count for each species at each site (from Lloyd et al., 1991).

Criteria	Specification
Count unit	Recommended unit (see Census Methods chapter) preferred to others.
Date	Recommended time of year (see Census Methods chapter) preferred to others.
Count accuracy	Counts marked 'Accurate Count' preferred to those given as 'Minimum Estimate' and 'Maximum Estimate'.
If two or more counts were selected based on the above criteria, the following criteria were applied:	
Count year	Most recent year up to 1987 (counts from 1988 were used only if no previous counts were available or if previous counts fulfilled fewer of the above criteria).
Method	Land-based counts were preferred to those made from boats, except at colonies where land-based counts were incomplete.

INLAND COLONIES

No inland colonies were surveyed during Operation Seafarer, all totals listed alongside SCR and Seabird 2000 counts in this book are for coastal colonies only. Counts from inland colonies were contained in the SCR data imported into the Recorder 2000 database. Coverage of inland sites during the SCR census was incomplete and was not included in the administrative area and country totals reported in Lloyd *et al.* (1991). Inland sites were defined by Lloyd *et al.* (1991) as being within a 1-km OS grid square that did not contain any coastline, except in Orkney and Shetland, where all sites were considered coastal. However, it was not stated in the SCR database whether or not a site was considered inland or coastal. Thus, in order to separate coastal from inland sites in both the Seabird 2000 and SCR data, the following criteria were applied. Using GIS, sites were defined as coastal if they were situated within 5 km of the mean high-water mark (OS Boundary-Line ™©

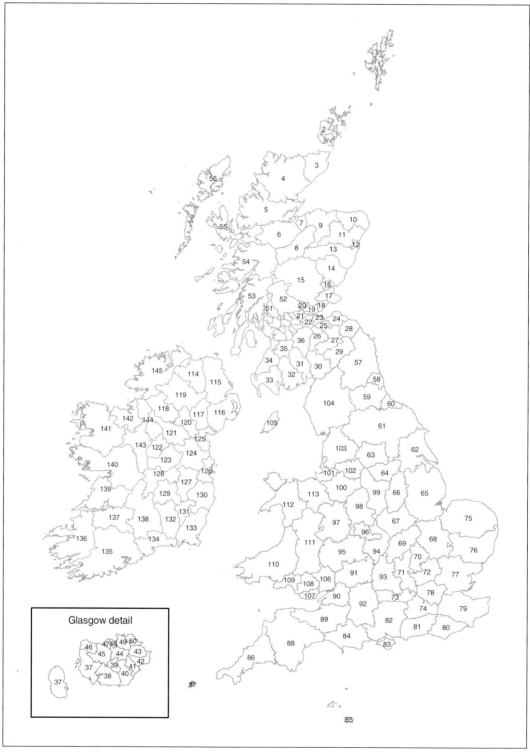

Figure 4   Administrative boundaries used to summarise Seabird 2000 data.

Scotland

1	Shetland
2	Orkney
3	Caithness
4	Sutherland
5	Ross & Cromarty
6	Inverness
7	Nairn
8	Badenoch & Strathspey
9	Moray
10	Banff & Buchan
11	Gordon
12	City of Aberdeen
13	Kincardine & Deeside
14	Angus
15	Perth & Kinross
16	City of Dundee
17	Northeast Fife
18	Kirkcaldy
19	Dunfermline
20	Clackmannan
21	Falkirk
22	West Lothian
23	City of Edinburgh
24	East Lothian
25	Midlothian
26	Tweedale
27	Ettrick & Lauderdale
28	Berwickshire
29	Roxburgh
30	Annandale & Eskdale
31	Nithsdale
32	Stewartry
33	Wigtown
34	Kyle & Carrick
35	Cumnock & Doon Valley
36	Clydesdale
37	Cunninghame
38	Kilmarnock & Loudon
39	Eastwood
40	East Kilbride
41	Hamilton
42	Motherwell
43	Monklands
44	City of Glasgow
45	Renfrew
46	Inverclyde
47	Clydebank
48	Bearsden & Milngavie
49	Strathkelvin
50	Cumbernauld & Kilsyth
51	Dumbarton
52	Stirling
53	Argyll & Bute
54	Lochaber
55	Skye & Lochalsh
56	Western Isles–Comhairle nan eilean

England

57	Northumberland
58	Tyne & Wear
59	Durham
60	Cleveland
61	North Yorkshire
62	Humberside
63	West Yorkshire
64	South Yorkshire
65	Lincolnshire
66	Nottinghamshire
67	Leicestershire
68	Cambridgeshire
69	Northamptonshire
70	Bedfordshire
71	Buckinghamshire
72	Hertfordshire
73	Berkshire
74	Surrey
75	Norfolk
76	Suffolk
77	Essex
78	Greater London
79	Kent
80	East Sussex
81	West Sussex
82	Hampshire
83	Isle of Wight
84	Dorset
85	Channel Islands
86	Cornwall
87	Isles of Scilly
88	Devon
89	Somerset
90	Avon
91	Gloucestershire
92	Wiltshire
93	Oxfordshire
94	Warwickshire
95	Hereford & Worcester
96	West Midlands
97	Shropshire
98	Staffordshire
99	Derbyshire
100	Cheshire
101	Merseyside
102	Greater Manchester
103	Lancashire
104	Cumbria
105	Isle of Man

Wales

106	Gwent
107	South Glamorgan
108	Mid Glamorgan
109	West Glamorgan
110	Dyfed
111	Powys
112	Gwynedd
113	Clwyd

Northern Ireland

114	Co. Londonderry
115	Co. Antrim
116	Co. Down
117	Co. Armagh
118	Co. Fermanagh
119	Co. Tyrone

Republic of Ireland

120	Co. Monaghan
121	Co. Cavan
122	Co. Longford
123	Co. Westmeath
124	Co. Meath
125	Co. Louth
126	Co. Dublin
127	Co. Kildare
128	Co. Offaly
129	Co. Laois
130	Co. Wicklow
131	Co. Carlow
132	Co. Kilkenny
133	Co. Wexford
134	Co. Waterford
135	Co. Cork
136	Co. Kerry
137	Co. Limerick
138	Co. Tipperary
139	Co. Clare
140	Co. Galway
141	Co. Mayo
142	Co. Sligo
143	Co. Roscommon
144	Co. Leitrim
145	Co. Donegal

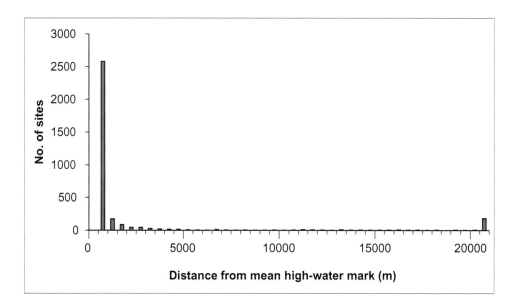

Figure 5   Frequency histogram of the number of seabird colonies counted during Seabird 2000 and their distance from the coast (mean high-water mark).

Crown copyright). This 5-km coastal buffer zone was based on a frequency histogram of the number of colonies and their distance from the coast (Fig. 5). For distances greater than 5 km, there was no discernable pattern in the frequency distribution, suggesting that there is little, if any, coastal influence on the position of colonies situated more than 5 km from the coast and that these are effectively 'inland'. The 5-km buffer was not applied to colonies in Orkney, Shetland and the Western Isles, where all colonies were considered coastal.

URBAN GULL COLONIES

Specialist surveys of gulls nesting on roofs and other man-made structures were conducted in 1974–76 (Monaghan & Coulson, 1977) and in 1994–95 (Raven & Coulson, 1997). The results of these surveys were contained within the SCR Database and were imported into the Recorder 2000 database. GIS was used to associate sites counted during the two surveys with 'urban, man-made' sites surveyed in Seabird 2000, so that direct comparisons between counts in the different surveys could be made on a site-by-site basis. Chapters of *Larus* spp. gulls contain tabulated totals of the total number of pairs and total number of colonies in each administrative area and country in the 1974–76, 1994–95 and Seabird 2000 surveys of urban/roof-nesting gulls.

SKUAS

Lloyd *et al.* (1991) reported 'complete' coverage for both species during the SCR Census, quoting the period 1985–87. Whilst most counts were from this period, particularly Shetland (conducted in 1985–86, see Ewins *et al.*, 1987), surveys of skuas in Orkney were conducted in 1982 (Meek *et al.*,

1985). Counts of Arctic Skuas in Caithness were taken from the NCC Upland Bird Survey in 1979–80 (Reed *et al.*, 1983). Coverage was less complete during Operation Seafarer, as the main focus was on coastal breeding seabirds and those skuas breeding more than 1 km inland (mostly Arctic Skuas) were largely missed. Other surveys of skuas have been conducted between all three censuses and are referred to in detail in the relevant species chapters.

TERNS

Neither Operation Seafarer nor the SCR Census achieved full coverage of coastal-nesting terns and neither census surveyed inland-nesting Common and Arctic Terns. This was partly because other national surveys or counts of important concentrations had been organised at irregular intervals. For example, Lloyd *et al.* (1975) summarised counts from 1969–1974 and Thomas (1982) coordinated a survey of Britain and Ireland in 1975–79. Lloyd *et al.* (1991) incorporated counts from the All-Ireland tern survey in 1984 (Whilde, 1985) into the results of the SCR Census, and we also compare Seabird 2000 counts in Ireland with the 1984 survey. In addition to inland sites, the major gaps in coverage of terns during the SCR Census in 1985–88 were in Shetland and Orkney. We have not used any counts from Orkney and Shetland conducted in 1985–88 and have instead compared Seabird 2000 counts of the Northern Isles with a complete survey conducted in 1980 (Bullock & Gomersall, 1981). A subsequent survey of terns in the Northern Isles in 1989 (Avery *et al.* 1983) was also used for comparison. Counts of large concentrations of terns, such as in the Northern Isles and in Britain and Ireland as whole, are best conducted in a single year to avoid errors associated with terns moving between sites in different years (see chapter on Census Methods).

BLACK GUILLEMOTS

During Operation Seafarer (1969–70), counts were conducted along with other cliff-nesting seabirds during June, outside the recommended period for censusing Black Guillemots and were not comparable with the pre-breeding counts made in late March–early May in Seabird 2000 (see chapter on Census Methods). Prior to, during and subsequent to the main SCR Census fieldwork in 1985–88, pre-breeding counts of Black Guillemots were conducted throughout their range in Britain and Northern Ireland. These were extracted from the SCR Database, spanning a total period of 1982–1991. The majority of counts were probably included in Lloyd *et al.* (1991), apart from those conducted in 1991 in parts of Argyll & Bute and southwest Scotland (Kyle & Carrick, Stewartry and Wigtown). Counts within each administrative area were conducted within 1–3 years, a comparable time period with those of Seabird 2000. No direct comparison was made with SCR Census counts of Black Guillemots in the Republic of Ireland, as these were all conducted in June. Seabird 2000 was the first comprehensive pre-breeding census of Black Guillemots in the Republic of Ireland.

INTERNATIONAL CONTEXT

Within each species chapter there is a table giving a breakdown of the international distribution of the species, based on the latest population estimates for each country or region in which the species is known to breed. Lloyd *et al.* (1991) presented international population estimates, which they used to place the results of the SCR Census into a global context. Lloyd *et al.* (1991) drew mainly on population estimates published by the International Council for Bird Preservation (Croxall *et al.*, 1984; Croxall, 1991). Whilst no more recent figures exist for some areas, notably parts of northeast Asia, there have been more recent initiatives to survey and collate estimates of seabird populations in other regions, e.g. by the European Bird Census Council (Hagemeijer & Blair, 1997; BirdLife International/EBCC, 2000) and reviews of North American population estimates published in the *Birds of North America*, by the American Ornithologist's Union.

Where possible, population estimates are broken down by subspecies. The population estimates from Seabird 2000 for Britain (including the Isle of Man and the Channel Islands) and Ireland are expressed separately as a percentage of the world population and of the relevant biogeographic population. The biogeographic population is used to assess the international significance of colonies and is one of the criteria used to designate sites as SPAs under Article 4 of the EU Birds Directive (1979). The separate contexts of Britain and Ireland arise from the fact that these are the relevant frames of reference under the Directive. The definition of the biogeographic population of each species is prescribed in Stroud *et al.* (2001).

In estimating the sizes of the global and biogeographic populations of breeding seabirds a minimum and a maximum estimate were derived from the best information available from each country in which the species breeds. These are simply the total of the minimum estimates for each country and the total of the maximum estimates. In cases where the published population estimate is not given as a range then clearly the (single) estimate was used in deriving the relevant international total estimate. No rounding conventions were adopted, as many of the published minimum and maximum estimates for individual countries have already been rounded; whilst some of these may be of specious accuracy, to apply a further, arbitrary rounding convention would compound any error associated with them. However, and again to avoid seeming accurate in the absence of it, the total minimum and maximum global and biogeographical estimates were rounded to the next lowest order of magnitude (Table 3).

In determining the biogeographical importance of breeding seabird populations in Britain and Ireland, again a minimum and a maximum value were derived. The former was computed by dividing the minimum total British or Irish population estimated from the present survey by the maximum biogeographical estimate, and the latter was derived by dividing the maximum British or Irish estimate by the minimum biogeographical estimate. The global importance of British and Irish populations were assessed in similar fashion. Minimum and maximum values for biogeographical and global importance were rounded to only one decimal place, again to avoid spurious accuracy.

Table 3   Rounding convention applied to breeding population size estimates.

Population size estimate	Population size estimate rounded to nearest:
1–999	10
1,000–9,999	100
10,000–99,999	1,000
100,000–999,999	10,000
≥1,000,000	100,000

Northern Fulmar *Fulmarus glacialis*

Mark L. Tasker

INTRODUCTION

Northern Fulmars are one of the commonest seabirds around northern Britain, where the lay-person may mistake them for gulls. They are present year-round, with no pronounced migration once they are adult; rather they disperse from colonies following the breeding season, to return early the following year. Typically they nest near the top of grassy cliffs on relatively wide ledges, but have more recently taken to nesting on flatter ground atop islands and even under boulders and in puffin burrows. They feed at sea on a wide variety of marine foods.

The spectacular growth in the numbers and distribution of Northern Fulmars in the British Isles must be one of the best documented of any bird species. Most of the population was surveyed at regular intervals during the 20th century (e.g. Harvie-Brown, 1912; Fisher & Waterston, 1941; Fisher, 1966; Cramp *et al.*, 1974; Lloyd *et al.*, 1991), and records of breeding in new areas pepper local and national ornithological literature. In summary, prior to the mid-18th century, Northern Fulmars bred in only 1–2 colonies in Iceland and in St Kilda (Western Isles). A spread started around Iceland at this time, and the Faeroes were colonised in the mid-19th century. This spread continued east and, in 1878, Foula (Shetland) was colonised. New colonies appeared successively further south around Britain and Ireland over the following century, and the species now breeds in France, Denmark and Germany.

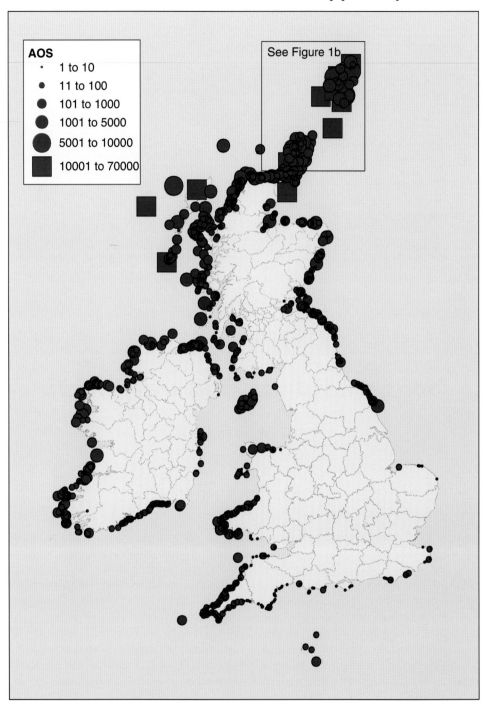

Figure 1a   Abundance and distribution of breeding Northern Fulmars in Britain and Ireland 1998–2002.

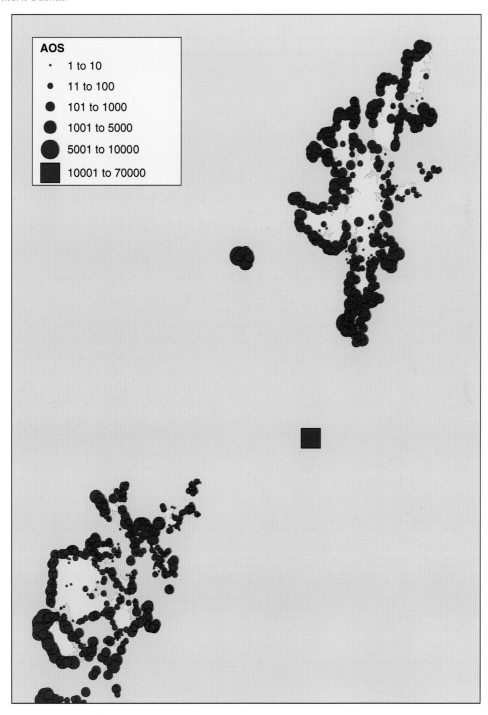

Figure 1b   Abundance and distribution of breeding Northern Fulmars in Orkney and Shetland 1998–2002.

In parallel with this dramatic increase in distribution, there has been a huge growth in population size. Surveys before 1939 in all colonies except St Kilda (where there were no counts) indicated growth rates of 13–19% per annum. These rates decreased from *c.*8% per annum in 1939–49 to 4% per annum in 1969–87. In St Kilda, rates of increase changed from 6% to 3% per annum in the latter two periods.

CENSUS METHODS

There were only a very few, minor gaps in coverage during Seabird 2000, notably Sula Sgeir (Western Isles) and Inishnabro (Kerry), representing a considerable improvement since the SCR Census (1985–88) when several relatively important sections of coast were not censused. Lloyd *et al.* (1991) estimated that at least 10% of Northern Fulmars were not counted in Co. Antrim, Co. Kerry, Co. Clare and Co. Mayo, whilst 40% were missed in Co. Donegal. Overall, Lloyd *et al.* (1991) estimated about one-quarter of Ireland's Northern Fulmars were not counted. The quality of coverage during Operation Seafarer (1969–70) was more difficult to ascertain, as some large sections of coastline were covered rapidly or late in the breeding season.

The recommended count unit for Northern Fulmars in Seabird 2000 was the Apparently Occupied Site (AOS). This is the same unit as was used in Operation Seafarer (1969–70) and in the SCR Census (1985–88). The small number of counts submitted as Apparently Occupied Nests or Apparently Occupied Territories were treated as if they were of AOS, since, for this species, there is no practical difference in these measures (as the site is usually a nest and the territory). A small proportion of counts in each of the three censuses were of individuals. These counts were divided by two (following the treatment of Lloyd *et al.*, 1991) in order to provide an estimate of AOS. The small proportion of individuals counted will not have affected overall estimation of trends. Northern Fulmars have a long period of immaturity (around ten years), but individuals may occupy sites before breeding starts. Thus, the number of AOS includes these non-breeders, as well as failed breeders and those that go on to breed successfully.

During Seabird 2000, 64% of Northern Fulmars were counted during the recommended date period and time of day. A further 24% were counted during the correct date period, but at an unrecorded time of day, whilst 9% were counted at the wrong time of day but during the correct date period. A mere 3% were counted on the wrong date and at the wrong time of day. During the SCR Census (1985–88), 83% of counts were on an appropriate date, but time of day was not recorded. Both time of day and date are important in minimising variability in the number of non-breeders counted. Some of the AOS counted will inevitably contain non-breeders, which tend to arrive at the colony after breeders and depart before them, and are more variable in their attendance early in the morning and late at night (Dott, 1975). They also tend to leave sites in windy or wet conditions.

During Seabird 2000, 76% of Northern Fulmars were counted in good weather conditions and weather conditions were not recorded in a further 16% of counts. Eight percent were counted in poor weather conditions. Weather conditions were not recorded in the SCR Census (1985–88).

CURRENT STATUS AND TRENDS

Seabird 2000 estimated a total of 537,991 AOS Britain and in Ireland, of which 90% were in Scotland, 7% in Ireland, 2% in England, the Channel Isles and the Isle of Man, and 1% in Wales

Table 1   Numbers of breeding Northern Fulmars (AOS) in Britain and Ireland 1969–2002.

Administrative area or country	Operation Seafarer (1969–70)	SCR Census (1985–88)[4]	Seabird 2000 (1998–2002)	Percentage change since Seafarer	Percentage change since SCR	Annual percentage change since SCR
Shetland	116,137	221,035	188,544	62%	−15%	−1.2%
Orkney	42,444	83,755	90,846	114%	8%	0.6%
North coast Caithness		*11,230*	*9,688*		*−14%*	*−1.1%*
East coast Caithness		*20,901*	*20,269*		*−3%*	*−0.2%*
Caithness total	25,922	32,131	29,957	16%	−7%	−0.5%
Northwest coast Sutherland		*21,488*	*23,200*		*8%*	*0.6%*
Inland Sutherland		*100*	*114*		*14%*	*1.1%*
East coast Sutherland		*346*	*136*		*−61%*	*−7.6%*
Sutherland total	17,947	21,934	23,450	31%	7%	0.5%
West coast Ross & Cromarty		*3,231*	*2,565*		*−21%*	*−1.7%*
East coast Ross & Cromarty		*1,508*	*1,638*		*9%*	*0.6%*
Ross & Cromarty total	3,867	4,739	4,203	9%	−11%	−0.9%
Moray	261	317	569	118%	79%	4.3%
Banff & Buchan	2,177	3,192	5,146	136%	61%	3.3%
Gordon	810	974	1,017	26%	4%	0.3%
City of Aberdeen	66	381	225	241%	−41%	−4.1%
Kincardine & Deeside	1,173	4,027	3,135	167%	−22%	−1.9%
Angus	522	820	1,185	127%	45%	2.6%
Perth & Kinross			2			
Northeast Fife	478	556	887	86%	60%	3.9%
Kirkcaldy	3	500	401	13267%	−20%	−1.8%
Dunfermline		138	161		17%	1.3%
City of Edinburgh	37	147	228	516%	55%	3.7%
East Lothian	364	871	1,051	189%	21%	1.5%
Berwickshire	764	1,283	1,060	39%	−17%	−1.4%
Stewartry	41	42	84	105%	100%	6.1%
Wigtown	328	376	147	−55%	−61%	−6.5%
Kyle & Carrick	131	374	465	255%	24%	1.7%
Cunninghame	53	277	237	347%	−14%	−1.1%
Argyll & Bute	3,804	6,482	8,467	123%	31%	2.0%
Lochaber	989	1,774	1,586	60%	−11%	−0.8%
Skye and Lochalsh	1,421	6,383	4,726	233%	−26%	−2.3%
Western Isles–Comhairle nan eilean[1]	65,328	112,132	118,073	81%	5%	0.4%
Scotland Total	**285,067**	**504,640**	**485,852**	**70%**	**−4%**	**−0.3%**
Northumberland	248	410	1,078	335%	163%	6.9%
Tyne and Wear	126	247	234	86%	−5%	−0.4%
Durham	5			−100%		
Cleveland	266	160	219	−18%	37%	2.2%
North Yorkshire	360	920	733	104%	−20%	−1.5%
Humberside	546	960	1,245	128%	30%	2.0%
Norfolk	146	181	91	−38%	−50%	−4.8%
Suffolk		9	0		−100%	
Kent	27	265	53	96%	−80%	−11.4%
East Sussex	5	31	111	2120%	258%	11.1%
Isle of Wight		69	15		−78%	−9.4%
Dorset	45	74	94	109%	27%	1.7%
Channel Islands		200	317		59%	3.9%
Cornwall	869	1,663	1,692	95%	2%	0.1%

Table 1 continued.

Administrative area or country	Operation Seafarer (1969–70)	SCR Census (1985–88)[4]	Seabird 2000 (1998–2002)	Percentage change since Seafarer	Percentage change since SCR	Annual percentage change since SCR
Isles of Scilly	17	92	180	959%	96%	5.8%
Devon	380	817	471	24%	−42%	−4.1%
Somerset		5	10		100%	5.5%
Cumbria	23	115	65	183%	−43%	−4.7%
Isle of Man	586	2,463	3,147	437%	28%	1.9%
England, Isle of Man and Channel Islands Total	**3,649**	**8,681**	**9,755**	**167%**	**12%**	**0.9%**
South Glamorgan			31			
West Glamorgan	1	5	18	1700%	260%	8.9%
Dyfed	459	1,767	2,870	525%	62%	3.8%
Gwynedd	407	902	509	25%	−44%	−3.9%
Clwyd	58	67	46	−21%	−31%	−2.4%
Wales Total	**925**	**2741**	**3,474**	**276%**	**27%**	**1.7%**
Great Britain, Isle of Man & Channel Islands Total	**289,641**	**516,062**	**499,081**	**72%**	**−3%**	**−0.2%**
Co. Londonderry	400	684	1,255	214%	83%	4.2%
Co. Antrim	1,821	2,792	4,706	158%	69%	4.0%
Co. Down	18	64	31	72%	−52%	−4.4%
Co. Meath		5			−100%	
Co. Dublin	130	704	766	489%	9%	1.0%
Co. Wicklow	48	125	160	233%	28%	1.9%
Co. Wexford	230	614	520	126%	−15%	−1.2%
Co. Waterford	323	973	683	111%	−30%	−2.7%
Co. Cork	540	2,059	1,569	191%	−24%	−2.0%
Co. Kerry[3]	4,214	3,278	4,941	17%	51%	3.5%
Co. Clare	1,957	3,163	4,231	116%	34%	2.1%
Co. Galway[2]	440	706	1,467	233%	108%	6.0%
Co. Mayo	5,415	3,248	12,750	135%	293%	11.4%
Co. Sligo	271	367	359	32%	−2%	−0.2%
Co. Donegal	3,512	1,733	5,472	56%	216%	10.1%
All-Ireland Total	**19,319**	**20,515**	**38,910**	**101%**	**90%**	**5.4%**
Britain and Ireland Total	**308,960**	**536,577**	**537,991**	**74%**	**0%**	**0.0%**

Notes

[1] Sula Sgeir not counted in Seabird 2000 (3,196 AOS in 1985–88)

[2] Inishbofin and Inishmore, Aran Isles not counted in 1985–88 (146 AOS and 262 AOS respectively in 1990)

[3] Inishnabro not counted in Seabird 2000 (864 AOS in 1985–88)

[4] The figures for the SCR are actual counts and do not include adjustments to totals made in order to account for unsurveyed colonies (see Lloyd *et al.*, 1991)

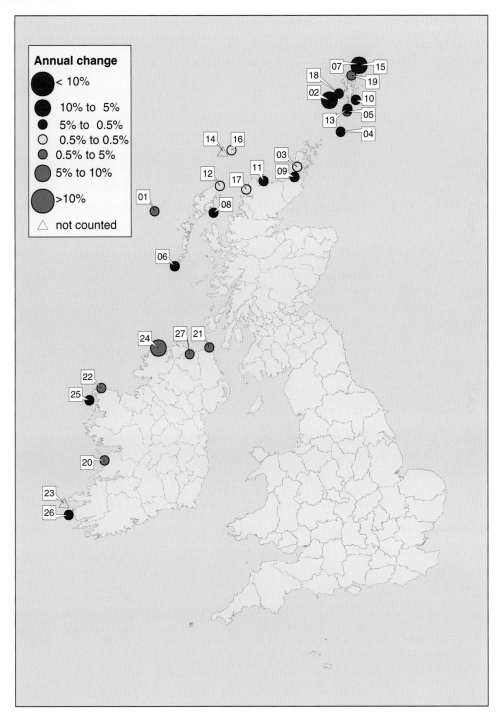

Figure 2   Changes in the number of breeding Northern Fulmars (AOS) at major colonies in Britain and Ireland between the SCR Census (1988–88) and Seabird 2000 (1998–2002). Major colonies are those that contained the top 50% of the national populations during the SCR Census in Britain and in Ireland. Numbers correspond to colonies listed in Table 2.

Table 2   Changes in the number of breeding Northern Fulmars (AOS) at major colonies in Britain and Ireland between the SCR Census (1985–88) and Seabird 2000 (1998–2002). Major colonies are those that contained the top 50% of the national populations during the SCR Census in Britain and in Ireland. ID corresponds to colony symbols in Fig. 2.

ID	Colony	SCR Census (1985–88)	Seabird 2000 (1998–2002)	Percentage change since SCR	Annual percentage change since SCR	Percentage of population in Britain or Ireland 1998–2002
1	St Kilda	62,786	68,448	9%	0.7%	13.7%
2	Foula	46,800	21,106	−55%	−6.0%	4.2%
3	Hoy and South Walls	37,465	35,858	−4%	−0.3%	7.2%
4	Fair Isle	26,995	20,424	−24%	−2.0%	4.1%
5	SW Mainland, Shetland: The Nev to Kame	10,154	17,240	70%	4.2%	3.5%
6	Mingulay	9,000	8,424	−6%	−0.5%	1.7%
7	Unst: Saxavord (SSSI)	7,773	5,475	−30%	−2.9%	1.1%
8	Shiant Islands	6,816	4,387	−36%	−3.3%	0.9%
9	Dunnet Head (SSSI)	6,747	5,465	−19%	−1.6%	1.1%
10	Noss	6,347	4,999	−21%	−2.1%	1.0%
11	Whiten Head	4,301	2,697	−37%	−3.5%	0.5%
12	Lewis: Cellar Head	4,060	3,812	−6%	−0.5%	0.8%
13	St Ninian's Isle	4,031	3,191	−21%	−1.8%	0.6%
14	Sula Sgeir	3,916	nc			
15	Unst: Burrafirth to The Keen	3,912	1,772	−55%	−6.2%	0.4%
16	North Rona	3,738	3,520	−6%	−0.5%	0.7%
17	Handa	3,574	3,550	−1%	0.0%	0.7%
18	Mainland Shetland: Mu Ness to Deepdale Burn	3,107	1,622	−48%	−4.9%	0.3%
19	Yell: West Sand Wick to Stacks of Stuis	2,836	3,474	22%	1.6%	0.7%
20	Cliffs of Moher	3,097	3,566	15%	1.3%	9.2%
21	Rathlin Island	1,482	2,032	37%	2.3%	5.3%
22	Benwee Head	1,377	1,986	44%	3.1%	5.1%
23	Inishnabro	864	nc			
24	Horn Head	843	1,675	99%	5.9%	4.3%
25	Duvillaun Islands	811	638	−21%	−1.8%	1.7%
26	Puffin Island	701	447	−36%	−3.0%	1.2%
27	Binevenagh, Gortmore & Downhill inland cliffs	684	870	27%	1.7%	2.3%

(Table 1). They are distributed throughout Britain and Ireland where there is suitable cliff-nesting habitat either along mainland coasts or on offshore islands. Hence they are absent from low-lying coastlines such as that along much of eastern England. As in previous surveys, the main concentrations of breeders were on the northern and western islands of Scotland. A few colonies were found inland on rocky outcrops, the largest of these (114 AOS) was at Carrol Rock, Loch Bora (Sutherland), 7 km from the coast.

The growth of the Northern Fulmar population in Britain and Ireland that occurred throughout the 20th century appears to have slowed or stopped in most areas sometime between the SCR Census (1985–88) and Seabird 2000, with the total population estimates of both censuses virtually identical (Table 1). The total number of AOS in Shetland, Orkney and the Western Isles represented almost three-quarters of all those breeding in Great Britain and Ireland combined. It follows, therefore, that changes in numbers on these three island groups will have a profound influence on overall trends in Great Britain. Between Operation Seafarer (1969–70) and the SCR Census (1985–88), Northern Fulmar numbers on all three island groups more or less doubled. However, the rate of change between island groups differed. The rates of increase declined considerably in both Orkney and the Western Isles to just 8% and 5% respectively between the SCR Census (1985–88) and Seabird 2000. In Shetland, numbers actually declined by *c*.15% since the SCR Census (1985–88). Numbers at most of the largest colonies during the SCR Census had declined in Seabird 2000, most notably on Foula, by 55% to 21,106 AOS, and by 24% to 20,424 on Fair Isle (Table 2). Some colonies in Shetland did increase, with the biggest of these of 70% on southwest Mainland.

The decline on Foula has meant that the second-largest colony in Britain and Ireland is now on Hoy and South Walls (Orkney), which had, in comparison, changed very little in size since the SCR Census (1985–88). In the Western Isles, 58% of the population were on St Kilda, the largest colony in Britain and Ireland, which increased by 9% since the SCR Census to over 68,000 AOS. Conversely the second- and third-largest colonies in the Western Isles, on Mingulay and on the Shiant Islands, decreased by 6% to 8,424 AOS and by 36% to 4,387 AOS (Table 2).

Numbers in the next two most important areas of the UK and Ireland, Caithness and Sutherland, were almost exactly the same as in the SCR Census (1985–88). Changes in other parts of Britain were a mixture of increases and decreases, with an overall slight increase (Table 1). Colonisation of Suffolk, first recorded in the 1980s, had failed and appears to also be failing in Kent.

The story in Ireland is different from Great Britain in that the population has continued to increase at a similar rate as it did between Operation Seafarer (1969–70) and the SCR Census (1985–88), and has almost doubled again since the latter census. On the south coast (Co. Wexford, Co. Waterford and Co. Cork) numbers have decreased by 24%, but this has been more than offset by massive apparent increases in Co. Mayo and Co. Donegal. It is a little difficult to determine how much of this increase is due to improved coverage and how much is due to a real increase in numbers. However, substantial increases were found at some of the largest colonies surveyed during both censuses, e.g. 37% on Rathlin Island (Co. Antrim) and 44% at Benwee Head (Co. Mayo). Conversely, the colonies on Puffin Island (Co. Kerry) and on the Duvillaun Islands (Co. Mayo) decreased by 36% and 21% respectively. But overall the population in Ireland, although relatively small, is continuing to grow at a much faster rate than in Britain.

CAUSES OF CHANGE

Recent changes in the trajectory of the Northern Fulmar population and its component parts in Britain and Ireland cannot be considered in isolation from the longer term changes noted in this population, nor from changes occurring in other parts of the species' range. The causes of long-term increase in the Northern Fulmar population have been much debated in the ornithological literature. Fisher (1952) considered the most likely explanation to be the provision of extra food by humans— first in the form of whale remnants from the fleets that devastated the North Atlantic whale populations, and later as offal from offshore trawlers. Wynne-Edwards (1962) considered that the timing of the expansion did not correlate well with the rise of these fisheries. Instead, he suggested that the colonisation may have been aided by a genetic change in the boreal Northern Fulmar population, and that this was a natural evolutionary change unaided by man. Salomonsen (1965) felt that only a small proportion of the Northern Fulmar population had expanded its range, co-incident with the warming of the eastern Atlantic. In considering the two main arguments, Bourne (1966) suggested that offal had permitted an increase in winter survival of Northern Fulmars. Brown (1970) found that Northern Fulmar distribution in the western Atlantic was closely linked with specific oceanographic factors, which led him to favour Salomonsen's view over that of Fisher. Brown (1970) also pointed out that detailed knowledge of diet was required before it was possible to decide the relative importance of natural and anthropogenic factors. Salomonsen's and Wynne-Edwards' suggestions do not fully accord with more recent changes in populations in Atlantic Canada and Alaska (Lensink, 1984; Stenhouse & Montevecchi, 1999b).

If past increases in Northern Fulmar breeding numbers are to be accounted for by changes in foods, then it would be logical to assume that recent changes in food supply might also cause changes in the fulmar population. There are three current main food types: zooplankton, small fish and offal from fisheries. The proportions of these food types consumed appear to have changed through time, and this change differs spatially. There have been no studies to determine if diet varies by age of the bird; this may be important, as nearly all studies of diet have concerned the food fed to chicks at nesting sites.

The level of the food chain that a bird is feeding at is reflected in the isotopic composition of its feathers. Studies of Northern Fulmar feathers from museum and current specimens show a change from a diet fairly high in the food chain around 1910 to one further down the chain at present (Thompson *et al.*, 1995). This change is supported by studies of mercury concentration in feathers; mercury becomes more concentrated further up the food chain. Studies of museum specimens indicate that mercury concentrations in Northern Fulmar feathers have decreased through time, in contrast to many other species whose concentrations have increased during the past century due to industrial outputs (Thompson *et al.*, 1992).

Studies in the early 1980s of chick diet at St Kilda (Furness & Todd, 1984) found that 71% of food samples were of pelagic zooplankton with only a limited proportion of small fish. This zooplankton would have been available at the surface only by night. In contrast, the same authors found that chicks on Foula were fed predominantly (72%) on sandeels. In the mid-1990s, studies by Hamer *et al.* (1997) at these two colonies found that fish offal from fishing vessels predominated in the diets of Northern Fulmar chicks on Foula, whilst 90% of samples at St Kilda contained small juvenile fish.

Many studies at sea have found that Northern Fulmars are the dominant species in flocks of scavengers feeding on offal around trawlers (Hudson & Furness, 1989; Camphuysen *et al.*, 1993, 1995). Camphuysen *et al.* (1993, 1995) found that the peak in numbers of Northern Fulmars at trawlers occurred in different months in different parts of the North Sea, with the peak in the northwest North Sea occurring in August, and in the central-western North Sea in May. Camphuysen & Garthe (1997) pointed out that Northern Fulmar distribution at sea is correlated much more strongly with the distribution of hydrographic features than it is with fishing vessels. Thompson & Furness (1995) found changes in isotopic composition of feathers of Northern Fulmar indicated a seasonal change in diet. In summary, the diet of Northern Fulmars varies geographically and temporally, both within and between years.

Information on changes in quantity and availability of major foods may explain fulmar population changes. The annual abundance of the key zooplankton, the copepod *Calanus finmarchicus*, in the northern North Sea, has declined steadily since the 1950s and there is strong evidence that this is correlated to some aspects of climate change (Colebrook, 1986; Stephens *et al.*, 1998; Heath *et al.*, 1999). The North Atlantic Oscillation (NAO) is an atmospheric pressure differential that drives

Northern Fulmars scavenging from a commercial long-lining vessel in the Norwegian Sea (Terje Lislevand/RSPB)

A dead Northern Fulmar caught on the hook of a commercial long-line in the Norwegian sea (Terje Lislevand/RSPB)

weather patterns in northern Europe producing cyclical change in climatic variables such as temperature (air and sea), rainfall and storm frequency (Hurrell *et al.*, 2003), and has the potential to affect populations of marine organisms. Indeed, positive values of NAO, which prevailed for most years in 1980–2000, were associated with lower abundance of zooplankton (Planque & Taylor, 1998) and lower recruitment of sandeels (Arnott & Ruxton, 2002) in the northeast Atlantic and North Sea. Furthermore, Thompson & Ollason (2001) found that over a 40-year study of a colony at Eynhallow (Orkney), the likelihood of breeding Northern Fulmars attending the colony and their hatching and fledging success were all negatively related to NAO index. It is therefore possible that declines in breeding numbers of Northern Fulmars elsewhere in the Northern Isles may be related to a sustained positive NAO. The mechanism by which this could happen, i.e. by reducing the abundance of prey, is difficult to demonstrate, but there is evidence to suggest that the abundance of certain prey species has declined in recent years. Overall, there has been about a 50% decrease in mean annual abundance of *C. finmarchicus* since the late 1960s. While *C. finmarchicus* was not present in the diets of Northern Fulmar chicks examined in Shetland in the mid-1990s (Hamer *et al.*, 1997), this species comprises up to 70% of the larger zooplankton over a wide area of the northeast Atlantic in summer (Heath *et al.*, 1999). This decrease implies a general decrease in the total productivity of the area. Changes in abundance of such an important species seem likely to force dietary changes in predators.

Sandeels were an important item in the diet of Northern Fulmars in Shetland in the 1980s (Furness & Todd, 1984). The sandeel stock in these waters is regarded as being isolated from other stocks in the North Sea, and is consequently managed separately, but it has not been assessed systematically in all years. The quantities of sandeels landed from the fishery rose from 8,000 tonnes in 1974 to peak at over 50,000 tonnes in 1982, followed by a drop to very low levels in 1989. This was due to a severe reduction in quantities of sandeel present around Shetland. The fishery was closed for the early 1990s, and reopened at a relatively low level in the late 1990s, regulated to avoid catching quantities that might affect the food supply of seabirds. The size of the stock has since not reached the levels of the early 1980s.

The quantities of other small fish in the waters off the main Northern Fulmar breeding area are evaluated annually by scientific surveys. Numbers of first-year cod and whiting have approximately halved in surveys when comparing the periods 1976–85 and 1991–2000 (EC, 2001). Declines in numbers of first-year saithe and haddock have also occurred. The herring is the only major species not to have shown a decline in the numbers of young fish in the North Sea over these periods; however, the majority of this age class occurs in areas away from the islands of northern and western Scotland.

Of the fish targeted by fishermen in the northern North Sea, east of Scotland, major stocks of cod and whiting have become severely depleted or are in a critical state following declines that commenced in the 1970s (EC, 2001). Annual landings of cod in the North Sea in the ten years prior to 1985 averaged about 260,000 tonnes, whilst in the ten years to 2000 the figure was 100,000 tonnes. The equivalent figures for whiting were *c*.150,000 tonnes and 60,000 tonnes. Landings of haddock and saithe have also declined. The amounts of offal discharged by these fleets will have correspondingly declined over the period.

A further and more recent pressure is the growing use of line and hook (longline) fisheries in the northeast Atlantic. Norwegian vessels use sets of lines with 30,000–40,000 baited hooks per day. Northern Fulmars become caught on these as they try to take the bait as lines are launched from the vessel. A study in 1997–98 of the Norwegian offshore fleet conservatively estimated that about 20,000 Northern Fulmars are taken per year (Dunn & Steel, 2001). If these figures are extrapolated to include equivalent fleets in the Faeroes and Iceland, some 50,000–100,000 birds might be taken per year in the northern Atlantic. Further studies are required to fully assess the extent of this bycatch.

The lack of precise knowledge of diet through time and throughout the year means that it is difficult to fully assess the effects of these changes in prey quantities on Northern Fulmars. The more general decline in all major possible foods may have stabilised the population in most of the main areas of distribution and even reduced it in some, by exacerbating negative density-dependant effects already acting on the burgeoning population, e.g. through competition for food. The fact that the main population decline occurred in Shetland might be indicative of its already large size, combined with recent localised reductions in food supply. For example, this might indicate that reductions in sandeels and offal have had a greater affect than the reductions in more natural foods. Given the relatively restricted area of decline, it would seem likely that the problems are probably occurring within the feeding range of the Shetland Northern Fulmars when they are at their colonies. The Britain and Ireland Seabird Monitoring Programme figures for Northern Fulmar chick production show a slight decline over the years since 1985 (Seabird Monitoring Programme reports, e.g. Mavor *et al.*, 2001), but there was much variability between years. Shetland does not differ from other areas in this respect. This might imply that mortality rates in the Shetland population (either of immatures or adults) have increased, but without long-term examination of ringing recovery data, it is impossible to assess this possibility. Perhaps adults and/or immatures from the more northerly populations in Britain, such as Shetland, form a more significant part of the bycatch in the northeast Atlantic long-line fishery?

The lack of recent growth at some colonies may simply be due to a limited number of suitable nest sites, particularly on small islands. On some islands, Northern Fulmars appear to be increasingly nesting away from cliff edges, further inland on flatter ground. Often the surrounding ground is so flat that in light winds, adults have great difficulty in taking off from the nest site and would be easily taken by land predators such as foxes or American Mink, if present. Thus, island colonies free of land predators are more likely to expand into areas away from the island's perimeter. Northern Fulmar nests that are not built on ledges against steep cliffs appear to be more open to predation from the air (i.e. by gulls, crows, skuas) and so 'inland' nests are often hidden under boulders or even in old puffin burrows.

INTERNATIONAL CONTEXT

Northern Fulmars breed around the North Atlantic, from Newfoundland in the west, to Svalbard and Novaya Zemlya in the north, and northern France in the southeast. The species also breeds around the North Pacific, in Alaska and eastern Russia (Table 3). The vast majority of European Northern Fulmars nest in Iceland, but achieving anything more than an approximate population estimate has, so far, been impossible. Dunnet (1997) estimated the Icelandic population to be 10–20 million pairs, but more recent estimates place this at 1–2 million pairs (BirdLife International/EBCC, 2000). The populations in Britain and in Ireland amount to approximately 12–18% and 1% of the Atlantic population and comprise the subspecies *F. g. glacialis* (Table 3). Approximately equal numbers occur in the Faeroes as in Britain and Ireland combined (BirdLife International/EBCC, 2000). Long-term trends in populations in these other parts of the Atlantic range have been described earlier, but none has been counted as frequently as those of Britain and Ireland. Populations in Iceland, the Faeroes and Norway are still increasing (BirdLife International/EBCC, 2000). The population has increased in Alaska (Lensink, 1984) and the colonisation of Atlantic Canada appears to be gathering pace (Stenhouse & Montevecchi, 1999).

Table 3   International context.

Country or region	Subspecies	Number of pairs		Year	Source
		Min	Max		
Great Britain, Isle of Man and Channel Isles	glacialis	500,000	500,000	1998–2002	Seabird 2000
All Ireland	glacialis	39,000	39,000	1998–2002	Seabird 2000
Denmark	glacialis	0	5	1993–96	BirdLife International/ EBCC (2000)
Faeroes	glacialis	600,000	600,000	1995	BirdLife International/ EBCC (2000)
France	glacialis	1,155	1,155	1997–2001	Cadiou & Hemery (in press)
Germany	glacialis	53	53	1996	BirdLife International/ EBCC (2000)
Greenland	glacialis	80,000	80,000	1996	BirdLife International/ EBCC (2000)
Iceland	glacialis	1,000,000	2,000,000	1990	BirdLife International/ EBCC (2000)
Norway	glacialis	6,000	7,000	1990	BirdLife International/ EBCC (2000)
Norway (Jan Mayen)	glacialis	80,000	80,000	1990s	BirdLife International/ EBCC (2000)
Norway (Svalbard)	glacialis	100,000	500,000		BirdLife International/ EBCC (2000)
Russia (Western)	glacialis	26,000	26,000	1980–90	BirdLife International/ EBCC (2000)
Canada (Eastern)	glacialis	302,000	302,000		Hatch & Nettleship (1998)
Russian (Eastern)	rogersii	1,150,000	1,450,000		Kondratyev et al. (2000)
USA (Alaska)	rogersii	1,500,000	1,500,000	1975–80	Lensink (1984)

Biogeographic region	Subspecies	Min	Max	Min % GB	Max % GB	min % Ireland	max % Ireland
Atlantic*	glacialis	2,700,000	4,100,000	12.2%	18.5%	1.0%	1.4%
World	all	5,400,000	7,100,000	7.0%	9.3%	0.5%	0.7%

* Stroud *et al.* (2001)

Manx Shearwater *Puffinus puffinus*

Stephen F. Newton, Kate Thompson and P. Ian Mitchell

INTRODUCTION

Most of the world population of Manx Shearwaters breed in Britain and Ireland. Their breeding range extends from Newfoundland (Robertson, 2002) through Iceland and northwest Europe (Brooke, 1990) to Madeira (Câmara, 2001) and the Azores (Groz *et al.*, 2001). Two other, recently separated species found in Europe, the Balearic (*P. mauretanicus*) and Yelkouan Shearwaters (*P. yelkouan*), breed solely in the Mediterranean, and five additional closely related taxa occur in the Pacific (British Ornithologists' Union, 2001; Brooke, 1990; Sangster *et al.*, 2002).

The worldwide population of Manx Shearwaters is estimated at 338,000–411,000 pairs, of which 305,000–374,000 breed in Britain and Ireland (see below). Yet, despite its abundance, and extensive research spanning over 70 years into its ecology and trans-equatorial migration patterns (Brooke, 1990; Wernham *et al.*, 2002), the Manx Shearwater remains one of the least familiar of our breeding seabirds.

The Manx Shearwater's air of mystery extends back over a millennium to Viking sagas which tell of a fleet of ships anchored off the Calf of Man in 1014 being attacked at night by fearsome birds with wild calls (Williamson, 1973). The Norse naming of Trollval (mountain of the Trolls) on Rum, which remains a breeding stronghold for Manx Shearwaters today, seems also likely to have been inspired by their eerie calls and burrowing habits (Love, 2001). Rather less romantically, Manx Shearwater colonies were, for many centuries, exploited as both local food source and revenue earner, principally through export of barrels of salted fledglings. Such records date back to the 14th century in the Isles of Scilly (Williamson, 1940). Early-18th century records from the eponymous colony on the Calf of Man indicate harvests of up to 10,000 chicks per annum (BRSM, 1941). On Mingulay a barrel of young birds reportedly also once formed part of each crofter's annual rent to the laird (Elwes, 1869), whilst on Rum, the earliest reference to the shearwater as a food source (*'certaine foullis which will be taken in these mountains and are exceedingly fatt'*) was by Timothy Pont writing in the late-16th century (Love, 2001).

Such accounts offer tantalising evidence of the historical distribution and potential abundance of Manx Shearwaters. The locations and, to a lesser extent, relative importance, of a number of colonies, as well as the international significance of the British and Irish populations, were known to Victorian naturalists. McPherson (*c.*1898) listed Shetland, Orkney, St Kilda, Rum, Eigg, Skye Islets, Treshnish Isles, Annet, Skomer, mainland Gwynedd, Rathlin, Great Skellig and Lambay as breeding sites, and Barrington (1888) recognised Skomer as being perhaps the largest Manx Shearwater colony in Europe. However, the Vikings' emphasis on the nocturnal and underground habits of Manx Shearwaters is the key to the lack of comprehensive data on distribution and breeding numbers prior to the current Seabird 2000 survey. As stated succinctly by Cramp *et al.* (1974): *'Manx Shearwaters are difficult to census owing to their nocturnal habits on land and to their burrow nesting'*.

In 1969–70, Operation Seafarer (Cramp *et al.*, 1974) documented 26 proven breeding sites in Britain and Ireland, and provided order of magnitude population estimates for most, based largely on subjective assessments. The total population was estimated at 175,000–300,000 or more pairs. Pioneering attempts at systematic colony census, by sample counts of burrows with obvious visual signs of occupancy and by mark-recapture of individual birds, had been undertaken on Rum (Wormell, 1976) and on Skomer and Skokholm (Brooke, 1990) respectively. However, as detailed below, there are inherent problems with both these approaches which preclude direct comparisons between them or with more recent estimates. By the time of the SCR Census in 1985–88 (Lloyd *et al.*, 1991), relatively little new systematic survey had been attempted and the total Manx Shearwater breeding population in Britain and Ireland was estimated as 250,000–300,000 pairs in 40 or more colonies. Virtually nothing could be concluded about population trends, either overall or at individual colony level.

Around the time of the SCR Census (1985–88), James & Robertson (1985) found that a quantifiable proportion of incubating birds would respond to tape-recordings of calls. This permitted the development of an accurate, precise and replicable survey method, which, crucially, enables surveys to be undertaken during daylight hours. The adoption of tape playback methods in Seabird 2000 enabled the first truly quantitative count of the number of Manx Shearwaters nesting in Britain and Ireland to be obtained, against which future trends can be monitored.

CENSUS METHODS

There are several fundamental difficulties inherent in obtaining accurate estimates of the numbers of breeding pairs of Manx Shearwaters. The first of these is that Manx Shearwaters nest underground, often in areas also used by Atlantic Puffins and/or rabbits, and are active at their colonies only at night. Secondly, many non-breeders visit colonies during the breeding season and spend time in burrows unoccupied by breeding birds. Thirdly, some colonies cover large areas, including treacherous terrain, such as boulder fields, within which burrow densities are highly variable.

The world's largest colony of Manx Shearwaters is situated above 450m on the mountains of the island of Rum (Lochaber). (Kate Thompson)

The world's second largest Manx Shearwater colony is on the low-lying island of Skomer (Dyfed) (Matt Parsons)

Prior to Seabird 2000, a number of attempts were made to census Manx Shearwaters by counting burrows showing evidence of recent use, e.g. the presence of freshly dug soil at entrances (e.g. Wormell, 1976). However, the use of such visual signs is inappropriate at some colonies as it is impossible to distinguish between burrows used by breeding pairs and those simply visited by prospecting birds, nor between burrows of Manx Shearwaters and those of Atlantic Puffins or even rabbits. Occasionally, some burrows occupied by breeding Manx Shearwaters show little visual evidence of their presence (pers. obs.), and in certain habitat such as boulder fields or in high or impenetrable vegetation (e.g. gorse) burrow entrances may be indistinct or difficult to see.

The tape playback technique potentially enables many of these problems to be overcome and also compares favourably with alternative approaches such as the more intrusive and labour intensive chick mark-recapture technique (Gibbons & Vaughan, 1998). It involves eliciting vocal responses to taped calls by incubating adults during daylight hours in the incubation period, when non-breeders are generally absent from colonies (as confirmed by Smith *et al.*, 2001). A calibration factor is applied to the number of responses obtained to enable the number of Apparently Occupied Sites (AOS), the prescribed count unit for this species, to be estimated.

The tape playback survey methods adopted for Seabird 2000 followed those detailed in Walsh *et al.* (1995) and Gilbert *et al.* (1998a). Most surveys used a taped call of a male Manx Shearwater, to which only males are thought to respond, but not all do so. Therefore, the number of responses elicited during a playback survey must be adjusted for the differing response rate of the sexes in order to estimate the number of AOS present. James & Robertson (1985) derived a correction factor of 1.98 from published data for Skomer on average durations of male and female incubation shifts and on response rates of both males and females to male calls (Brooke 1978a,b). They also derived a correction factor of 1.08 for responses to composite taped calls of both males and females. However, work on Leach's and European Storm-petrels has shown response rate to vary considerably between different colonies (see relevant species chapters) and Manx Shearwater calls also exhibit considerable geographic variation (James, 1985). Therefore, at larger, colonies response rates were estimated using repeated visits to fixed calibration plots (see also chapter on Census Methods and Appendix II).

Calibration plots necessitate daily visits to a study plot containing a reasonable number of occupied burrows for a period of around one week. Tape playback is undertaken at all burrows and those where a response is heard are marked. Each day, the number of responses and the cumulative number of occupied burrows are recorded. These data are used to estimate the absolute number of occupied burrows in the plot and the initial (day 1) response rate, which is applied to the more extensive sampling strategy employed throughout the colony. As detailed in Table 1, the response rates from such calibration plots were also applied to counts of responses for adjacent islands. Where no such colony-specific calibration factor was available, the adjustment factor of James & Robertson (1985) was adopted and was eventually applied to *c*.4% of the total estimated population of Britain & Ireland (Table 2). The effects of this on the accuracy of the population estimate are unknown. For example, application of the 'standard' 1.98 factor to counts of responses to tape playback on Skomer

Table 1　Response rates to tape playback of male calls by Manx Shearwaters.

Colony and administrative area	Response rate (95% CLs)	Other colonies estimated using measured response rate
Puffin, Kerry	0.44 (0.30–0.58)	Great Skellig, Scariff, Deenish
Inishtooskert, Kerry	0.32 (0.17–0.47)	Inishnabro, Inishvickillane, Great Blasket
Cruagh, Galway	0.55 (0.46–0.63)	High, Inishshark
Skomer, Dyfed	0.43 (not given)	Skokholm, Middleholm

(Smith *et al.*, 2001) and Cruagh (Newton & Mitchell, 2001) would have resulted in respective population estimates of AOS, 16% lower and 9% higher respectively than those based on site-specific adjustment factors.

The most appropriate timing for tape playback surveys is the mid- to late-incubation period, when the maximum number of egg-laying pairs is occupying burrows. The timing of egg-laying has been studied intensively on the Pembrokeshire (Dyfed) islands of Skomer and Skokholm (Brooke, 1990), where laying commences in April and the majority of the breeding population have laid by late May. Seabird 2000 surveys were thus targeted to the period late May to early June, although logistic constraints meant that some were conducted earlier in May and continued into late June.

In Britain over 90% of the population is thought to be on Rum and on the Welsh islands of Skokholm, Skomer and Middleholm, and all of these colonies were surveyed for Seabird 2000 (Smith *et al.*, 2001; Murray & Shewry, 2002). The Rum colony presents very considerable challenges, as burrows are distributed in widely varying densities over a series of steep mountain slopes. A ground survey in 2000 was used to map the overall limits of the main colony and to define two strata of apparently high and low burrow densities. Manx Shearwaters also breed at low densities elsewhere on Rum, but these are estimated to hold no more than a few thousand pairs. During the incubation period in 2001 two surveys were carried out in parallel. Firstly, the number of AOS (as identified from visual signs of burrow use) were counted in 650 randomly placed sample quadrats (20 m²). The mean number of AOS in the quadrats in each stratum were used to estimate the total number of AOS across the whole colony (Murray & Shewry, 2002). Secondly, within each quadrat a taped call of a male Rum shearwater was played at the entrance of all potential burrows and responses noted. No calibration studies were undertaken and the 1.98 correction factor given by Walsh *et al.* (1995) was used to estimate the number of AOS (Murray & Shewry, 2002).

On Skomer, Skokholm and Middleholm all burrows deemed suitable for occupancy by Manx Shearwaters were counted during winter 1997–98. The following summer, tape playback was performed at 5% of the burrows on each island. The number of responses was adjusted by a response rate measured on Skomer, concurrently with the survey (Smith *et al.*, 2001).

Elsewhere, the first comprehensive surveys were conducted on the Isles of Scilly (Cornwall) in 2000 (Heaney *et al.*, 2002), on Lundy (Devon) in 2001 (Price & Booker, 2001) and on the Treshnish Isles (Argyll & Bute) in 2000 (Offer, 2000). In the St Kilda archipelago (Western Isles), the main Manx Shearwater colony on Hirta was surveyed systematically for the first time using playback (Mitchell *et al.*, 2003). The colony on the adjacent island of Dun was surveyed less intensively, but numbers there were an order of magnitude less than on Hirta. Similarly, the colonies on Soay and Boreray were also judged too small to warrant full systematic surveys; instead, nocturnal visits to colony areas in late June and early July 2000 provided qualitative population estimates.

Cramp *et al.* (1974) and Lloyd *et al.* (1991) listed all sites in Britain and Ireland that contained evidence of possible or definite breeding during Operation Seafarer and the SCR Census of 1985–88, in addition to other records made outwith the two censuses. This evidence is summarised in Table 2 and was used as a basis for selection of sites to survey during Seabird 2000. The main gaps in coverage in Britain were in the Northern Isles, where only relict populations apparently remain, Bearasay off Lewis (Western Isles), Eigg and Muck in the Small Isles (Lochaber), and the Sanda Islands off Kintyre (Argyll & Bute). However the combined population of all these islands is thought to be no more than 1,000 AOS (Table 2).

In Ireland, those islands with probably the largest populations were surveyed as a first priority. Time limitations prevented some smaller colonies or potential sites from being surveyed during Seabird 2000 (Table 2). On five of these, breeding by Manx Shearwaters had been previously confirmed or strongly suspected and the probable size of the colony estimated (Table 2). Of these, only Inishtearaght (Co. Kerry) was thought to contain a sizeable colony of around 1,000 pairs, whereas the other four were thought to each hold fewer than 100 pairs. Four more sites are historically suspected to contain shearwater colonies but no attempt to confirm breeding has been made in at least the last 30 years. Significant colonies in Ireland could have been overlooked during Seabird 2000, as Cruagh Island clearly demonstrated.

Cruagh Island, off the western tip of Connemara (Co. Galway) was not known to support any seabirds of note and was almost certainly not visited during Operation Seafarer (1969–70) or the SCR Census (1985–88). In 2000, a concerned member of the public contacted BirdWatch Ireland with a report of several hundred dead black and white birds, smaller than gulls, and thought to be Oystercatchers, in various states of decomposition lying around burrow entrances. The following year, we visited the island and found that the dead 'oystercatchers' were in fact dead Manx Shearwaters, depredated by Great Black-backed Gulls. A subsequent survey found over 3,000 AOS, the sixth-largest colony in Ireland.

When an island was visited for the first time, preliminary playback surveys were conducted to confirm breeding and the extent of sub-colonies was mapped. The size of these sub-colonies determined whether a survey was conducted of the whole area or only a sample area was surveyed and then an estimate made of the total number of AOS over the whole colony. Population estimates for the larger colonies are crucially dependent upon the sampling, mapping and extrapolation methods adopted to estimate overall population size from sample plots. The methods used to survey each colony are summarised in Table 2. The implications of the methods adopted at individual colonies during Seabird 2000 for comparisons with previous (and future) population estimates are discussed below.

CURRENT STATUS AND TRENDS

During Seabird 2000 there were 332,267 AOS (95% CLs 305,072–374,067) of Manx Shearwaters at 40 colonies surveyed in Britain and Ireland, with 50% in Wales, 38% in Scotland, 11% in Ireland and fewer than 1% in England and the Isle of Man (Table 3). Coverage was incomplete in Ireland and Scotland, with up to 14 more colonies possibly present. But, as outlined above, there were not believed to be any major colonies overlooked, thus we have made no attempt to account for these gaps in the total population estimate.

Over 90% of the British population is on the islands of Rum (Lochaber) and the Pembrokeshire islands of Skomer, Skokholm and Middleholm. The remaining 36 colonies contribute very little to the population apart from the large colony on Bardsey (Gwynedd; Table 2). Lloyd *et al.* (1991) estimated the British population at 220,000–250,000 pairs, which would suggest that the Seabird 2000 estimate of 295,089 (95% CLs 277,803–313,263) represents a fairly stable population, although any detailed comparison is impossible, as no comprehensive national survey has previously been completed. A better idea of population trends can be obtained by comparing previous estimates at individual colonies.

The 'super-colony' on the three Pembrokeshire islands held 151,000 AOS in 1997–98 (Smith *et al.*, 2001) and is the largest in the world. Of these, 67% were on Skomer, 31% on Skokholm and 2% on Middleholm. It is difficult to assess whether this population is increasing or decreasing, as no complete census had previously been conducted on any of the three islands. However, on Skokholm, Smith *et al.* (2001) suggest that there may have been a 30% increase over the last 30 years, based on estimates using mark-recapture of fledglings conducted in the mid-1960s. There have been several attempts to estimate the size of the population on Skomer over the last 30 years, incorporating a variety of methods (see Smith *et al.*, 2001 for a review). For instance, Brooke (1990) estimated the

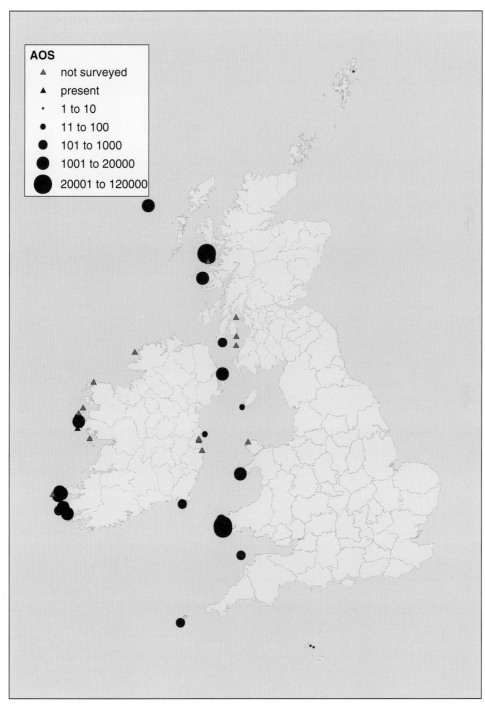

Figure 1   Abundance and distribution of breeding Manx Shearwaters in Britain and Ireland 1998–2002.

Table 2   *Numbers of Manx Shearwaters (AOS) at colonies in Britain and Ireland (1999–2002) compared to previous evidence of breeding given by* Cramp et al. *(1974) and* Lloyd et al. *(1991).*

Administrative area or country	Colony	Method	Year	AOS	95% lower confidence limit	95% upper confidence limit	Cramp et al. 1974	Lloyd et al. 1991
Shetland	Horse of Burravoe	1, 2	1994	0				P
Shetland	Lamb Hoga, Fetlar	2, 6	2002	7	7	7	c.100 pairs	P
Shetland	Foula	1, 3	2001	0			P	P
Orkney	Enegars, Hoy	1, 2	2002	0			2 colonies: 1–9 pairs + 10–99 pairs	40–50 pairs
Western Isles	St Kilda: Hirta	3, 6, 7	1999	4,581	3,371	5,687	P	P
Western Isles	St Kilda: Dun	3, 7	1999	222			P	P
Western Isles	St Kilda: Soay	1, 3	2000	P			P	P
Western Isles	St Kilda: Boreray	1, 3	2000	P?			P	P
Lochaber	Canna	2,6	2001	2			1,000+ pairs	c.1,000 pairs
Lochaber	Muck			nc				P
Lochaber	Rum	2,7	2001	120,000	107,000	134,000	c.70,000 pairs	97,000–135,000 pairs (Wormwell 1976), c. 150,000 pairs (Thompson & Thompson 1980)
Lochaber	Eigg	8	1999	250	200[1]	300[2]	10–99 pairs	70–100 pairs
Argyll and Bute	Treshnish Isles	3,6	2000	1,283			P	P
Argyll and Bute	Sanda	8	1999	200				50–100 pairs
Argyll and Bute	Inchmarnock, Bute	1	2002	1?				
Cunninghame	Pladda Island, Arran			nc				(dead bird found in a burrow 1979, also P 1981)
Kyle and Carrick	Ailsa Craig			?				
Devon	Lundy	4,6	2001	166			c.100 pairs	c.1,200 pairs
Isles of Scilly	Annet	4,6	2000	123			800–900 pairs	50–300 birds
Isles of Scilly	Shipman's Head, Bryher	4,6	2000	12				1977: 25–30 pairs
Isles of Scilly	St Agnes	4,6	2000	5				1977: 500 pairs, P (1983)
Isles of Scilly	Round Island	4,6	2000	34				P (1983: 24 AOB)
Isles of Scilly	Gugh	4,6	2000	22				
Isles of Scilly	St Helen's	4,6	2000	5				
Channel Islands	Little Sark	8	2000	5				10–20 AOB (1989)
Channel Islands	Jethou	8	2000	5				5–10 AOB (1989)
Isle of Man	Calf of Man	3,6	2001	34			'very small numbers'	P (1983: 32 AOB)
Dyfed	Skokholm	5,6	1998	46,200[3]			30,000–40,000 pairs	P
Dyfed	Skomer	5,6	1998	101,800	98,824	104,768	c.60,000 pairs	P (1981: 100,000 pairs)
Dyfed	Middleholm	5,6	1998	3,000[3]			100 pairs	2,000+ pairs (1983)
Dyfed	Cardigan Island	1	1999–2001	0				1980–84: 50 chicks introduced annually from Skomer. Deserted egg found in 1984. No subsequent breeding
Dyfed	Ramsey	3,6	1999	950	900[1]	1,000[2]		165 pairs (1992)
Gwynedd	Bardsey	2,6	2001			16,183	c.2500 pairs	4000–5000 pairs
Gwynedd	Carmel Head			nc			P	1972–82: birds calling over land
Co. Antrim	Rathlin	1		0?			1000–9999	320 birds
Co. Down	Big Copeland; Copeland Islands	3,7	2002–03	1,766	1,651	2,007	c.300 pairs total on Copeland Islands	c.700 pairs total on Copeland Islands

Administrative area or country	Colony	Method	Year	AOS	95% lower confidence limit	95% upper confidence limit	Cramp et al. 1974	Lloyd et al. 1991
Co. Down	Lighthouse Island; Copeland Islands	3,7	2000	2,867	1,938	4,239	c.300 pairs total on Copeland Islands	c.300 pairs total on Copeland Islands
Co. Dublin	Lambay	3,6	2002	25			50–100	
Co. Dublin	Ireland's Eye			nc			<20 burrows	
Co. Dublin	Howth Head			nc			several	<15 birds (1984)
Co. Wicklow	Bray Head			nc			10 burrows	
Co. Wexford	Great Saltee	7	2002	150			c.20 pairs	P
Co. Wexford	Little Saltee	8	2001	100			c.30 pairs (1981)	
Co. Kerry	Scariff	5	2000	1,960	1,491	2,859	thought to breed (1001–10,000 pairs in 1973)	
Co. Kerry	Deenish	5	2000	351	267	512		11–100 pairs (1978)
Co. Kerry	Puffin Island	5	2000	6,329	4,815	9,235	10,000–99,999 pairs	1001–10,000 pairs
Co. Kerry	Great Skellig	5	2001	738	561	1,077	1000–9999 pairs	P
Co. Kerry	Great Blasket	5	2001	3,584	2,445	6,705	thought to breed	P? (1988)
Co. Kerry	Inishvickillane	5	2001	643	439	1,204	100–999 pairs	101–1000 pairs (1988)
Co. Kerry	Inishtearaght			nc			100–999 pairs	800–1200 pairs (1988)
Co. Kerry	Inishnabro	5	2000	5,611	3,828	10,498	100–999 pairs	101–1000 pairs (1988)
Co. Kerry	Inishtooskert	5	2000	9,696	6,616	18,142	100–999 pairs	1001–10,000 pairs (1988)
Co. Kerry	Illauntannig, Magharees	5	2001	0				
Co. Galway	Corrigeenagowlra			nc			(suspected in 1942)	
Co. Galway	Friar	5	2001	0		nc		
Co. Galway	High Island	5	2001	22	19	26	10–99 pairs	c.100 pairs
Co. Galway	Cruagh	5	2001	3,286	2,879	3,965	nc	
Co. Galway	Inishshark	5	2001	51	45	61	nc	
Co. Galway	Doonnahinneena, Inishbofin	1	2000	P		nc		
Co. Galway	Davillaun	5	2001	0			100–500 pairs	
Co. Galway	Slyne Head/ Illaunamid	1	1995	P			c.15	c.80 pairs (1980)
Co. Mayo	Inishturk			nc			4 AOB	nc
Co. Mayo	Clare Island			nc			one bird calling	
Co. Mayo	Kid Island			nc			nc	
Co. Donegal	Aranmore Island			nc			nc	nc

Method code		Notes	
1	Determined presence/absence	[1] Min	
2	AOS determined by visual signs of burrow occupancy	[2] Max	
3	AOS determined using tape playback of male call with adjustment factor 1.98	[3] Confidence limits not given by Smith et al. (2001)	
4	AOS determined using tape playback of male and female calls with adjustment factor 1.08	P	present and confirmed breeding
5	AOS determined using tape playback using site specific adjustment factor—see table 1.	nc	not counted (i.e. presence/absence not determined); also applies to sites that have historical evidence of breeding (i.e. prior to 1969) but were not visited during Operation Seafarer (see Cramp et al., 1974)
6	Complete count of AOS / responses		
7	Sample count of AOS / responses		
8	Best guess		

total population at 100,000 pairs from sample counts of fledglings. The only previous playback survey conducted on Skomer was in 1995 (Gibbons & Vaughan, 1998), but this was confined to the area of the island known as 'The Neck', which held 26,500 AOS (95% CLs 21,000–32,000) in 1995, compared to 18,807 AOS during the complete census in 1997–98. Smith *et al.* (2001) argue that the 1995 survey may have overestimated the number of AOS present and been biased towards dense areas because of the small proportion of total area (i.e. 1%) that was sampled.

On Rum there were an estimated 120,000 AOS (95% CLs 107,000–134,000) in 2001 (Murray & Shewry, 2002). The Manx Shearwaters on Rum, in contrast to all other colonies, nest at altitudes of 457–800 m covering a total colony area of 148 ha, although the core of the population is within

50 ha. The burrows are concentrated in 'greens' where droppings from the birds have enriched the surrounding vegetation. Wormell (1976) estimated that between 1965 and 1969 there was a total of 116,000 AOS (95% CLs 97,000–135,000) within an estimated colony area totalling *c.*31 ha, derived from, probably flawed, interpretation of 1946 aerial photographs (Philips, 1982; Furness, 1997a; Murray & Shewry, 2002). In 1982, Philips (1982) estimated 79,000 AOS (95% CLs 69,000–88,000) over the same area, using a different sampling regime. In both cases, burrows were counted in July–August, when many non-breeders are active in the colonies (Brooke, 1990), so may have overestimated the number of burrows occupied by breeding pairs. In addition, the sample quadrats were much larger than used in 2001 and confined to the highest density parts of the colony within the obvious 'greens'.

In July 1990, Furness (1990) counted the number of AOSs in 160 circular quadrats (50 m^2) placed randomly within areas mapped as occupied by Manx Shearwaters in a 1985–1988 ground survey of the colony. This gave a population estimate of 62,800 AOS (95% CLs 20,100–105,500) over a similar area to that estimated by Wormell (1976). These CLs are much wider than Wormell's (1976) or Phillips' (1982) as they include estimates for possible errors associated with both mapping and measuring the colony area. Between 1985 and 1995, Furness (1997a) also examined changes in densities of AOS within 105 non-random 100 m^2 square quadrats placed in blocks designed to sample large and small 'greens' as well as 'peripheral' colony areas, including some unoccupied ground. During the periods 1985–90 and 1990–95 there were declines in mean densities of AOS in these quadrats of 2.3% and 2.4% respectively, higher than the 2% estimated as attributable to inter-observer variation. However, the variance in numbers of burrows per quadrat was very high and the observed changes in densities (paired t-test) were statistically insignificant. Whether the observed declines are indicative of a real decline in the colony over this period is unclear (Furness, 1997a; Murray & Shewry, 2002).

Results from the parallel tape playback survey conducted in 2001 can be re-analysed with the calibration plot exercise undertaken in 2003. This yielded an estimate of 112,600 AOS but with rather wide 95% CLs (83,000–159,000). The visual count of occupied burrows was adopted by Seabird 2000 based on the judgement of the field team responsible for the work. Notwithstanding, the tape playback estimate is close enough to the visual count to indicate that the newer technique has potential and can be used to help design a robust long-term monitoring strategy for the Rum colony.

Adjacent to Rum are the islands of Canna, Eigg and Muck. On Canna, Manx Shearwaters ceased to breed in 2002 (Swann, 2003). The population was believed to be in the order of 1,000–15,000 pairs between the mid-1970s and mid-1980s, but by 1993 there were fewer than 150 pairs (Swann, 1995, 2000). A comprehensive tape playback survey in 1997 suggested that only 65 of 952 potential Manx Shearwater burrows were occupied by breeding pairs within the main colony area (Swann, 1997). Subsequent annual checks of *c.*100 burrows charted the demise of the species on the island (Swann, 2000). No systematic surveys have been undertaken on Eigg or Muck, but no more than a few hundred pairs are estimated to breed at these sites.

The largest concentration in Scotland outside Rum is on St Kilda (Western Isles), where the main breeding concentration (3,443 AOS) was nesting amongst the immense boulders of Carn Mor on Hirta (Mitchell *et al.*, in prep.). Manx Shearwaters have bred at a number of other islands in the Western Isles, notably Mingulay, Pabbay and Berneray (Elwes, 1869; Gray, 1871; Cramp *et al.*, 1974), but there are no recent records from these sites. In the 1960s, a colony was present on the island of Bearasay in Loch Roag, Lewis (Robson & Wills, 1963; Andrew, 1965), but the present status of this is unknown.

The limited information available for the Northern Isles suggests that the already small breeding populations recorded by Operation Seafarer (1969–70) and the SCR Census (1985–88) have further declined, with a maximum of 10 AOS remaining on Fetlar.

On the Treshnish Isles (Argyll & Bute), a Manx Shearwater colony of 1,283 AOS was confined to the main island of Lunga. The use of systematic tape survey found that colonies are more widespread in suitable habitat throughout the island than previously thought (Offer, 2000). The colony on the Sanda Islands (Argyll & Bute), which was first noted in 1978, was estimated to hold *c.*200 AOS (R. Morton, pers. comm.). Occasional finds of depredated Manx Shearwaters on land suggest that there may possibly be very small colonies at other sites in the Firth of Clyde (e.g. Pladda, Inchmarnock). Prospecting birds were heard on the ground on the Isle of May (northeast Fife) on some nights in late July–early August 1997 (D. Hemsley, *in litt.*), but there have been no subsequent records. Manx Shearwaters remain confined to a breeding range on the north, west and south coasts of Britain.

Table 3   Numbers of breeding Manx Shearwaters (AOS) in Britain and Ireland 1999–2002.

Administrative area or country	AOS	95% lower confidence limit	95% upper confidence limit	Colonies counted	Colonies not counted
Shetland	7	7	7	1	
Western Isles–Comhairle nan eilean	4,803	3,593	5,909	1[1]	
Lochaber	120,252	107,202	134,302	4	
Argyll & Bute	1,483	1,483	1,483	2	1[2]
Cunninghame	P?			0	1
Kyle & Carrick	P?			0	1
Scotland Total	**126,545**	**112,285**	**141,701**	**8**	**3**
Channel Islands	10	10	10	2	
Devon	166	166	166	1	
Isles of Scilly	201	201	201	6	
Isle of Man	34	34	34	1	
England, Channel Islands and Isle of Man Total	**411**	**411**	**411**	**10**	
Dyfed	151,950	148,924	154,968	4	
Gwynedd	16,183	16,183	16,183	1	
Wales Total	**168,133**	**165,107**	**171,151**	**5**	
Great Britain, Channel Islands and Isle of Man Total	**295,089**	**277,803**	**313,263**	**23**	**3**
Co. Down	4,633	3,589	6,246	2	
Co. Dublin	25	25	25	1	2[3]
Co. Wicklow	P?			0	1
Co. Wexford	250	250	250	2	
Co. Kerry	28,912	20,462	50,231	9	1[4]
Co. Galway	3,358	2,942	4,052	3	3[5]
Co. Mayo	P?			0	3
Co. Donegal	P?			0	1
All-Ireland Total	**37,178**	**27,269**	**60,804**	**17**	**11**
Britain and Ireland Total	**332,267**	**305,072**	**374,067**	**40**	**14**

Notes
[1] Four islands of St Kilda treated as one colony
[2] Possibly breeding on Inchmarnock
[3] Possibly breeding on Ireland's Eye and at Howth Head
[4] Present on Inishtearaght, but not counted
[5] Present on Inishbofin and Slyne Head but not counted, possibly breeding on Corrigeenagowlra

The other large colony in Britain is on Bardsey Island (Gwynedd) with a visual burrow count of 16,183 AOS in 2001. Tape playback indicated a somewhat smaller breeding population of 9,779 AOS (Leaper *et al.*, in prep.), but this was based on a correction factor of 1.98, as no calibration for response rate was conducted. Elsewhere in Wales, a further 900 AOS were estimated for Ramsay Island (Dyfed). Experiments to establish a colony on Cardigan Island in the early 1980s appear to have been unsuccessful (H. Roderick, pers. comm.) as none was recorded in 1999–2001. Cadman (1936) apparently found Manx Shearwaters nesting on the Pembrokeshire mainland but no subsequent information is available.

The only colonies in England were on Lundy (Devon) and the Isles of Scilly. At the latter, Heaney *et al.* (2002) found a total of 201 AOS on six of 14 islands, and confirmed the long-recognised importance of Annet (e.g. McPherson, *c*.1898) as the principal colony, with 123 AOS. The current population estimate is much lower than previous ones, e.g. 900 pairs in 1974 (Allen, 1977), 375–530+ pairs in 1977 (Harvey, 1983) and 500–700 in 1999 (Robinson, 1999), but the variety of methods used to assess burrow occupancy preclude any definite conclusion that the population is declining (Heaney *et al.*, 2002). On Lundy, tape playback at over 7,000 potential burrows in May 2001 yielded only 154 responses (Price & Booker, 2001). This is very much lower than recent estimates of several thousand pairs, based on counts of all potentially suitable burrows in areas known to be visited by Manx Shearwaters at night in the pre-breeding season, or on counts of birds at sea (Thomas, 1981; Taylor, 1985). However, it is more in line with Southern & Tucker's (1944) observations in July 1942, when 19 definitely occupied burrows were found in an area found to hold 9 AOS in 2001.

In the Channel Islands, Manx Shearwaters have established a tentative toehold on Sark and Jethou within the last few decades (Hill, 1994), which in the early 1990s may have held up to 50 occupied burrows in total. Small numbers of chicks have fledged successfully, but cats and Brown Rats are active predators at these colonies (Hill, 1994) and the prospects for their expansion, or indeed long-term survival, seem poor. Information submitted to Seabird 2000 indicates that the colonies are only just hanging on with estimates of 5 AOS on each island.

At the Calf of Man (Isle of Man), small numbers of shearwaters were found ashore and visiting burrows at night in early July 1999. Subsequently, bird observatory staff have attempted diurnal tape playback and in 2001 17 responses were elicited (T. Bagworth, pers. comm.), which would indicate the presence of 34 AOS. Subsequent surveys indicate that the population is increasing, with 50 AOS in 2003 (C. Sharpe, pers. comm.).

In Ireland the population was roughly similar to the estimate of the SCR Census (1985–88) and the review of Brooke (1990), both of which gave numbers of *c*.30,000 AOS at 25–28 colonies/sites. On the basis of Seabird 2000 tape playback surveys, Ireland supports a breeding population of 37,178 AOS (95% CLs 27,269–60,804), with more than 30,000 in the Republic of Ireland and *c*.5,000 in Northern Ireland (Tables 2–3).

Islands off the Co. Kerry coast have long been known to support the bulk of the Irish breeding population. The colonies can be split into three island groups: Scariff and Deenish; Puffin Island and Great Skellig, and the Blasket Islands (five main islands). Tape playback surveys were carried out in 2000–01 on all islands, with the exception of Inishtearaght in the Blasket group. Together, these islands support an estimated 28,912 AOS (Table 2), with the largest colonies on Inishtooskert (9,696 AOS) and on Puffin Island (6,329 AOS). The presence of a significant colony on the largest island of the group, Great Blasket, was confirmed by Seabird 2000. This island had been overlooked, and underestimated, by many earlier seabird expeditions, perhaps because of its size and because it lacks any other obvious diurnal seabird populations. The colony is perhaps more dispersed than others, with small sub-colonies scattered along the slight promontories of the south coast, although a significant concentration is present at the southwest tip, Canduff, closest to the other outer Blasket Islands. Elsewhere in Co. Kerry, the only other islands with the potential to support colonies are the Magharees, off Castlegregory, on the north side of the Dingle Peninsula. The largest island of the group is Illauntannig and here tape playback was used, with no responses detected, during a brief visit.

In Co. Galway, there was a previously undocumented colony of 3,286 AOS on the island of Cruagh, off the western tip of Connemara. Co. Galway and Co. Mayo are very rich in islands, but both Operation Seafarer and the SCR Census found very few to have evidence of breeding by Manx Shearwaters (Table 2). Elsewhere in Co. Galway, small numbers (fewer than 100 AOS) were found breeding on High Island and Inishshark, where colonies had previously been detected (Ruttledge, 1950). S. Berrow (*in litt.* 2000) reported the presence of Manx Shearwater burrows, together with a dead adult on Doonnahinneena, a small islet just off the coast of Inishbofin, a site also known to Ruttledge (1950). In Co. Mayo, the only colonies are thought to be on Inishturk, Kid Island (off Broadhaven Bay) and possibly mainland cliffs and small islands near Porturlin. Seabird 2000 fieldworkers attempted to land on Kid Island but were thwarted by rough seas. Kid Island is the most northerly documented colony in the Republic (Ruttledge, 1950; Brooke, 1990). The apparently large gap in the distribution of Manx Shearwater colonies, from here north and east to Co. Antrim, is possible due to lack of coverage or awareness amongst Irish seabird workers, as there is no shortage of islands off north Co. Mayo and Co. Donegal. There is an urgent need to survey such sites for nocturnal seabirds given the recent range expansion of American Mink to many of the inner Co. Donegal islands (J. P. Hillis, pers. comm.; E. Magee, pers. comm.). 'Former' sites in Co. Mayo known to Ruttledge (1950), including the Porturlin cliffs, and the nearby islet of Illaunakonoge, should also be visited to assess whether Manx Shearwaters can persist at mainland sites.

The Copeland Islands (Co. Down), off the southern approach to Belfast Harbour, hold the largest two colonies of just five off the east coast of Ireland. Lighthouse Island holds the larger of the two colonies, 2,867 AOS, compared to 1,766 AOS on the largest island, Big Copeland. The presence of the bird observatory on Lighthouse Island has lead to a history of censusing Manx Shearwaters using mark-recapture ringing, but this is the first time playback has been used. They are fairly dispersed on Big Copeland where the latter method is particularly useful as the birds often nest underneath old stone walls and other raised field boundaries all across the island. The most northerly colony was formerly on Rathlin Island (Co. Antrim). Manx Shearwaters have disappeared from their former nesting areas and local expert opinion (L. McFaul, pers. comm.) considers that only 'inaccessible' grassy ledges/slopes on the north side of the island may still support a tiny number of birds. Given that access to such ledges is precarious, tape playback was only attempted on one night and no responses were elicited. Hence, nesting cannot be confirmed for the island.

The only other colonies on the east coast were on Lambay Island (Co. Dublin: Newton, 2002), Great Saltee and Little Saltee (Co. Wexford). Systematic surveys were not carried out on the latter two islands for Seabird 2000, but the total of 150 AOS estimated for Great Saltee is based on visual burrow counts and numbers of adults and fledglings recorded during night-time ringing operations. A similar number are thought to nest on Little Saltee.

Previous surveys have alluded to the presence of several small colonies on islands and headlands around Co. Dublin and north Co. Wicklow: Ireland's Eye, Howth Head and Bray Head, but no surveys were undertaken during Seabird 2000. There is a paucity of islands along the south coast of Ireland, between the Saltees and west Co. Cork until one reaches the vicinity of Cape Clear and Roaringwater Bay, and thus Manx Shearwater colonies are thought to be absent. Tape playback could prove otherwise, especially in Co. Cork, where Manx Shearwaters are suspected of breeding on the Bull and Cow Rocks.

CAUSES OF CHANGE

Alien mammalian predators have long been recognised as significant, and potentially devastating, predators of island avifaunas (Atkinson, 1985). Among seabirds, Manx Shearwaters are potentially highly vulnerable to such predators, especially Brown Rats, on account of their burrow-nesting habits, population dynamics, and adaptation to prolonged desertion of viable eggs or chicks.

Historical evidence, in the form of letters between 1786 and 1789, suggest that Manx Shearwaters were exterminated at their eponymous colony on the Calf of Man by Brown Rats that escaped from a wrecked ship at about that time (BRSM, 1941). However, the absence of systematic records over the period between *c.*1730 and the mid-19th century, during which Brown Rats became widely established in Britain and Ireland (Corbett & Southern, 1977) makes it impossible to assess the overall historical impact on Manx Shearwater populations. Current distribution patterns are certainly suggestive of a negative impact, with major colonies now confined largely to sites not colonised by Brown Rats. The obvious exception to this is Rum, where Thompson (1987) suggests that the unique location of the extant colony in mountain terrain ringed by moorland may at least in part explain the apparent lack of impact of a very substantial Brown Rat population. Fortunately, feral cats, which are active predators of Manx Shearwaters at colonies from Shetland (M. Smith, pers. comm.) to the Channel Islands (Hill, 1994), are absent from the Rum colonies, and the island's managers (Scottish Natural Heritage) permit only neutered cats to be kept as pets by island residents. Both Brown and Black Rats are present on Lundy, although their current impact on breeding Manx Shearwaters requires investigation.

Circumstantial evidence suggests that predation of eggs, chicks and adults by Brown Rats and cats was a causal factor in the recent rapid demise of the once substantial Manx Shearwater colony on Canna (Swann, 2000). However, it is not clear which underlying environmental factors might have driven the apparent increase in predator activity at the colony. Reductions in Manx Shearwater breeding success caused by external factors, such as poor food supply or increased rainfall (Swann, 2000; Thompson & Furness, 1991), could have increased the availability of deserted eggs or dead chicks whilst milder winters could have increased overwinter survival of predators. Whatever the ultimate cause of the cessation of regular nesting on Canna, it serves as a sobering reminder that systems are far from static and that vigilance, through appropriate systematic monitoring, is an essential prerequisite to effective conservation action. Determining the actual level of predation, and its potential effect on populations, is extremely difficult as it requires quantitative information on populations of predators and prey, on predators' food intake and diet and on prey population dynamics (Moors & Atkinson, 1984). However, recent developments in the use of stable isotopes to determine diet offer a new set of tools to assist in determining the extent to which introduced mammals may rely on seabirds (e.g. Stapp, 2002; Keitt *et al.*, 2002).

The fate of the Manx Shearwater colony on Canna, plus indications of increasing rat predation on other seabirds there (Swann, 2000), has prompted the island's owners (National Trust for Scotland) to implement localised rat and cat control measures, and to instigate a study into the feasibility of undertaking a rat eradication programme (Patterson, 2001). Following the successful precedents set by conservation managers in New Zealand (Veitch & Bell, 1990) and elsewhere, several rat eradication projects have recently been implemented in the UK (e.g. Zonfrillo & Monaghan, 1995). On Skomer, contingency procedures, recently developed for Ramsey Island, will be implemented should rats ever arrive (Brown, 2001).

In Ireland, virtually all extant colonies on the west coast are on uninhabited islands. Some have summer residents based on them, for example on Great Skellig (Co. Kerry), up to ten or more archaeological heritage workmen and guides live on the island. The *status quo* on Great Blasket is

Manx Shearwater chick in a burrow on Skomer in late July (photographed using a video endoscope) (JNCC)

certainly about to change. The island has had no permanent residents since its evacuation in 1954. The possible increase in the size on the colony since then may be attributable to the probable demise of any domestic cats left behind following evacuation. However, some landowners are now spending more time in residence on the island and increased development is likely. Plans are also well advanced for the construction of a new pier that would eliminate the need to transfer visitors from ferries into inflatable dinghies for landing. This may increase the likelihood of Brown Rats reaching the island and although conservation organisations have expressed their concerns to the planning authorities, it remains to be seen whether any anti-rat contingency plans will be developed to protect the Manx Shearwater colony. On the east coast, two of the known colonies also support rat populations: Great Saltee has Brown Rats and Lambay has both Brown and Black Rats. Both colonies are small and are perhaps limited in their size, distribution and breeding success by the rats.

Ferrets were deliberately introduced to Rathlin in 1988, since when breeding Manx Shearwaters, if still present, are believed to be confined to inaccessible grassy ledges on the cliffs (L. McFaul, pers. comm.). One unusual predator, and scavenger, of Manx Shearwaters on Rum are Red Deer which obtain scarce minerals from the shearwaters' bones. Furness (1988) estimated that up to 4% of Manx Shearwater fledglings on Rum may be taken by Red Deer. This level of fledgling mortality is unlikely to affect the breeding population.

Unlike Brown Rats, which can target breeding adults, eggs and chicks in burrows, avian predators at Manx Shearwater colonies normally only take birds in the air or on the ground. As breeding adults tend to fly quickly to and from colonies and spend little time on the ground (Brooke, 1990), such predation is likely to focus mainly on prospecting non-breeders and on fledglings, thus reducing the potential impact on the breeding population. Both Corkhill (1973) on Skomer and Brooke (1990) on Skokholm regarded Great Black-backed Gulls as having no significant impact on Manx Shearwater populations. However, in the 1960s and 1970s Great Black-backed Gulls on Skomer were the subject of a major control programme, which saw the population drop from 260 to fewer than 80 pairs. The current population (*c*.60 pairs) is not regarded as a threat to other breeding seabirds (Brown, 2001).

In the Isles of Scilly, Harvey 1983 (in Heaney *et al.*, 2002) suggested that apparent declines on Annet might be due to expanding gull populations, but no quantitative data are available to assess this (Heaney *et al.*, 2002). On Rum, resident Golden Eagles were found not to be significant predators of the island's Manx Shearwater population (Thompson, 1987).

At St Kilda, the recent rapid expansion in the Great Skua population (see Great Skua chapter) has led to concern as to possible impacts on other seabirds. In 1996, Great Skuas were estimated to have taken 455 Manx Shearwaters (Phillips *et al.*, 1999a). Given an estimated Shearwater population of around 5,000 pairs (Table 2), with an associated visiting non-breeding population of *c.*5,000 birds and assuming 10% annual adult mortality (Brooke, 1990), Great Skua predation has the potential to roughly equal 30% of the total estimated annual adult mortality. The actual impact on the breeding population is difficult to assess as many of the birds taken may be non-breeders, and it is unknown to what extent any increase in mortality due to Great Skuas might be compensated by decreases in rates due to other factors. In global conservation terms, the significance of the St Kilda Great Skua population far exceeds that of the Manx Shearwater population. However, given the relatively high rate of predation suggested, and rapid recent expansion of the St Kilda Great Skua population, future monitoring of this interaction would be of interest.

Where they occur together, Manx Shearwaters and Atlantic Puffins compete for burrows and in some cases, the latter have been cited as responsible for displacing Manx Shearwaters. Elwes (1869) says of Mingulay that '*about 100 years ago, however, the Puffins which before were not numerous began to increase very much and drove the Shearwaters from the holes which they occupied in the cliffs and now they have completely supplanted them*'. On Skomer, both species can successfully usurp the other and overall competitive advantage varies with geographical location on the island (Ashcroft, 1976, in Brooke, 1990).

Climate change, and especially any increase in the incidence of heavy rainfall during the incubation period, could adversely affect Manx Shearwater populations through increased incidence of flooding of burrows and consequent mortality of eggs or young chicks. Using simple models relating breeding success to burrow quality, as determined by likelihood of flooding during heavy rainfall during incubation, Thompson & Furness (1991) concluded that alteration of the rainfall regime on Rum would alter the colony size at which population stability would be achieved. Climatic changes could potentially also render colonies more prone to physical damage through soil erosion, although this has to date apparently been more problematic for some east-coast Atlantic Puffin colonies than for Manx Shearwaters (Brown, 2001). Climate change might potentially also affect the incidence of the disease Puffinosis, which is currently estimated to kill an insignificant 4% or fewer Manx Shearwater fledglings on Skomer and Skokholm each year (Brooke, 1990), although there is no proven link between weather and incidence of the disease. Thompson (1987) also found that the average laying date on Rum could be substantially delayed by poor weather in the pre-laying period, with consequent potential implications for average breeding success.

Given their relatively pelagic habits during the breeding season (Brooke, 1990), and apparent ability to utilise a variety of prey when feeding young (Thompson, 1987), Manx Shearwaters may be less prone than some seabirds to complete breeding failures associated with localised reductions in the availability of particular prey. However, monitoring on Canna has revealed occasional incidences of extremely poor breeding success, apparently associated with food shortages (Swann, 1995).

The historical impact of the collection of large numbers of Manx Shearwaters for food (see Introduction) in the British Isles is impossible to assess, although as mainly fledglings were taken such harvests were potentially sustainable (Brooke, 1990). In the 1960s and 1970s, substantial numbers of adult Manx Shearwaters from the Pembrokeshire colonies were deliberately caught on baited lines by fishermen in the Bay of Biscay, but the scale of this mortality has apparently substantially declined in recent years (Brooke, 1990; Wernham *et al.*, 2002). However, the impact of accidental bycatch in expanding longline fisheries operating in the Manx Shearwater's wintering grounds has yet to be assessed (Wernham *et al.*, 2002).

Manx Shearwaters, particularly fledglings, can be disorientated by and attracted to artificial light sources, particularly on moonless or foggy nights. Birds disorientated by lights around settlements may be grounded and vulnerable to predation by domestic cats (pers. obs.). Where lighthouses are situated close to colonies, some birds may be killed by collision with buildings, but systematic records at Bardsey suggest that the scale of such mortality is insignificant (Jones, 2001).

Seabird 2000 has demonstrated that the British and Irish Manx Shearwater population is larger than previously thought. Although we have no conclusive evidence of significant overall population changes, it would be complacent to suggest the population is secure. Clearly there are problems on Canna where it is difficult to separate the effect of food shortage and egg/chick predation in the demise of the colony. Breeding success is monitored at Skomer, where it is usually high, and a series of monitoring plots to measure population size using tape playback have also been established (Poole *et al.*, 2001). There is an urgent need to establish a more comprehensive monitoring programme for Manx Shearwaters across Britain and Ireland given their global importance for the species.

INTERNATIONAL CONTEXT

Outside Britain and Ireland, knowledge of Manx Shearwaters is rather poor and in these areas researchers are still in the discovery phase of understanding their distribution and status. However, combining Seabird 2000 estimates for Britain and Ireland with those from elsewhere gives an estimated world population of 338,000–411,000 pairs, of which Britain holds 68–93% and Ireland 7–18% (Table 4). Therefore, the colonies on St Kilda, Rum, Skomer, Skokholm, Bardsey, Puffin Island, Inishnabro, Inishtooskert, the Copeland Islands, and possibly Great Blasket and Cruagh would qualify as internationally important using a threshold of 3,700 pairs, i.e. 1% of the mid-point of estimated world population (Stroud *et al.*, 2001).

Two Faeroese colonies, Skúvoy and Sandoy, and the Vestmannaeyjar archipelago in Iceland would also qualify. The Manx Shearwater populations in the Faeroe Islands and Iceland are estimated at around 25,000 and 7,000–10,000 AOS respectively (BirdLife International/EBCC, 2000; Einarsson, 2000). To our knowledge, no intensive and systematic censuses have been undertaken and it is far from clear how these figures have been generated. In Iceland, breeding Manx Shearwaters are confined to the Westmann Islands. In both Iceland and the Faeroes, young Manx Shearwaters are legal quarry, but they are no longer taken in Iceland, whereas on the Faeroes they are still collected for human consumption. Skúvoy (Faeroe Islands) formerly held 10,000 AOS, the largest colony in the archipelago, according to Heath & Evans (2000), whereas others suggest 3,000–6,000 AOS between 1961 and 1981. Olsen (2003) suggests that Skúvoy has suffered a major decline in recent years due to unsustainable harvesting. Whether or not these levels of exploitation are more widespread in the archipelago remains to be seen, but the population estimate of 25,000 AOS may be too high.

Spanish and Portuguese populations of Manx Shearwaters are rather small and confined to the Atlantic archipelagos of Madeira, Azores and the Canary Islands, where population trends are unknown. In the northwest Atlantic, Manx Shearwaters have apparently colonised some islands off Canada (Newfoundland), although numbers are tiny and their persistence appears precarious.

Table 4   International context.

Country or region	Number of pairs		Year	Source
	Min	Max		
Great Britain, Channel Isles & Isle of Man	280,000[1]	310,000[2]	1999–2002	Seabird 2000
All Ireland	27,000[1]	61,000[2]	2000–2003	Seabird 2000
Faeroe Islands	25,000	25,000	1995	BirdLife International/EBCC (2000)
France	192	192	1999	Cadiou *et al.* (In press)
Iceland	7,000	10,000	1990	Icelandic Institute of Natural History (2000)
Portugal (Azores & Madeira)	500	900	1991–97	BirdLife International/EBCC (2000)
Spain (Canaries)	200	500	1987	BirdLife International/EBCC (2000)
Canada (Newfoundland)	1	5[3]		Robertson (2002)

Biogeographic region	Min	Max	Min % GB	Max % GB	Min % Ireland	Max % Ireland
World*	340,000	410,000	68.3%	91.2%	6.6%	17.9%

* Stroud *et al.* (2001)

Notes

[1] 95% lower confidence limit

[2] 95% upper confidence limit

[3] Robertson (2002) indicated less than 5

European Storm-petrel *Hydrobates pelagicus*

P. Ian Mitchell and Stephen F. Newton

INTRODUCTION

The European Storm-petrel presented the greatest challenge of all 25 species during Seabird 2000. In the absence of any recognised method for surveying breeding European Storm-petrels, the previous two censuses of seabirds in Britain and Ireland had to largely guess at the location of the colonies, let alone their size. European Storm-petrels are pelagic, returning to land only to breed, and choose to nest on remote offshore islands where nocturnal access is often difficult and dangerous. They nest below ground, appearing above ground only during darkness. European Storm-petrels are much more widespread in Britain and Ireland than Manx Shearwaters and Leach's Storm-petrels (see relevant chapters) These characters of storm-petrel distribution and behaviour have meant that obtaining estimates of breeding numbers has been virtually impossible, and indeed Cramp *et al.* (1974) stated that in order *'to locate these* [colonies] *and to provide some assessment of the total population would require a mammoth effort devoted solely to these ends'*.

The presence of birds at a site at night does not necessarily prove they are breeding there. Hundreds of thousands of European Storm-petrels have been caught in mist-nets and ringed all around Britain and Ireland, including areas outside their breeding range, such as eastern Scotland and England (Fowler, 2002). The petrels are caught at night, attracted to the nets by tape-lures (i.e.

recordings of their call played through loud-speakers). European Storm-petrels attracted to tape-lures tend to be non-breeders or 'wanderers' (Furness & Baillie, 1981; Fowler & Okill, 1988). Mark-recapture has estimated there to be 60,000 of these wanderers around Shetland (Fowler & Hounsome, 1998) moving randomly through the area and often covering large distances of over 200 km in three days or less, and often visiting other locations throughout the northeast Atlantic breeding range, e.g. Iceland and Norway (Fowler, 2002). Wanderers were thought to come close to shore at night to visit colonies and prospect for future mates and nest sites, but recent evidence suggests that European Storm-petrels move close inshore at night to exploit intertidal benthic organisms that migrate into the water column during high tides (D'Elbee & Hemery, 1997), which is probably why large numbers can be attracted to mist-nets by tape-lures placed away from breeding colonies.

During the last two censuses presence or absence of breeding European Storm-petrels was assessed from the following a) distinctive oily smell on the ground in likely habitat, b) presence of eggs or chicks (these are usually difficult or impossible to see), c) a bird singing from a burrow voluntarily or in response to tape-recording of the call of a European Storm-petrel, and, d) corpses found in a burrow or in likely nesting habitat. In 1969–70, Cramp *et al.* (1974) used historical accounts to identify likely locations of colonies and attempted to visit as many as possible. Subsequently, Lloyd *et al.* (1991) reported that during the late 1970s and 1980s breeding had been confirmed or suspected at 34 islands/archipelagos in Scotland, 28 in Ireland, ten islands in the Isles of Scilly, two in the Channel Islands, one on the Calf of Man and four in Wales. Breeding had also been confirmed or suspected at an additional 31 sites during 1968 and 1972 (see Cramp *et al.*, 1974) but these had not been revisited since. This gave a total of at least 110 sites that needed to be visited during Seabird 2000. All of the colonies were thought to be confined to the western coasts of Britain and Ireland, with the main concentrations in Shetland and the islands along the Atlantic Frontier of northwest Scotland and Ireland (mainly Co. Kerry, Co. Mayo and Co. Donegal: Lloyd *et al.*, 1991).

In the absence of any accurate method for counting European Storm-petrels during the last two censuses, the size of colonies was expressed as orders of magnitude. Lloyd *et al.* (1991) estimated there to be 20,000–150,000 pairs breeding in Britain and 50,000–100,000 pairs in Ireland.

A major aim of Seabird 2000 was to improve on the current estimate of numbers of European Storm-petrel breeding in Britain and Ireland. Recent developments in the use of tape playback for surveying the species have enabled us to obtain the first quantitative population estimate of numbers breeding in Britain and Ireland.

CENSUS METHODS

All of the colonies were surveyed in 1999–2001, except the Treshnish Isles (Argyll & Bute), which were visited in 1996, Mousa (Shetland), in 1996, and the islands of Eilean nan Ron, Eilean Iosal, Eilean Hoan, and Rabbit (all in Sutherland), in 1995. In all, 164 islands were surveyed in Britain, the Isle of Man and the Channel Islands using tape playback (Tables 2), including 98 islands where presence of breeding European Storm-petrels had not previously been suspected or confirmed. Coverage was not possible on 13 islands where breeding was confirmed and on four islands where breeding was suspected during at least one of the last two censuses (Table 2). There were a further eight islands from which historical records suggestive of breeding exist that were not visited during both previous censuses (see Cramp *et al.*, 1974; Table 2). It is highly unlikely that any substantial colonies (i.e. greater than order 1 or 2) were missed.

In the Republic of Ireland, a total of 16 islands was surveyed during 2000 and 2001 (Tables 2). Breeding was confirmed on another four islands (Table 2), but time constraints prevented a full

An Adult European Storm-petrel incubating in a nest chamber during the day on Hirta, St Kilda. This image was taken using a video endoscope (JNCC)

playback survey, so a rough estimate of apparently occupied sites (AOS) was made based on the density of AOS on nearby islands and the area of suitable habitat. There are a further 31 sites in the Republic of Ireland where European Storm-petrels were either proved breeding or strongly suspected of breeding in the past but were not surveyed during Seabird 2000 (Table 2). Breeding had previously been confirmed at 16 of these and rough population estimates were available for ten, which were added to the Seabird 2000 playback survey results to provide a total estimate of AOS for the Republic of Ireland (Table 3). The estimated colonies accounted for 40% of the total population in the Republic of Ireland (Table 3). It is highly unlikely that any other substantial colonies (i.e. greater than order 1–2) were missed. Major geographical gaps in coverage comprised islands between the main concentrations of colonies in west Co. Kerry and northwest Co. Mayo, and between the latter and west Co. Donegal. Neither area was thought to hold major colonies and there are few suitable islands in Co. Clare, Co. Sligo and Co. Leitrim. The south and west Connemara archipelago represented the largest concentration of islands that were not surveyed. No colonies have ever been found in Northern Ireland.

Where possible, all suitable habitat on an island was covered systematically. However, at some colonies large sub-colonies could not be completely surveyed due to time constraints. In such cases, an estimate of the density of burrows was obtained and multiplied by the area of the colony sampled to obtain an estimate of the number of AOSs. Even within suitable habitat the distribution of European Storm-petrel AOSs was highly patchy. This further reduces the precision of the final population estimate of AOSs.

The entrances to the nest sites of European Storm-petrels are indistinct, very difficult to find and tend to show little sign of use. Therefore, counting AOSs using visual signs of use, as with Atlantic Puffins and Manx Shearwaters is unsuitable for European Storm-petrels. The methods used to census European Storm-petrels during Seabird 2000 followed those of Gilbert *et al.* (1998a) that were based on research by Ratcliffe *et al.* (1998e). The method relies on the fact that European

Storm-petrels are highly vocal at their colonies and that vocalisation can be elicited from incubating adults by playing taped calls. There are two main types of calls issued by European Storm-petrels in response to playback. The purr call (often referred to as the churr or song) is uttered exclusively by males (James, 1984) and usually from the burrow rather than in flight. The flight or terr-chick call is uttered by both sexes and is associated with aerial courtship chases, but is also given from the burrow (Cramp & Simmons, 1977). James (1984) found that when recordings of the purr and flight calls (of both sexes) were played to European Storm-petrels incubating in burrows, more responded to the purr calls than to the flight calls. In fact, all males responded to the purr call, whereas only *c*.45% of females responded. Males responded with either a purr and a flight call or a flight call only.

During Seabird 2000, an AOS was defined by a response to a tape recording of a purr call with either a purr or flight call, elicited during the day. There were occasionally instances where two or more birds responded from apparently the same AOS. This was indicative of two pairs of petrels using the same entrance to two separate nest chambers. Unlike Leach's Storm-petrels, where both members of a pair may respond simultaneously, European Storm-petrels do not sing duets (James, 1984).

The optimum time of year to conduct playback surveys is during periods of maximum daytime attendance at the burrows when maximum response rates can be achieved. On Mousa, Shetland, Ratcliffe *et al.* (1998e) found peak attendance (90%) to occur in mid-July, coinciding with the incubation period. Incubation in European Storm-petrels lasts 40 days and both adults take an equal role, with shifts of on average three days (1–5: Cramp & Simmons, 1977). Chicks are brooded for 6–7 days after hatching but are then left alone during the day, with adults returning almost every night to feed them. Incubation periods and hence optimum times for conducting playback can vary between colonies within Britain and Ireland. Laying on Mousa (Shetland) occurs around two weeks earlier than at colonies on Priest Island (west Ross & Cromarty), Annet (Isles of Scilly), Skokholm (Dyfed) and Inishtooskert (Co. Kerry), and three weeks earlier than on Inishglora (Co. Mayo: Ratcliffe *et al.*, 1988b). These differences in laying date may not just be due to geography, since within individual colonies timing of laying can vary considerably by up to several weeks (Cadiou, 2001. During Seabird 2000 all surveys were conducted during July and probably coincided with periods of maximum attendance. Attendance by non-breeders is a potential problem as they will visit the colony and occupy burrows during the day for up to 3–4 days. However, the extent of overestimation of breeding population by including non-breeders was estimated at just 0.4% (Ratcliffe *et al.*, 1998e).

The main problem with the tape playback method for European Storm-petrels is that even if most adults in a colony are in attendance during the survey, not all of them will respond to the recording of the purr call. Therefore the counts of responses need to be adjusted by the proportion of birds responding so that the number of AOS at a colony is not underestimated. Appendix II details how the proportion of responding birds or response rate was estimated at colonies during Seabird 2000. Once the response rate has been estimated the number of responses is multiplied by the reciprocal of the response rate to estimate the number of AOS.

Table 1 shows the response rate measured in 16 plots on 11 islands and shows that response rate varied significantly between different colonies. Ratcliffe *et al.* (1998e) found that response rate may vary between years at some colonies. Therefore, at the majority of colonies, response rate was measured at the same time as the playback surveys were being undertaken. The only exceptions were on the Isles of Scilly where response rate was measured on Annet in 1996, but the playback survey was undertaken in 2000, and on St Kilda where the response rate was measured on Hirta in 1999 and the playback survey on the other islands in the group was conducted in 2000. The majority (95%) of the British population estimate was derived from colonies where response rate had been

Table 1   *Response rates to tape playback of purr calls by European Storm-petrels.*

Administrative area or country	Response rate (95% CLs)	Source
Yell Islands (Linga, Bigga, Samphrey, Copister, Brother), Shetland	0.43 (0.34–0.52)	Fowler (2001)
Mousa, Shetland	0.25 (0.23–0.27)	Ratcliffe *et al.* (1998e)
Auskerry, Orkney		
Grassland (rabbit burrows)	0.53 (0.39–0.66)	Mitchell & Williams (unpubl.)
Boulder beach	0.59 (0.41–0.77)	Mitchell & Williams (unpubl.)
Stone ruins	0.56 (0.36–0.76)	Mitchell & Williams (unpubl.)
North Rona, Western Isles	0.40 (0.36–0.44)	Murray *et al.* (in prep.)
Hirta, St Kilda, Western Isles	0.43 (0.21–0.58)	Mitchell *et al.* (2003)
Treshnish Isles, Argyll & Bute	0.37 (0.23–0.51)	Ratcliffe *et al.* (1998e)
Priest Island, west coast Ross & Cromarty		
Boulder beach	0.47 (0.40–0.54)	Mayhew *et al.* (2000)
Stone Wall	0.42 (0.38–0.45)	Mayhew *et al.* (2000)
Scree	0.48 (0.45–0.50)	Mayhew *et al.* (2000)
Heath/grassland	0.36 (0.27–0.45)	Mayhew *et al.* (2000)
Annet, Isles of Scilly	0.35 (0.25–0.47)	Ratcliffe *et al.* (1998e)
Puffin Island, Co. Kerry	0.35 (0.26–0.43)[1]	Newton & Mitchell (2001)
Inishglora, Co. Mayo	0.34 (0.25–0.42)[3]	Newton & Mitchell (2001)
Inishvickillane, Co. Kerry	0.36 (0.34–0.39)[2]	Newton & Mitchell (2001)

Notes

[1] Response rate on Puffin Island used to estimate AOSs on Great Skellig

[2] Response rate on Inishvickillane used to estimate AOSs on Inishtooskert

[3] Response rate on Inishglora used to estimate AOSs on all other Irish islands survyed using playback

determined either on the same island or in the same group of islands (see Table 2). On islands where response rate calibration was not carried out (see Table 2), the number of AOS was estimated using the median of the response rates (0.42) measured at the colonies listed in Table 1, giving an adjustment factor (1/0.42) of 2.4. The minimum and maximum response rates (0.25–0.59) were used to attach 'confidence limits' to the estimate of AONs. In the Republic of Ireland, the response rate derived on Puffin Island (Table 1) was applied to Great Skellig and that from Inishvickillane (Table 1) was used for Inishtooskert. The response rate derived from Inishglora (Table 1) was used to estimate the number of AOSs at colonies elsewhere in Co. Mayo and Co. Donegal (Table 2).

Variation in response rate between different colonies may result from significant geographical differences in the purr calls of European Storm-petrels, creating so-called dialects (James, 1985). James (1985) found call structure of European Storm-petrels on Mousa to be most different from those on Puffin Island (Co. Kerry). Ratcliffe *et al.* (1998e) noted that European Storm-petrels on Mousa responded more readily to calls recorded at other colonies and were significantly more likely to respond to calls recorded on Great Skellig, also in Co. Kerry, suggesting that petrels are more likely to respond to more distinct dialects. During Seabird 2000 response rate was determined for exactly the same recording that was used in the playback survey.

Counting the number of responses in a colony can also be prone to error in terms of ensuring that all the birds that are likely to respond to the tape within the survey area actually hear the tape, and that the surveyor actually hears the response. Gilbert *et al.* (1998a) recommended playing the tape within 2 m of potential burrows for 10 seconds. Detection rate by the bird and, in turn, the surveyor are both likely to vary in different habitats based upon depth of burrow, denseness of vegetation, depth of boulder beach etc. On Priest Island, Mayhew *et al.* (2000) found that the response rate of

European Storm-petrels nesting in cracks in peat on heath and grassland habitats was significantly less than that of petrels nesting amongst scree (see Table 1). In contrast, Mitchell & Williams (unpubl.) found no significant difference in the response rate of European Storm-petrels nesting in old rabbit burrows, in the ruins of stone buildings and in boulder beach on Auskerry. However, on islands where there are highly distinct nesting habitats, it is advisable to carry out response rate calibrations for each habitat.

CURRENT STATUS AND TRENDS

Seabird 2000 represents the first comprehensive survey of European Storm-petrels in Britain and Ireland, thus we have listed in Table 2 the population estimates (AOS) for all colonies surveyed, plus a summary of the status of each colony during Operation Seafarer (1969–70; Cramp *et al.*, 1974) and the SCR Census (1985–88; Lloyd *et al.*, 1991). Cramp *et al.* (1974) gave further details of historical records, i.e. prior to 1969, of each colony, including those not visited during Operation Seafarer. Table 3 summarises Seabird 2000 counts by administrative area and country. Previously confirmed or suspected colonies that were not surveyed during Seabird 2000 and those that appeared to be extinct during Seabird 2000 are also listed in Table 2. Other sites were surveyed by playback during Seabird 2000 for which there was no previous or current evidence of breeding.

In Britain and Ireland, European Storm-petrels were found at 95 colonies, containing 82,820 AOS (95% CLs 71,356–100,025). This is likely to be an underestimate, since not all previously suspected or confirmed colonies were surveyed during Seabird 2000 (Table 2). Despite 24 potential sites in Britain not being surveyed during Seabird 2000, it is unlikely that more than 5% of the present estimate have been missed. In Ireland however, at least 12 of the 31 potential colonies are thought hold substantial numbers (Table 2). If previous estimates for these colonies are added to the Seabird 2000 count, the total population of Britain and Ireland would be around 125,000 AOS (Table 3), of which Ireland would hold around 80%, Scotland 17%, Wales 2% and England and the Channel Isles 1%. In Britain, the population of European Storm-petrels is dispersed over at least 77 islands, whereas the population in Ireland is more concentrated in 18–30 colonies (Table 3). Colonies were confined to the Northern Isles, northwest Scotland, southwest Wales, the Isles of Scilly, the Channel Islands and western Ireland. Only one mainland colony was found, in caves at Danish Cellar near Erris Head (Co. Mayo). This colony was chanced upon by a local boatman and it is possible that other such sites remain undetected along the coasts of Britain and Ireland.

In Britain, there was a total of 25,710 AOS (95% CLs 21,043–33,517), with the majority (83%) in Scotland. Distribution does not appear to have changed significantly over the last 30 years. Compared to records of confirmed or suspected breeding given in Lloyd *et al.* (1991) and Cramp *et al.* (1974), and historical records (see Cramp *et al.*, 1974), there were 28 new island colonies and 15 extinct colonies (Table 2).

The largest colony in Britain was on Mousa (Shetland) which held 6,800 AOS in 1996 (Ratcliffe *et al.*, 1998a). Elsewhere in Shetland, 69 islands were surveyed and colonies found on four of the Scalloway Islands (95 AOS), on four skerries off Whalsay (6 AOS), on Colsay (2 AOS) and on 14 small islands around Yell (600 AOS), which included six new colonies (Table 2). There was an unknown number breeding on Fair Isle and possibly a substantial colony in inaccessible geos at Lambhoga on Fetlar (J. Fowler, pers. comm.). A survey of Foula failed to elicit any responses to playback and this once large colony may now be restricted to low numbers on inaccessible ledges (S. Gear, pers. comm.). In Orkney 2,023 AOS were found on 14 islands, of which the largest colonies were on Auskerry (994 AOS) and on Sule Skerry (309 AOS).

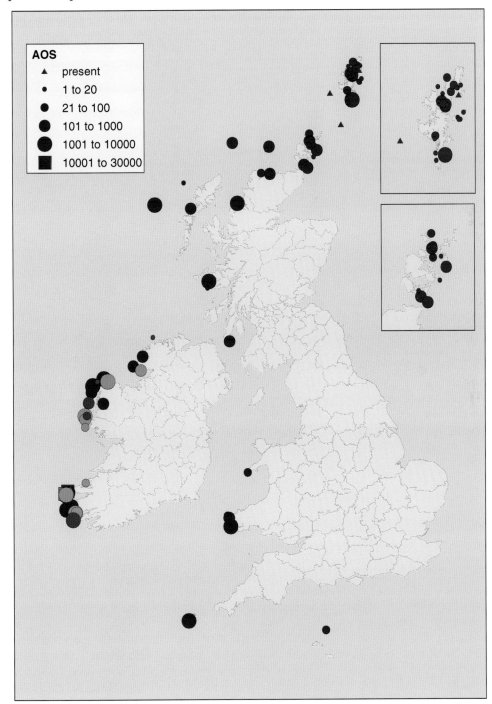

Figure 1   Abundance and distribution of breeding European Storm-petrels in Britain and Ireland 1999–2001.

Table 2   Numbers of European Storm-petrels (AOS) at sites surveyed in Britain and Ireland (1999–2002) compared to previous evidence of breeding given by Cramp et al. *(1974) and Lloyd* et al. *(1991).*

Administrative area or country	Site	Method	Year	AOS[3]	95% lower confidence limit	95% upper confidence limit	Cramp et al. 1974[1]	Lloyd et al. 1991[2]
Shetland	Colsay, SW Mainland	1	2000	2			nc	
Shetland	Eynhallow	1	2000	0				15 calling birds in one group
Shetland	Fair Isle	1	2002	P			10–99 pairs	>5 pairs
Shetland	Foula	1	2002	P (suspected)			101–999 pairs	P (1988)
Shetland	Isbister Holm, Whalsay	1	2000	1				
Shetland	Lamb Hoga, Fetlar	1	2002	P			>16 pairs	P
Shetland	Mousa	2,5	1996	6,800	4,800	8,800	P	P (possibly >1000 pairs in 1983)
Shetland	Noss	1	2002	0			P	regular finds of birds killed by cats
Shetland	Papa Stour			nc			P (suspected)	
Shetland	Scalloway Islands:							
	Black Skerry	1	2000	0				
	Easter Score Holm	1	2000	0				
	Flotta	1	2000	0				
	Fore Holm	2,4	2000	75				
	Green Holm	1	2000	0				
	Greena	1	2000	0				
	Hildasay	1	2000	0				
	Hoggs of Hoy	1	2000	0			10–99 pairs	
	Holm of Burwick	1	2000	0				
	Holm of Maywick	1	2000	0				
	Hoy	1	2000	0			10–99 pairs	
	Junk			nc			10–99 pairs	
	Kirk Holm	1	2000	0				
	Langa	1	2000	0				
	Linga	1	2000	0				
	Little Harva	2,4	2000	5				
	Little Harva	1	2000	0				
	Merry Holm	1	2000	0				
	North Cheynes	1	2000	0				
	North Harva	1	2000	0				
	Oxna	1	2000	0				
	Papa	1	2000	0				
	Sanda Little	1	2000	0				
	Sanda Stour	2,4	2000	15				
	South Cheynes	1	2000	0				
	South Harva	1	2000	0				
	Spoose Holm	1	2000	0				
	West of Hoggs	1	2000	0				
Shetland	Whalsay, East Skerries: East Linga	1	2000	2				
	Mista/Mooa	1	2000	2				
	North Benelip	1	2000	1				
Shetland	Yell:							
	Bigga	2,4	1999–2001	46	44	48	P (suspected)	<50 pairs
	Brother	2,4	1999–2001	101	96	106		5 pairs
	Copister Broch	2,4	1999–2001	107	102	112		150–200 pairs
	Daaey	2,4	1999–2001	9			10–99 pairs	P (suspected 1982–83)
	Fish Holm	1	1999	0				
	Gloup Holm	2,4	1999–2001	23				
	Gruney	2,4	1999–2001	12				
	Haaf Gruney	2,4	1999–2001	9			10–99 pairs	P (1982–83)
	Hascosay	1	1999	0			P	P (1983)
	Holm of Heogaland	1	1999	0				

Administrative area or country	*Site*	*Method*	*Year*	*AOS[3]*	*95% lower confidence limit*	*95% upper confidence limit*	*Cramp* et al. *1974[1]*	*Lloyd* et al. *1991[2]*
Shetland	Yell:							
	Holm of							
	Westsandwick	2,4	1999–2001	5				
	Kay Holm	2,4	1999–2001	92	87	97		
	Lamba	2,4	1999–2001	14				
	Linga (HU5598)	2,4	1999–2001	59	56	62	>2 pairs	adult found dead in burrow
	Linga (HU4673)	1	2001	0				
	Little Holm	1	1999	0				
	Little Roe	1	2000	0				
	Lunna Holm	1	2001	0				
	Muckle Holm	1	1999	0				
	Orfasay	2,4	1999–2001	5				
	Samphrey	2,4	1999–2001	113	108	119	P (suspected)	<50 pairs
	Sinna Skerry	1	1999	0				
	Sligga Skerry	1	2000	0				
	Sound Gruney	1	1999	0			P (suspected)	P (suspected 1982–83)
	Sweinna Stack	1	1999	0				
	Tinga Skerry	1	1999	0				
	Urie Lingey	2,4	1999–2001	5			10–99 pairs	P (suspected 1982–83)
	Uyea	1	2000	0			nc	
	Uynarey	1	1999	0				
	Wedder Holm	1	2000	0				
	Wether Holm	1	1999	0			nc	
Orkney	Auskerry	2,5	2001	994	372	3,196	150 pairs	P
Orkney	Copinsay	1	2001	0				
Orkney	Copinsay: Black Holm	1	2000	0				
Orkney	Copinsay: Ward Holm	1	2000	0				
Orkney	Corn Holm	3,4	2000	2	2	3		
Orkney	Faray	3,4	2000	21	16	28		
Orkney	Holm of Faray	3,4	2000	38	29	50	nc	
Orkney	Holm of Huip	1	2000	0				
Orkney	Holm Of Papa	3,4	2000	85	64	113		40 pairs
Orkney	Holms of Spurness	1	2000	0				
Orkney	Hunda	1	2001	0				
Orkney	Kili Holm	1	2000	0				
Orkney	Linga Holm	3,4	2000	2	2	3		
Orkney	Little Green Holm	3,4	2000	31	23	41		
Orkney	Little Linga	1	2000	0				
Orkney	Muckle Green Holm	3,4	2000	12	9	16	P (suspected)	
Orkney	Muckle Skerry			nc			P	
Orkney	Pentland Skerries	3,4	2000	102	77	134	nc	>2 AOB
Orkney	Red Holm	1	2000	0				
Orkney	Rusk Holm	3,4	2000	135	102	178	30 pairs	P
Orkney	Skea Skerries			nc			10–99 pairs	
Orkney	Sule Skerry	2,4	2001	309	309	309	P	1,000–10,000 pairs
Orkney	Switha	3,4	2000	7	5	9	P (suspected)	>4 AOS
Orkney	Swona	3,4	2000	130	98	172		
Orkney	Wart Holm	3,4	2000	2	2	3	10–99 pairs	
Argyll & Bute	Sanda	6	1999	200				50–100 pairs
Argyll & Bute	Soa	3,4	1999	3				
Argyll & Bute	Staffa	3,4	1999	5				
Argyll & Bute	Treshnish Isles	2,5	1996	5,040			P (suspected)	
Lochaber	Canna	1	2001	0			P (suspected)	
Skye & Lochalsh	Ascrib Islands			nc			nc	
Ross & Cromarty	Longa (Loch Gairloch)			nc			P	

Table 2 continued

Administrative area or country	Site	Method	Year	AOS[3]	95% lower confidence limit	95% upper confidence limit	Cramp et al. 1974[1]	Lloyd et al. 1991[2]
Ross & Cromarty	Summer Isles: Bottle Island	3,4	2001	33	25	44		
	Carn nan Sgeir	3,4	2001	2	2	3		
	Eilean Dubh	3,4	2001	31	23	41		
	Preist Island	2,5	1999	4,400	3,300	6,100	P	
Sutherland	Edrachillis Bay: Calbha Beag	1	2001	0				
	Eilean na Bearachd	1	2001	0				
	Eilean na Rainich	1	2001	0				
	Meal Beag	1	2001	0				
Sutherland	Eilean Hoan	3,4	1995	54	41	72		
Sutherland	Eilean Iosal	3,4	1995	99	75	131		
Sutherland	Eilean nan Ron	3,4	1995	288	218	381	P	P (suspected)
Sutherland	Faraid Head			nc			P (suspected)	
Sutherland	Island Roan			nc			P	
Sutherland	Meall Mor			nc				P
Sutherland	Rabbit Island	3,4	1995	7	5	9		
Caithness	Stroma			nc			P	
Western Isles	Berneray			nc				P (1985)
Western Isles	Boreray, North Uist	1	2001	0			P (suspected)	
Western Isles	Campay, Loch Roag	1	2001	0				
Western Isles	Coppay	1	2001	0				P (1988)
Western Isles	Flannan Isles: Eilean a' Ghobha	1	2001	0				
	Eilean Mor	3,4	2001	7	5	9	nc	P (1988)
	Eilean Tighe	1	2001	0				
	Roareim	1	2001	0				
	Sgeir Toman	1	2001	0				
	Soray	1	2001	0				
Western Isles	North Rona	2,4	2001	368	335	413	P	P
Western Isles	Old Hill	1	2001	0				
Western Isles	Shiants			nc			P (suspected)	
Western Isles	Shillay	3,4	2001	328	298	368	P (suspected)	
Western Isles	St Kilda: Boreray	2,4	1999–2000	84	62	171	P	P
Western Isles	St Kilda: Dun	1	2000	0			P	P
Western Isles	St Kilda: Hirta	2,4	1999–2000	508	376	1,000	P	P
Western Isles	St Kilda: Soay	2,4	1999–2000	529	387	1,071	P	P
Western Isles	Sule Sgeir	2,4	2001	9			P	P
Channel Islands	Burhou (Guernsey)	3,4	2002	60	49	83	1000–9999 pairs	<100 pairs
Channel Islands	Godin			nc			P (suspected)	
Channel Islands	Grand Amfroque (Herm)			nc			nc	
Channel Islands	Great Casquet			nc			nc	
Channel Islands	Icho Tower Reef			nc			1–9 pairs	
Channel Islands	Les Etacs (Alderney)			nc			nc	
Channel Islands	L'Etac de Serk			nc			nc	P (several AOS)
Cornwall	Carter's Rock			nc			nc	
Cornwall	Gull Rock, Falmouth			nc			nc	

Administrative area or country	Site	Method	Year	AOS[3]	95% lower confidence limit	95% upper confidence limit	Cramp et al. 1974[1]	Lloyd et al. 1991[2]
Cornwall	Gulland Rock			nc			nc	
Devon	Lundy	1	2001	0				
Devon	Thatcher Rock			nc			nc	
Isles of Scilly	Annet	2,4	2000	938	797	1,079	1000–9999 pairs	>500 pairs
Isles of Scilly	Castle Bryher	2,4	2000	17			nc	
Isles of Scilly	Daymark, St Martin's	1	2000	0				
Isles of Scilly	Gorregan	2,4	2000	49			1–9 pairs	P (1974, 1983)
Isles of Scilly	Great Crebawethan	1	2000	0				P (1974)
Isles of Scilly	Great Ganilly	1	2000	0				
Isles of Scilly	Gugh	1	2000	0			nc	50 pairs (1974)
Isles of Scilly	Gweal	1	2000	0				
Isles of Scilly	Illiswilgig	2,4	2000	3				
Isles of Scilly	Innisvouls	1	2000	0				
Isles of Scilly	Maiden Bower	1	2000	0				
Isles of Scilly	Melledgan	2,4	2000	140			nc	P (1974)
Isles of Scilly	Men-a-vaur	2,4	2000	20			nc	
Isles of Scilly	Menawethan	1	2000	0				
Isles of Scilly	Mincarlo	2,4	2000	17				P (1977)
Isles of Scilly	Norwethal	1	2000	0				
Isles of Scilly	Nournour	1	2000	0				
Isles of Scilly	Puffin Island	1	2000	0				
Isles of Scilly	Rosevean	2,4	2000	37			nc	P (1974, 1983)
Isles of Scilly	Rosevear	2,4	2000	57			nc	P (1974, 1983)
Isles of Scilly	Round Island	2,4	2000	183			nc	P
Isles of Scilly	Samson	1	2000	0				
Isles of Scilly	Scilly Rock	2,4	2000	14			nc	
Isles of Scilly	Seal Rock	1	2000	0				
Isles of Scilly	St Agnes	1	2000	0				50 pairs (1974)
Isles of Scilly	St Helen's	1	2000	0				
Isles of Scilly	Tean	1	2000	0				
Isles of Scilly	White Island, St Martin's	1	2000	0				
Isle of Man	Calf of Man			nc				>1 AOS
Dyfed	Careg Rhoson	2,4	1999	51				
Dyfed	Middleholm			nc			1–9 pairs	P
Dyfed	North Bishop	2,4	1999	57				
Dyfed	Ramsey	2,4	1995	102				
Dyfed	Skokholm	2,5	2001	2,450	2,300	2,600	5000–7000 pairs	P
Dyfed	Skomer	2,4	2000	110			10–1000 pairs	500 pairs
Gwynedd	Bardsey (Ynys Enlli)	2,4	2002	35			P	P (1984)
Co. Cork	Bull and Cow Rocks			nc (3500)			1000–9999	P
Co. Cork	Cape Clear Island			nc			P (suspected)	P (suspected)
Co. Cork	Fastnet Rock			nc			P	
Co. Kerry	Beginish	2,5	2000	450			10–99 pairs	P
Co. Kerry	Deenish			nc (700)				400–1000 (1991)
Co. Kerry	Great Blasket			nc			P	
Co. Kerry	Great Skellig	2,5	2000, 2002	9,994	8,135	13,454	1000–9999 pairs	P
Co. Kerry	Illaunboy			nc			nc	
Co. Kerry	Inishnabro			nc (3000)			100–999 pairs	1000–5000 pairs (1988)
Co. Kerry	Inishtearaght			nc (15,000)			10,000–99,999	10,000–20,000 pairs (1988)
Co. Kerry	Inishtooskert	2,5	2000	27,297	25,197	28,903	1000–9999 pairs	5000–20,000 pairs (1988)
Co. Kerry	Inishvickillane	2,5	2000	6,394	5,903	6,771	10,000–99,999 pairs	10,001–100,000 pairs (1988)

Table 2 continued

Administrative area or country	Site	Method	Year	AOS[3]	95% lower confidence limit	95% upper confidence limit	Cramp et al. 1974[1]	Lloyd et al. 1991[2]
Co. Kerry	Magharee Islands			nc (55)			10–99 pairs	P
Co. Kerry	Puffin Island	2,5	2000	5,177	4,214	6,969	1000–9999 pairs	P (1988)
Co. Kerry	Scariff			nc (5500)	1,000	10,000	1000–9999	
Co. Clare	Mattle Island			nc				P (1984)
Co. Clare	Mutton Island			nc			P (1960's)	P (1984)
Co. Galway	Brannock Islands			nc			P (suspected)	
Co. Galway	Corrigeenagowlra			nc			nc	
Co. Galway	High Island	4	1999	60	53	70		c.1000 pairs
Co. Galway	Illaunamid, Slyne Head			nc (50)				c.50 pairs (1980)
Co. Galway	Inishark			nc (5100)			P (suspected)	200–10,000 (1991)
Co. Galway	Inishbofin	1	2000	nc (100)			few pairs (1950s-60s)	probably <100 pairs
Co. Mayo	Bills Rocks	6	2001	500				P (1983), possibly >1000 pairs
Co. Mayo	Black Rock	2,5	2001	171	138	232	1–9 pairs	P
Co. Mayo	Caher			nc			P	
Co. Mayo	Carrickawilt			nc			nc	
Co. Mayo	Clare Island			nc			P (suspected)	
Co. Mayo	Danish Cellar	6	2001	5				
Co. Mayo	Duvillaun Beg	2,5	2001	950	769	1,292	P (1966)	P
Co. Mayo	Duvillaun More			nc			nc	
Co. Mayo	Illaunmaster			nc (8625)				7500–10,000 pairs (1980)
Co. Mayo	Inishdalla			nc			nc	
Co. Mayo	Inishglora	2,5	2001	1,788	1,448	2,432		10,000+ pairs (1979)
Co. Mayo	Inishkea North	2,5	2001	59	48	80		
Co. Mayo	Inishkea South	1	2001	0				
Co. Mayo	Inishkeeragh	2,5	2001	1,635	1,324	2,224		P
Co. Mayo	Inishturk			nc			P (suspected)	
Co. Mayo	Kid Island			nc			nc	
Co. Mayo	Pig Island	2,5	2001	68	55	92		
Co. Mayo	Stags of Broadhaven	2,5	2001	1,912	1,548	2,600	P(1960's)	P
Co. Sligo	Inishmurray			nc				P (1986)
Co. Donegal	Inishbeg			nc			P (suspected)	
Co. Donegal	Inishduff			nc (225)			P (suspected)	200–250 pairs
Co. Donegal	Inishkeeragh	1	2001	0			P (suspected)	
Co. Donegal	Islands in Gweedore Bay			nc			P (suspected)	
Co. Donegal	Rathlin O'Birne	2,5	2001	159	129	216	100–999 pairs	500–1000 pairs
Co. Donegal	Roaninish	2,5	2001	491	398	668	250–300 pairs (1953–57)	1001–10,000
Co. Donegal	Torglass			nc			nc	
Co. Donegal	Tory Island			nc (50)			P	probably <100 pairs
Co. Donegal	Umfin			nc			nc	

Method code

1	determined presence/absence
2	AOS determined using tape playback of male purr call using site specific adjustment factor – see table 1.
3	AOS determined using tape playback of male purr call using median British adjustment factor of 2.4 (see text).
4	complete count of responses
5	sample count of responses
6	best guess

Notes

[1] records are from 1969–70 unless otherwise stated

[2] records are from 1985–87 unless otherwise stated

[3] values in parenthese are the mid-points of estimates from previous surveys of colonies that were not surveyed during Seabird 2000

nc   not counted (i.e. presence / absence not determined); also applies to sites that have historical evidence of breeding (i.e. prior to 1969) but were not visited during Operation Seafarer (see Cramp *et al.*, 1974)

P   present breeding

Table 3   *Numbers of breeding European Storm-petrels (AOS) in Britain and Ireland 1999–2002.*

Administrative area or country	Surveyed AOS	95% lower confidence limit	95% upper confidence limit	Number of colonies surveyed
Shetland	7,503	5,478	9,529	26
Orkney	1,870	1,110	4,255	14
Northwest coast Sutherland	449	339	594	4
West coast Ross & Cromarty	4,466	3,350	6,188	4
Argyll & Bute	5,248	5,248	5,248	4
Western Isles–Comhairle nan eilean	1,833	1,472	3,041	7
Scotland Total	**21,370**	**16,997**	**28,855**	**59**
Channel Islands	60	49	83	1
Isles of Scilly	1,475	1,334	1,616	11
England and the Channel Islands Total	**1,535**	**1,383**	**1,699**	**12**
Gwynedd	35	35	35	1
Dyfed	2,770	2,620	2,920	5
Wales total	**2,805**	**2,663**	**2,963**	**6**
Great Britain and the Channel Isles Total	**25,710**	**21,043**	**33,517**	**77**
Co. Kerry	49,313	43,899	56,097	5
Co. Galway	60	53	70	1
Co. Mayo	7,087	5,835	9,457	9
Co. Donegal	650	526	884	3
Republic of Ireland Total	**57,110**	**50,313**	**66,508**	**18**
Britain and Ireland Total	**82,820**	**71,356**	**100,025**	**95**
	Estimated AOS	Min	Max	Estimated number of colonies
Co. Cork	3,500	2,000	5,000	1
Co. Kerry	24,305	12,420	36,190	5
Co. Galway	5,250	310	10,150	3
Co. Mayo	8,625	7,500	10,000	1
Co. Donegal	275	210	340	2
Republic of Ireland Total Estimated	**41,955**	**22,440**	**61,680**	**12**
Republic of Ireland Total Estimated and Surveyed	**99,065**	**72,753**	**128,188**	**30**

In the Western Isles, European Storm-petrels were confined mainly to the remotest outer islands. In the St Kilda archipelago a total of 1,121 AOS was found on the islands of Hirta, Boreray and Soay, but were absent from Dun (Mitchell *et al.*, in prep.). On all three islands there was a strong preference for nesting in stone structures, which was also evident on North Rona, where boulder beach was also important. A survey of six of the Flannan Isles found only 9 AOS on the largest island, Eilean Mor (Newton & Mitchell, 2001). The only inshore island colony is on Shillay in the Sound of Harris, where 328 AOS were found in two small boulder fields.

Off the Scottish mainland, there were concentrations on four islands off north Sutherland (Mainwood *et al.*, 1996), the Summer Isles (West Ross & Cromarty) and the Treshnish Isles (Argyll

& Bute) (Table 2). The latter was surveyed in 1996 (Gilbert *et al.*, 1998a) and is the second-largest colony in Britain, with 5,040 AOS. The third-largest British colony is on Priest Island (4,400 AOS) in the Summer Isles (Mayhew *et al.*, 2000), where breeding was confirmed on three other islands, although there may be more colonies in the group (A. R. Mainwood, pers. comm.).

Outside Scotland, breeding European Storm-petrels were confined to five Welsh islands (a total of 2,770 AOS) including Britain's fourth-largest colony, of 2,450 AOS, on Skokholm (Vaughan, 2001), 11 of the Isles of Scilly, England (1,475 AOS; Heaney *et al.*, 2002) and 60 AOS on Burhou, in the Channel Islands.

Very few colonies have previously been surveyed using playback (or any other accurate method) before Seabird 2000, so it is impossible to measure regional or national trends. On Mousa, Ratcliffe *et al.*'s (1998d) count of 6,800 AOS (4,800–8,800 95% CLs) in 1997 appears to represent a significant increase on the previous estimate of 4,500–5,000 AOS in 1992 by Suddaby (1992). However, Ratcliffe *et al.* (1998d) advised caution in interpreting this apparent trend given the different methods used in the two surveys. The population on Auskerry has declined significantly since 1995 by 79% to 994 AOS (95% CLs 994–3,196) in 2001 (Mitchell & Williams, unpubl.). Some 85% of the European Storm-petrels on Auskerry nest in old rabbit burrows and it in this habitat that the greatest decline has occurred, although numbers nesting in old ruins and boulder beach declined by 67% since 1995. On Priest Island, the population appears to have doubled between 1996 (Mainwood *et al.*, 1996) and 1999 (Mayhew *et al.*, 2000). However, the number of responses elicited by playback in 1999 was only 7% greater than that in 1996. The discrepancy between the two surveys' estimates of AOSs is more likely to be attributable to Mainwood *et al.* (1996) overestimating response rate using data obtained on Skomer (James & Robertson, 1985), whereas Mayhew *et al.* (100) measured response rate directly in calibration plots on Priest Island (see Appendix II). On Skokholm there appears to have been a 43% decline, from 3,500 AOS in 1995 (Vaughan & Gibbons, 1996) to 2,000 AOS in 2001 (Vaughan, 2001), as determined by two identical playback surveys. This decline may be a long-term trend since at least the late 1960s when Scott (1970) estimated 5,000–7,000 AOS, although his methods were not comparable with playback. Perrins (1997) suggested that the colony on the nearby island of Skomer may have also declined at some point during the latter half of the 20th century. However, during six playback surveys conducted on Skomer between 1981 and 2000 numbers have remained remarkably constant (Brown & Easton, 2000).

In the Republic of Ireland, the playback survey of 18 islands found a total of 57,110 (95% CLs 50,313–66,508). If the estimates for the 12 colonies that were not surveyed during Seabird 2000 are added, then the Republic of Ireland would hold around 99,000 AOS. Most of these (74%) would be in Co. Kerry, with 16% in Co. Mayo, 6% in Co. Galway, 4% in Co. Cork and 1% in Co. Donegal (Table 3). There are also thought to be two colonies in Co. Clare and one in Co. Sligo (Table 2).

Around two-thirds of European Storm-petrels in Co. Kerry were surveyed by tape playback and were concentrated in two groups of islands: the Blasket Islands off the Dingle Peninsula and the islands off the Iveragh Peninsula (e.g. Puffin Island and Great Skellig). The Blaskets contain the largest colony in Britain and Ireland of 27,297 AOSs on Inishtooskert, which to date is the largest colony anywhere in the world to be censused using tape playback. Two other islands in the Blaskets were surveyed: Inishvickillane (6394 AOS) and Beginish (450 AOS). Earlier estimates suggested Inishvickillane held the largest of the Blasket colonies (Table 2). Nesting habitat on the two islands is highly contrasting with the Inishvickillane colony concentrated in monastic ruins and the most extensive series of stone walls in the Blasket Islands, whereas Inishtooskert contains few stone walls and most petrels nest on steep vegetated slopes dominated by ling heather. The other islands in the Blaskets known to have breeding European Storm-petrels, but not surveyed during Seabird 2000, are thought to contain large numbers. The population on Inishtearaght was suggested to be even larger

Inishtooskert, Kerry holds around 27,000 pairs of European Storm-petrels the largest colony to be surveyed in the world to date (Alyn Walsh)

than Inishvickillane (10,000–20,000 AOS; Lloyd *et al.*, 1991). Inishnabro is physically similar to Inishtooskert, but its vegetation is very different, comprising very tussocky *Armeria*, highly burrowed by Manx Shearwaters and Atlantic Puffins. Thus, the population of European Storm-petrels is likely to be considerably less dense than on Inishtooskert (see Table 2 for estimates). Great Blasket, the largest island in the group, has never been thoroughly surveyed for European Storm-petrels, although Cramp *et al.* (1974) claimed they were definitely breeding there. Further north, off the Iveragh Peninsula, the mountainous but largely grassy Puffin Island contained 5,177 AOS, all in natural sites owing to the almost complete absence of stonework. In contrast, nearby, the equally precipitous and largely rocky island of Great Skellig supported 2,654 AOS in man-made structures, including the extensive network of stone steps and pathways that link the landing place with lighthouses and the monastery on the northeastern summit. The latter contains a large number of dome-like 'beehive' cells and lower walls that support many nesting petrels. Access to other potential petrel nesting habitat on steep vegetated (sea campion and rock sea spurrey) slopes was extremely hazardous, but the number of responses obtained in accessible areas was used to used to extrapolate an estimate of 9,994 AOS in similar habitat over the rest of the island. The population estimates for the Co. Kerry islands surveyed during Seabird 2000 are in reasonable accord with what was essentially guesswork during earlier surveys (Cramp *et al.*, 1974; Evans & Lovegrove, 1974; Lloyd *et al.*, 1991), which suggest that most of the islands each hold in the order of 1,000–10,000 AOS (see Table 2).

Islands off the extreme northwest corner of Co. Mayo have been thought to support the second major concentration of breeding European Storm-petrels in Ireland, but previous assessments appear to have overestimated the size of these colonies (Table 2). For instance, Inishglora and its near neighbour Inishkeeragh have been visited regularly by seabird ringers who have mist-netted very large numbers of European Storm-petrels. The ease of capture of the petrels gave the impression of vast numbers nesting, e.g. the estimate of 10,000 pairs for Inishglora alone, cited in Lloyd *et al.* (1991). Tape playback surveys found a much smaller breeding population, of 1,788 AOS on Inishglora and 1,635 AOS on Inishkeeragh. These low estimates are perhaps attributable to relatively poor natural habitat. Both islands have extensive boulder beaches, though seawater possibly penetrates quite far and renders only the uppermost part dry enough for nesting. Ruined stone walls and some monastic remains are also present but, with few exceptions, densities are much lower than equivalent habitats in Co. Kerry. Other major colonies in Co. Mayo were located at Duvillaun Beg (950 AOS, mainly in boulder beaches) and on the Stags of Broadhaven (1,912 AOS), where the petrels were nesting amongst the burrows of Leach's Storm petrels in well-vegetated, peat-covered slopes. Other colonies in Co. Mayo were shown to be relatively small (Table 2), but included three new colonies on Pig Island, Inishkea North and in the mainland caves of Danish Cellar (see above). Illaunmaster is often considered amongst the largest colonies in Ireland, but unfortunately was not visited during Seabird 2000. It is a fairly steep, well-vegetated island, with no stone walls or boulder beaches. It is very different from Inishglora or Inishkeeragh, and is perhaps closer in appearance to the Stags of Broadhaven, albeit considerably larger. The estimate of 7,500–10,000 AOS cited in Lloyd *et al.* (1991) may be reasonable in the light of experience elsewhere in the area. Of all the Irish colonies, this one should be given priority in any future tape playback survey.

In the northern part of the range in Ireland, only three colonies were censused in Co. Donegal. The population of 159 AOS on Rathlin O'Birne was much smaller than the 1,000 pairs estimated by ringers visiting the site previously (Table 2). However, the playback estimate of 491 AOS on Roaninish was similar to that suggested by Wilson (1959), who mapped occupied sites by intensive nocturnal visits over several successive days. Birds were absent from Inishkeeragh (Table 2) despite an abundance of potential nesting habitat in stone walls.

FACTORS CONTROLLING DISTRIBUTION AND NUMBERS

In the few colonies where repeated playback surveys have enabled trends to be determined, an impression can be obtained of what factors may be important in controlling other colonies around Britain and Ireland. On Auskerry the large decline between 1995 and 2001 was caused by a reduction in available breeding habitat. The majority of petrels breeding on Auskerry in 1995 occupied old rabbit burrows (Wood, 1997), but subsequent increases in stocking levels of sheep on the island have resulted in the destruction of 65% of the rabbit burrows (Mitchell & Williams, unpubl.). Reduction in breeding habitat may also result from competition for such areas with other ground nesters. For instance, on Sule Skerry the 300 pairs found in 2001 (Williams, unpubl.) was an order of magnitude less than predicted in 1986 (Lloyd *et al.*, 1991). Since the mid-1980s, the resident puffin population has increased sharply and now occupies most of the surface of the island. European Storm-petrels were restricted to old walls and under boulders at the edge of the puffin colony, rather than within it as was previously thought, probably because storm-petrel burrows would be untenable with the intensive digging of the puffins. Habitat degradation has also been suggested as a possible cause for the decline on Skokholm (Perrins, 1997).

The availability of suitable nesting habitat is a major determinant of the size and distribution of European Storm-petrel colonies. Rocky habitat, whether natural (e.g. boulder beach, stable scree) or man-made (e.g. dry stone walls, stone buildings/ruins) was present on virtually all of the islands containing colonies, and was always occupied to some extent by nesting petrels. However, at some of the largest colonies, where rocky habitat may be limited, nesting tends towards other habitats. For instance, on Priest Island, in the Summer Isles (Ross & Cromarty), 62% of AOS were found in cracks in peat under dense vegetation in heathland habitat. Similar habitat was occupied on the other Summer Isles and islands off north Sutherland (e.g. Eilean Hoan). In the Republic of Ireland nesting on softer ground appeared much more common than in Britain. For instance, on the Stags of

Broadhaven, European Storm-petrels were nesting exclusively among tussocky vegetation in soft peat, habitat more usually associated with the Leach's Storm-petrels that nest alongside them on these islands. Most of the European Storm-petrels on Inishtooskert were nesting in soft ground and around 20% of the breeding population had dispensed with burrows altogether, simply nesting atop peat below a dense cover of ling heather. Such 'open-plan burrows' amongst heather may be under threat from trampling by sheep, and grazing may also increase the spread of bracken, resulting in the loss of heather cover (Beatty *et al.*, 1997).

On some islands, numbers were clearly being limited by factors other than available habitat. On St Kilda, for instance, particularly on Hirta and Dun, there are large areas of suitable habitat totally unoccupied by European Storm-petrels. On these islands predation by Great Skuas poses a serious threat. Since the early 1990s, the skua population on St Kilda has increased exponentially from around 42 pairs in 1986 to 229 in 1996 (Phillips *et al.*, 1999a). These, together with non-breeding birds, are thought to take around 7,450 European Storm-petrels each year (Phillips *et al.*, 1999c), i.e. over three times the number of breeding adults estimated present in 1999–2000. We do not know where the skuas are depredating the petrels (i.e. at sea or at the colony) so it is impossible to gauge what proportion of the depredated petrels are breeding adults and non-breeders, and whether all the breeders are from the St Kilda colony. Also, the lack of any previous population estimate makes it impossible to assess the impact the predation has had on the resident storm-petrel population. On the Welsh islands of Skomer and Skokholm Little Owls have apparently become storm-petrel specialists, and Perrins (1997) suggested that their introduction to the islands in 1920s caused a decline in numbers of European Storm-petrels on Skomer.

Generally, avian predators have less of a devastating effect on petrel colonies compared to mammals. The underground burrows protect eggs, chicks and adults from avian predators such as gulls, crows, skuas and raptors. It is no coincidence that all but two of the colonies listed in Table 2 (i.e. Foula and Fetlar) are on islands free of mammalian predators. On Foula, Shetland, predation by feral cats has reduced a once sizeable colony of 100–999 AOS (Cramp *et al*, 1974) to just a few pairs that are confined to remote inaccessible ledges alongside the island's few remaining Leach's Storm-petrels. The effect of mammals on the distribution of European Storm-petrels is clearly demonstrated by a survey of the Isles of Scilly conducted in 2000 by Heaney *et al.* (2002), where out of 28 islands visited, petrels were absent from all those colonised by rats. In Britain and Ireland, the only exception to nesting on islands by European Storm-petrels was a colony of 5 AOS in caves at Danish Cellar (Co. Mayo). Such sites are utilised elsewhere, for example Benidorm off the Mediterranean coast of Spain (Mínguez, 1994), but are very difficult to find and are probably present elsewhere in mainland Britain and Ireland. Caves that are only accessible from the sea offer safe haven from most mammalian predators, although in Spain cave-nesting European Storm-petrels are depredated by Yellow-legged Gulls (Mínguez, 1994).

The distribution of European Storm-petrel colonies in Britain and Ireland is strongly influenced by proximity to the North Atlantic. The only North Sea colonies are off eastern Orkney and Shetland, and the only Irish Sea colonies are in Wales. However, European Storm-petrels have a much less restricted range than Leach's Storm-petrels, which are reliant on breeding sites adjacent to deep oceanic water for feeding (see relevant species chapter). During the breeding season (May–September), European Storm-petrels share the deep-water feeding areas of Leach's Storm-petrels, but are also present in similar densities in shallower water over the shelf, all along the north and west coasts of Britain and Ireland (Pollock *et al.*, 2000a,b). Very low numbers feed in the North Sea, southeast of the Northern Isles (Hall *et al.*, 1987). European Storm-petrels have a fairly eclectic diet of small fish and zooplankton, which they usually glean from the surface (Cramp & Simmons, 1977), but have been recorded diving below the surface (Griffiths, 1981; Jensen, 1993). They sometimes associate with fishing boats, scavenging discards and offal, and forage in wakes of ships

(Pollock *et al.*, 2000a,b). European Storm-petrels are rarely seen feeding close inshore during the day (but see Riddiford & Riddiford, 1984; Koerts, 1992; Stegeman, 1990). However, recent evidence shows they move inshore at night in order to feed on intertidal benthic crustaceans (*Eurydice* spp.) that migrate into the water column during nocturnal high tides (D'Elbee & Hemery, 1997). *Eurydice* spp. were found to comprise 37% of the diet of European Storm-petrels breeding on two French islands in the Bay of Biscay. D'Elbee & Hemery (1997) suggest that this ability to exploit an inshore food source enables European Storm-petrels to evade avian predators that are more concentrated near the coast, and permits them to feed close to their colonies when returning to land to mate, incubate and feed young. This no doubt also enables them to nest at colonies considerable distances from their main feeding grounds along the continental shelf edge.

The presence of blood-sucking (haematophagous) ectoparasites (e.g. the dermanyssid mite, flea *Xenopsylla grantiosa*) significantly reduce the growth rate of chicks European Storm-petrels in Spain, which may reduce fledging success and subsequent survival (Merino *et al.*, 1999). However, it is unclear how ectoparasites impact the overall productivity and growth of populations of European Storm-petrels. Studies of ectoparasites on European Storm-petrels have been restricted to non-haematophagous taxa such as mallophaga (i.e. feather lice; Fowler & Miller, 1984; Fowler *et al.*, 1984). Other types of ectoparasites are thought to have sub-lethal effects on adult storm-petrels. Zonfrillo (1996) suggested that the small numbers (1–2% of birds caught) of European Storm-petrels observed by bird ringers to have injured feet or in some cases missing completely (Murray, 1984; Bowey, 1995; Stonehouse, 1996; Sultana & Borg, 1996) were caused by parasitic larvae of a marine trematode worm. The larvae wrap themselves around the legs of petrels, cutting the blood supply to the foot, which withers and eventually drops off. Murray (1984) suggested such foot injuries may be caused by a disease similar to puffinosis that causes mortality in fledgling Manx Shearwaters. It is unknown what effect these injuries have on the long-term survival and productivity of European Storm-petrels.

INTERNATIONAL CONTEXT

European Storm-petrels, as their name suggests, are confined to breeding colonies in Europe, but may also breed on islands off the coasts of Morocco and Algeria, North Africa, but no survey has ever been undertaken (Zotier *et al.*, 1992). There are two subspecies. The most numerous, constituting 97% of the global population is *H. p. pelagicus*, which breeds in Britain and Ireland and on other islands along the east Atlantic coast, from the Westmann Islands off southern Iceland to the Bay of Biscay and as far south as the Canary Islands off northwest Africa. The northeastern limit to the range of *H. p. pelagicus* is in the Barents Sea, on at least two islands off Norway (Barrett & Strann, 1987; Anker-Nilssen, 2000). The size and distribution of colonies along the Atlantic coasts of France and Spain are well understood. Most of the French population is in 16–18 colonies on islands off Brittany, with two more, totalling 15 pairs (minimum) off Biarritz (Cadiou *et al.*, in press). The Spanish population of *H. p. pelagicus* (2,000 pairs) is scattered among 45 islands along the Atlantic coast. The largest concentration of European Storm-petrels outside Britain and Ireland are in the Faeroe Islands (150,000–400,000 pairs) and off the south coast of Iceland (50,000–100,000 pairs), concentrated on Elliday, in the Westmann Islands (Icelandic Institute of Natural History, 2000). The wide-ranging population estimates for the Faeroes and Iceland are based largely on guesswork. Despite the accurate population estimates of most colonies in Britain and Ireland, it is difficult to assess their international significance and thus conservation status (i.e. designation of colonies as Special Protection Areas under the EU Birds Directive 1979) given the uncertainty of the size of the

Icelandic and Faeroese populations. Hence, there is a strong international need to survey European Storm-petrels in the Faeroes and in Iceland much more accurately, so that the international importance of individual colonies can be assessed and international site designation can be assigned with greater confidence.

However, if the 95% CLs of the population estimates for Britain and Ireland (including estimates for those colonies not surveyed during Seabird 2000) are added to population estimates from elsewhere in Europe, the total population of *H. p. pelagicus* is 300,000–680,000 pairs, of which Ireland holds 10.7–42.7% and Britain 3.1–11.1% (Table 4). Therefore, the colonies on Mousa, Treshnish Isles, Inishtooskert, Puffin Island, Inishvickillane and Great Skellig qualify as internationally important, using a threshold of 4,900 pairs, i.e. 1% of the mid-point of estimate of the world population of *H. p. pelagicus* (the comparative biogeographic population for British and Irish colonies defined by Stroud *et al.*, 2000).

H. p. pelagicus winters off the coast of southern Africa, venturing into the Indian Ocean, as far north as Mozambique. European Storm-petrels ringed in Ireland and the Irish sea coast of Britain show a much greater tendency to be recovered off the Atlantic coast of France than Scottish breeders (Fowler, 2002) and are thought to be a separate subpopulation from their northern neighbours (Furness & Baillie, 1981).

The other subspecies, *H. p. melitensis*, is confined mainly to the Mediterranean, but is also known to breed in the Adriatic Sea, on the Vis archipelago off the Croatian coast (Lovric & Obradovic, 1988) and on Prassoudha, in the Greek Aegean (Akriotis & Handrinos, 1986). *H. p. melitensis* is thought to remain in the Mediterranean throughout the year. Hashmi & Fliege (1994) observed large numbers of European Storm-petrels entering the Mediterranean from the Atlantic during autumn. However, there is no ringing evidence to suggest that *H. p. pelagicus* from Britain and Ireland ever enter the Mediterranean (Fowler, 2002).

Table 4   International context.

Country or region	Subspecies	Number of pairs		Year	Source
		Min	Max		
Great Britain, Isle of Man and Channel Isles	*pelagicus*	21,000[1]	34,000[2]	1999–2002	Seabird 2000
All Ireland	*pelagicus*	73,000[1]	128,000[2]	2000–02	Seabird 2000
Faeroes	*pelagicus*	150,000	400,000	1995	BirdLife International/EBCC (2000)
France (Atlantic)	*pelagicus*	750	810	1997–2000	Cadiou *et al.* (2002)
Iceland	*pelagicus*	50,000	100,000	1990	Icelandic Institute of Natural History (2000)
Norway	*pelagicus*	1,000	10,000	1994	Gjershaug *et al.* (1994)
Portugal (Madeira & Salvagems)	*pelagicus*	?	?		
Spain (Canary Islands)	*pelagicus*	595	1,000	1990s	Martí & del Moral (2003)
Spain (mainland Atlantic)	*pelagicus*	580	1,590	1990s	Martí & del Moral (2003)
Algeria	*melitensis*	?	?		Zotier *et al.* (1992)
Croatia (Adriatic)	*melitensis*	P	P		Lovric & Obradovic (1988)
France (Mediterranean incl. Corsica)	*melitensis*	200	300	1997–2000	Cadiou *et al.* (2002)
Greece (Aegean)	*melitensis*	10	30		Akriotis & Handrinos (1986)
Italy (incl. Sardinia)	*melitensis*	1,500	2,000	1988–97	Zotier *et al.* (1992)
Malta	*melitensis*	2,500	10,000		Massa & Sultana (1990–91) in Zotier *et al.* (1992)
Morrocco	*melitensis*	?	?		See Zotier *et al.* (1992)
Spain (Balearics)	*melitensis*	2,138	4,268	1990s	Aguilar (1992), Amengual *et al.* (1999)
Spain (Mediterranean)	*melitensis*	918	1,264	1990s	Martí & del Moral (2003)

Biogeographic region		Min	Max	Min % GB	Max % GB	Min % Ireland	Max % Ireland
Atlantic (northeastern)	*pelagicus*	300,000	680,000	3.1%	11.3%	10.7%	42.7%
World*	all	310,000	690,000	3.0%	11.0%	10.6%	41.3%

* Stroud et al. (2001)

Notes

[1] 95% lower confidence limit

[2] 95% upper confidence limit

Leach's Storm-petrel *Oceanodroma leucorhoa*

P. Ian Mitchell

INTRODUCTION

Leach's Storm-petrel is a truly oceanic species, only returning to remote island colonies under hours of darkness. It ranges widely in both the Atlantic and Pacific Oceans. In the east Atlantic, the Leach's Storm-petrel '*but brushes a wing-tip at the British Isles*' (Atkinson 1948) in that breeding is confined to just eight remote islands and archipelagos along the Atlantic Frontier.

Obtaining estimates of breeding numbers has been virtually impossible, due to the species' nocturnal and subterranean breeding habits, and accessing the remote colonies during the hours of darkness is often difficult and dangerous. Attempts to gauge the size of colonies based on the number of birds active above ground has led to the most wide-ranging population estimate of any bird species in Britain and Ireland (Stone *et al.*, 1997). Lloyd *et al.* (1991) estimated there to be a total of 10,000–100,000 pairs breeding on two islands in Shetland, one in Orkney, three island groups and one island in the Western Isles, and on one island group off Co. Mayo, Ireland.

A major aim of Seabird 2000 was to improve on the current estimate of numbers of breeding Leach's Storm-petrel in Britain and Ireland. Recent developments in the use of taped call playbacks for surveying European Storm-petrels and Manx Shearwaters were adapted to obtain the first quantitative population estimate of Leach's Storm-petrels breeding in Britain and Ireland.

Leach's Storm-petrel and newly-hatched chick in a burrow during the day on Hirta, St Kilda in early July (photographed using a video endoscope) (JNCC)

CENSUS METHODS

In British and Irish colonies, the entrances to burrows are indistinct and very difficult to see, as they are small and often obscured with rank vegetation, particularly where grazing animals are absent. Furthermore, burrows tend to show little sign of use. Therefore, counting apparently occupied burrows, as used with Atlantic Puffins and Manx Shearwaters, is not suitable for Leach's Storm-petrels. The methods used to census Leach's Storm-petrels during Seabird 2000 followed those of Gilbert *et al.* (1998a) and were based on similar methods developed for surveying European Storm-petrels (Ratcliffe *et al.*, 1998e). The method relies on the fact that both storm-petrels are highly vocal at their colonies and that vocalisation can be elicited from incubating adults by playing taped calls.

Tape playback surveys were undertaken on four islands in the St Kilda archipelago, on six of the Flannan Isles, the adjacent islands of North Rona and Sule Sgeir, North Hill (all in the Western Isles), Sule Skerry (Orkney), Gruney, Foula (Shetland) and the Stags of Broadhaven (Co. Mayo). All these sites were previously known to hold colonies of Leach's Storm-petrels (see below).

Where possible, all suitable habitat on an island was systematically investigated by tape playback. However, on St Kilda there were three large sub-colonies where time constraints did not permit complete coverage. In such cases, an estimate of the density of burrows was obtained and multiplied by the area of the colony sampled to estimate the number of AOS. Even within suitable habitat, the distribution of Leach's Storm-petrel AOS was highly variable. On Boreray, St Kilda, Mitchell *et al.* (2003) sampled 10% of the area of a sub-colony, covering 11.6 ha, using 464 quadrats (25 m^2) to achieve an estimate of burrow density that could detect changes of only greater than 20%. However, on Dun, St Kilda, time constraints meant that only 1.8% of the sub-colony of 14.7 ha could be surveyed, yet produced an estimate of similar accuracy to that on Boreray.

The playback method involves playing recordings of a male chatter call in the vicinity of burrows in order to elicit responses of birds within them. The chatter call is used for nest defence and male–male competition (Huntington *et al.*, 1996), and so only males will respond to taped male calls (Taoka *et al.*, 1989b). Playing chatter calls at burrows can also elicit purr chip call or screech call responses and all these are counted as AOS. On occasion, European Storm-petrels will respond to taped calls of Leach's Storm-petrels, but their vocalisations are easily distinguishable.

The main problem with the tape playback method is determining what proportion of incubating adults at any one time will actually respond to the taped calls. The method used to estimate response rate of Leach's Storm-petrels is identical to that used for European Storm-petrels and Manx Shearwaters, and is detailed in Appendix II (see also Gilbert *et al.*, 1998a). The response rates estimated at British colonies are shown in Table 1.

Table 1   Response rates to tape playback of male chatter call by Leach's Storm-petrel.

Colony and administrative area	Response rate (95% CLs)
St Kilda: Boreray, Western Isles [daytime 2000][1]	0.382 (0.338–0.422)
St Kilda: Boreray, Western Isles [dusk 2000]	0.518 (0.449–0.579)
Flannan Isles, Western Isles[2]	0.295 (0.245–0.342)
North Rona, Western Isles[3]	0.434 (0.288–0.580)

Notes
[1] Response rate on Boreray used to estimate AOSs on other island in St Kilda
[2] Response rate on Flannan Isles used to estimate AOSs on Old Hill
[3] Response rate on North Rona used to estimate AOSs on Sula Sgeir

A response rate calibration plot for a tape playback survey of Leach's Storm-petrel on Boreray, St Kilda. The small yellow flags mark the barely distinguishable entrances to Leach's Storm-petrel burrows (Andy Webb)

On Boreray, St Kilda, the response rate during the day (07.10–17.15), when the playback surveys were conducted, was significantly lower than at dusk (22.10–23.30). This demonstrates the need to undertake playback calibrations at the same time of day as playback surveys are being conducted. The response rate of 0.38 obtained from the Boreray daytime plot in 2000 was used to calculate the number of AOS from the counts of responses on all islands in the archipelago. The response rate on St Kilda lies between those estimated on the Flannan Isles and on North Rona (Table 1). This inter-colony difference in response rate has also been found in European Storm-petrels (see previous chapter). The call used at these three Leach's Storm-petrel colonies was originally recorded on St Kilda (British Sound Library), so it appears that males from other colonies react differently to the St Kildan chatter call. It may be that dialects exist within Leach's Storm-petrel populations. Indeed, Ainley (1980) found differences between the chatter and purr calls of Leach's Storm-petrels breeding on Guadalupe, Mexico, and other colonies in the Pacific and Atlantic. It remains to be seen whether or not males respond differently to similar or more distinct chatter calls than their own.

CURRENT STATUS AND TRENDS

In Britain, Leach's Storm-petrels are confined to two island groups, plus three individual islands in the Western Isles, and two islands in Shetland (Table 2 and Fig. 1). There is just one colony in Ireland, with an estimated 310 AOS. These colonies are all on islands at the extreme western edge of the region. The total British and Irish population is estimated at 48,357 AOS (95% CL's; 36,741–65,194).

An estimated 45,433 AOS were found on St Kilda, representing 94% of the British and Irish population (Mitchell *et al.*, 2003). Leach's Storm-petrels were first recorded on St Kilda in 1818 (see Cramp *et al.*, 1974) and this has long been regarded as the largest colony in Britain (Ainslie & Atkinson, 1937; Lloyd *et al.*, 1991). The largest sub-colony in the archipelago, of 27,704 AOS, was on the island of Dun. The burrows on Dun were virtually invisible, hidden in a thick sward on unconsolidated ground, broken by boulders and by puffin burrows, which were very dense in places. Sheep-grazing on Boreray and Soay has created grassy slopes that are much more consolidated and have a closely cropped sward, which held 12,093 AOS and 2,031 AOS, respectively. Even in this type of habitat, Leach's Storm-petrel burrows were very indistinct and showed few signs of use. On Hirta, 3,605 AOS were found in the grassy margins of boulder-strewn habitat and at the base of cleits. There is also thought to be a small colony on Stac an Armin (Harris & Murray, 1977), but this site was not visited during the Seabird 2000 surveys in 1999–2000.

On the Flannan Isles, a survey in 2001 found a total of 1,425 AOS on six islands that were deemed to have sufficient habitat (Newton & Mitchell, 2001). They were recorded as present on the Flannans in both previous censuses (Cramp *et al.*, 1974; Lloyd *et al.*, 1991), but visits were confined to the largest island, Eilean Mor. Anderson *et al.* (1961) found the colony extent on Eilean Mor to be similar to that first mapped by Atkinson & Ainslie (1940) in 1937. More recently, a joint Scottish National Heritage / Joint Nature Conservation Committee expedition in 1996 gained the impression of hundreds or possibly low thousands of Leach's Storm-petrels (K. Thompson, pers. comm). In 2001, there were actually more Leach's Storm-petrels on Eilean Tighe than on the Eilean Mor (Table 2), yet it was only in 1955 that breeding was proven there (Atkinson & Roberts, 1955). The last confirmed breeding on the four other islands (Table 2) was in 1959 (Anderson *et al.*, 1961). On all the islands in the group, Leach's Storm-petrels favoured lush areas of Mayweed. Their numbers on the outer islands appeared to be limited by the depth of soil available. On Eilean Mor, Leach's Storm-petrels were found nesting among the densest areas of Atlantic Puffin burrows, sharing entrances with the puffins.

The third-largest colony, of 1,132 AOS, was on North Rona (Murray *et al.*, in press). Some 35% of the AOS were in man-made stone structures, predominantly the village ruins, which held 328 AOS. This was almost identical to the 327 occupied burrows found in the village in 1936 by Ainslie & Atkinson (1937). In the intervening period, Robson (1968) and Love (1978) both considered the

Table 2   Numbers of Leach's Storm-petrels (AOS) at colonies in Britain and Ireland (1999–2002) compared to previous evidence of breeding given by Cramp et al. (1974) and Lloyd et al. (1991). ID denotes the position of each island group in Figure 1.

ID	Administrative area or country	Colony	Method	Year	AOS	95% lower confidence limit	95% upper confidence limit	Cramp et al. 1974[1]	Lloyd et al. 1991[2]
1	Shetland	Foula	1,6	2001–02	15	3	30	P (suspected)	P; P (1974; Mainwood, 1975); 50 pairs (1976)
2	Shetland	Gruney	2,4	2000	20				<50 pairs (1982; Fowler, 1982)
3	Orkney	Sule Skerry	1	2001	0			1 AOS (1933; Robinson, 1934)	>5 pairs
4	Western Isles	St Kilda:							
		Hirta	2,5	1999–2000	3,605	2,758	4,925	P	P
		Dun	2,5	1999	27,704	20,430	38,506	P	P
		Boreray	2,5	2000	12,093	9,283	15,671		3200–6400 AOS
		Soay	2,4	2000	2,031	1,839	2,296		P
		St Kilda Total			45,433	34,310	61,398		
5	Western Isles	Flannan Isles:							
		Eilean Mor	2,4	2001	567	492	676	P	P (1988)
		Eilean Tighe	2,4	2001	630	544	759	P (1955; Atkinson & Roberts, 1955)	
		Soray	2,4	2001	112	96	135	P (1959; Anderson et al., 1961)	
		Sgeir Toman	2,4	2001	51	44	61	P (1959; Anderson et al., 1961)	
		Roareim	2,4	2001	14	12	16	P (1959; Anderson et al., 1961)	
		Eilean a' Ghobha	2,4	2001	51	44	61	P (1959; Anderson et al., 1961)	
		Flannan Isles Total			1,425	1,232	1,708		
6	Western Isles	Old Hill, Loch Roag	3,4	2001	17	15	20		
7	Western Isles	Bearasay, Loch			nc			2 AOS (1955; Atkinson & Roberts, 1955)	
8	Western Isles	Campay, Loch Roag	1		0				
9	Western Isles	Haskeir			nc			1 AOS (1939)	
10	Western Isles	North Rona	2,4	2001	1,132	849	1,700	P	P; 500 pairs (1972)
11	Western Isles	Sule Sgeir	3,4	2001	5	3	7	400 pairs (1939: Atkinson 1948)	P; 15 pairs (1980)
	Scotland Total				**48,047**	**36,432**	**64,883**		
12	Kerry	Great Skellig	1	2002	0			P (suspected 1965; Ruttledge, 1966)	
13	Mayo	Stags of Broadhaven	1,6	2001	310			P (suspected; 1945 & 1947)	>200 pairs (1982; Waring & Davis, 1983)
14	Mayo	Inishglora	1	2002	0				
	Ireland Total				**310**				
	Britain & Ireland Total				**48,357**	**36,742**	**65,193**		

Method code

1   Determined presence/absence
2   AOS determined using tape playback of male purr call
    using site specific adjustment factor – see Table 1.
3   AOS determined using tape playback of male purr call
    using adjustment factor estimated at an adjacent site – see Table 1.
4   Complete count of responses
5   Sample count of responses
6   Best guess

Notes

[1]   records are from 1969–70 unless otherwise stated
[2]   records are from 1985–87 unless otherwise stated
nc   not counted (i.e. presence / absence not determined)
P   present breeding

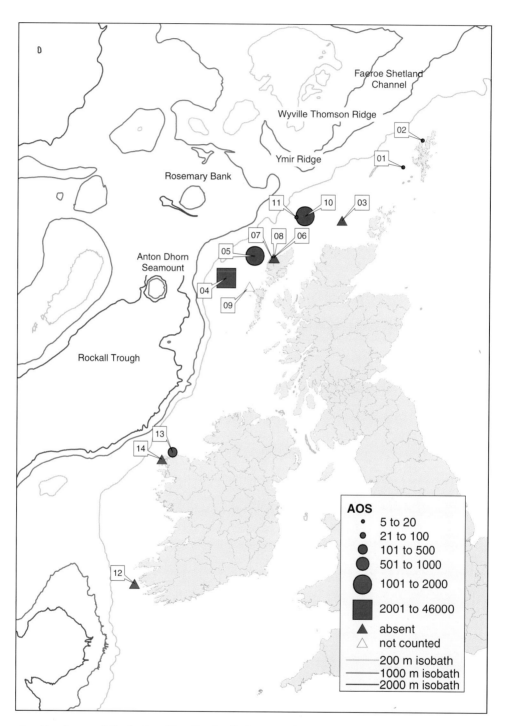

Figure 1   Abundance and distribution of breeding Leach's Storm-petrels in Britain and Ireland 1999–2001. ID number corresponds to colonies listed in Table 2. Bathymetry data supplied by METOC (UKHO) Licence no. 032003/005.

The island of Dun (background), barely separated from Hirta (foreground) in the St Kilda archipelago holds the largest colony of Leach's Storm-petrels in Britain and Ireland (Tim Dunn)

The Stags of Broadhaven, Co. Mayo hold Ireland's only known colony of Leach's Storm-petrel (Alyn Walsh)

village population to be little different from 1936. However, in 1958, Bagenal & Baird (1959) estimated the village population at 2,000–3,000 pairs, based on ringing and recapture, with a total island population of *c.*5,000 pairs. P. G. H. Evans, cited in Lloyd *et al.* (1991) estimated the entire population, including that of the village, at 500 pairs in 1972.

Some 17 km west of North Rona, the small island of Sula Sgeir was first confirmed as a breeding site of Leach's Storm-petrels in the 1930s (Atkinson, 1948). In 1939, John Ainslie and Robert Atkinson reported '*as soon as darkness fell, the night air was alive with* [Leach's Storm-] *petrels: we guessed a population of some 400 pairs, as many as. . .on North Rona*' (Atkinson, 1948). However, in 2001, Murray *et al.* (in press) were successful in eliciting only two responses to playbacks, suggesting 3–7 pairs, based on the response rate on North Rona. These were confined to the walls of bothies, and suitable breeding habitat elsewhere was limited by extensive soil erosion and high densities of nesting Northern Fulmars that have expanded substantially since Ainslie and Atkinson's visit in 1939.

On Sule Skerry, 56 km west of Orkney, Lloyd *et al.* (1991) reported more than 5 AOS in 1986, with the only previous record of confirmed breeding in 1933 (Robinson, 1934). However, during a seven-night stay in 2001, diurnal playback and nocturnal searches failed to find any AOS's, despite Leach's Storm-petrels being regularly caught in mist-nets during the breeding season.

In Shetland, breeding was first confirmed on the island of Foula in 1974 (Mainwood, 1975). Lloyd *et al.* (1991) simply listed the species as present in 1986. In 2001, nocturnal visits found birds calling from burrows, suggesting 3–30 AOS, although much of the suitable habitat was inaccessible. Breeding was confirmed in 2002, by one bird responding to diurnal playback (S. Gear, pers. comm.). The only other colony in Shetland was found in 1980, on the small island of Gruney in the Ramna Stacks (Fowler & Butler, 1982). The small colony of 20 AOS has been monitored annually since 1991, using an endoscope to investigate burrows, and numbers have remained stable since then (Ellis *et al.*, 1988).

The 'newest' colony in Britain is on the island of Old Hill in Loch Roag, northwest Lewis (Western Isles). Atkinson & Roberts (1955) suggested its suitability for Leach's Storm-petrels, but it was 1994 before breeding was confirmed and around 25 AOS were found on a nocturnal visit (A. Rothwell, pers. comm.). In 2001, a thorough diurnal playback survey yielded only five responses, equivalent to 17 AOS, assuming a response rate of 0.295 calculated on the Flannan Isles, 40 km to the west (Table 1). Atkinson & Roberts (1955) found 2 AOS on the nearby island of Bearasay in 1955. Unfortunately, sea conditions prevented us from landing in 2001, but the adjacent island of Campay was visited, where no responses were elicited by diurnal playback.

It is highly unlikely that any other substantial colonies exist in Scotland, since, during the course of Seabird 2000, many suitable petrel islands were visited during late June and July (see European Storm-petrel chapter). There may be an occasional pair on some other northwestern islands, but the only other island previously reported to hold Leach's Storm-petrel that was not visited during Seabird 2000, is Haskeir, off North Uist (Western Isles). A Leach's Storm-petrel was found in a burrow on Haskeir in 1939 (Freeman, 1940 cited in Cramp *et al.*, 1974), though none was found in 1955 by Atkinson & Roberts (1955).

The only Leach's Storm-petrel colony in Ireland is on the Stags of Broadhaven, (Co. Mayo). Leach's Storm-petrels were recorded as present (but not necessarily breeding) on two of the four Stags, Chackbeg and Chackmore in 1945 and 1947 (Ruttledge, 1994). This site was not subsequently visited until 1982, when breeding was confirmed on Chackbeg (Waring & Davis, 1983). A diurnal playback survey was carried out on Chackmore in 2001, but not until late July, when chicks had already started hatching, so diurnal attendance by adults would be lower than during incubation by an unknown amount. Response rate, therefore, would likely be less than the 0.30–0.43 found at other Leach's Storm-petrel colonies (Table 2). Bad weather prevented a visit to the other Stags, but a rough total of 310 AOS was estimated for the four islands based on area of suitable habitat (Newton

& Mitchell, 2001). Breeding has yet to be confirmed on any other islands off western Ireland since the 1880s, when eggs were taken from two islands in Co. Mayo and two in Co. Kerry (see Cramp *et al.*, 1974). Ruttledge (1966) carried out an extensive search for breeding Leach's Storm-petrels on various west-coast islands but heard birds calling on only the Stags of Broadhaven and on Great Skellig, Co. Kerry. A reconnaissance playback survey of Great Skellig, in 2002, failed to elicit any responses, as did a similar survey of Inishglora, Co. Mayo (S. F. Newton, pers. comm.).

FACTORS CONTROLLING DISTRIBUTION AND NUMBERS

The lack of an accurate population estimate prior to Seabird 2000 makes it impossible to assess whether there have been any significant changes in the numbers of breeding Leach's Storm-petrels in Britain and Ireland. But the various quantitative accounts described above suggest no major shift in distribution has occurred, at least during the last 70 years. However, the results of Seabird 2000 provide a baseline on which to assess future changes. By examining what controls the current distribution of Leach's Storm-petrels in Britain and Ireland, we may be able to predict what factors are likely to have an impact on the population in years to come.

An important determinant of where Leach's Storm-petrels breed, and by far the greatest threat to existing populations, is the presence of predatory mammals. Being ground-nesters, Leach's Storm-petrels are particularly susceptible to mammalian predators and, around the world, they nest exclusively on islands that are generally free of indigenous mammals. In Britain and Ireland, all the islands occupied by Leach's Storm-petrels have historically had no mammalian predators, except Foula where feral cats have no doubt restricted occupied sites to the most inaccessible slopes and outcrops (S. Gear, pers. comm.). In addition, during the present study, an American Mink was found in a holt on the island of Old Hill, and it is unlikely that the small Leach's Storm-petrel colony there will persist as long as the mink does. Mink are proficient swimmers and are capable of colonising inshore islands, such as Old Hill. On more remote offshore islands, the potential threat from colonisation by mink or other land predators, such as Brown Rats, still exists through their accidental introduction from boats visiting the islands. Ironically, the most likely island for such an occurrence is St Kilda, the largest colony in the east Atlantic. At St Kilda, the main island of Hirta is inhabited by workers on a radar-tracking installation, which is occasionally supplied by landing craft, and the island is also frequently visited by leisure boats. Every measure must be taken to prevent rats going ashore from these boats.

Avian predators can also have a severe effect on Leach's Storm-petrel colonies. However, their underground burrows offer some protection for the eggs, chicks and adults from avian predators, such as gulls, crows, Great Skuas and raptors. Adult Leach's Storm-petrels are at greatest risk from aerial predators when they appear above ground in their colonies at night. Leach's Storm-petrels in Japan reduce their chance of predation from Slaty-backed Gulls by timing their return to land with the darkest period of the night, depending on the lunar cycle (Watanuki, 1986). However, on St Kilda, predation by Great Skuas poses a serious threat. Since the early 1990s, the Great Skua population on St Kilda has increased exponentially, from around 42 pairs in 1986 to 229 in 1996 (Phillips *et al.*, 1999a), and, together with non-breeding birds, are thought to take around 14,850 Leach's Storm-petrels each year (Phillips *et al.*, 1999b). A recent survey, in 2003, of the largest sub-colony of Leach's Storm-petrel in St Kilda, on Dun, suggests that breeding numbers have declined by 48% since the Seabird 2000 survey in 1999 (P. I. Mitchell, unpubl. data). If the populations on Boreray, Hirta and Soay have declined by a similar proportion we would expect the total population on St Kilda to have declined by almost 44,000 birds since 1999. This is not far short of the 60,000

Leach's Storm-petrels that Phillips *et al.* (1999c) predicted would be depredated by Great Skuas during the same period. The Great Skuas may also take non-breeding Leach's Storm-petrels, which also visit the islands at night, but the numbers involved are unknown.

On the other side of the Atlantic, on Great Island, Newfoundland, a high level of predation (an estimated 49,000 petrels taken from a population of 270,000 in 1997) by the resident Herring Gulls (1,640 pairs) has had surprisingly little effect on the Leach's Storm-petrel population (Stenhouse *et al.*, 2000). The predation of adult petrels on Great Island may be counteracted by immigration from nearby islands, such as Baccalieu, which has over three million breeding pairs and no Herring Gulls (Sklepkovych & Montevecchi, 1989). The level of immigration to St Kilda is unknown, but may be low as St Kilda probably holds the majority of the Leach's Storm-petrel breeding population in the eastern Atlantic (see below).

Furness (1997b) suggested that the recent reductions of fish discards in the North Sea and northeast Atlantic has lead to an increase in the proportion of seabirds in the diet of Great Skuas breeding in Scotland. Great Skuas nest at four, and large gulls are present at all, Leach's Storm-petrel colonies (Table 3). On Foula, it is surprising that there are any Leach's Storm-petrels breeding at all, as the island also holds the largest Great Skua colony in the world, as well as a population of feral cats. On North Rona, the population of Leach's Storm-petrels probably faces heavy predation from the large colony of Great Black-backed Gulls, as well as from 19 pairs of Great Skuas, but the impact these are having is unknown. On Eilean Tighe, Flannan Isles, the single pair of Great Skuas nesting in the group has acquired a taste for Leach's Storm-petrels, judging from the pellets near their nest (pers. obs.). It is important that we start to monitor the effects of aerial predators on Leach's Storm-petrels, particularly on St Kilda and North Rona, where the impact may be considerable. However, devising a management solution for reducing predation by a globally scarce species like the Great Skua is unlikely to be straightforward.

Given that Leach's Storm-petrels are mainly confined to islands free of mammalian predators, why do they not breed on more mammal-free islands around Britain and Ireland? European Storm-petrels are equally dependant on mammal-free islands, but are much more widespread, breeding on over 100 islands along the north and west coasts of Britain and west coast of Ireland (see the previous chapter). European Storm-petrels tend to prefer rockier habitat, but most of the islands occupied by European Storm-petrels also harbour potentially suitable nesting habitat for Leach's Storm-petrels. Indeed, on St Kilda, North Rona, and the Stags of Broadhaven, both species nest side by side in identical habitat. Thus, whilst availability of breeding habitat may limit the number of Leach's Storm-petrels breeding on a particular island, it does not explain why they are not as widespread as European Storm-petrels. This is more likely to be explained by a fundamental difference in their feeding habits.

Table 3   Number of predators present (breeding pairs) at colonies of Leach's Storm-petrels.

Island colony	Great Skua	Great Black-backed Gull	Herring Gull	Lesser Black-backed Gull	Others
St Kilda	229	32	34	30	
Flannans	1	55	20	9	
North Rona	19	983	40	3	
Sule Sgeir	0	0	8	0	
Old Hill	0	36	0	0	corvids
Gruney		15	0	0	corvids
Foula	2,293	16	15	0	Feral cats
Stags of Broadhaven	0	10	4	0	corvids

Regurgitated pellet of a Great Skua containing the remains of a Leach's Storm-petrel complete with BTO leg-ring (Ian Mitchell)

European Storm-petrels feed on scraps that they glean off the surface and are often associated with fishing vessels in both inshore waters and beyond the shelf break. In contrast, Leach's Storm-petrels feed on macro-zooplankton (e.g. myctophids, amphipods, euphausiids; Montevecchi *et al.*, 1992) and, in the east Atlantic (during the breeding season), are confined to areas beyond the continental shelf break (deeper than 200 m), being concentrated over the continental slope (200–1,000 m) and in deeper water (1,000–>2,000 m; Pollock *et al.*, 2000a). Therefore, it would seem logical for Leach's Storm-petrels to nest as close as possible to their feeding grounds, i.e. deep oceanic water. Indeed, colony size is significantly negatively correlated with proximity to the $_{r,8}$ 1,000 m isobath ($_{r,8} = 0.726$, $P<0.01$; Fig. 2) for all sites in Table 2 and figure 1, including those islands where no Leach's petrels have been found breeding during Seabird 2000. All the British and Irish Leach's Storm-petrel colonies are 37–67 km from the shelf break (200 m isobath) and 65–119 km from the bottom of the continental slope (1,000–2,000 m).

As the southwesterly North Atlantic drift current hits this steep slope, cold nutrient-rich upwellings create ideal conditions for plankton blooms, and Leach's Storm-petrels gather to feed in such areas (Brown, 1988). St Kilda and the Flannans are ideally placed for accessing upwellings of water from over 2,000 m deep, and the main concentrations of Leach's Storm-petrels during the early part of the breeding season, in May–June, are found around the Anton Dhorn Seamount and Rosemary Bank (Fig. 1; Pollock *et al.*, 2000a). North Rona is closer to the Yimir and Wyville Thompson ridges (Fig. 1), where there are also considerable concentrations of feeding Leach's Storm-petrels, particularly in August (Pollock *et al.*, 2000a). Much lower densities of feeding Leach's Storm-petrels occur northeast of the Wyville Thompson ridge, west of Shetland. The slope is less steep to the west of the Shetland colonies of Foula and Gruney (where the 200 m and 1,000 m isobaths are 41–52 km apart) and low numbers were observed feeding above it throughout the breeding season

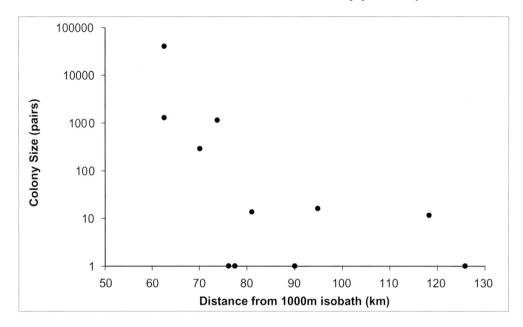

Figure 2   Relationship between colony size (plotted on a log-scale axis) and proximity of deep oceanic water (1,000 m isobath). Spearman rank correlation $r_{s,8}$ = 0.726, P<0.05.

and further out into the deeper water of the Faeroe–Shetland channel in August (Pollock *et al.*, 2000a).

Of all the islands on the west coast of Ireland that are occupied by European Storm-petrels, the Stags of Broadhaven are closest to the shelf edge and the bottom of the slope. At this location, the slope is very steep, and the Stags are just 83 km from the 2,000 m isobath on the edge of the Rockall Trough (Fig. 1), which holds the main concentration of feeding birds off western Ireland (Pollock *et al.*, 2000b). Inishglova is also close to the deep water yet none were found breeding here and perhaps some other unknown factor is affecting the island's suitability to nest Leach's Storm-petrels. The distance to the bottom of the continental slope increases sharply for islands south and north of here, possibly explaining why these small rocks hold the only colony of Leach's Storm-petrels in Ireland.

INTERNATIONAL CONTEXT

There are around 9,000,000–10,600,000 pairs of breeding Leach's Storm-petrel in the world (Table 4, see Huntington *et al.*, 1996). Around half breed in the North Atlantic, but Britain only holds around 1% of these, with over 98% in the west. In the east Atlantic, it is difficult to put the British population into context, because the size of the other main population, on the Westmann Islands off southern Iceland, has not been systematically surveyed, but is thought hold 80,000–150,000 pairs (Icelandic Institute of Natural History, 2000). The only other colonies in the east Atlantic are in the Faeroes and Norway. The first Leach's Storm-petrels confirmed breeding in Norway, were found on Hernyken, in the Røst archipelago (Lofoten Islands) in 1989 (Anker-Nilssen & Anker-Nilssen, 1993) and is the most northerly Leach's Storm-petrel colony in the world. A second colony was found further south on Erkna, off western Norway, in 1996 (Olsen, 1996 cited by Anker-Nilssen, 2000b), and the total Norwegian population is thought to be 100–1,000 pairs (Gjershaug *et al.*, 1994).

On the other side of the Atlantic, there are around 4,800,000 breeding pairs, 97% of which breed on islands around Newfoundland, Canada (Table 4). These include the largest colony in the world, of 3,360,000 breeding pairs, on Baccalieu Island (Sklepkovych & Montevecchi, 1989). They also breed off Quebec, Nova Scotia and New Brunswick, Canada, and south into Maine, USA, with fewer than 10 pairs in Massachusetts, USA. Some colonies in Newfoundland have been subject in recent years to increased levels of predation by Herring Gulls. Herring Gull populations have benefited from feeding on landfill sites and fisheries discards. However, since the eastern Canadian ground-fishery moratorium, in 1992, gulls have turned increasingly to smaller seabirds, including Leach's Storm-petrels, as an alternative food source (Russell & Montevecchi, 1996; Regehr & Montevecchi, 1997), in a similar scenario to the depredation of Leach's Storm-petrels by Great Skuas in Scotland (see above). The level of predation from gulls can vary within a season and is indirectly controlled by the inshore movements of spawning capelin, which have become progressively later in recent years. Thus, if there are few capelin close inshore when the gull chicks first hatch, depredation of Leach's Storm-petrels is high. However, once capelin move inshore, gull predation on Leach's Storm-petrels is significantly reduced (Stenhouse & Montevecchi, 1999a).

There are four currently recognised subspecies of Leach's Storm-petrel (Power & Ainley, 1986). Nominate *O. l. leucorhoa* breeds in the north Atlantic and north Pacific. *O. l. chapmani* is confined to the Los Coronados and San Benito islands, off Baja California, Mexico, and is usually dark-rumped. On the Pacific island of Guadalupe, off Mexico, *O. l. socorroensis* is predominantly dark-rumped and breeds during the summer, whilst the larger and mainly white-rumped *O. l. cheimomnestes* breeds in winter.

In the eastern Pacific, *O. l. leucorhoa* breed on islands along the coast of North America from the Aleutian Islands, Alaska, to southern California. Alaska holds the most substantial breeding colonies, totalling around 2,000,000–3,500,000 pairs (Sowls *et al.*, 1980). In Mexico, *O. l. chapmani* is concentrated on the San Benito islands, where 1,200,000 birds (i.e. *c.*600,000 pairs) were estimated breeding in 1999 (see Wolf, 2002). On Guadalupe, the estimated population of *O. l. socorroensis* and *O. l. cheimomnestes* in the 1960s were 4,000 and 3,000 birds (i.e. *c.*2,000 and 1,500 pairs) respectively, but no more-recent surveys of these rare subspecies have been conducted (Wolf, 2002). On both sides of North America, introduced mammals (e.g. dogs, cats, rats, Skunk) have led to extinctions of Leach's Storm-petrels on some islands (Huntington *et al.*, 1996). Aleutian Islands' populations, previously devastated by introduced foxes, are now recovering following removal of the foxes and active re-introductions of Leach's Storm-petrels.

In the western Pacific, there are thought to be about 350,000 birds (i.e. *c.*175,000 pairs) of *O. l. leucorhoa* breeding in Russia, on three groups of islands; Commander, Sakhalin and Kuril (Litvinenko & Shibaev, 1991). However, all of these islands appear to be inhabited by mammalian predators, such as the Red Fox, and introduced species such as Arctic Fox, Sable and Brown Rat. Elsewhere, there are around 500,000 pairs breeding in Japan (Watanuki *et al.*, 1988).

The first breeding by Leach's Storm-petrel in the southern hemisphere was confirmed in 1997 on Dyer Island, South Africa, when 19 nest sites with calling birds produced at least three young (Whittington *et al.*, 1999). Breeding is also suspected on at least two other islands in South Africa. Leach's Storm-petrels have also been found prospecting on the Chatham Islands, New Zealand, but have yet to be confirmed breeding there.

Table 4　International context.

Country or region	Subspecies	Number of pairs		Year	Source
		Min	Max		
Great Britain, Isle of Man and Channel Isles	*leucorhoa*	37,000[1]	65,000[2]	1999–2001	Seabird 2000
All Ireland	*leucorhoa*	310	310	2001	Seabird 2000
Faeroe Islands	*leucorhoa*	1,000	1,000	1995	BirdLife International / EBCC (2000)
Iceland	*leucorhoa*	80,000	150,000		Icelandic Institute of Natural History (2000)
Norway	*leucorhoa*	100	1,000	1994	Gjershaug *et al.* (1994)
Canada (Atlantic)	*leucorhoa*	4,793,364	4,793,364	1980–91	Huntington *et al.* (1996)
USA (Atlantic)	*leucorhoa*	19,138	19,138	1970s	Huntington *et al.* (1996)
South Africa		3	19	1986–87	Whittington *et al.* (1999)
Canada (Pacific)	*leucorhoa*	550,000	550,000	1980s	Rodway (1991)
Japan	*leucorhoa*	500,000	500,000		Watanuki *et al.* (1988)
Mexico	*chapmani*	600,000	600,000	1999	Wolf (2002)
Mexico (Guadalupe Is.)	*cheimomnestes*	1,500	1,500	1968	Wolf (2002)
Mexico (Guadalupe Is.)	*socorroensis*	2,000	2,000	1968	Wolf (2002)
Russia (NW Pacific)	*leucorhoa*	175,000	175,000	1970s–1980s	Litvinenko & Shibaev (1991) (see also Kondratyev *et al.*, 2000)
USA (Alaska)	*leucorhoa*	2,000,000	3,500,000	1970's	Sowls *et al.* (1978)
USA (Pacific)	*leucorhoa*	237,182	237,182		Huntington *et al.* (1996), Wolf (2002)

Biogeographic region		Min	Max	Min % GB	Max % GB	Min % Ireland	Max % Ireland
North Atlantic*	*leucorhoa*	4,900,000	5,000,000	0.7%	1.3%	0.0%	0.0%
World	all	9,000,000	10,600,000	0.3%	0.7%	0.0%	0.0%

* Stroud *et al.* (2001)

Notes

[1]　95% lower confidence limit

[2]　95% upper confidence limit

Northern Gannet *Morus bassanus*

Sarah Wanless and Mike P. Harris

INTRODUCTION

The Northern Gannet is the largest and one of the most striking of all the seabirds in the northern hemisphere. Gannets are birds of the open sea, frequently reaching the outer limits of the continental shelf, but skeins can also be seen most months of the year passing many headlands of Britain and Ireland en route to and from colonies or feeding grounds. The species is endemic to the North Atlantic with two widely separated populations, one in the northeast Atlantic with colonies from Brittany north to Murmansk and west to Iceland, the other in eastern Canada. Outside the breeding season, birds from all colonies migrate south, with some European birds crossing the equator off Africa and others entering the Mediterranean. Although there is no evidence of intermixing of the east and west Atlantic populations, birds ringed as chicks at the Canadian colonies on Funk Island and Bonaventure Island have been recovered on or off the coasts of Ireland, Spain, Portugal and northwest Africa (Harris & Wanless, 1999).

The sight of these brilliant white birds plunging arrow-like into shoals of mackerel, herring or other medium-sized pelagic fish is the highlight of many a summer seawatch. The deployment of activity loggers has shown that there are two types of dives (Garthe *et al.*, 2000). In the first, probably aimed at large pelagic fish near the surface, the time spent underwater is short with birds attaining depths of only a few metres. In the second, birds spend over a half a minute underwater and reach depths of over 20 m, apparently feeding on much deeper schools of fish. Gannets can also be seen feeding on the surface, greedily swallowing gullet-loads of sandeels only a few inches long. Substantial numbers of gannets follow trawlers as they haul their nets and when their catches are being sorted and gutted. Satellite tracking has revealed that, when feeding chicks, adults may travel huge distances, the maximum recorded foraging ranges being 540 km from Bass Rock and 240 km from Great Saltee (Hamer *et al.*, 2001).

There is a long tradition of counting Northern Gannets and changes in numbers are better documented than for any other seabird. Many of the smaller colonies are counted each year and censuses of the whole population have been made in the early 1900s, 1939, 1969–70, 1984–85 and 1994–95 (Gurney, 1913; Fisher & Vevers, 1944; Cramp *et al.*, 1974; Murray & Wanless, 1986; Wanless, 1987; Lloyd *et al.*, 1991; Murray & Wanless, 1997). Even a census of the British and Irish population is a formidable undertaking as many gannetries are on remote and inaccessible islands and require aerial surveys. A complete census was carried out in 1994/95 (Murray & Wanless, 1997) and therefore full coverage of the species was not a top priority for Seabird 2000. However, counts were made of 14 of the 21 colonies in Britain and Ireland in 1998–2000, which allow the size and status of the population to be updated.

CENSUS METHODS

Northern Gannets are highly traditional in where they breed and most colonies have been occupied for decades, and many for centuries. Gannetries are often large, always obvious and noisy, and many are tourist attractions. Where new colonies are established, prospecting birds are often present for several years, alerting local birdwatchers that colonisation is possible. Even so, the exact year of colonisation can be missed. For instance, four pairs of gannets reared chicks among Common Guillemots at Troup Head in the Moray Firth in 1988. Prospecting birds were seen patrolling these cliffs in 1986, but despite the area being on the Scottish mainland and relatively easy to visit, there is no record of the species' status in 1987. Thus, we will never know if the first year of breeding was 1987 or 1988 (Wanless *et al.*, 1996). Typically, initial colonisation by a few pairs is followed by a rapid increase in numbers.

Gannets breed in wild, spectacular and frequently remote places. Most gannetries are on isolated and inaccessible offshore islands, often with difficult access for ornithologists, or on imposing mainland cliffs where the birds are generally safe from man, foxes and other large ground-predators. Nests at small gannetries or those where birds breed along stretches of indented cliffs are relatively straightforward to count, although this can still be a time-consuming business, since there are usually areas of the colony that can only be viewed and counted from the sea. During direct counts, the count unit was Apparently Occupied Nest (AON). In the photographs from aerial surveys (see below) it was usually possible to see whether one or two birds were present at a site, but the actual nest was barely visible. The count unit used for aerial surveys was therefore the Apparently Occupied Site (AOS). For simplicity, counts of AON and AOS from different colonies are combined to give a total population estimate expressed as AOS. Precise totals are presented in Table 1, but since these suggest a spurious accuracy, rounded totals (to the nearest 100) are used in the text.

In the 1994–95 census 11 colonies were surveyed by direct counts of every nest, from either land or sea or both. However, such techniques are not feasible for the large and/or remote gannetries of St Kilda (Western Isles), Grassholm (Dyfed), Little Skellig (Co. Kerry), Sule Stack (Orkney), Sula Sgeir (Western Isles), Ailsa Craig (Kyle & Carrick), the Flannan Isles (Western Isles), Ortac (Channel

Isles) and Les Etacs (Channel Isles). At these colonies, counts of nests were made from photographs taken from the air or, less commonly, from the sea. The first five of these colonies were counted in the same way as in the previous surveys conducted in 1968–70 and 1984–85. The colonies on Ortac and Les Etacs were also previously surveyed using aerial photographs in 1984. The Bass Rock was counted directly in 1968–70 and from aerial photographs in 1985 and 1994.

During aerial surveys in 1994–95, the number of AOS was estimated from either large prints, or slides that were projected onto sheets of paper pinned on the wall. AOSs were counted, usually by blocking them off one-by-one. Unless it is possible to enter a gannetry to demarcate the limits of breeding birds on the ground, there is the risk of slightly overestimating the size of the colony from aerial photographs by including prospecting birds that typically congregate at the perimeter. A further problem is the need to draw up a composite of photographs that can lead to some sites being counted twice or some areas being missed. Such errors have been estimated at 4–5% (Boyd, 1961; Dixon, 1971). Despite these drawbacks, an aerial photographic survey is generally preferred for large colonies, since it gives a permanent record of the extent of the colony and allows repeated counts to be made by several observers in relative comfort. Even so, the problem of counting error remains since tests have shown that counts of gannet AOSs from photographs made by different people can vary by as much as 17%, so where possible, independent counts of each colony should be made by several people and the mean count used as the population estimate (Harris & Lloyd, 1977). New automated techniques for counting gannets from electronic images of aerial photographs can be as accurate as a human counter (Chardine, 2000). However, fully automated techniques are unlikely to be applicable to any but the highest quality photographs of relatively level terrain that occurs on few of the British and Irish gannetries, such as Grassholm or the top of Stac Lee, St Kilda.

There is an additional problem when counting methods need to be altered as a colony gets bigger. This is well illustrated by two counts made only three days apart in 1994 of the gannets on the Bass Rock, a colony that has grown so dramatically that it is now difficult to reach vantage points without causing disturbance. The first count in 1994 was made by Bryan Nelson using the same methods that he had used at this colony for over 40 years, i.e. mainly from photographs taken from the sea and land, combined with visual estimates for the remaining areas. Counts of birds were made and these were converted to AOS assuming a single bird to pair ratio of 10:1. He considered his count of 27,300 AOS to be an underestimate by 10% and accordingly increased his estimate to 30,000 AOS. The second count in 1994 was based on high-quality aerial photographs in which it was often possible to establish whether or not an AOS had nest material present (Murray & Wanless, 1997). The average of two counts from the aerial photographs was 39,800 AOS, 33% higher than that from the land-based survey. The aerial survey could have included non-breeders, but even if only definite AONs were counted on the aerial photographs (i.e. those AOS where nest material was visible), the total of 34,400 AON was still 15% higher than in the land-based survey. It thus appears that the aerial survey provided much better coverage of the colony. This example highlights the problems with changing methodology and cautions against being too dogmatic when comparing counts without some local knowledge. There is now a very strong case that large colonies should be surveyed by aerial photography, or where this is difficult or dangerous, photography from the sea. Where possible, land-based visits should also be made to check the extent of the colony and ensure that birds are not nesting in areas invisible from the air (Chardine, 2000).

Fortunately the pattern of change in the numbers of gannets has been remarkably consistent over almost a century, so that population trends are very obvious even though there may be concerns about the accuracy of a few individual counts.

Fourteen gannetries that together held 26% of the total British and Irish population in 1994/95 were subsequently censused during Seabird 2000 (1998–2000). Grassholm, Ortac and Les Etacs were counted from aerial photographs (S. Murray, J. Hooper/La Societe Gurnesiaise, unpubl.). The

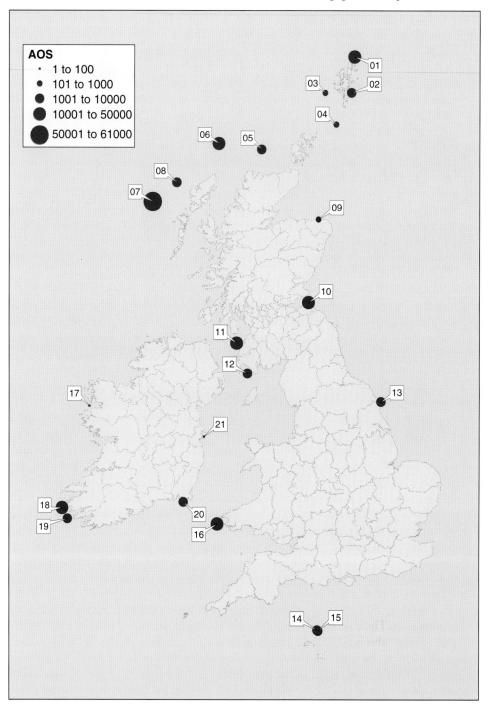

Figure 1   Abundance and distribution of breeding Northern Gannets in Britain and Ireland 1994–1995. Numbers correspond to colonies listed in Table 1.

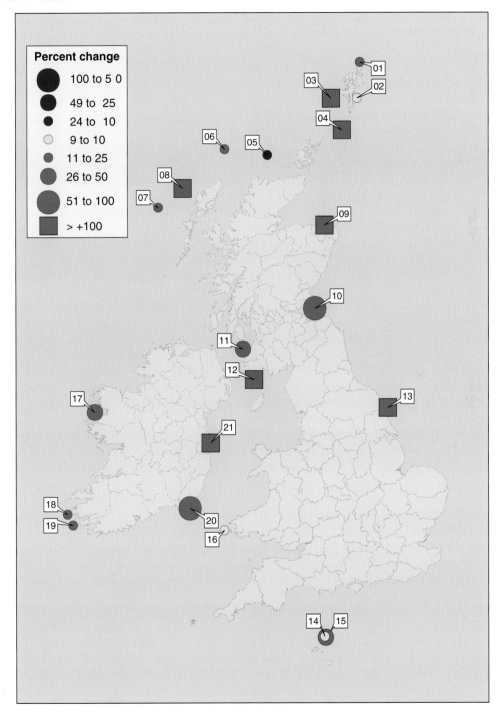

Figure 2 Changes in the number of breeding Northern Gannets (AOS/AON) at all colonies in Britain and Ireland 1984–85 to 1994–95. Numbers correspond to colonies listed in Table 1.

remaining colonies were counted directly. Projected estimates of AOSs at those colonies not counted during Seabird 2000 were calculated using the 1994–95 counts at each colony and the colony-specific mean annual rates of increase prior to 1994–95 (Moss *et al.*, 2002). A comparison of projected totals with counts of 12 colonies that were censused in Seabird 2000 (excluding the 3–4 pairs on Clare Island, and the Flannan Isles where recent counts have been erratic) suggested that, on average, the projected counts were 6–7% too low.

CURRENT STATUS AND TRENDS

The 1994–95 census of Northern Gannets in Britain and Ireland reported a total of 231,600 AOS dispersed among 21 colonies (Table 1). The majority (72%) were in Scotland (12 colonies), with 13% in Ireland (five), 12% in Wales (one), 2% in the Channel Islands (two) and <1% in England (one). The world's largest colony was on St Kilda: 60,400 AOS dispersed between Boreray (33,000 AOS) and its offshore stacks of Stac Lee (14,400 AOS) and Stac an Armin (13,000 AOS). The next largest colonies, in descending order, were on the Bass Rock, Ailsa Craig and Grassholm. At the other end of the scale there were 3 AON on Clare Island, where the species first bred in 1978, and 45 AON on Ireland's Eye, where breeding was first recorded in 1989. One or two birds, sometimes with nests, were recorded ashore on two different islands in the Shiant Islands (Western Isles) at various times between 1975 and 1995, but regular breeding appears not to have occurred and it is doubtful whether the Shiant Islands should really be included as a gannetry. A single pair was recorded breeding on Rockall, 300 km west of St Kilda in 1992 (Belaoussoff, 1993). It is possible that gannets have attempted to nest here in other years but, as Rockall is rarely visited by ornithologists, an accurate assessment of its status is problematical. The chances of a pair successfully rearing a chick must be very low because even during summer, waves sometimes break right over the rock. Northern Gannets have been recorded breeding in some bizarre locations. For instance, for four seasons an individual held a site on a roof-top at Seaford, East Sussex (Palmer, 2001).

Between 1969–70 and 1984–85 the Northern Gannet population of Britain and Ireland increased at a mean rate of 2.0% per annum and this rate remained unchanged over the next ten years. However, the rate of increase varied greatly between colonies, being significantly higher at smaller colonies, even though there still appeared to be much room for expansion at most of the larger colonies (Murray & Wanless, 1997). Counts at eight gannetries surveyed ten or more times since 1900 are shown in Fig. 3. These clearly demonstrate the rapid expansion in small colonies following initial colonisation. The erratic counts from St Kilda are considered to be more likely to be due to counting errors associated with censusing gannets when they nest on large, steep and broken cliff-faces, rather than real fluctuations in numbers.

Two colonies, on Sule Stack and Grassholm, appeared to have decreased between the mid-1980s and the mid-1990s (Table 1), but it was unclear whether these were real declines. The 1995 photographs of Sule Stack were excellent but those taken in 1985 were of only moderate quality. There was no evidence of a major change in the extent of the colony and the decline of 17% could therefore be partly due to the 1985 count being too high. The aerial photographs of Grassholm used for the 1994 count were of poor quality, but comparison with photographs taken in 1991 and 1999 suggested that numbers remained stable between 1984 and 1994 before increasing at 2.2% per annum subsequently (S. Murray, pers. comm.).

The estimated size of the population in Britain and Ireland during Seabird 2000 (i.e. combining the actual counts and projected totals) was 259,300 AOS. Numbers at 13 of the colonies actually counted during Seabird 2000 showed an increase. The only colony to register a decrease was on the

Table 1   Numbers of breeding Northern Gannets (AOS/AON) in Britain and Ireland 1968–2000. 14 colonies only in 1998–2000 and extrapolated estimates (in italics) for the seven other colonies are also shown. ID corresponds to colony symbols in Fig. 2, were surveyed.

ID	Colony	Admin area	1968–70	1984–85	1994–95	Percentage change 1968–95	Percentage change 1984–1995	1998–2000
1	Hermaness	Shetland	5,894	9,904	11,993	103%	21%	16,386
2	Noss	Shetland	4,300	6,900	7,310	70%	6%	8,017
3	Foula	Shetland	0	124	600		384%	723
4	Fair Isle	Shetland	0	258	975		278%	1,123
5	Sule Stack	Orkney	4,018	5,900	4,888	22%	−17%	*5,137[1]*
6	Sula Sgeir	Western Isles–Comhairle nan eilean	8,964	9,143	10,440	16%	14%	*10,703[1]*
7	St Kilda	Western Isles–Comhairle nan eilean	52,099	50,050	60,428	16%	21%	*61,340[1]*
8	Flannan Isles	Western Isles–Comhairle nan eilean	0	414	1,438		247%	1,244
9	Troup Head	Banff and Buchan	0	2	530[3]		26400%	1,085
10	Bass Rock	East Lothian	8,077	21,591	34,397	326%	59%	*44,110[1]*
11	Ailsa Craig	Kyle & Carrick	13,058	22,811	32,456	149%	42%	*35,825[1]*
12	Scar Rocks	Wigtown	450	770	1,952	334%	154%	1,670
	Scotland Total[2]		**96,860**	**127,867**	**167,407**	**73%**	**31%**	***187,363***
13	Bempton	Humberside	18	780	1,631		109%	2,552
14	Ortac	Channel Islands	1,000	1,985	2,098	110%	6%	2,500
15	Les Etacs	Channel Islands	2,000	2,536	3,380	69%	33%	3,450
	England, Isle of Man and Channel Islands Total		**3,018**	**5,301**	**7,109**	**136%**	**34%**	**8,502**
16	Grassholm	Dyfed	16,128	28,600	27,500[4]	71%	−4%	30,688
	Wales Total		**16,128**	**28,600**	**27,500[4]**	**71%**	**−4%**	**30,688**
	Great Britain, Isle of Man and Channel Islands Total		**116,006**	**161,768**	**202,016**	**74%**	**25%**	***226,553***
17	Clare Island	Co. Mayo	0	2	3		50%	3
18	Little Skellig	Co. Kerry	20,000	22,500	26,436	32%	17%	*28,799[1]*
19	Bull Rock	Co. Cork	1,500	1,511	1,815	21%	20%	*1,879[1]*
20	Great Saltee	Co. Wexford	155	710	1,250	706%	76%	1,930
21	Ireland's Eye	Co. Dublin	0	17	45		165%	147
	All-Ireland Total		**21,655**	**24,740**	**29,549**	**36%**	**19%**	***32,758***
	Great Britain and Ireland Total		**137,661**	**186,508**	**231,565**	**68%**	**24%**	***259,311***
	Number of colonies		**15**	**21**	**21**	**40%**	**0%**	**21**

Notes

[1] Not surveyed in 1998–2000. Extrapolated estimate for 1999 based on previous colony-specific trends.

[2] Birds, sometimes with nests, have also been reported on two of the Shiant Islands (see text)

[3] Minimum count

[4] Estimate

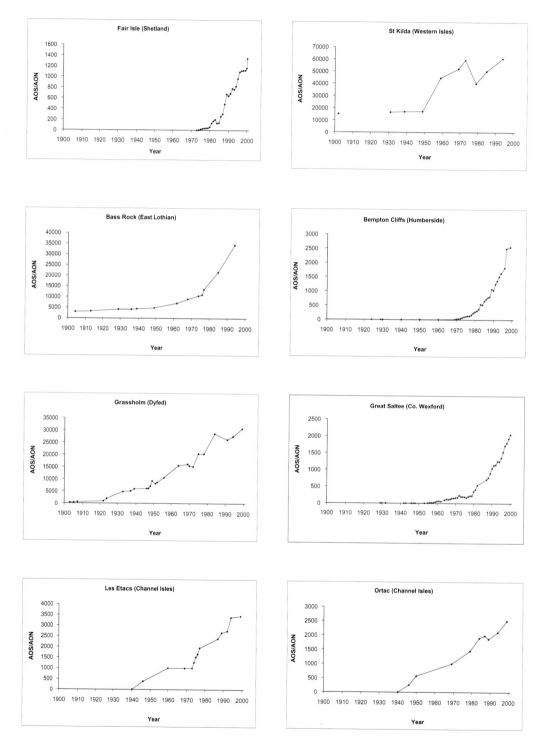

Figure 3   Changes in the number of Northern Gannets AOS/AON at colonies in Britain and Ireland 1900–2000.

a)

b)

c)

The extent of the Northern Gannet colony on the Bass Rock, Firth of Forth in a) 1969, b) 1984, c)2000. (Bryan Nelson)

Flannan Isles (Table 1). Assessments of the larger gannetries not surveyed during Seabird 2000 indicated that numbers had increased substantially on Ailsa Craig (B. Zonfrillo, pers. comm.) and the Bass Rock (Nelson, 2002), and that there had been little change on St Kilda (S. Murray, pers. comm.). These trends are very much in line with those estimated in 1994–95. No updated assessment was available for the large colony on Little Skellig but, to judge from recent counts, it seems unlikely that numbers have increased substantially.

CAUSES OF CHANGE

Nelson (2002) considered that the increase in total numbers of Northern Gannets could be seen, not as a population explosion, nor an extension of range such has occurred in the Northern Fulmar, but rather as a recovery from prolonged and extensive persecution. As far as can be judged, in recent decades there has been a decline in all the likely causes of mortality and breeding losses for this species.

Up until about a century ago large numbers of gannets were killed both for human consumption and baiting lobster and crab creels, and there can be little doubt that numbers were limited by human interference. Some legal killing of chicks still occurs, for instance in Iceland (up to 1,000 per annum; A. Petersen, pers. comm.) and the Faeroes. On Sula Sgeir, the men of Ness, Isle of Lewis, are licensed to take 2,000 nearly fledged young (known as gugas) each year for salting and then sale and consumption, both locally and abroad. If gannets here have the same nesting success as elsewhere in Scotland, this harvest represents *c*.30% of the young produced each year. Between 1985 and 2001 some 33,690 were reported killed, only in 1999, when 1,690 gugas were taken, was the reported annual total not exactly 2,000 (Scottish Executive figures). Although a tally is kept during the hunt, photographs of the piles of plucked gannets being salted (Beatty, 1992) suggest that more than the reported 2,000 may be killed in a year. In addition to the actual 'take', many more chicks must die by falling off cliffs or being unable to return to their nests during the inevitable disturbance. Although the overall gannet population of Scotland can easily sustain these losses, more regular censuses need to be made, as should an assessment of the true losses of young directly and indirectly attributable to the hunt. The timing of breeding of gannets tends to show little annual variation (Nelson, 2002). However, breeding on Sula Sgeir appears to have been very late in 1999 since the men of Ness reported unusually high numbers of very young gannets (and also Northern Fulmars), although the young were of high quality (www.reidio.com/fios29.htm). Young gannets tend to return and breed at their natal colonies, thus, not surprisingly, numbers at Sula Sgeir have increased much more slowly than predicted for a colony of this size (Table 1). Gannets at other British and Irish colonies appear to be mostly safe from humans, although there are rumours that chicks have been harvested on the Flannan Isles in recent years.

Direct information on the causes of gannet mortality is difficult to obtain. About half the recoveries of birds ringed in Britain and Ireland suggest a cause of death—the commonest being caught in fishing gear, either on baited hooks or in nets (34%), being shot or deliberately caught in some way for food (24%), or being oiled (22%: Wanless, 2002). The level of deliberate killing undoubtedly declined during the latter part of the last century. Gannets are quite commonly found washed ashore with oil on their plumage but losses due to oiling are unlikely to have any serious effect on the population, unless a major spill occurs immediately adjacent to a colony during the breeding season (Nelson, 2002). Such data are inevitably severely biased and give no indication of the birds dying from starvation or other less obvious causes in the open sea.

Like most other top marine predators, gannets suffer a wide range of effects resulting from man's activities. Perhaps the most insidious are chemicals entering the environment which the birds have not previously been exposed to. These are often fat-soluble and, despite being in extremely low levels, become concentrated within the food chain and may reach quite high levels in predators. Gannet eggs can have high levels of organochlorine residues, notably DDE, the principal metabolite of DDT found in vertebrate tissue. In birds, these chemicals are known to cause thinning of the eggshell, resulting in breakage of the egg. In the gannet egg, thinning occurs mainly in the soft chalky vaterite outer layer of the shell that is often worn away during incubation (Cooke, 1979). Routine monitoring of eggs collected from several British and Irish colonies has shown that organochlorine and mercury levels are too low to cause reductions in breeding success (Newton *et al.*, 1990). Long-term declines in organochlorine levels in eggs collected at Ailsa Craig and the Bass Rock between 1971 and 1997 presumably reflect the reduction in use of these chemicals (Newton *et al.*, 1998). The effect of pollution on the survival of full-grown gannets remains unknown.

Its generalised diet has permitted the gannet to switch prey as human fisheries have systematically reduced the stocks of herring, mackerel and other species on which it often appears to depend. The role of fishing in supplying discards as an easy food source is unclear. Although the rate of population increase of *c.*2% per annum has been sustained for a long period, it is slow compared with that of the Australian population of the Australasian Gannet *Morus serrator,* which increased at 6% per annum between 1980 and 2000 (Bunce *et al.*, 2002) and by other seabirds in Britain and Ireland with similar demographic parameters. Thus, like the Northern Gannet, the Common Guillemot and Atlantic Puffin both have a single egg-clutch, rear 0.7–0.8 chicks per annum, have adult survival rates of 90–95% and do not commence breeding until 4–6 years old, yet both have achieved rates of increase of 5% or more over several decades. The Northern Fulmar also lays a single egg, breeding success is typically only 0.4–0.5 young per year, birds do not start to breed until they are 6–12 years old and survival is again high (Cramp & Simmons, 1977). Despite these constraints, the Northern Fulmar has increased at 4% per annum in Britain and Ireland for over 100 years. What then has prevented the Northern Gannet from achieving a comparable rate of sustained increase? All four species have high adult survival rates, so the most likely explanation appears to be that the gannet survives less well during the period between fledging and recruiting to the breeding population. This is probably the largest gap in our knowledge of the Northern Gannet and attention should now focus on obtaining empirical data on the survival of both adults and chicks.

Modelling based on observed population parameters for 34 gannetries in the east Atlantic, and the observation that most gannetries increase in size by gradual expansion at the perimeter, suggested that small colonies could sustain faster growth following their initiation only by recruiting birds from other colonies. Furthermore, once a colony had more than about 600 breeding pairs many of the young reared there did not recruit to the natal colony (Moss *et al.*, 2002). This was a mechanistic model and assumed that breeding density remained constant but the observations could also be viewed as an expression of density dependence. Direct measurements of the lengths of feeding trips have shown that these are positively correlated with colony size, both among colonies of different size in the same year, and within colonies as they change size (Lewis *et al.*, 2001a). Perhaps competition for food during the breeding season results in potential recruits moving elsewhere where competition for food is less intense.

Among the larger, generally slower growing gannetries, the Bass Rock stands out as having shown a higher proportional increase (326%) between Operation Seafarer and the 1994–95 census than the others (St Kilda 16%, Sula Sgeir 22%, Little Skellig 32%, Grassholm 71%, Ailsa Craig 149%). The seven counts made of the Bass Rock between 1960 and 1994 suggest an annual increase of 4.5–5.5%, depending on which 1994 count is used (see above). This must mean that either productivity, immature and/or adult survival, levels of philopatry or immigration are substantially higher on the Bass Rock than elsewhere (Nelson, 2002). If numbers on the Bass Rock and St Kilda continue to increase at their current rates then the Bass Rock could become the world's largest gannetry within the next ten years, assuming, as seems probable, that there is room for at least 65,000 nests.

INTERNATIONAL CONTEXT

Most of the world's gannetries have been counted in recent years and combining these counts suggests a world population of 390,000 pairs, with 59% in Britain and 8.5% in Ireland (Table 2). The six more or less complete surveys of this species spanning almost a century show a remarkably consistent increase of 2.0% per annum (Fig. 4).

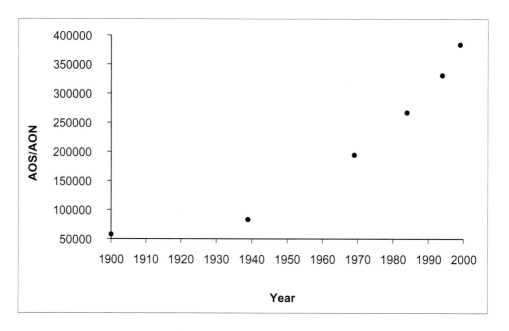

Figure 4   The world population of Northern Gannets 1900–99.

Since the establishment of the first colony in 1947, numbers of Gannets nesting in Norway have increased to 3,800–3,900 pairs in 1999 and 4,000–4,500 pairs in 2002. Whilst the population in north Norway of 2,000–2,500 pairs has changed little over the last decade, numbers breeding in the different colonies in the region have fluctuated greatly with some being abandoned and new ones being established (Barrett & Folkestad, 1996; R. T. Barrett, pers. comm.). The southern colony on Runde had 1,455 AON in 1995 and about 1,800 AON in 1999, but numbers have since declined slightly (R. T. Barrett, pers. comm.). The first Russian colony was established on the Kola Peninsula in 1995 (Krasnov & Barrett, 1997) and had increased to 35 pairs in 1998. Its subsequent development is, however, unknown (Yu. V. Krasnov, pers. comm.).

The only French colony, on Rouzic, continues to increase, with 14,900 AON in 1999 and 15,100 AON in 2000 (Siorat, in press a). However, during the 1990s gannets attempted to nest on pleasure boats at two marinas in the French Mediterranean, some 600 km south of the nearest colony and over 3,000 km away by sea (Bouillot, 1999). The German colony on Helgoland, founded in 1991, goes from strength to strength with 69 AON in 1999 and 128 AON in 2002 (Schneider, 2002). The most recent count of the Faeroese colony of Mykinesholmur was 2,340 AOS in 1996 (Skov *et al.*, 2002). Numbers at colonies in southwest Iceland increased from 22,000 to 23,000 AOS between aerial surveys in 1989 and 1994, whereas in the smaller colonies in east Iceland, the change was more rapid with 1,550 AOS in 1984 and 2,300 AOS in 1994 (Gardarsson, 1995). Aerial photo inventories in 1999 indicated a total North American population of 77,700 site-holding pairs (Chardine, 2000).

Table 2   International context.

Country or country	No. pairs	No. colonies	Year	Source
Great Britain, Isle of Man			1998–	
and Channel Isles	230,000	16	2000	Seabird 2000
All Ireland	33,000	5	1999	Seabird 2000
Faeroe Islands	2,340	1	1996	Skov *et al.* (2002)
France	14,900	1	1999	Siorat (in press).
Germany	69	1	1999	Schneider (2002)
Iceland	25,400	5	1994	Gardarsson (1995)
Norway	3,850	5	1999	R. T. Barrett (pers. comm.)
Russia	35	1	1998	Yu. V Krasnov (pers. comm.)
Canada	77,700	6	1999	Chardine (2000)

Biogeographic region	Number of pairs	% GB	% Ireland
World	390,000	59.0%	8.5%

Great Cormorant *Phalacrocorax carbo*

Robin M. Sellers

INTRODUCTION

Historically, British and Irish Great Cormorants have been regarded as primarily coastal birds, both in the breeding and non-breeding seasons, but during the past 40 years there have been some marked changes in their demography. Most leave the breeding colonies shortly after the chicks become independent and depart in a generally southerly direction. These 'orientated movements' are not strictly migratory, and are probably best considered dispersive, though once a first-year bird has found a suitable place to winter, it will tend to return there in subsequent winters. Formerly birds wintered on coasts and estuaries but from about 1960 there has been a gradual shift of wintering quarters inland, to the extent that almost every lowland lake of any consequence in Britain and Ireland now has its complement of Great Cormorants. More recently they have begun to breed inland in trees, and from modest beginnings this subpopulation has become an important component of the British and Irish population. The growth of the inland-breeding population in England has been fuelled by the immigration of the subspecies *P. c. sinensis* from continental Europe (see below).

The population of the endemic subspecies of Great Cormorant in Britain and Ireland, *P. c. carbo*, breeds predominantly on the coast and increased by 35% between Operation Seafarer (1969–70) and the SCR Census (1985–88). Numbers in Ireland more than doubled during this period and by 1985–88 held 44% of the population of Britain and Ireland, with 28% in Scotland, 15% in Wales and 13% in England, the Channel Islands and Isle of Man (Table 1; Lloyd *et al.*, 1991). The numbers breeding increased throughout Ireland (except in Co. Clare and Co. Kerry), but the largest increases were on the east coast, in Co. Dublin (230%) and in Co. Down, where there were none during Operation Seafarer, but by the SCR Census there were 310 AON on five islands in Strangford Lough. However, some doubts have been expressed about the completeness of the coverage of Great Cormorant colonies in Ireland during Operation Seafarer (Hutchinson, 1989), thus the increase in the Irish population between Operation Seafarer and the SCR Census may have been exaggerated. In contrast, the population in Scotland decreased by 13% during the same period, due to substantial declines in Shetland, Caithness and the Western Isles, whereas numbers elsewhere were either stable or increased. In England, the Channel Islands and Isle of Man, the population increased by 24%, the largest increases were in the northeast (Northumberland to North Yorkshire), Devon and Cumbria; the only declines were in Cornwall and the Isle of Wight. In Wales, the population increased slightly by 14%.

Increases in breeding populations and the increased use of inland waters for breeding and wintering have done nothing to allay anglers' fears that Great Cormorants have a detrimental effect on catches. Although the problems may often be exaggerated, there is little doubt that Great Cormorants do sometimes have an appreciable effect on fish stocks, for example at certain fish farms and put-and-take lakes (Russell *et al.*, 1996; Feltham *et al.*, 1999). It comes as no surprise, therefore, that the Great Cormorant has probably received the worst press of any British or Irish seabird over the past decade or so, and the species' impact and management continue to be potent issues with obvious implications for its general well-being.

CENSUS METHODS

Great Cormorants construct a large nest of sticks, twigs and, where available, seaweed, and for the most part are straightforward to count. The count unit for Great Cormorants adopted in Seabird 2000 was the Apparently Occupied Nest (AON). Great Cormorants are social and build their nests quite close to one another in distinct and usually well-defined colonies, typically varying in size between 10 and 400 AON in Britain and Ireland. Colonies are generally located on stacks, rocky islets, cliffs or rocky promontories and are usually easy to locate, as the entire area within the colony quickly becomes whitewashed with guano. Colonies on cliffs tend to be somewhat more fragmented, and care needs to be taken in identifying the limits of such colonies. Many colonies persist in the same place for long periods, but others, often the smaller ones, come and go or show sudden shifts in location. The presence of a colony in one year is no guarantee that there will be one there the following year, and small colonies in new locations are easily overlooked. These shifts introduce an element of uncertainty where counts from a number of years have to be combined, as was the case with Operation Seafarer (1969–70), the SCR Census (1985–88) and Seabird 2000 (1999–2002). To reduce this problem, an effort was made during Seabird 2000 to reduce the number of years over which counts were obtained within as large an area as possible. This was achieved to some extent, in that 63% of administrative areas were surveyed in a single year and a further 21% in two successive years (Table 1). On a larger scale, all inland colonies in England and all colonies in north mainland Scotland (east Sutherland to Lochaber) and in the Firth of Forth were counted in single years. Conversely, counts in Wales were spread over four years (1999–2002).

Unlike many other seabirds, the timing of breeding by different pairs within the same colony of

Great Cormorants is not always synchronous. This means that there is no guarantee that a single count of the nests will reflect precisely the true number of breeding attempts. Counts made too early will miss late starters, counts made in middle of the season will miss the early failures (nest material from deserted nests is quickly removed by other birds and incorporated into their own nests), whilst late counts will not only miss the early failures but potentially early fledgings as well. A better estimate of the total number of nesting attempts can be made by making several counts during the breeding season, but this requires detailed records of the location of individual nests to be kept and can be very time-consuming. This is not feasible at many colonies and in practice very few studies have been carried out in which this approach was adopted. Virtually all of the Seabird 2000 counts, as well as those from Operation Seafarer and the SCR Census and most of those from the extensive monitoring that has taken place over the past three decades, have utilised the 'single count at the optimum period' approach. For comparative purposes these points are of minor significance but they do mean that the absolute number of nests is generally somewhat underestimated.

The recommended period for counting Great Cormorants during Seabird 2000 was 1 May–25 June. For most British and Irish colonies this is likely to coincide with the end of incubation or the early nestling stage, when the chicks are brooded continuously by their parents. This is the time when the number of birds with nests is likely to be at a maximum and also when the nests are at their most obvious since each will have an adult sitting. Timing of breeding according to calendar date varies between years and, occasionally, breeding may be advanced or delayed by several weeks depending on weather conditions. Fortunately, this seems not to have been true of the Seabird 2000 counts. Even within seasons there can be considerable variation in the timing of breeding between neighbouring colonies and there is also some geographical variation around Britain and Ireland. During Seabird 2000, 70% of counts were made on the recommended dates and 17% outside the recommended dates, compared to 51% and 10% respectively during the SCR Census (dates were not given for the remaining 13% and 39%).

Finding newly established, inland, tree-nesting colonies in England also poses some difficulties, partly as a result of their small size (founding numbers are usually less than ten pairs) and that they tend to be in places free of human disturbance, away from public view. Furthermore, there has been a tendency for the existence of such colonies to be kept confidential until they have become better established and to protect the birds from being 'discouraged', as has happened in a number of places. After several years, the trees in these colonies become covered in guano and eventually this kills them. Well-established tree-nesting colonies on the continent bear more than a passing resemblance to a war zone, such is the destruction that the birds' guano can wreak (see van Eerden & Zijlstra, 1985). Tree-nesting colonies usually become much more obvious as they age. Once located, nests in trees are usually difficult to count accurately from a distance and counts are best made from within the colony. Counts should be made when there are eggs or small young in the nests, although this may lead to an increased risk of predation by crows. However, entry into colonies late in the breeding cycle should be avoided as this runs the risk of accidentally inducing larger chicks to jump out of their nests in a hapless attempt to evade 'capture'. Further information on the recommended procedure for censusing tree-nesting colonies is given in Gilbert *et al.* (1998a).

Coverage of colonies in Seabird 2000 seems to have been good. However, eight colonies in Ireland were not counted, and two inland colonies in England were neglected because of difficulties concerning access. For the Irish colonies not counted, best guesses of size were based on recent subjective estimates and counts made during the SCR Census (1985–87) and rounded to the nearest ten (or to the nearest five for colonies of less than 10 AON) and are highlighted in Fig. 1. The estimated Irish colonies were of 200 AON on the Keeragh Islands (Co. Wexford), 20 AON on Mattle Island (Co. Clare), 150 AON on Rinn Island and Scilly Island, Lough Derg (Co. Tipperary), 150 AON on Lough Cutra, 200 AON on Deer Island (both in Co. Galway), 60 AON on Slieve League, 50 AON on the Garvan Isles and 5 AON on Glashedy Island (all in Co. Donegal). These colonies accounted for 17% of the total population in Ireland. A special effort was made following the conclusion of Seabird 2000 to contact County Bird Recorders and other people with an interest in Great Cormorants to ensure that no inland colonies established during the three years of the survey were overlooked; several new ones were found, and counts from these have been included in Seabird 2000.

CURRENT STATUS AND TRENDS

Seabird 2000 found a total of 13,628 AON in Britain and Ireland, of which 38% were in Ireland, 27% in Scotland, 23% in England, the Isle of Man and the Channel Islands, and 13% in Wales (Table 1). Of the total population, 85% were nesting in 232 coastal colonies and 15% in 35 inland colonies (for definitions of inland and coastal, see chapter on Data Processing and Analysis)[1]. The coastal colonies were distributed around almost the whole of Britain and Ireland, but with a distinctly western bias (Fig. 1). Colonies were either absent from, or present in low numbers in, all areas with little suitable breeding habitat, i.e. the east and south coasts of England between the Humber Estuary and the Isle of Wight, the Bristol Channel, and northwest England from the Dee Estuary to west Cumbria. There were noticeably few in northeast Scotland between Inverness and the Firth of Forth, and in northwest Sutherland, probably due to a lack of suitable nesting habitat. The east coast of Ireland also had few colonies, but most were large, particularly those in Co. Dublin and Co. Wexford. England held the most inland colonies (29), with five in Ireland and one in Wales. The English inland colonies were mostly in southern and eastern administrative areas, but extended west to Warwickshire and north to Cumbria (Fig. 1).

The 35% increase in the coastal population of Great Cormorants that occurred in Britain and Ireland between Operation Seafarer (1969–70) and the SCR Census (1985–88) had slowed to just 7% since 1985–88 (Table 1). However, a growth in the inland-breeding population of England has meant that the total population, including both inland and coastal colonies, has increased by 15% since the SCR Census. In 2000 there were 1,334 AON breeding at inland colonies in England. All but three of the English inland colonies have been established since the SCR Census (1985–88). The largest of these, at Abberton Reservoir (Essex), has increased from 151 AON in 1986 to 370 AON in 2000, whilst colonies at Narford (Norfolk) and at Little Paxton Gravel Pits (Cambridgeshire) were both established in 1988 and grew to 12 AON and 129 AON respectively in 2000. The only Welsh inland colony, at Craig yr Aderyn (Gwynedd), was first recorded in 1645 and recently has remained stable at 65 AON compared to 57 in 1986. All but one of the inland colonies in Ireland were on islands in Lough Derg, which held a total of 788 AON in 1985, situated in Co. Galway, Co. Tipperary and Co. Clare. During Seabird 2000 only the colonies in Co. Galway were surveyed and had remained stable at 112 AON compared to 125 AON in 1985. The other inland colony was at Lough Cutra (Co. Galway) which had 166 AON in 1985 but was not surveyed during Seabird 2000.

The 7% increase in the population breeding on the coasts of Britain and Ireland belies quite marked regional differences in trends, with strong growth in some, little change in others and substantial declines in the rest (Table 1).

In northern Scotland the 48% decline in numbers of Great Cormorants in Shetland, Caithness and Sutherland between Operation Seafarer (1969–70) and the SCR Census (1985–88) continued

---

[1] In contrast to previous accounts (e.g. Lloyd *et al.* 1991), the following colonies are considered as coastal here: Loch an Tomain (Western Isles), Mochrum and Castle Lochs (Wigtown), and Loch of Strathbeg (Banff & Buchan)

Table 1   Numbers of breeding Great Cormorants (AON) in Britain and Ireland 1969–2002.

Administrative area or country	Operation Seafarer (1969–70) AON	SCR Census (1985–88) AON	SCR Census (1985–88) colonies	Seabird 2000 (1999–2002) AON	Seabird 2000 (1999–2002) colonies	Years	Percentage change since Seafarer	Percentage change since SCR	Seabird 2000 inland and coastal AON
				Coastal Colonies Only					
Shetland	502	395	8	192	4	1999	−62%	−51%	192
Orkney	590	604	11	412	7	1999–2000	−30%	−32%	412
East coast Caithness		235	6	107	4	2000		−54%	107
Caithness total	828	235	6	107	4	2000	−87%	−54%	107
Northwest coast Sutherland		88	6	76	3	2000		−14%	76
East Coast Sutherland				2	1	2000			2
Sutherland total	56	88	6	78	4		39%	−11%	78
West coast Ross & Cromarty		93	5	82	3	1999–2000		−12%	82
East coast Ross & Cromarty		40	1	245	1	1999		513%	245
Ross & Cromarty total	276	133	6	327	4		18%	146%	327
Moray	1								
Banff & Buchan				9	1	2000			9
Gordon				48	2	2001			48
City of Aberdeen		12	2						
Kincardine & Deeside		1	1	88	2	1999–2002		8700%	88
Angus				29	2	2001			29
Kirkcaldy				85	1	1999			85
Dunfermline		137	1	100	1	1999		−27%	100
East Lothian	152	231	3	190	2	1999	25%	−18%	190
Berwickshire	1	41	1	36	2	2000	3500%	−12%	36
Stewartry	124	217	4	313	4	2000–2003	152%	44%	313
Wigtown	148	442	4	389	4	2000	163%	−12%	389
Kyle & Carrick	97	96	1	307	5	1999–2000	216%	220%	307
Cunninghame	14			51	1	1999	264%		51
Argyll & Bute	61	119	10	231	13	1999–2000	279%	94%	231
Lochaber	45			23	1	2000	−49%		23
Skye & Lochalsh	151	124	12	166	9	1998–2001	10%	33%	166
Western Isles–Comhairle nan eilean	392	111	7	445	9	1999–2002	14%	301%	445
Scotland Total	**3,438**	**2,986**	**83**	**3,626**	**82**		**5%**	**21%**	**3,626**
Northumberland	214	238	1	144	2	2000	−33%	−39%	144
Tyne & Wear	25	75	1	248	1	1999	892%	231%	248
Cleveland	18	81	2	68	3	2000	278%	−16%	68
North Yorkshire		45	2	25	2	1999–2002		−44%	27
Humberside	20					2000			47
Lincolnshire						2000			100
Nottinghamshire						2000			98
Leicestershire						2000			67
Cambridgeshire						2000			179
Northamptonshire						2000			28
Bedfordshire						2000			9
Berkshire						2000			25
Norfolk						2000			52
Suffolk						2000			30
Essex						2000–01			371
Greater London						2000			252
Kent						2000			151

				Coastal Colonies Only					
Administrative area or country	Operation Seafarer (1969–70) AON	SCR Census (1985–88) AON	colonies	Seabird 2000 (1999–2002) AON	colonies	Years	Percentage change since Seafarer	Percentage change since SCR	Seabird 2000 inland and coastal AON
East Sussex		4	1	2	1	1999–2000		−50%	77
Isle of Wight	184	39	2	90	1	2001	−51%	128%	90
Dorset	122	138	3	150	3	2000–01	23%	9%	150
Channel Islands	62	113	5	115	4	1999–2000	85%	2%	115
Cornwall	206	128	12	199	25	1999–2000	−3%	55%	199
Isles of Scilly	50	52	3	56	5	1999	12%	8%	56
Devon	178	335	21	181	13	2000–01	2%	−46%	181
Avon	39	39	1	72	1	1999	85%	85%	72
Oxfordshire						2000			5
Warwickshire						2000			43
Staffordshire						2000			45
Derbyshire						2000			1
Cumbria	1	46	1	80	2	1999–2000	7900%	74%	81
Isle of Man	35	102	7	134	4	1999	283%	31%	134
England Total	**1,154**	**1,435**	**62**	**1,564**	**67**		**36%**	**9%**	**3,145**
West Glamorgan	10								
Dyfed	550	636	16	268	13	1999–2001	−51%	−58%	268
Gwynedd	908	1032	13	1366	12	1999–2002	50%	32%	1431
Wales Total	**1,468**	**1,668**	**29**	**1,634**	**25**		**11%**	**−2%**	**1,699**
Great Britain, Isle of Man & Channel Islands Total	**6,060**	**6,089**	**174**	**6,824**	**174**		**13%**	**12%**	**8,470**
Co. Antrim	108	426	2	385	2	1999–2000	256%	−10%	385
Co. Down		310	5	278	1	2000		−10%	278
Co. Dublin	317	1,048	3	1539	4	1999	385%	47%	1539
Co. Wicklow		3	1						
Co. Wexford	388	473	2	473[1]	2	2000	22%	0%	473[1]
Co. Waterford	79	431	15	247	10	1999–2000	213%	−43%	247
Co. Cork	38	477	15	366	6	1999–2002	863%	−23%	366
Co. Kerry	117	52	4	69	6	1999–2001	−41%	33%	72
Co. Tipperary						2000			150[2]
Co. Clare	162	42	6	28[3]	2	2002	−83%	−33%	28[3]
Co. Galway	153	473	5	360[4]	2	1999–2001	135%	−24%	632[4,5]
Co. Mayo	159	416	6	172	7	1999–2000	8%	−59%	222
Co. Sligo	118	205	1	179	2	1999	52%	−13%	179
Co. Donegal	311	361	14	640[6]	14	1999–2002	106%	77%	640[6]
All-Ireland Total	**1,950**	**4,717**	**79**	**4,736**	**58**		**143%**	**0%**	**5,211**
Britain and Ireland Total	**8,010**	**10,806**	**253**	**11,560**	**232**		**44%**	**7%**	**13,628**

Notes

[1] Includes an estimate of 200 AON at Keeragh Island that was not counted during Seabird 2000.

[2] An estimate of 150 AON at Rinn and Scilly Islands, Lough Derg that were not counted during Seabird 2000.

[3] Includes an estimate of 20 AON at Mattle Island that was not counted during Seabird 2000.

[4] Includes an estimate of 200 AON on Deer Island that were not counted during Seabird 2000.

[5] Includes an estimate of 150 AON at Lough Cutra that were not counted during Seabird 2000.

[6] Includes estimates of 60 AON at Slieve League, 50 AON on the Garvan Islands and 5 AON on Glashedy Island that were not counted during Seabird 2000.

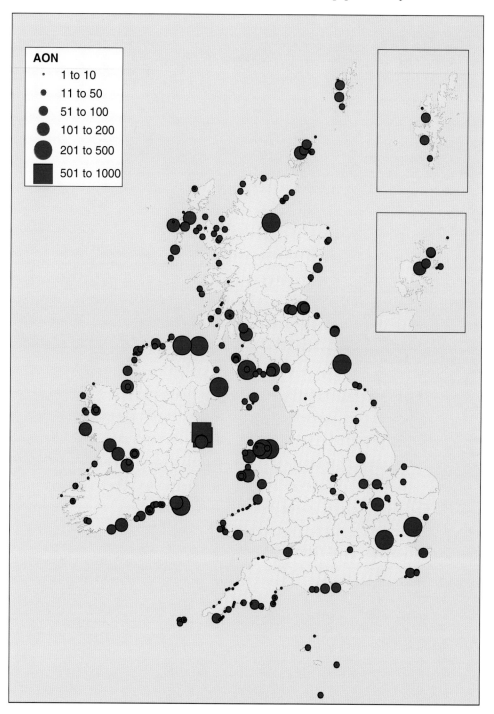

Figure 1   Abundance and distribution of breeding Great Cormorants in Britain and Ireland 1998–2002.

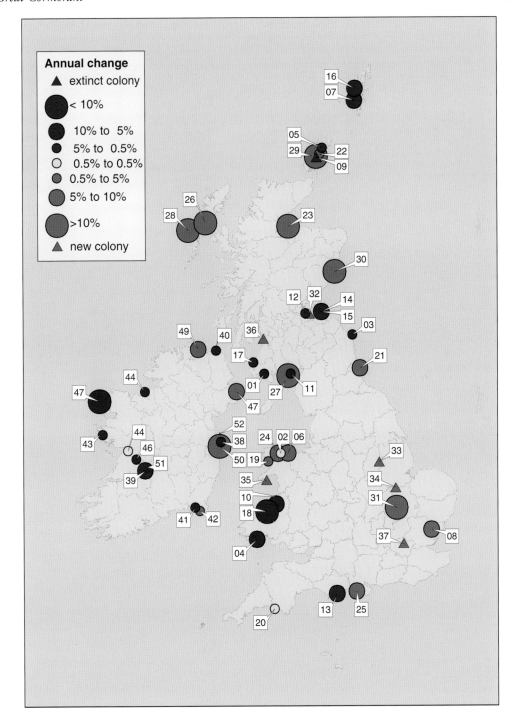

Figure 2   Changes in the number of breeding Great Cormorants (AON) at major coastal and inland colonies in Britain and Ireland between the SCR Census (1985–88) and Seabird 2000 (1999–2002). Major colonies are those that contained the top 50% of the British population or the top 60% of the Irish population during the SCR census and during Seabird 2000. Numbers correspond to colonies listed in Table 2.

Table 2   Changes in the number of breeding Great Cormorants (AON) at major coastal and inland colonies in Britain and Ireland between the SCR Census (1985–88) and Seabird 2000 (1999–2002). Major colonies are those that contained the top 50% of the British populations of the top 60% of the Irish populations during the SCR census and during Seabird 2000. ID corresponds to colony symbols in Fig. 2.

ID	Colony	SCR Census (1985–88)	Seabird 2000 (1999–2002)	Percentage change since SCR	Annual percentage change since SCR	Percentage of populations in Britain or Ireland 1999–2002
1	Mochrum Loch & Castle Loch	425	343	−19%	−1.6%	4.0%
2	Anglesey: Puffin Island	370	353	−5%	−0.3%	4.2%
3	Farne Islands	238	144	−39%	−3.3%	1.7%
4	St Margaret's Island	238	69	−71%	−7.9%	0.8%
5	Calf of Eday	223	138	−38%	−3.2%	1.6%
6	Little Ormes Head	198	428	116%	5.6%	5.1%
7	Shetland Mainland: Clett Stacks	165	94	−43%	−4.6%	1.1%
8	Abberton Reservoir[1]	151	370	145%	6.7%	4.4%
9	Taing Skerry[2]	146	0	−100%		0.0%
10	Llanddeiniol	140	69	−51%	−5.3%	0.8%
11	Port o' Warren	138	126	−9%	−0.7%	1.5%
12	Car Craig[3]	137	100	−27%	−2.6%	1.2%
13	Gad Cliff	110	43	−61%	−6.5%	0.5%
14	Craigleith[3]	109	56	−49%	−5.4%	0.7%
15	The Lamb[3]	104	134	29%	2.0%	1.6%
16	Muckle Roe: Erne Stack (Shetland)	98	56	−43%	−4.6%	0.7%
17	Dyke Foot to Downan Point	96	83	−14%	−1.2%	1.0%
18	Trwyn Crou to Cwmtydu	92	7	−92%	−18.1%	0.1%
19	Ynys yr Adar group	88	138	57%	3.0%	1.6%
20	Great Mew Stone	87	84	−3%	−0.3%	1.0%
21	Marsden Rock	75	248	231%	8.9%	2.9%
22	Little Green Holm	46	85	85%	4.2%	1.0%
23	North Sutor	40	245	513%	13.7%	2.9%
24	Anglesey: Bwrdd Arthur to Fedw Fawr	35	125	257%	9.1%	1.5%
25	Isle of Wight: Main Bench Cliffs	27	90	233%	9.0%	1.1%
26	Sound of Harris: Lingay & Scaravay	15	112	647%	15.4%	1.3%
27	Balcary Point	13	95	631%	12.5%	1.1%
28	Monach Islands	13	158	1115%	19.5%	1.9%
29	Holm of Boray[2]	6	165	2650%	29.1%	1.9%
30	Yellow Ark	1	85	8400%	40.6%	1.0%
31	Paxton Pits[1]	1	129	12800%	50.1%	1.5%
32	Inchkeith[3]	0	85			1.0%
33	Besthorpe[1]	0	98			1.2%

ID	Colony	SCR Census (1985–88)	Seabird 2000 (1999–2002)	Percentage change since SCR	Annual percentage change since SCR	Percentage of populations in Britain or Ireland 1999–2002
34	Deeping St James[1]	0	100			1.2%
35	St Tudwall's Islands	0	112			1.3%
36	Lady Isle	0	198			2.3%
37	Walthamstow Reservoir	0	252			3.0%
38	Lambay	1,027	675	−34%	−3.0%	13.0%
39	Lough Derg: Rinn Island[1]	400	nc			
40	Sheep Island	380	344	−9%	−0.7%	6.6%
41	Keeragh	239	nc			
42	Little Saltee	234	273	17%	1.0%	5.2%
43	Lough Scannive	218	160	−27%	−1.9%	3.1%
44	Galway Bay: Deer Island	205	nc			
45	Ardboline & Horse Island	205	179	−13%	−1.0%	3.4%
46	Lough Cutra[1]	166	nc			
47	Duvillaun Islands	154	20	−87%	−14.5%	0.4%
48	Strangford Lough: Bird Island	89	278	212%	9.2%	5.3%
49	Inishowen/Crockduff −Croaghdoo	62	225	263%	9.7%	4.3%
50	Ireland's Eye	19	306	1511%	23.8%	5.9%
51	Lough Derg: Scilly Island[1]	17	nc			
52	Skerries: St Patrick's Island	0	558			10.7%

nc = not counted

Notes

[1] Inland

[2] There is considerable interchange of breeding birds between Taing Skerry and Holm of Boray

[3] There is considerable interchange of breeding birds between the four colonies in the Firth of Forth

at a similar rate, with the Seabird 2000 population estimate 47% lower than the SCR Census (Table 1). The biggest decline occurred in Caithness where a population of 828 AON at 12 colonies in 1969 had declined by 87% to just 107 AON at four colonies in 2000. The timing and rate of decline varied between colonies and at one (Ceann Leathad) numbers actually increased in the 1970s and 1980s, reaching a maximum of 49 AON in 1993, but have fallen since (Budworth *et al.*, 2000). Of the colonies at which regular breeding no longer occurs, breeding ceased at four in the 1970s, one in the 1980s and two in the 1990s. In Orkney the decline started only after the SCR Census (1985–88) when there were 605 AON, which fell to 491 AON in 1995 (Wood, 1995) and 412 AON in 1999–2000. In these four administrative areas there has been a 60% decline in the combined population of Great Cormorants since Operation Seafarer (1969–70).

Further south in east Ross & Cromarty, the size of the colony along the cliffs of North Sutor has fluctuated from 193 AON in 1969 to just 40 AON in 1985, and then peaked at 288 AON in 1995, before falling back to 245 AON in 1999. During Operation Seafarer (1969–70), there was only one pair of Great Cormorants breeding on the coast between east Ross & Cromarty and East Lothian on the south side of the Firth of Forth. By the SCR Census (1985–88) there were just 12 pairs in Aberdeen, 1 AON in Kincardine & Deeside and 137 AON on Car Craig (Dunfermline), but by Seabird 2000 there was a total of 174 AON at seven colonies between Banff & Buchan and Angus, and a new colony of 85 AON on Inchkeith (Kirkcaldy) and 100 AON on Car Craig. On the south side of the Firth of Forth (East Lothian), the combined population on the islands of The Lamb and Craigleith has changed little from 213 AON in 1986–87 to 190 AON in 1999.

Cormorant colonies in northwest and western Scotland (west Ross & Cromarty to Argyll & Bute) were mostly small to medium in size, and fairly well separated from one another, although somewhat more common and closer together in Argyll & Bute than further north. Overall, there was an increase in breeding numbers of 49% between 1985–88 and 1999–2000, continuing the increase of 30% between 1969–70 and 1985–88. Much of this change can be traced to a substantial increase in the number of colonies in Argyll & Bute, from three in 1969–70 to 13 in 1999–2000. Quite what is driving this increase is uncertain (see below).

In the Western Isles there was a 13% increase between Operation Seafarer (1969–70) and Seabird 2000 to 445 AON at nine colonies. However, during the SCR Census, a total of only 111 AON were recorded in seven colonies (Table 1). The substantial colony at Loch an Tomain on the east side of North Uist was omitted from the results of the SCR Census (Table 1) and from Lloyd *et al.* (1991). This colony held 113 AON in 1981 (Counsell, 1983), but this had fallen to 53 AON the following year and by 1983 the colony appears to have been abandoned (Counsell, 1983). No young were fledged in 1982, and it seems that the colony had been subject to severe disturbance, probably human. It was not until 1997, when there were 44 AON, that it was appreciated that the birds had returned. Quite where they were during the SCR Census is a mystery. Furthermore, another reasonably large colony in the Western Isles, on the Monach Islands, held 300 AON in 1978 and 158 AON during Seabird 2000, but only 13 AON in 1987 during the SCR Census (1985–88). Again, where these birds were during the SCR Census is unknown, but it seems very likely that the published figure for the Western Isles at this time (Lloyd *et al.*, 1991) was underestimated by 200–250 AON. If so, it would suggest a constant rate of increase between the three censuses.

In southwest Scotland (i.e. Cunninghame to Stewartry) there has been a sustained growth in numbers during the past 30 years. Between 1969–70 and 1985–88 the population doubled and then increased by 40% between 1985–87 and Seabird 2000. There were particularly large increases in the number of breeding Great Cormorants in Kyle & Carrick, notably at the cliff-nesting colonies between Dove Cove and Portandea, and the formation of a new colony on Lady Isle (196 AON in 2000). On the north Solway coast the increase in numbers has occurred despite the loss of some colonies, and the one on a wartime structure in Rigg Bay (Wigtown) moved south 1 km to the cliffs at Cruggleton in 2000.

There was another colony on a wartime structure across the Solway in northwest England at Grune Point (Cumbria). Numbers there have remained remarkably constant at about 40–60 AON since 1984 when regular counts began (the colony seems to have been established only a few years before this). The only other coastal colony in Cumbria, that on St Bees Head, numbered around 25 AON and was established in about 1990, although birds have bred here on a number of occasions during the past century. Numbers in northeast England (Northumberland to North Yorkshire) remained virtually unchanged between the SCR Census (1985–88) and Seabird 2000. There was a substantial decrease in numbers breeding on the Farne Islands (Northumberland), and an even more marked increase in numbers over the same period at Marsden Rock (Tyne & Wear), 75 km away and the nearest colony to the south (Table 2). It seems possible this was, in part, due to a shift of birds from one colony to the other. The size of the population on the coast of southwest England (Isle of Wight to Avon) and the Channel Isles has remained remarkably stable over the last 30 years, with 841 AON in Operation Seafarer (1969–70), 844 AON in the SCR Census (1985–88) and 863 AON in Seabird 2000 scattered in 52 colonies.

In addition to Operation Seafarer, the SCR Census and Seabird 2000, surveys of Great Cormorants breeding in Wales were also conducted in 1994 and again in 1996 following the *Sea Empress* oil spill (Sellers, 1994; Sellers & Hughes, 1996). There was a steady increase in numbers between 1969 and 1994, little change between the 1994 (when there were 2,291 AON in 29 colonies) and 1996 surveys (2,182 AON in 28 colonies), but a 25% decline between 1996 and 2000, bringing the population back almost exactly to its level in 1985–88. Most of the increases between 1969–70 and 1994 occurred in colonies in Gwynedd, in particular the two largest on Puffin Island and at Little Ormes Head. The decline between 1996 and 2000 has, however, occurred throughout the Welsh colonies, but was rather more pronounced in Dyfed (40% decrease) than elsewhere (*c*.20% decrease).

The coastal population in Ireland appears to have remained stable since the SCR Census (Table 1). However, during Seabird 2000 some colonies were not counted (see Census Methods) which contained 12% of the coastal population during the SCR Census. The largest colony in Britain and Ireland was 675 AON on Lambay Island (Co. Dublin), which was also the largest during the SCR Census (1985–88) when it held 1,027 AON (Lloyd *et al.*, 1991). The apparent decrease between the two censuses was simply caused by a movement of some birds to found new colonies at nearby St Patrick's Island and Ireland's Eye. The three islands now hold a combined total of 1,539 AOS (in 1999), a 50% increase on the original Lambay Island colony since 1985–88. Elsewhere, there were notable declines in the coastal population in the south and west of the Republic of Ireland (i.e. Co. Waterford, Co. Wexford, Co. Cork, Co. Galway, Co. Mayo: Table 1). These declines take into account those colonies not actually counted during Seabird 2000 (see Census Methods) and the declines in Co. Waterford previously noted by Smiddy (1998), but the possibility that some additional colonies were not counted during Seabird 2000 cannot be entirely eliminated. However,

Colony of coastal-nesting Great Cormorants at Forvie, Gordon (Matt Parsons)

the largest colonies during the SCR Census in these administrative areas have all declined since (Table 2). The only large colonies outside Co. Dublin to have increased in size between the SCR Census (1985–88) and Seabird 2000 were on Bird Island, Strangford Lough (Co. Down) and at Inishowen Head (Co. Donegal; Table 2).

CAUSES OF CHANGE

Persecution by man has long been a major influence on Great Cormorant numbers in many parts of the species' European range including Britain and Ireland. As more enlightened attitudes have prevailed and the Great Cormorant has been afforded legal protection, so its numbers have generally increased (van Eerden *et al.*, 1995). In the Republic of Ireland large numbers were formerly shot under a government-run bounty scheme, which, between 1973 and 1976, accounted for no less than 3,527 birds (Macdonald, 1987). Full protection came with the passing of the Wildlife Act (1976), and almost immediately breeding numbers in the Republic of Ireland began to increase. In Britain, equivalent protection was afforded by Wildlife & Countryside Act 1981, implemented under Article 4.2 of the EC Directive on the Conservation of Wild Birds. Overall numbers in Britain have increased, but only slowly (a few per cent per annum), and these increases certainly predate the passing of this legislation. It may simply be that the 1981 Act codified attitudes that had begun to change a decade or two earlier, but the matter is made more complicated by the marked shift in the winter quarters of British (and Irish) coastal birds already noted above. What is unclear is whether this shift was driven by the attraction of birds to the growing number of inland waters stocked with fish, or deteriorating stocks in coastal waters, or, perhaps more credibly, some combination of the two. The impact of such a shift for overwinter survival, and hence for breeding numbers, is unknown, but it can hardly have resulted in a reduction in numbers, and the conjecture is that it is at least partly responsible for the general upward trend in Great Cormorants breeding in British and Irish coastal waters.

Persecution has often taken the form of shooting and this has been a major cause of mortality in Great Cormorants in Britain and Ireland in the past, and continues to account for appreciable numbers. For instance, of 172 recoveries of birds ringed at the Mochrum Loch colony (Wigtown) between 1919 and 1939, 62% had been shot (Stuart, 1948). In Caithness, 23% of recoveries of birds ringed before 1980 had been shot, falling to 9% thereafter (Budworth *et al.*, 2000). With the passing of the Wildlife & Countryside Act 1981 it has been illegal to shoot Great Cormorants in Britain, unless under license. Licenses to kill Great Cormorants to prevent serious damage to fisheries can be obtained, but only after it has been demonstrated that serious economic damage is occurring to the fishery, that this is attributable to Great Cormorants and that attempts have been made to prevent such damage. Precise details of how many have been legally shot are not generally available, but from 1983 to 1992, between 26 and 51 licenses were issued annually in Britain, and these resulted in the deaths of about 4,000 Great Cormorants (Kirby *et al.*, 1996). However, some unlicensed shooting undoubtedly still occurs. At fish farms in Scotland, Carss (1994) found a mean of 1,643 Great Cormorants killed each year between 1984 and 1987, representing around 20% of the (then) Scottish population and well in excess of the numbers shot under license. The most recent analysis suggests that, depending on age, 15–20% of Great Cormorant ringing recoveries in Britain in 1965–94 were of birds that had been shot, the equivalent figure for Ireland being 30–40% (Wernham *et al.*, 1999). Drowning in nets was also a significant cause of mortality during this period, accounting for 15–20% of recoveries in Britain and 20–30% in Ireland (Wernham *et al.*, 1999).

Mortality in the Great Cormorant is age-dependent, with *c.*55% dying in their first year of life, 25% in their second, and 15% in their third and each subsequent year (Wernham *et al.*, 1999). There is some regional variation in these figures, with immature Scottish birds having the highest mortality. There has also been an upward trend in such rates over the past 40 years, as the population has increased, evidence perhaps of density-dependent mortality. Concurrently, and for reasons which remain obscure, there has been a sharp decline in the proportion of ringed birds reported dead.

Higher rates of annual mortality in immatures compared to adults is a characteristic feature of seabird demography (see chapter on Causes of Seabird Population Change). In Great Cormorants, this differential mortality may be a direct consequence of differences in foraging ability between adults and immatures. Adult cormorants are adept at catching fish but these are skills which have to be honed in their first and, to a lesser extent, their second year of life. Significant differences between first-year and adult birds have been found in prey capture rates and in success in swallowing prey for birds taking eels in the Severn Estuary, where, because of high turbidity, the birds were effectively feeding blind, circumstances in which skill is likely to be at a premium (R. M. Sellers, unpubl.). In still waters with low turbidity, first-year and adult birds possess similar prey capture rates, but adults take appreciably larger fish and consumed about four times more mass of food per feeding bout (Hughes *et al.*, 1999).

Food is undoubtedly an important factor in determining population levels and trends of Great Cormorants, but establishing cause and effect relationships between the two has proved surprisingly elusive. The clearest indication comes from north Norway, where there was a marked reduction in breeding numbers of cormorants in 1986–87. This followed winters with low sea temperatures, and low numbers of capelin and other fish on which Great Cormorants prey. Positive correlations have been found in Norway between sea temperature in December and the number of birds wintering and also breeding the following spring (Røv, 1994; Debout *et al.*, 1995). A similar event occurred in Pembrokeshire in 1991, when the number of nests constructed was much reduced and many birds made no attempt to breed. The cause seems to have been a period of abnormally cold and persistent northerly winds during April and the first part of May, which, it was suggested, confined fish to deep water where they were unavailable to Great Cormorants (Debout *et al.*, 1995).

Food availability is a key determinant of colony size in Norwegian and French coastal waters, as suggested by the positive correlation between colony size and the amount of available shallow water for feeding (Debout *et al.*, 1995). This is probably true of British coastal Great Cormorants, but definitive studies have yet to be undertaken. Competition for limited food supplies is also implicit in the finding in Wales and Norway that smaller colonies tend to be closer to each other than larger ones (Debout *et al.*, 1995).

Oil spills may claim small numbers of Great Cormorants, but neither of the recent major spills in British coastal waters (the *Braer* in 1993 and *Sea Empress* in 1996) appear to have caused any major decrease in breeding numbers, nor any long-term effect on productivity (Okill *et al.*, 1993; Sellers & Hughes, 1996; Newson *et al.*, 1997). However, although both spills occurred close to cormorant colonies, they happened at times of year when the majority of birds were in their wintering areas, typically 50–200 km away. The potential for mass mortality remains should a spill occur near to colonies during the breeding season.

Reproductive success in coastal-breeding Great Cormorants seems generally to be in the range 1.8–2.4 chicks per pair (e.g. Sellers & Hughes, 1996; Newson *et al.*, 1997; Andrews & Day, 1999; Newson, 2000). Occasional near-total failures have been recorded and, although these seem to be inconsequential to the general fortunes of cormorants in Britain and Ireland, further investigation would be valuable (Debout *et al.*, 1995). There is evidence of reduced reproductive success at a colony in The Netherlands as a result of the accumulation of persistent organochlorine contaminants derived from pesticides. Significant reductions in eggshell thickness were found, as well as reduced clutch size, hatching success and survival of young (Boudewijn & Dirksen, 1995). These and other contaminants such as heavy metals (notably mercury) have been found in the livers of Great Cormorants in several other countries including Germany (Scharenberg & Schultz, 1992), Poland

(Fabczak *et al.*, 1997), Romania (Fossi *et al.*, 1984) and Ireland (Wilson & Early, 1986), often in amounts which approach those likely to pose a threat to reproduction. Except for the Dutch case already mentioned, nowhere in Europe are these a serious concern, and certainly nothing on the scale of the effects on Double-crested Cormorants, *P. auritus*, found in the Great Lakes of North America (Ludwig *et al.*, 1995). A more recent development has been the discovery of accumulated polybrominated diphenyl ethers (used as fire retardants) in the livers of British cormorants; the long-term toxicity of these environmentally persistent compounds is unknown (Law *et al.*, 2002).

Given the list of potential impacts on Great Cormorant breeding numbers discussed above, what have been the main causes behind the dramatic decline in the numbers breeding in northern Scotland? Surprisingly, during this decline, productivity in this region remained the highest of any coastal population in Britain (Budworth *et al.*, 2000). Even during the sandeel shortages in Shetland in the 1980s, cormorants were well able to provision their chicks with food and suffered no obvious ill effects from a dearth of sandeels (Okill *et al.*, 1992). In Caithness the decline has been caused by high annual adult mortality, which is around 20% higher than anywhere else in Britain (Budworth *et al.*, 2000). However, the cause of this is unknown, but appears more likely to occur during the non-breeding season. Great Cormorants from colonies in northern Scotland winter along the salmon rivers of northeast Scotland. Control of cormorants through licensed and unlicensed shooting may be responsible for the high adult mortality of northern breeders, as may food supply in these wintering areas and both possibilities warrant further investigation.

Emigration from northern Scotland offers a possible partial explanation for the declines, but increases in the wintering areas of these birds (mainly the Moray Firth and the east coast of Scotland) are insufficiently large to account for anything other than a small fraction of the losses. Shifts of breeding birds within the Northern Isles and northern Scotland may, however, account for why the declines in Shetland and Caithness appeared to occur a decade or so before those in Orkney. A gradual deferral of the age of first breeding might be another explanation, but this seems intrinsically unlikely in a declining population (Budworth *et al.*, 2000).

Perhaps the most spectacular development concerning Great Cormorants in Britain and Ireland in recent decades has been the establishment and rapid growth of inland breeding in England. This rapid expansion has undoubtedly been fuelled by an abundant food supply from inland waters stocked with fish, combined with low levels of intra-specific competition. As a consequence, inland-breeding Great Cormorants achieve significantly higher rates of productivity (2.3–3.0 chicks per pair) than coastal breeders (Newson, 2000; Carss & Ekins, 2002). Given the huge increases in numbers in neighbouring parts of the continent and that these new inland colonies are almost exclusively in trees, a habitat more typical of the continental race, *P. c. sinensis*, it has not unnaturally been assumed that the inland-breeding birds in England derive from the continent. There have certainly been sightings of colour-ringed birds from The Netherlands, Denmark and Germany breeding in England (Sellers *et al.*, 1997). Recent DNA analysis has confirmed that *P. c. sinensis* was breeding at England's oldest inland colony at Abberton Reservoir (Essex), but also showed that 50% of the occupants were *P. c. carbo* (Goostrey *et al.*, 1998; Winney *et al.*, 2001). Other recent investigations, using the shape of the gular pouch to distinguish between the two subspecies, have shown the percentage of *carbo* to be higher in older inland colonies (Newson, 2000). It thus appears that the English inland colonies have been established by *P. c. sinensis* from the continent, which have subsequently been joined by *P. c. carbo*, presumably from colonies in Britain and Ireland. Secondary colonisation from the established inland colonies also seems to play a part. It is presumably no coincidence that numbers breeding at Abberton Reservoir (Essex) were more or less constant in 1989–91, when the colonies at Paxton Pits (Cambridgeshire), Besthorpe (Nottinghamshire) and Walthamstow Reservoir (Greater London) were formed (Sellers *et al.*, 1997). The continued growth is also fuelled by the recruitment of birds hatched on mainland Europe

(Newson, 2000; Carss & Ekins, 2002). Many of these new inland colonies have been established at sites used as winter roosts. Given the large number of roost sites (Hughes & Sellers, 1998) and the availability of suitable feeding areas nearby, further expansion of the inland-breeding habit in England (and beyond) seems inevitable.

INTERNATIONAL CONTEXT

Great Cormorants have one of the widest distributions of any species of cormorant, being found throughout most of Europe, southern Asia, Australasia, northwest, southern and East Africa, and in more limited numbers in Greenland, eastern Canada, and the northeast USA (Table 3). There is great uncertainty as to just how many Great Cormorants there are worldwide, but a recent estimate suggests a figure of around 600,000 breeding pairs (R. M. Sellers, unpubl.). Most authorities recognise five subspecies as shown in Table 3. In Britain and Ireland, *P. c. sinensis* is confined to the inland colonies in England. Assuming that all English inland colonies are composed solely of *sinensis*, except at Abberton Reservoir, which is 50% *P. c. carbo* (Goostrey *et al.*, 1998), there are probably 1,400 AON of *sinensis* and 7,100 AON of *carbo* in Britain. Britain and Ireland hold just under a quarter of the world population of *carbo* (13–14% in Britain and 10% in Ireland) and, after Norway, are the most important areas for this subspecies. The population of *carbo* generally appears buoyant with modest increases apparent in most parts of its range, and has expanded its range in northwest Russia, from the north coast of the Kola Peninsula into the White Sea Region (Røv *et al.*, 2000).

The British population of *sinensis* constitutes only 0.4–0.5% of the world population of this subspecies, situated within the Western Palearctic. *P. c. sinensis* is concentrated in Denmark, The Netherlands, Sweden, Germany, Poland, Ukraine and the area of Russia around the Volga Delta (Table 3). What is remarkable is that only half a century ago *sinensis* was rare in western Europe with a population to be reckoned in thousands. The growth in numbers appears to have begun in the 1970s following protection, first in The Netherlands (1965) and shortly afterwards in Denmark (1971), and has continued ever since (van Eerden & Gregersen, 1995). With numbers growing in the core of its range, the birds expanded into Germany, north into Sweden, east into Poland, and more recently into the Baltic States and Belarus, west into Britain, south into Belgium and France, and southeast to the Czech Republic, Slovakia, Croatia etc. There is some evidence that numbers are leveling off at the epicentres of this phenomenal expansion, but growth continues elsewhere, despite many control measures, mostly unauthorised, being taken. There is little reason to believe that this expansion will not continue in central and eastern Europe for some time to come.

The sizes of established colonies of *sinensis* in Europe typically number many hundreds to several thousands of pairs, the largest on record is 8,380 AON in 1992 at Oostvaardersplassen, The Netherlands (van Eerden & Gregersen, 1995). Colonies numbering many hundreds or thousands of breeding pairs are generally typical of the other subspecies of Great Cormorant. The largest such colony is of 20,000 pairs of *P. c. novaehollandiae* at Blowering Dam, New South Wales, Australia, in 1974 (del Hoyo *et al.*, 1992). Population trends outside Europe and North America are difficult to judge, but in recent decades there appear to have been increases in Japan (Fukada, 2000) and numbers in Malawi seem to be higher now than they have been for some time (Wilson & Van Zegeren, 1996). Elsewhere in Asia and Africa, where Great Cormorants are primarily if not exclusively inland birds, loss of wetland habitat poses a real threat and the limited available evidence suggests some declines may be taking place. Despite regional and local differences in status, overall the world population of Great Cormorants is probably healthier now than it has been for several centuries.

Table 3   International context.

Country or region	Subspecies	Number of pairs		Year	Source
		Min	Max		
Great Britain, Isle of Man and Channel Islands	*carbo*	7,100	7,100	1999–2002	Seabird 2000
Great Britain, Isle of Man and Channel Islands	*sinensis*	1,400	1,400	2000	Seabird 2000
All Ireland	*carbo*	5,200	5,200	1999–2002	Seabird 2000
Albania	*sinensis*	400	1,000	1992	Snow & Perrins (1998)
Austria	*sinensis*	0	5		BirdLife International / EBCC (2000)
Belarus	*sinensis*	1,200	1,500	1988–98	BirdLife International / EBCC (2000)
Belgium	*sinensis*	272	272	1995	Ulenaers *et al.* (1997)
Bosnia	*sinensis*	3	10		estimate based on Hagemeijer & Blair (1997)
Bulgaria	*sinensis*	1,000	1,300	1990–97	BirdLife International / EBCC (2000)
Croatia	*sinensis*	6,000	8,000		BirdLife International / EBCC (2000)
Czech Republic	*sinensis*	500	650	1985–95	BirdLife International / EBCC (2000)
Denmark	*sinensis*	40,126	40,126	2002	Bregnballe *et al.* (2002)
Estonia	*sinensis*	3,500	3,500	1998	BirdLife International / EBCC (2000)
Finland	*sinensis*	1,392	1,392	2002	Rusanen *et al.* (2002)
France	*carbo*	1,909	1,913	1997–99	Cadiou *et al.* (2002)
France	*sinensis*	1,425	1,474	1997–99	Cadiou *et al.* (2002)
Germany	*sinensis*	20,055	20,055	2001	Bregnballe *et al.* (2002)
Greece	*sinensis*	1,000	1,500	1995	Handrinos & Akriotis (1997)
Greenland	*carbo*	2,000	3,000	1976–95	Boertmann & Mosbech (1997)
Hungary	*sinensis*	1,700	1,800	1998	BirdLife International / EBCC (2000)
Iceland	*carbo*	2,200	2,200	1995	A. Petersen quoted in Boertmann & Mosbech (1997)
Italy	*sinensis*	487	487	1995	Carpegna *et al.* (1997)
Italy (Sardinia)	*sinensis*	30	40	1980	H. Schenk quoted in de Juana (1984)
Kazakhstan (west of River Ural), Georgia, Azerbaijan	*sinensis*	2,500	2,500		very approximate estimate only
Latvia	*sinensis*	150	150	1993	Baumanis *et al.* (1997)
Lithuania	*sinensis*	2,000	3,000	1996–98	BirdLife International / EBCC (2000)
Macedonia	*sinensis*	30	30		estimate based on Hagemeijer & Blair (1997)
Moldova	*sinensis*	3,000	5,000	1990	BirdLife International / EBCC (2000)
Netherlands	*sinensis*	19,205	19,205	2000	Bregnballe et al. (2002)
Norway	*carbo*	25,150	25,150	2000	Røv *et al.* (2002)

Country or region	Subspecies	Number of pairs		Year	Source
		Min	*Max*		
Poland	*sinensis*	8,077	8,077	1992	Przybysz *et al.* (1997)
Romania	*sinensis*	13,000	13,000	1998	BirdLife International / EBCC (2000)
Russia	*carbo*	1,681	1,681	1995–96	Røv & Paneva (2000), T. Paneva & J. Krasnov quoted in Boertmann & Mosbech (1997)
Russia	*sinensis*	30,000	45,000	late 1980s–early 1990s	Snow & Perrins (1998)
Serbia	*sinensis*	100	100		estimate based on Hagemeijer & Blair (1997)
Slovakia	*sinensis*	190	190	1994–95	Musil *et al.* (1997)
Spain	*sinensis*	1	2		BirdLife International / EBCC (2000)
Sweden	*sinensis*	27,300	27,300	2000	Bregnballe *et al.* (2002)
Turkey	*sinensis*	1,600	3,000		BirdLife International / EBCC (2000)
Ukraine	*sinensis*	17,300	21,000	1998	BirdLife International / EBCC (2000)
Eastern Palearctic[3]	*sinensis*	100,000	100,000		order of magnitude estimate only
Southern & Western Africa[4]	*lucidus*	100,000	100,000		order of magnitude estimate only
Northwest Africa[5]	*maroccanus*	10,000	10,000	1996–97	order of magnitude estimate only
Canada	*carbo*	6,300	6,300	1986–95	Lock *et al.* (1994)
USA	*carbo*	165	165	1995	J. Drury quoted in Boertmann & Mosbech (1997)
Australia, New Zealand, New Guinea, Chatham Islands	*novaehollandiae*	100,000	100,000		order of magnitude estimate only

Biogeographic region		*Min*	*Max*	*Min % GB*	*Max % GB*	*Min % Ireland*	*Max % Ireland*
World* N. Atlantic	*carbo*	52,000	53,000	13.4%	13.7%	9.8%	10.0%
Palearctic	*sinensis*	300,000	330,000	0.4%	0.5%		
World	all	570,000	590,000	1.4%	1.5%	0.9%	0.9%

* Stroud *et al.* 2001

Notes

[1] Taken to be all British cormorants except those breeding in English inland colonies, plus 50% of the colony at Abberton Reservoir

[2] Taken to be all cormorants breeding in English inland colonies, minus 50% of the colony at Abberton Reservoir

[3] Present in Burma, Bangladesh, China, India, Iran, Japan, Kazakhstan (east of River Ural), Russia, Turkmenistan, Uzbekistan.

[4] Present in Namibia, South Africa, Mozambique, Botswana, Malawi, Zambia, Zimbabwe, Ethiopia, Kenya, Uganda, Tanzania

[5] Present in Mauritania, Western Sahara, Morocco, Senegal

European Shag *Phalacrocorax aristotelis*

Sarah Wanless and Mike P. Harris

INTRODUCTION

The European Shag is endemic to the northeast Atlantic and the Mediterranean. An inshore species that is almost never observed out of sight of land, it takes a wide range of small fish that it catches on or near the seabed over both sandy and rocky substrates. In Britain and Ireland, it is commonest in the north and west (Fig. 1). Although not truly migratory, British and Irish Shags in their first and second years of life disperse widely. Populations on North Sea coasts suffer from periodic wrecks when severe weather and difficulties in finding food force younger birds south, and sometimes inland, resulting in the deaths of many birds (Potts, 1969).

Like most seabirds, the shag is a colonial breeder. In some areas, birds nest in small groups spread along several kilometres of coast making it difficult to delimit colonies. However, in general, colonies are discrete and range in size from a few to several thousand pairs. Colonies are normally on cliffs or offshore islands. Numbers in Britain and Ireland increased substantially during the 20th century. For instance, in 1905 there were only ten pairs in east Britain between the rivers Tay and Humber, but by 1965 there were 1,900 pairs: an average rate of increase of 10% per annum (Potts, 1969). During Operation Seafarer (1969–70) the British and Irish population was estimated at just under 34,000 pairs, and by the SCR Census (1985–88) numbers had increased to 43,000 pairs. This pattern was not apparent in Shetland and Orkney where numbers declined by 38% and 30%, respectively. Numbers have subsequently declined in most parts of Britain and Ireland.

CENSUS METHODS

European Shags build substantial and conspicuous nests, and the prescribed count unit during Seabird 2000 was the Apparently Occupied Nest (AON). These nests superficially appear straightforward to count, but there are, however, several major problems associated with a widespread survey of this species: i) detection of nests, ii) a prolonged and very variable breeding season, and iii) occasional years when many adults do not breed.

Shags nest in three distinct habitats. The first is among, or under, boulders, often at the base of cliffs that are only accessible from the sea. Off-duty birds standing around on the rocks signal the presence of most boulder colonies, but small colonies are difficult to count accurately and are easily overlooked. Nests in such habitat are hidden from view and are best counted by entering the colony and searching for them. The second type of habitat is steep cliff where the birds breed, often at low density, on small ledges and in caves. Here nests are easily missed. Many of these areas are best counted from the sea, e.g. during seven years at one Shetland colony, the land-based count averaged 31% lower than the sea-based counts (M. Heubeck, pers. comm.). Most of the coastline of western Scotland, between Cape Wrath (Sutherland) and Kintyre (Argyll & Bute), including the islands of Skye, Mull, Jura and Islay, was searched for nests from boats during Seabird 2000. Coverage of the highly scattered small colonies along this coast was substantially better than the previous two censuses

An incubating European Shag (Andy Webb)

and the declines noted in this area (see below) are almost certainly real. The third breeding habitat used by shags consists of broad open ledges or offshore skerries, rather like those preferred by Great Cormorants. Noteworthy examples of this are the islands in the Firth of Forth (southeast Scotland) and the Farne Islands (Northumberland). Nests here are generally easily counted, although there is still a risk of missing pairs nesting in caves.

The European Shag has an exceptionally prolonged and highly variable breeding season. In Britain, eggs have been reported in every month of the year except September and October. Whilst many late records refer to infertile eggs (that are sometimes incubated for several months) or multiple replacement clutches, double-brooding (i.e. the raising of two successive broods in the same year) does occur, albeit very rarely (Wanless & Harris, 1997). Within a colony, the timing of breeding varies greatly between years, e.g. on the Isle of May, Firth of Forth, first egg dates during the 1990s ranged from 1 March (1998) to 16 May (1993) and median laying dates from 11 April to 30 June (pers. obs.). Thus, a one-off count will inevitably miss pairs that have not yet built nests and those that have already failed (since neighbours soon dismantle unattended nests).

Ideally, a single count should be made when the maximum number of nests is occupied but, since the timing of breeding is so variable, this is impossible to predict until laying has actually started. Over 83% of counts for Seabird 2000 were made between 15 May and 25 June, which was the recommended counting period. To judge from repeated counts, 60–80% of the total number of nests built in a season would have been expected to have been active at this time (Harris & Forbes, 1987). For seven years on the Isle of May, the total number of breeding sites with well-built nests was determined by detailed censuses made through the season. These totals were compared with the number estimated by a single count between 1 and 19 June. On average, the one-off count underestimated the cumulative total by 24% (range 11–34%). This underestimate was due to some pairs not breeding at the time of the one-off count, some active nests being missed and a few pairs that failed early in the season moving to another site for the replacement laying.

There is increasing awareness that in many seabird species some adults do not breed every year, and in the northeast Atlantic the European Shag is perhaps the most extreme and certainly best-documented example (Aebischer, 1986; Aebischer & Wanless, 1992; Harris & Wanless, 1996). Acute non-breeding can produce large reductions in the apparent status of a colony, and also a strong bias on trends should such an event coincide with a census. Such non-breeding events tend to be localised, such that national trends are unlikely to be explained by this phenomenon. An unexpectedly low count at a colony where there are many apparently unattached adults in breeding plumage should alert the counter to the real possibility that a substantial number of adults might not be breeding that year.

All the problems described above will result in underestimation of the population, possibly by one-third or more. However, past counts will all have suffered from similar problems and it is therefore reasonable to suppose that the long-term trends shown by Operation Seafarer, the SCR Census and Seabird 2000 are real. The potential biases do, however, need to be borne in mind when assessing annual changes using just single well-separated counts.

CURRENT STATUS AND TRENDS

In Britain and Ireland the main breeding strongholds of the European Shag are in the north and west, with no colonies at all between Flamborough Head (Humberside) and the Isle of Wight (Fig. 1). The gap appears to be due mainly to a lack of suitable nesting habitat, although a single pair bred in Kent in 1928–29 (Harrison, 1953). Indeed, a shortage of safe places to roost may contribute to the wrecks of young birds in southern England (Coulson, 1986). There has been relatively little change in the numbers and distribution of colonies since the first complete census was undertaken as part of Operation Seafarer in 1969–70. Most of the few colonies that appear to have been established in recent years were probably overlooked previously. Some substantial colonies, for instance in the Sound of Jura (Argyll & Bute) and the East Noup on Fetlar (Shetland), have, however, been abandoned and no breeding was recorded in North Yorkshire (where Operation Seafarer reported 45 nests) by the SCR Census or Seabird 2000.

Seabird 2000 estimated the total British and Irish population at 32,306 AON with 66% in Scotland, 19% in England (including the Isle of Man and the Channel Islands), 12% in Ireland, and 3% in Wales, with the main concentrations in Shetland, Orkney, the Firth of Forth, the Farne Islands and Argyll & Bute (Table 1, Fig. 1). Most of the largest colonies were on islands: 2,277 AON on Foula (Shetland), 1,287 AON on the Farne Islands, 1,122 AON on Lambay Island (Co. Dublin), 1,092 AON on the Isles of Scilly, 740 AON on Canna (Lochaber), 734 AON on the Isle of May, 724 AON on Sule Skerry (Orkney), 506 AON on the Shiant Isles (Western Isles) and 500 AON on the Sanda Islands (Argyll & Bute). The only mainland colony of comparable size was of 839 AON along the Berridale Cliffs (east Caithness).

The number of European Shags in both Scotland and Ireland appears to have declined by *c.*32% and 27% respectively since the SCR Census (1985–88), whilst totals for England and Wales have increased by 12% and 16% respectively. These changes are apparent in most major colonies (Fig. 2, Table 2). During the SCR Census, 62% of the total number of AONs were counted during the recommended dates with another 7% probably so, but the actual dates were not recorded. In Seabird 2000, 84% of AONs were counted in the recommended period, suggesting that a higher proportion of AONs were missed during the SCR Census. Thus, the apparent decline in numbers observed between the two censuses could have been even greater than recorded. In contrast, numbers were substantially higher in Dyfed, Cornwall, on the Isle of Man (but not on the Calf of Man), Kyle & Carrick, Cunninghame, and the east coast of Ross & Cromarty and Co. Mayo, where mostly only minor increases or no change had occurred between 1969–70 and 1985–88. Some of these increases are real. For instance, numbers at North Sutor (east Ross & Cromarty) have increased dramatically since 1990 (R. L. Swann, pers. comm.), whereas in other areas substantial numbers of nests may have been overlooked (or possibly birds had not nested in the relevant year) during the SCR Census (1985–88). Numbers in the Clyde area have also increased, possibly due to some redistribution of birds from colonies to the northwest. Other cases of increase may be more apparent than real. A total of 211 pairs was recorded in Kyle & Carrick in 1969/70, only 47 AON were reported 15 years later but the total had risen to 476 AON in Seabird 2000. This was partly due to almost 200 AON on Lady Isle where the species was not recorded breeding until 1996 (A. Hogg, pers. comm.). In such instances, there is always the possibility that nests had been overlooked in a previous survey or that counts had been made in a year when many birds did not breed.

In Britain and Ireland, the ranking in size of the 38 largest colonies (Table 2) remained largely unchanged between the SCR Census and Seabird 2000 (Spearman rank correlation $r_{s,38} = 0.78$, P <0.001). This suggests a gradual decline in numbers rather than any large-scale redistribution of breeders.

Since 1986, regular counts of AONs have been made at a number of colonies in Britain and these have been used in the Joint Nature Conservation Committee and Partners' Seabird Monitoring Programme to provide indices of the breeding population for four areas in northern Britain (Mavor *et al.*, 2002). These confirm the general picture of decline but suggest two rather different patterns. In northwest Scotland and Shetland numbers declined gradually during the late 1980s and early 1990s, perhaps in part as a result of increased adult mortality due to entanglement in nets during the early years of salmon-farming in these areas. Numbers in northwest Scotland have remained

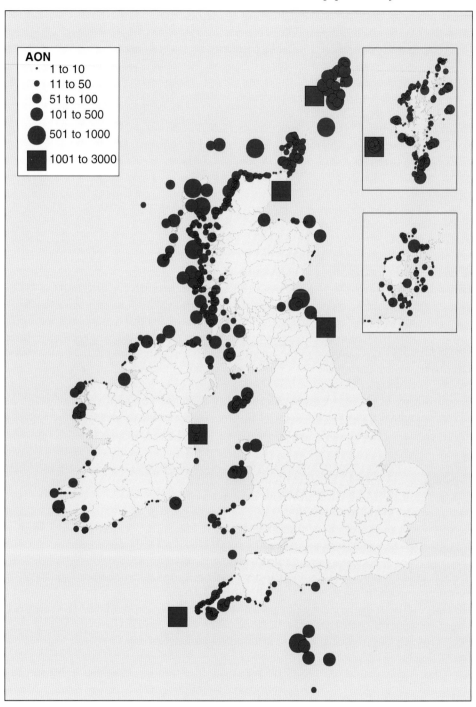

Figure 1   Abundance and distribution of breeding European Shags in Britain and Ireland 1998–2002.

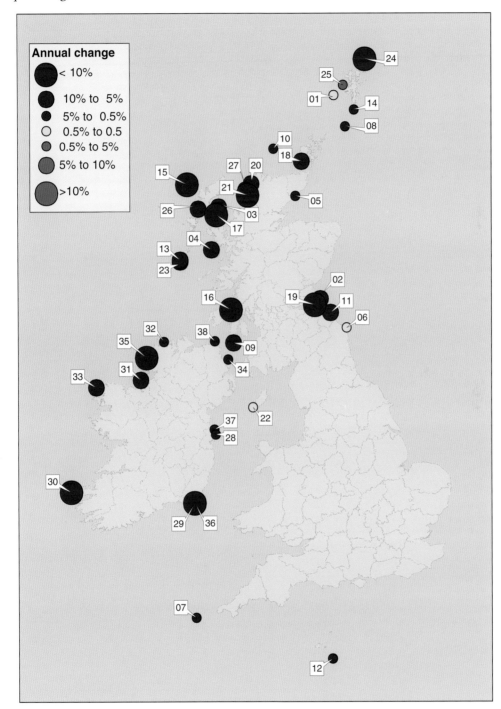

Figure 2   Changes in the number of breeding European Shags (AON) at major colonies in Britain and Ireland between the SCR Census (1985–88) and Seabird 2000 (1998–2002). Major colonies are those that contained the top 50% of the British population or the top 75% of the Irish population during the SCR Census. Numbers correspond to colonies listed in Table 2.

Table 1   Numbers of breeding European Shags (AON) in Britain and Ireland 1969–2002.

Administrative area or country	Operation Seafarer (1969–70)	SCR Census (1985–88)	Seabird 2000 (1998–2002)	Percentage change since Seafarer	Percentage change since SCR	Annual percentage change since SCR
Shetland	10,536	7,341	6,147	−42%	−16%	−1.3%
Orkney	3,724	2,539	1,872	−50%	−26%	−2.2%
North coast						
Caithness		*120*	*61*		*−49%*	*−5.0%*
East coast						
Caithness		*2,532*	*1,075*		*−58%*	*−6.4%*
Caithness total	1,595	2,652	1,136	−29%	−57%	−6.3%
Northwest coast						
Sutherland		*1,808*	*880*		*−51%*	*−5.3%*
Sutherland total	2,096	1,808	880	−58%	−51%	−5.3%
West coast Ross &						
Cromarty		*474*	*505*		*7%*	*0.5%*
East coast Ross &						
Cromarty		*30*	*270*		*800%*	*15.7%*
Ross &						
Cromarty total	594	504	775	30%	54%	3.0%
Moray		1	33		3200%	31.0%
Banff & Buchan	243	552	656	170%	19%	1.2%
Gordon	10	23	25	150%	9%	0.6%
City of Aberdeen	3	4	3	0%	−25%	−2.0%
Kincardine &						
Deeside	37	54	13	−65%	−76%	−9.6%
Angus	28		21	−25%		
North East Fife	880	1,916	734	−17%	−62%	−6.6%
Kirkcaldy		12	21		75%	4.8%
Dunfermline		28	7		−75%	−10.9%
City of Edinburgh		24	33		38%	2.7%
East Lothian	438	996	298	−32%	−70%	−9.3%
Berwickshire	149	641	349	134%	−46%	−4.5%
Stewartry	12	5	3	−75%	−40%	−4.5%
Wigtown	129	156	55	−57%	−65%	−7.2%
Kyle & Carrick	211	47	476	126%	913%	19.9%
Cunninghame	22	11	109	395%	891%	19.3%
Argyll & Bute	1,774	3,093	3,341	88%	8%	0.6%
Lochaber	1,173	2,063	973	−17%	−53%	−5.5%
Skye & Lochalsh	660	2,389	866	31%	−64%	−7.5%
Western Isles–						
Comhairle						
nan eilean	2,763	4,701	2,661	−4%	−43%	−4.5%
Scotland Total	**27,077**	**31,560**	**21,487**	**−21%**	**−32%**	**−2.9%**
Northumberland	164	1,255	1,299	692%	4%	0.3%
North Yorkshire	45		0	−100%		
Humberside	13	31	32	146%	3%	0.2%
Isle of Wight	10	1	4	−60%	300%	9.0%
Dorset	55	84	67	22%	−20%	−1.6%
Channel Islands	570	1,443	1,403	146%	−3%	−0.2%

Administrative area or country	Operation Seafarer (1969–70)	SCR Census (1985–88)	Seabird 2000 (1998–2002)	Percentage change since Seafarer	Percentage change since SCR	Annual percentage change since SCR
Cornwall	686	680	1,109	62%	63%	3.6%
Isles of Scilly	1,000	1,199	1,092	9%	−9%	−0.8%
Devon	138	241	260	88%	8%	0.6%
Isle of Man	567	575	912	61%	59%	3.6%
England Total	**3,248**	**5,509**	**6,178**	**90%**	**12%**	**0.9%**
West Glamorgan	2	1	1	−50%	0%	0.0%
Dyfed	198	167	230	16%	38%	2.4%
Gwynedd	350	617	683	95%	11%	0.7%
Wales total	**550**	**785**	**914**	**66%**	**16%**	**1.1%**
Great Britain, Isle of Man and Channel Islands total	**30,875**	**37,854**	**28,579**	**−7%**	**−25%**	**−2.1%**
Co. Antrim	195	378	281	44%	−26%	−2.2%
Co. Down	23	62	20	−13%	−68%	−8.3%
Co. Dublin	271	1,736	1,359	401%	−22%	−1.9%
Co. Wicklow	5	8	19	280%	138%	6.9%
Co. Wexford	327	504	268	−18%	−47%	−4.5%
Co. Waterford	105	165	26	−75%	−84%	−13.0%
Co. Cork	215	419	221	3%	−47%	−4.3%
Co. Kerry	449	432	208	−54%	−52%	−5.6%
Co. Clare	131	70	49	−63%	−30%	−2.6%
Co. Galway	152	49	43	−72%	−12%	−1.1%
Co. Mayo	214	259	504	136%	95%	5.4%
Co. Sligo	34	241	104	206%	−57%	−6.3%
Co. Donegal	880	793	625	−29%	−21%	−1.9%
All-Ireland Total	**3,001**	**5,116[1]**	**3,727**	**24%**	**−27%**	**−2.4%**
Britain and Ireland Total	**33,876**	**42,970**	**32,306**	**−5%**	**−25%**	**−2.1%**

Note

[1] The total of 5,116 AON represents actual counts. Lloyd *et al.* (1993) estimated there to be a total of 8,800 AON in Ireland in 1985–88 in order to account for unsurveyed colonies.

approximately stable since 1993, whereas in Shetland there has been a very gradual increase (Heubeck, 2003). Less complete counts at many other colonies (e.g. Great Saltee, Sanda Islands; Fig. 3) lend support to the suggestion that a widespread decline began in the late 1980s. In contrast, in southeast Scotland and the Farne Islands numbers were stable or continued to increase until 1993 when numbers crashed following the unprecedented mortality of breeding adults in February–March 1994 (Figs. 3–4). During this wreck some 3,000–5,000 mainly adult Shags from colonies in northeast Britain died following an unusually prolonged period of onshore winds (Harris & Wanless, 1996). Numbers on the Farne Islands have subsequently increased rapidly, whereas recovery has been much slower on the Isle of May (Fig. 4) and other colonies in southeast Scotland. Regular counts at Annet (Isles of Scilly) and St Alban's Head (Dorset) show no evidence of a decline in the south of Britain (Fig. 3).

Table 2   Changes in the number of breeding European Shags (AON) at major colonies in Britain and Ireland between the SCR Census (1985–88) and Seabird 2000 (1999–2002). Major colonies are those that contained the top 50% of the British population or the top 75% of the Irish population during the SCR Census. ID corresponds to the colony symbols in Fig. 2.

ID	Colony	SCR Census (1985–88)	Seabird 2000 (1998–2002)	Percentage change since SCR	Annual percentage change since SCR	Percentage of population in Britain or Ireland 1998–2002
1	Foula	2,400	2,277	−5%	−0.4%	8.0%
2	Isle of May	1,916	734	−62%	−6.6%	2.6%
3	Shiant Islands	1,776	506	−72%	−9.2%	1.8%
4	Canna	1,447	740	−49%		
5	Berriedale Cliffs (SSSI)	1,428	839	−41%	−4.0%	2.9%
6	Farne Islands	1,248	1,287	3%	0.2%	4.5%
7	Isles of Scilly	1,199	1,092	−9%	−0.8%	3.8%
8	Fair Isle	1,099	663	−40%	−3.3%	2.3%
9	Sanda Islands	950	500	−47%	−5.2%	1.7%
10	Sule Skerry	874	724	−17%	−1.6%	2.5%
11	St Abb's Head to Fast Castle Head (SSSI)	626	329	−47%	−4.7%	1.2%
12	Jersey	525	423	−19%	−1.8%	1.5%
13	Mingulay	500	183	−63%	−7.5%	0.6%
14	Sumburgh Head	481	270	−44%	−4.0%	0.9%
15	Flannan Isles	400	77	−81%	−15.2%	0.3%
16	Corr Eilean & Eilean Ghamnha	345	70	−80%	−11.6%	0.2%
17	Fladda-chuain, Gaeilavore & Gearran Islands	345	46	−87%	−14.9%	0.2%
18	Hoy & South Walls	318	161	−49%	−4.9%	0.6%
19	The Lamb	301	76	−75%	−10.0%	0.3%
20	Handa	233	109	−53%	−5.3%	0.4%
21	Rubha Rodha	225	17	−92%	−16.8%	0.1%
22	Calf of Man	225	218	−3%	−0.2%	0.8%
23	Berneray	221	95	−57%	−6.3%	0.3%
24	Unst: Virdik to Brei Wick	209	8	−96%	−23.8%	0.0%
25	Papa Stour	195	240	23%	1.5%	0.8%
26	Harris: Toe Head	182	90	−51%	−5.3%	0.3%
27	Rhu Stoer	175	79	−55%	−5.5%	0.3%
28	Lambay Island	1,597	1,122	−30%	−2.9%	30.1%
29	Great Saltee	385	240	−38%	−3.3%	6.4%
30	Inishtooskert	275	3	−99%	−29.4%	0.1%
31	Inishmurray	237	104	−56%	−5.7%	2.8%
32	Horn Head	191	111	−42%	−4.4%	3.0%
33	Inishkeeragh	174	61	−65%	−7.2%	1.6%
34	The Maidens	161	97	−40%	−4.1%	2.6%
35	Roaninish	146	6	−96%	−23.5%	0.2%
36	Little Saltee	112	28	−75%	−10.9%	0.8%
37	St Patrick's Island (Skerries)	110	200	82%	4.7%	5.4%
38	Rathlin Island	109	58	−47%	−4.4%	1.6%

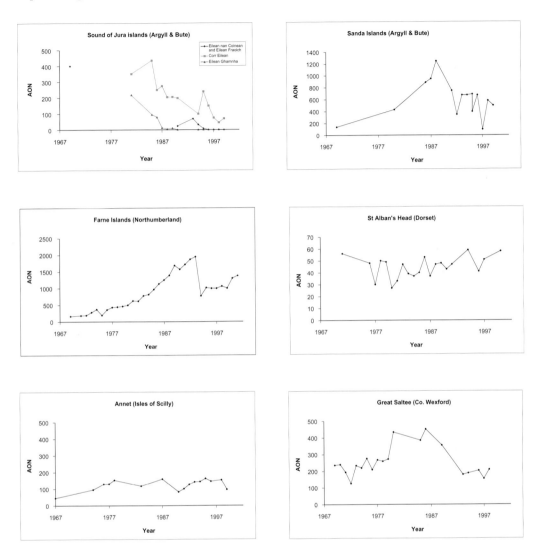

Figure 3 Number of breeding European Shags (AON) at colonies in Britain and Ireland where repeated counts were conducted 1967–2002 (data from Seabird Colony Register Database, JNCC/Seabird Group, Aberdeen; J.A.C. Craik pers. comm.).

CAUSES OF CHANGE

Potts (1969) attributed the spectacular increase in the numbers of European Shags on North Sea coasts of Britain during the first 60 years of the 20th century to a reduction in human exploitation for food (since the species is good to eat, although perhaps an acquired taste, and is still hunted legally in Iceland and the Faeroes) and persecution due to a perceived threat to fish stocks (Lambert, 2003). Since then, the species has undoubtedly benefited from the removal of the bounty offered for Great Cormorant beaks, following the introduction in Britain of the Wildlife and Countryside Act in 1981,

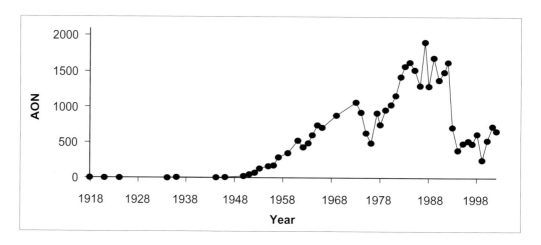

Figure 4   Number of breeding European Shags (AON) on the Isle of May 1918–2002.

which also outlawed hunting for food. The increase in the numbers of nests on Lambay, from 144 in 1969 to 1,597 in 1987, may have been due to a reduction in persecution in Ireland (Merne & Madden, 1999). Numbers may initially have been depressed by food limitation (Parslow, 1967), but Potts (1969) considered this unlikely, given the very small population at the end of the 19th century. However, it is now many decades since man's direct influence on the numbers of shags has swung from persecution to protection and we must look for other explanations for recent changes.

Shags often defer breeding in years when local conditions are unfavourable, and this may produce large decreases in population status that usually only last for a single year, but sometimes longer. The number of nests on the Isle of May has been counted almost annually for 50 years (Fig. 4) and data on breeding behaviour and productivity have been collected for several decades. In nine years between 1973 and 2001 substantial numbers of experienced adults on the Isle of May failed to breed. The abrupt decrease in the numbers of nests in the mid-1970s, which interrupted almost 40 years of constant increase, was initially (and quite understandably) attributed to an increase in adult mortality. However, analysis of ringing and retrapping data revealed that most of the missing adults had not died but had refrained from breeding for one or more years (Aebischer, 1986). In 1993 over 60% of experienced adults at this colony did not breed, although they were present in the colony and some held nest sites (Harris *et al.*, 1998). The situation was further complicated by 80% of the adults alive at the end of 1993 dying in a wreck in February 1994, caused by an exceptionally long period of onshore winds that led to either a shortage of food or the birds being unable to feed efficiently (Harris & Wanless, 1996). Thus, the decline in the breeding population actually occurred between 1993 and 1994, although the counts of nests, if taken as an indication of the population, would have indicated a severe reduction in numbers between 1992 and 1993. This highlights the usefulness of long-term detailed studies in interpreting the results of more extensive surveys.

Substantial non-breeding has also been noted on the Sanda Islands (Argyll & Bute) in 1995 and on Canna (Lochaber) in at least five years between 1970 and 2002 (Fig. 3). Non-breeding events are sometimes quite local, e.g. in 1993 non-breeding occurred at most colonies in the Firth of Forth but nothing unusual was noted on the Farne Islands less than 100 km away. Intriguingly, many adults on Canna (Lochaber) on the opposite side of Scotland also took a year off breeding. However, a sudden drop in numbers (apparent in almost all the time series shown in Fig. 3), need not necessarily indicate non-breeding as severe gales and predation by gulls or mammals prior to a census can also cause reductions in the numbers of nests (Aebischer, 1993; Craik, 1998).

The survival and productivity of European Shags is probably affected by availability of prey, and this in turn may affect population status. European Shags eat a wide variety of small fish, but in the British Isles the commonest food at all times of year, both in numbers and biomass, is the Lesser Sandeel (Harris & Wanless, 1991, 1997c). This small shoaling fish is abundant in many sandy areas and is a staple food of a wide variety of marine predators. It is also the target of a very large industrial fishery, with annual catches in the North Sea sometimes approaching one million tonnes. There is as yet no proven link between this fishery and the decline in numbers of the European Shag. However, at the Isle of May breeding success was positively, and significantly, correlated with the availability of sandeels for the local fishery. This suggests that this particular fishery, which took over 100,000 tonnes in 1993, could potentially have serious consequences for Shags (Rindorf *et al.*, 2000). Apart from the 1994 disaster, survival of adult Shags on the Isle of May has remained high and constant (at *c*.88% per annum) between 1967 and 2000, but unfortunately no survival data for adults or chicks are currently available for other colonies.

Shags are susceptible to mass adult mortality events that produce large declines in population status within a single year. Since recruitment rates are comparatively low, it may take the population many years to recover from such events. As already mentioned, recent declines in numbers in northeast England and southeast Scotland can be attributed to the wreck of spring 1994. Abrupt decreases in the size of breeding populations have followed severe local oiling incidents (e.g. at Sumburgh in 1993 after the *Braer* disaster: Heubeck, 1997) and natural events such as paralytic shell fish poisoning at the Farne Islands in 1968 and 1975, both of which led to increased adult mortality (Coulson *et al.*, 1968; Armstrong *et al.*, 1978).

The gradual declines noted at many other colonies are much harder to explain. There has certainly been no reduction in available breeding habitat and nesting success has remained high at most colonies where this has been monitored (Mavor *et al.*, 2002). Eggs and chicks in some colonies have suffered from predation by introduced mammals. The effects of prolonged predation by American Mink, illustrated by the decline in numbers of shags on Corr Eilean and Eilean Ghamnha in the McCormaig islands and their complete disappearance from Eilean nan Coinean and Eilean Fraoich, (all in the Sound of Jura, Argyll & Bute; Fig. 3: Craik, 1998). Increases in the Firth of Clyde may be due to birds moving from colonies affected by mink predation in Argyll & Bute. Numbers and productivity at Hermaness (Shetland), the most northern seabird colony in Britain, declined dramatically after the mid-1970s and this seems to be associated with predation by feral cats (Martin, 2002). In 1987 15 shag nests were recorded on Ailsa Craig, while in 2002 at least 50 pairs reared chicks; this increase seemed to be a direct result of the successful rat removal campaign in 1991–92 (Zonfrillo, 2001). The decline in numbers of nests on Canna in recent years may be due, at least in part, to the increasing numbers of rats there (R. Swann, pers. comm.). The effects of introduced mammals that are mainly nocturnal can be hard to detect, so predation might have a greater effect on breeding success than currently thought.

A decrease in the survival of adults and/or young birds between independence and their recruitment to the breeding population in their second or third years could obviously be responsible for the observed declines, but no good data are yet available. Ringing recoveries provide the only information on the causes of mortality and these suggest that during the last decade the proportions shot and drowned in nets were substantially lower than 20–40 years ago when most populations were increasing (Swann, 2000). The numbers of ringed birds recovered oiled appear to have increased in some areas (Harris & Swann, 2002a) and could be higher than reported since oil is not easy to see on black plumage. However, apart from major incidents near colonies, oiling is probably insufficient to have a major effect on population size. Shags accumulate various pollutants and heavy metals but there is no evidence to suggest that the current levels are having adverse effects on breeding or survival.

Despite there being a few long-distance movements, for instance chicks reared on Foula (Shetland) breeding 934 km away on Great Saltee (Co. Wexford) and 505 km away on the Farne Islands (Northumberland) (Harris & Swann, 2002a), most young Shags that survive recruit to their natal colony and, once they have bred, rarely move elsewhere (Aebischer, 1995). Thus it is unlikely that there has been a major redistribution of birds within Britain and Ireland except at a local scale. Some immatures from southern British and Irish colonies winter in northern France but there is no evidence that any of these have remained in that area and contributed to the large increase in the French population that occurred during the 1990s (Monnat & Pasquet, in press).

Although the European Shag is still numerous in Britain and Ireland, Seabird 2000 has revealed a widespread decline since the mid-1980s. Given that Britain and Ireland holds over 40% of the world population (see below), priority should be given to trying to understand the reasons for the recent decrease.

INTERNATIONAL CONTEXT

The problems associated with assessing the numbers of European Shags have been highlighted earlier. All estimates of populations must be treated as minima and used with caution. It is, however, important to place the British and Irish populations in an international context. Wanless & Harris (1997b) suggested a world population of 80,000–90,000 pairs in the mid-1990s. Additional data now available, together with counts from Seabird 2000, indicates a decline to around 73,000–83,000 pairs (Table 3). Britain and Ireland now hold around 35–40% and 4.5–5.1% respectively of the world population. Around 90% of European Shags belong to the subspecies *aristotelis*, which is confined to Atlantic coasts of Europe; Britain holds 40–44% of this subspecies, and Ireland 5.1–5.6%.

In 1975 there were 6,600 breeding pairs of *P. a. aristotelis* in Iceland (Gardarsson, 1979) but the population has increased substantially since then, probably as a result of a reduction in human hunting pressure, and is now estimated at 8,000–9,000 pairs (Petersen, 1998). There is no recent count of Shags in the Faeroes, but in 1987 the population was estimated at 1,000–2,000 pairs, and there is nothing to suggest a recent marked change (B. Olsen & J.-K. Jensen, pers. comm). The Norwegian population is currently estimated at 15,000–20,000 pairs (T. Anker-Nilssen, pers comm.; NINA unpubl.). Trends at Norwegian colonies over the last 35 years have been extremely variable; thus, whilst the southernmost colonies have increased at least ten-fold, the large colony on Runde (5,000 pairs in 1975) has decreased and numbers in northern Norway have remained fairly stable (Lorentsen, 2001). The reasons for these differences are unclear. The Russian population is currently about 350 pairs (Røv *et al.*, 2000). A survey of the French Atlantic coast in 1997–99 reported 6,100 nests, a 35% increase since the previous count ten years before (Monnat & Pasquet, in press). The breeding population on the Atlantic coast of Iberia was estimated at 3,062 pairs in 1995–99 (2,912 pairs in Spain and 150 in Portugal); the Cíes and Ons Islands (Galicia) held 2,050 pairs with numbers declining by 5% per annum, perhaps due to birds being caught in fishing gear (Velando & Freire, 2002; Velando & Alvarez, in press).

Birds breeding in the Mediterranean belong to the subspecies *desmarestii*. There are few recent surveys but the population in the Balearic archipelago is put at 1,050 pairs and is declining at 3–4% per annum (D. Oro, pers. comm.), and there were 971 nests in Corsica in 2002 (J.-C. Thibault & I. Guyot, pers. comm.). In the Mediterranean, shags of all ages are regularly reported drowned in fishing nets and there is concern that this mortality could be having a serious effect on breeding numbers. Using the above counts to update those in Wanless & Harris (1997b) gives a population of 7,000–10,000 pairs of *desmarestii*. Little is known of the northwest African race *riggenbachi*, although numbers have declined to no more than 20–40 pairs in Morocco (Thevenot *et al.*, 2003).

Table 3 International context.

Country or region	Subspecies	Number of pairs		Year	Source
		Min	Max		
Great Britain, Isle of Man and Channel Isles	*aristotelis*	29,000	29,000	1999–2002	Seabird 2000
All Ireland	*aristotelis*	3,700	3,700	1999–2002	Seabird 2000
Faeroes	*aristotelis*	1,000	2,000	1987–2001	B. Olsen & J.-K. Jensen (pers. comm)
France (Atlantic)	*aristotelis*	6,059	6,130	1997–99	Monnat & Pasquet (in press)
Iceland	*aristotelis*	8,000	9,000	1998	Petersen (1998)
Norway	*aristotelis*	15,000	20,000	1999–2001	T. Anker-Nilssen (pers. comm.), NINA unpubl.
Portugal (Atlantic)	*aristotelis*	150	150	1995–99	Velando & Alvarez (in press)
Russia	*aristotelis*	350	350	1999	Røv *et al.* (2000)
Spain (Atlantic)	*aristotelis*	2,912	2,912	1995–99	Velando & Alvarez (in press)
Albania	*desmarestii*	20	20		Wanless & Harris (1997)
Bulgaria	*desmarestii*	25	30	1970–85	Wanless & Harris (1997)
Croatia	*desmarestii*	2,000	4,000		Wanless & Harris (1997)
Cyprus	*desmarestii*	40	50		Wanless & Harris (1997)
France (Corsica)	*desmarestii*	971	971	2002	J. C. Thibault & I. Guyot (pers. comm.)
Gibraltar	*desmarestii*	7	8	2002	J. E. Cortes (pers comm)
Greece	*desmarestii*	1,000[1]	1,000[1]		Handrinos & Akriotis (1997)
Italy (Sardinia)	*desmarestii*	1,600	2,000	1983–93	Harris & Wanless (1997)
Spain (Balearics)	*desmarestii*	1,050	1,050	2002	D. Oro (pers. comm.)
Turkey	*desmarestii*	50	350		Wanless & Harris (1997)
Ukraine	*desmarestii*	250	400	1978	Wanless & Harris (1997)
Libya	*desmarestii*	50	50		Wanless & Harris (1997)
Tunisia	*desmarestii*	30	30	1975–90	Wanless & Harris (1997)
Morocco	*riggenbachi*	20	40		Thévenot *et al.* (2003)

Biogeographic region		Min	Max	Min % GB	Max % GB	Min % Ireland	Max % Ireland
NE Atlantic*	*aristotelis*	66,000	73,000	39.7%	43.9%	5.1%	5.6%
World	all	73,000	83,000	34.9%	39.7%	4.5%	5.1%

*Stroud *et al.* (2001)

Note

[1] at least 1,000 pairs

Arctic Skua *Stercorarius parasiticus*

Robert W. Furness and Norman Ratcliffe

INTRODUCTION

In Britain the Arctic Skua is confined as a breeder to north and west Scotland, at the southern extremity of its circumpolar, high-latitude breeding range. Most Scottish Arctic Skuas nest in moorland colonies close to aggregations of auks, kittiwakes and Arctic Terns from which they obtain food by piracy. In a few places, such as the moors of Caithness, Arctic Skuas nest further inland in rather scattered breeding territories, where feeding on berries, insects and small birds may be more important. Unlike their larger cousin, the Great Skua, Arctic Skuas do not normally scavenge behind fishing boats or feed as members in multi-species flocks of seabirds on surface shoals of fish. Arctic Skuas are simply too small to compete in such situations. Although numbers of Arctic Skuas nesting in Scotland increased in the 1970s and 1980s, most of their breeding sites have been established for many decades or centuries. Few new colonies have been formed and the breeding range has remained remarkably static.

CENSUS METHODS

Counting Arctic Skuas is made difficult by the scattered nature of territories in many areas, and by the ability of this species to occupy many separate patches of ground of quite variable habitat type. In Scotland there are only a few colonies where Arctic Skuas nest close together. For example, nests in Foula (Shetland) may be only 20–40 m apart, with a mean spacing of 72 m (Phillips, 2001), and concentrated in the few areas of the island that lack breeding Great Skuas. Even here, odd pairs can be found nesting up to 1 km away from the major aggregations. In areas such as Mainland Shetland and Caithness, single pairs may be scattered, often considerable distances from the coast, and might easily be overlooked. Coverage of areas known to hold breeding Arctic Skuas was thorough during Seabird 2000 and was also thought to be good for the SCR Census (Lloyd *et al.*, 1991, reported coverage for this species as 'complete'), but it was rather incomplete during Operation Seafarer (1969–70). As a result of the focus of effort on coastal surveys, Operation Seafarer missed many Arctic Skuas, especially those breeding more than 1 km inland (Ewins *et al.*, 1987, found that 40% of Arctic Skuas in Shetland in the early 1980s were nesting more than 1 km from the coast). Surveys of Arctic Skuas during the SCR Census were conducted in Orkney in 1982 (Meek *et al.*, 1985) and the total count was increased by 15% (Lloyd *et al.*, 1991) to make it comparable with the results of the survey of Arctic Skuas in Shetland conducted in 1985–86 (Ewins et al. 1987). The SCR Census also included counts from Caithness conducted in 1979–80 (Reed *et al.*, 1983), whereas all other areas were surveyed during the main census period of 1985–88. In 1992, further surveys were conducted of breeding Arctic Skuas in Orkney (Meek *et al.*, 1994) and in Shetland (Sears *et al.*, 1995).

The count unit for Arctic Skuas is the Apparently Occupied Territory (AOT). This is very similar to the number of breeding pairs, but also includes the small numbers of birds that are holding territory but not necessarily breeding. Proving breeding is difficult since Arctic Skua nests are not easy to locate, and chicks leave the nest within 1–3 days of hatching and can be extremely difficult to find when hiding somewhere in the territory. Even if chicks are found, it can be impossible in many cases to be sure whether particular chicks belong to one pair of adults or another. This is especially the case where Arctic Skuas nest at high density; chicks will often wander into neighbouring territories. Although Arctic Skuas usually breed annually once they have recruited into a colony, and usually return to exactly the same territory year after year, in seasons when food supply is particularly poor, birds may fail to lay (Catry *et al.*, 1998). This appears to have been the case during the main census of Arctic Skuas in Shetland in 2000–01 (Mavor *et al.*, 2002), and may have resulted in an underestimate of the number that would normally be breeding under more favourable conditions. Breeding success of Arctic Skuas in Shetland was also poor in 2000–01, and birds that lost eggs early may have shown low attendance in the territory, so that some breeding AOTs may also have been missed. The Shetland counts in 2002 were also affected by poor weather conditions, with a considerable area surveyed in fog. This may also have contributed to an underestimate of numbers in parts of Shetland. Apparently, counting conditions and breeding success during Seabird 2000 were better in other regions and should have had little impact on count accuracy.

Arctic Skuas return to territories during April and May, and are present on territory most of the time until July, when chicks fledge and adults start to depart for winter quarters in the southern hemisphere. Incubating birds can be difficult to detect among the grass and heather, and sometimes sit quite tightly while people pass by. This makes Arctic Skuas somewhat more difficult to locate and count than their larger relative the Great Skua. Dark-phase Arctic Skuas, which comprise the majority of the Scottish population, are least conspicuous, but even pale-phase individuals are easily overlooked against a background of heather, grass and rocks typically found on most territories.

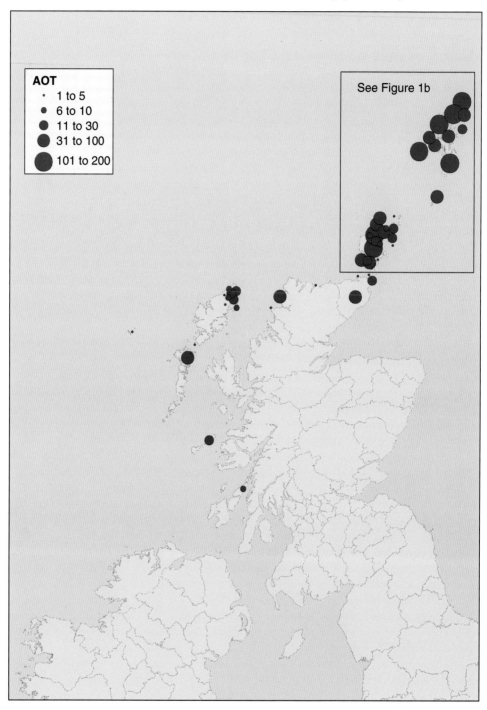

Figure 1a   Abundance and distribution of breeding Arctic Skuas in Britain 1998–2002.

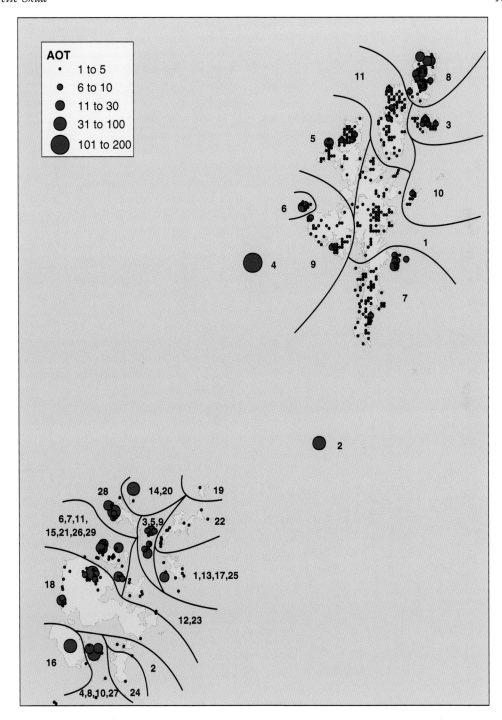

Figure 1b Abundance and distribution of breeding Arctic Skuas (AOT) in Orkney and Shetland 1998–2002. Numbers correspond to areas listed in Tables 1b, c.

As with the Great Skua, large and densely occupied colonies of Arctic Skuas tend to have traditional 'club' sites associated with the breeding area. Immatures gather at these clubs, and may establish 'practice' territories on the edge of a club and then be mistaken for territory-holding breeders.

The accuracy of Arctic Skua census counts has not been determined by formal testing of the methodology, but there can be considerable disagreement between independent counters. Probably, the accuracy of counts of Arctic Skuas is rather less than that of counts of Great Skuas, as the smaller species is more difficult to detect, and often more patchily distributed over larger areas. In several sites it nests in small and somewhat separated groups in peripheral areas adjacent to colonies of Great Skuas, and in these situations AOTs can easily be overlooked. Empirical data for Great Skuas suggest that counts can differ by up to 40% between different observers, so it seems likely that Arctic Skua counts may vary by even more than this. In particular, the older data on numbers (such as the 1969 Operation Seafarer counts), may be rather inaccurate as the local distributions of the species within regions of Scotland were not well known and many birds may have been overlooked. Comparisons of counts conducted in the three censuses should be treated with caution.

CURRENT STATUS AND TRENDS

The breeding range in Scotland has hardly changed over the last 150 years. In 1999–2002 the species nested mainly in Orkney and Shetland, but with inland colonies in Caithness and small numbers nesting in Sutherland, the Western Isles and on a few of the islands of Argyll (Fig. 1). This is almost identical to the breeding distribution of the Arctic Skua in Britain and Ireland reported in the 19th century (Holloway, 1996). Not only is the regional distribution virtually unchanged over 150 years, but also the local distribution of colonies among islands has altered only very slightly. Very few sites have been colonised during this period (one important exception is Handa (Sutherland) which was colonised in 1970, and another is Rubha Shois, in mainland Sutherland, colonised in 1987. Several sites in the Western Isles where Arctic Skuas nested in 1985 had not been recorded in earlier surveys, but may have been overlooked in the past, whilst only a handful of sites have suffered local extinction, e.g. Mull (Argyll & Bute), Islay (Argyll & Bute) and Barra (Western Isles).

Table 1a   Numbers of breeding Arctic Skuas (AOT) in Scotland 1969–2002.

Administrative area or country	Operation Seafarer (1969–70)	SCR Census (1985–88)	Seabird 2000 (1998–2002)	Percentage change since Seafarer	Percentage change since SCR
Shetland	709	1,946	1,120	58%	−42%
Orkney	256	1,190[1]	720	181%	−39%
Western Isles– Comhairle nan eilean	36	60	156	333%	160%
Caithness	10	57[2]	71	610%	25%
Sutherland	1	31	48	4700%	55%
Argyll and Bute	27	104	21	−22%	−80%
Scotland Total	**1,039**	**3,388**	**2,136**	**106%**	**−37%**

Notes

[1] Extrapolated from a count of 1,034 AOT in 1982 (Meek *et al.*, 1985) using previous trend data (Furness, 1986) to estimate numbers in 1986 (see Lloyd *et al.*, 1991)

[2] 47 AOT in Caithness were counted during the NCC moorland bird survey in 1979–80 (Reed *et al.*, 1983)

Table 1b   Numbers of breeding Arctic Skuas (AOT) in Orkney in 1982, 1992 and Seabird 2000 (1998–2002). ID corresponds to areas shown in Fig 1b.

ID	Local area	1982	1992	Seabird 2000 (1998–2002)	Percentage change since 1982	Percentage change since 1992
1	Auskerry	2	2	1	−50%	−50%
2	Burray (Hunda)	2	3	2	0%	−33%
3	Calf of Eday	22	14	7	−68%	−50%
4	Cava	nc	1	0		−100%
5	Eday	80	106	69	−14%	−35%
6	Egilsay	1	0	0	−100%	
7	Eynhallow	19	13	9	−53%	−31%
8	Fara	28	20	13	−54%	−35%
9	Faray (including Holm)	1	2	0	−100%	−100%
10	Flotta	26	80	66	154%	−18%
11	Gairsay	38	31	29	−24%	−6%
12	Helliar Holm	nc	1	1		0%
13	Holm of Huip	0	1	0		−100%
14	Holm of Papa Westray	1	2	0	−100%	−100%
15	Holm of Scockness	1	0	0	−100%	
16	Hoy and South Walls	406	211	72	−82%	−66%
17	Linga Holm	2	0	1	−50%	
18	Mainland	64	79	120	88%	52%
19	North Ronaldsay	1	1	1	0%	0%
20	Papa Westray	96	151	64	−33%	−58%
21	Rousay	96	137	115	20%	−16%
22	Sanday	25	28	21	−16%	−25%
23	Shapinsay	nc	10	6		−40%
24	South Ronaldsay	7	8	3	−57%	−63%
25	Stronsay	44	40	29	−34%	−28%
26	Sweyn Holm	1	1	1	0%	0%
27	Swona	nc	1	1		0%
28	Westray	45	98	88	96%	−10%
29	Wyre	3	2	1	−67%	−50%
	Total	1,011[1,2]	1,043	720	−29%	−31%

Notes   Description
nc   not counted
[1] Prior to extrapolation
[2] Meek *et al.* (1985) gave a total of 1,034 AOT

   Although the distribution of colonies has remained remarkably static over this long period, the sizes of many colonies have altered dramatically, and this has affected the relative importance of different regions of Scotland for breeding Arctic Skuas. Between Operation Seafarer (1969–70) and the SCR Census (1979–88), counts of Arctic Skuas increased in all the occupied regions of Scotland (Table 1a). This can be attributed in part to the greater coverage during the SCR Census, but where areas were covered thoroughly in both 1969–70 and in 1979–88, an increase was still evident. Lloyd *et al.* (1991) concluded that there was without doubt a considerable increase in breeding numbers of Arctic Skuas in Scotland in the 1970s and 1980s, with the increase apparently slowing during the latter decade. Between the SCR Census and Seabird 2000 the numbers of Arctic Skua AOTs fell sharply in Shetland, Orkney and Argyll & Bute, but increased in the Western Isles, Caithness and

Table 1c   Numbers of breeding Arctic Skuas (AOT) in Shetland in 1985–86, 1992 and Seabird 2000 (1998–2002).
ID corresponds to areas shown in Fig. 1b.

ID	Local area	1985-86[1]	1992[2]	Seabird 2000 (1998–2002)	Percentage change since 1982	Percentage change since 1992
1	East Mainland	190	177	84	−56%	−53%
2	Fair Isle	115	109	78	−32%	−28%
3	Fetlar	189	152	95	−50%	−38%
4	Foula	174	159	107	−39%	−33%
5	North Mainland	175	159	146	−17%	−8%
6	Papa Stour	94	101	47	−50%	−53%
7	South Mainland	324	344	154	−52%	−55%
8	Unst	279	339	189	−32%	−44%
9	West Mainland	173	139	77	−55%	−45%
10	Whalsay	41	25	25	−39%	0%
11	Yell	192	168	118	−39%	−30%
	Total	1,946	1,872	1,120	−42%	−40%

Notes

[1] Totals derived from raw data held on Seabird Colony Register database. Sears *et al.* (1995) gave a total of 1,912 AOT.

[2] Totals derived from raw data supplied by RSPB. Sears *et al.* (1995) gave a total of 1,878 AOT.

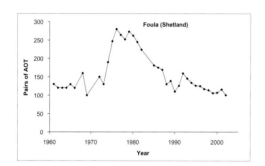

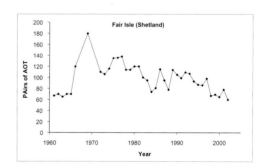

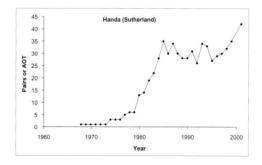

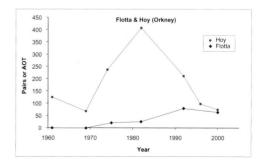

Figure 3   Numbers of breeding Arctic Skuas (AOT or pairs) at colonies where repeated counts have been conducted during 1961–2002.

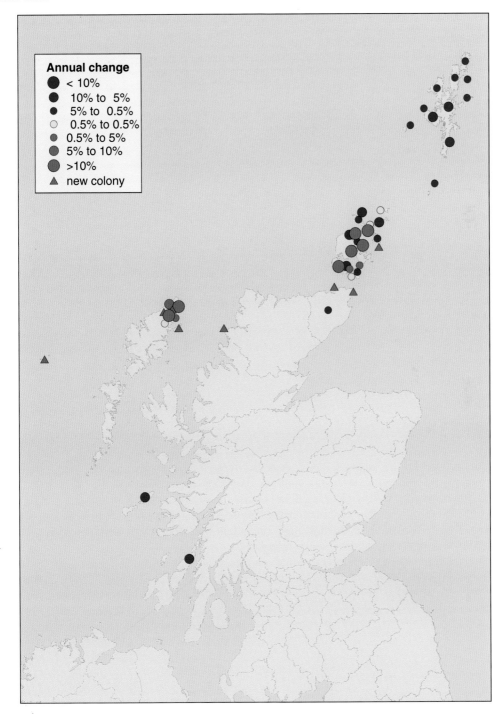

Figure 2   Changes in the number of breeding Arctic Skuas (AOT) at all colonies (except in Orkney and Shetland where change is denoted for each count area—see Fig 1b and Tables 1b, c for definitions) from 1979–88 to 1998–2002.

Table 2   Changes in the number of breeding Arctic Skuas (AOT) at major colonies or areas 1969–2002.

Colony/Area	AOT				Rank			
	Operation Seafarer (1969–70)	1982/85–86	1992	Seabird 2000 (1998–2002)	Seabird 2000 (1998–2002)	1992	1982/85–86	Operation Seafarer (1969–70)
Unst	80[1]	279	339	189	1	2	3	4
South Mainland Shetland	>70[2]	324	344	154	2	1	2	5
North Mainland Shetland	>50	175	159	146	3	6.5	7	9
Mainland Orkney	5	64	79	120	4	17	15	14
Yell	55	192	168	118	5	5	4	8
Rousay	11	96	137	115	6	11	11.5	12.5
Foula	100	174	159	107	7	6.5	8	3
Fetlar	200	189	152	95	8	8	6	1
Westray	67	45	98	88	9	15	16	7
East Mainland Shetland	No data	190	177	84	10	4	5	–
Fair Isle	180	115	109	78	11	12	10	2
West Mainland Shetland	No data	173	139	77	12	10	9	–
Hoy	68	406	211	72	13	3	1	6
Eday	11	80	106	69	14	13	14	12.5
Flotta	1	26	80	66	15	16	17	15
Papa Westray	25	96	151	64	16	9	11.5	10
Papa Stour	20	94	101	47	17	14	13	11

Notes

[1] Source: Bourne & Dixon (1974)

[2] Source: Everett (1982)

Sutherland (Table 1a). Moreover, because the sizes of the populations in Shetland and Orkney were much larger than in the other areas, the total population of Scotland decreased by 37% from 3,388 AOT (1979–88) to 2,136 AOT (1999–2002). Despite the large decrease in Shetland, the archipelago still held 52% of the Scottish population during Seabird 2000, whilst a further 34% were in Orkney. The largest decline has been in Argyll & Bute, the only region where Arctic Skua breeding numbers were less in Seabird 2000 than in Operation Seafarer.

Changes in numbers of AOTs in individual colonies showed pronounced variation, even between adjacent colonies (Fig. 2). For example, in Orkney, numbers decreased by almost 50% on Hoy and South Walls, from 406 to 211 AOT between 1982 and 1992, whilst numbers increased from 96 to 151 AOT on Papa Westray, 96 to 137 AOT on Rousay, 45 to 98 AOT on Westray, 80 to 106 AOT on Eday and from 26 to 80 AOT on Flotta during the same period (Table 1b). While numbers fell from 174 to 159 AOT on Foula between 1985 and 1992, numbers increased from 94 to 101 AOT at Papa Stour (Shetland), this colony being the nearest neighbour to the Foula colony and one known from ringing to receive recruits from Foula (Table 1c). The different dynamics of individual colonies have resulted in quite dramatic changes in ranking among the largest Arctic Skua colonies in Scotland. In particular, Hoy, which was ranked the largest colony in Scotland during the SCR Census fell to 13th place during Seabird 2000. Whereas Mainland Orkney, which ranked only 15th in the SCR Census, rose to fourth place in Seabird 2000. Changes in rank have been less pronounced in Shetland, although Unst climbed from third place during the SCR Census to become the largest colony in Seabird 2000 (Table 2). Changes in distribution were also evident within some of the islands. For example, Arctic Skuas on Unst (Shetland) formerly nested predominantly in the Hermaness area in the northwest corner of the island, but are now mostly in the southern half of Unst. Another feature of the ranking of the largest colonies of Arctic Skuas is the importance of areas of Shetland Mainland and Orkney Mainland for this species (Table 2). This contrasts with Great Skuas which are more numerous on the remoter islands where there is little human activity. It is unclear how much this distribution of Arctic Skuas on more disturbed areas is a consequence of the species moving away from areas with high concentrations of Great Skuas, but this is clearly the cause of recent declines in Arctic Skua numbers at Hermaness and on Hoy, for example, as discussed in the next section.

CAUSES OF CHANGE

Lloyd *et al.* (1991) identified loss of nesting habitat through agricultural change, and increasing Great Skua numbers, as the two most important factors affecting Arctic Skua numbers and distribution, but also mentioned the importance of reductions in sandeel availability around Shetland and local impacts of human disturbance and persecution. In addition to these factors that may affect breeding success or adult survival rates, the divergent changes in numbers at various neighbouring colonies mentioned above suggest that the rates of immigration and emigration have probably also been extremely important in determining the size of particular colonies.

Arctic Skuas prefer to nest in short vegetation, and avoid areas of long grass or rank heather. During the 1980s large areas of moorland in Orkney and Shetland were modified by application of lime and by ploughing and reseeding to produce higher quality grassland for grazing. These changes in some areas of Orkney were responsible for local declines in breeding numbers of Arctic Skuas (Meek *et al.*, 1985). However, it seems unlikely that the population size was affected as birds had plenty of alternative habitat available in Orkney and were certainly not habitat-limited in Shetland. The amount of agricultural intensification decreased during the 1990s, and this threat to Arctic Skuas has now probably become rather trivial. One trend in recent years has been a reduction in stocking of sheep and this may even affect Arctic Skuas by permitting vegetation to increase in height. However, few Arctic Skuas nest on improved grassland. In Jura (Argyll & Bute), plans were made to afforest much of the hill ground occupied by Arctic Skuas on the island. Whilst it is possible that habitat alteration has affected the birds there, it seems that much of the island remains as potential breeding ground for Arctic Skuas. Overall, it appears that changes in the quantity of suitable nesting habitat are unlikely to have contributed to the widespread and quite large declines in numbers of Arctic Skuas between the SCR census and Seabird 2000.

There is no doubt that Great Skuas have affected the fortunes of Arctic Skuas. The growth in numbers of Great Skuas has often involved the takeover of breeding habitat previously used by Arctic Skuas. Arctic Skuas were pushed off most of Hermaness by the spread of Great Skuas there in the 1970s and, on Foula, Arctic Skuas were forced off much of their former nesting habitat as Great Skua numbers increased in the 1960s and 1970s. Even after Great Skua numbers began to fall in the 1980s, their colony limits expanded to permit larger mean territory sizes, further compressing the distribution of Arctic Skuas and restricting them to nesting in high densities on the island's periphery (Phillips *et al.*, 1998) and in areas of greater human disturbance (which Arctic Skuas apparently tolerate better than Great Skuas do). Great Skuas can kill adult Arctic Skuas during territorial disputes, which can have an immediate affect on local Arctic Skua breeding numbers. However, on Foula in the 1970s, despite Great Skuas killing over 3% of Arctic Skua adults each year and 15% of the chicks, Arctic Skua numbers increased (Furness, 1987). In more recent years, Great Skuas killing

Arctic Skua adults on Foula has become less common, as Great Skuas are no longer moving into Arctic Skua territories, but Arctic Skua numbers have still declined. The huge decrease in the number of Arctic Skuas on Hoy, from 406 to 211 AOT between 1982 and 1992, seems to have coincided with the period of maximum expansion of the Great Skua colony there. By the mid-1990s Great Skuas nested over most of the Hoy uplands, and Arctic Skuas remained only in peripheral areas, in small, rather isolated, clusters (Furness, 2000). Under these conditions, Arctic Skuas find it extremely difficult to defend their fledglings from predation by Great Skuas. As the chicks learn to fly they almost inevitably wander into a Great Skua territory, and become a quick and easy meal (Phillips *et al.*, 1998). Although the evidence is only circumstantial, it seems highly likely that the increases in numbers of Arctic Skuas nesting on Flotta, and other Orkney islands, that occurred at the same time as the decrease on Hoy, were a result of recruits from the Hoy population emigrating to other sites as a consequence of the pressures exerted by Great Skua expansion on Hoy. Possibly some breeding adults may even have switched colony. There is no proof of this, but the changes in numbers were so large that it would be difficult to account for them without invoking abandonment of Hoy by some of the established breeders.

In contrast to the demise of Arctic Skuas at Hermaness and on Hoy, growth of numbers of Arctic Skuas on Handa (Sutherland) has progressed despite large increases in numbers of Great Skuas there. Possibly, the exceptionally high breeding success of both species on Handa may have permitted the two species to cohabit, and the conflict for space may not arise until numbers have increased still further or their food supply decreases.

In Shetland and Orkney in recent years, but especially in Shetland, Arctic Skua breeding success has been poor and much of this can be attributed to the reduced stock of sandeels (Phillips *et al.*,

Arctic Skua pale-phase adult at nest (P J Newman)

1996a,b). In Shetland, Arctic Skuas depend on their ability to steal fish from Atlantic Puffins, Black-legged Kittiwakes and Arctic Terns, and to a lesser extent from Common Guillemots and Razorbills (Caldow & Furness, 2001). With declines in numbers of several of these species, and low breeding success in all, there are fewer fish-carrying hosts for Arctic Skuas to kleptoparasitise. Lack of sandeels has clearly had a direct impact on Arctic Skuas in Shetland by reducing productivity, chick condition and survival. This has been especially evident in 2002–03, with large decreases in Arctic Skua breeding numbers at many Shetland colonies in these years of exceptionally low sandeel stock.

As a result of food shortage, foraging skuas spend longer away from their territory searching for feeding opportunities, and so are less able to defend their chicks from predation (Caldow & Furness, 2000). There is no doubt that an interaction also occurs between food availability and the extent of the Great Skua impact on Arctic Skuas. Declines in numbers of potential hosts and breeding failures of potential hosts are therefore both threats to the success of Arctic Skuas. The switching of Great Skuas to killing larger numbers of seabirds when discards or sandeels are in short supply therefore threatens Arctic Skuas both directly by an impact from predation of their chicks, and indirectly through the impact of Great Skuas on the populations of host species such as Black-legged Kittiwakes and Atlantic Puffins. With drastic reductions in the amounts of discards being produced in the haddock and whiting fisheries of the northwest North Sea expected in the next few years as a result of new conservation measures in the Common Fisheries Policy, there is every reason to expect this impact to increase in the short and medium term.

This impact can be seen already. Since Seabird 2000 surveys were completed on Shetland, numbers of Arctic Skua AOTs have decreased dramatically. For example, on Foula in 2001 Arctic Skuas nested in nearly all 116 AOTs, whereas in 2002, eggs were laid in only 84 territories out of a total of 101 AOTs. In 2003 the number of AOTs was almost impossible to count because attendance was so low and sporadic, and birds laid in only 47–48 territories. The immediate future prospects do not appear good for the Shetland Arctic Skuas during this period of depleted sandeel stock.

Human persecution of Arctic Skuas occurs at a few colonies, and this can affect adult survival rates and cause declines in numbers at affected colonies. The best-documented example of this is on Fair Isle (Shetland), where adult Arctic Skuas on territory have been shot to keep the size of the colony within limits by crofters concerned for the welfare of their sheep (Furness, 1987). O'Donald (1983) showed that the annual mortality rate of breeding adult Arctic Skuas on Fair Isle increased from 11% per annum in 1973–75, when there was no shooting, to around 25% per annum in 1976–78, when shooting was resumed. Modelling indicated that the level of shooting in 1976–78 would have led to the extinction of the colony if it had been sustained. Presumably it was not, as numbers of Arctic Skuas on Fair Isle may have fallen further, but have not approached extinction.

INTERNATIONAL CONTEXT

The Arctic Skua has a high-latitude circumpolar breeding distribution, with large populations in Russia, Alaska, Canada, Greenland, Svalbard, Iceland and Norway (Table 3). None of these have been censused in detail. The breeding numbers in what are probably the three largest populations (Russia, Alaska and Canada) are a matter for guesswork. Even within Europe or the biogeographical population of the northeast Atlantic (see Stroud *et al.*, 2001), numbers are not well known in the main breeding areas (Table 3), making it difficult to assess the international importance of the Scottish population. The Scottish population represents only about 0.6–2.5% of the world population of 85,400–335,000 pairs. At a more local level, it represents about 6.1–13.9% of the biogeographical population of breeding numbers in the northeast Atlantic. By comparison,

Anker-Nilssen *et al.* (2000) estimated that 25,000–39,000 pairs of Arctic Skuas breed around the Barents Sea.

Despite having a circumpolar breeding range, the Arctic Skua is considered monotypic; there is little difference in plumage or biometrics even between Atlantic and Pacific populations. This lack of subspecific differentiation suggests that there may be extensive gene-flow between Arctic Skua colonies, with recruits moving to breed in areas some distance from where they were born. The plumage polymorphism of this species is well known, and shows a strong latitudinal cline in the relative frequency of the dark and pale morphs, with a greater proportion of dark morphs further south (Phillips, 2001). Similarly, there is a slight trend for Arctic Skuas breeding at higher latitudes to be larger. These trends indicate that there are genetic differences between populations at different latitudes, which could be taken as an indication of limited gene-flow, but it is possible that these patterns represent strong selection in opposite directions at high- and low-latitude breeding sites. Ringing has not yet provided much evidence of the extent to which birds move between populations. Although there are many recorded movements of birds ringed as chicks in one colony to breed in another colony, these movements tend to be over distances of tens of kilometres, rather than hundreds or thousands. Current molecular genetic studies may shed some light on this question in the near future.

Table 3 International context.

| Country or region | Number of pairs | | Year | Source |
	Min	Max		
Great Britain (Scotland)	2,100	2,100	1999–2002	Seabird 2000
Faeroes	500	1,000	Early 1990s	Phillips (2001)
Finland	400	400	1980s	Phillips (2001)
Greenland	1,000	10,000	1980s	Evans (1984)
Iceland	5,000	10,000	1990s	Hagemeijer & Blair (1997)
Norway	5,000	10,000	1990s	Hagemeijer & Blair (1997)
Norway (Svalbard)	1,000	1,000	1994	Anker-Nilssen *et al.* (2000)
Sweden	400	500	1980s	Phillips (2001)
Canada	10,000	100,000	1980s	Furness (1987)
Russia	50,000	100,000	1980s	Ilyichev & Zubakin (1988)
USA (Alaska)	10,000	100,000	1980s	Furness (1987)
Biogeographic region	*Min*	*Max*	*Min % GB*	*Max % GB*
NE Atlantic*	15,000	35,000	6.0%	14.0%
World	85,000	340,000	0.6%	2.5%

* Stroud *et al.* (2001)

Great Skua *Stercorarius skua*

Robert W. Furness and Norman Ratcliffe

INTRODUCTION

The Great Skua, or Bonxie, is famous for its aggressive defence of territory against human intruders. The world population of this species is small (now *c.*16,000 apparently occupied territories), and it has a very restricted breeding range in the northeast Atlantic. The largest numbers nest in Shetland, Orkney and Iceland. However, its population has been increasing since 1900, and it has progressively extended its breeding range northeast into the Barents Sea, and south into the islands of west Scotland. It nested for the first time in Ireland during Seabird 2000. Closely related species breed in the Antarctic and subantarctic, and show strong adaptations to cold conditions and a predatory lifestyle. In Scotland, Great Skuas nest on coastal moorland, often in loose groups of scattered nests, but with some colonies numbering thousands of pairs. When nesting at low density in small colonies, most birds in the colony feed by killing birds (Furness, 1987). However, when nesting in large colonies, the majority feed on fish, including fishery discards, and only a small proportion specialise in killing seabirds (Votier *et al.*, in press). Ringing has shown that Great Skuas from Shetland have emigrated to form colonies in many other areas as far away as north Russia, but the majority of chicks return to their natal colony to establish a breeding territory (Klomp & Furness, 1992).

CENSUS METHODS

Coverage of Great Skua breeding areas in Seabird 2000 was good in most regions, but small areas of possible breeding habitat in parts of west and central mainland Shetland and Caithness were not surveyed. According to Lloyd *et al.* (1991), coverage of skuas in the SCR Census (1985–88) was 'complete'. However, surveys of Great Skuas in Orkney were actually conducted in 1982 (Meek *et al.*, 1985) and Lloyd *et al.* (1991) adjusted the 1982 count using observed trends (Furness, 1986) to estimate population size in 1986 to be comparable with the survey in Shetland conducted in 1985–86 (Ewins *et al.*, 1987). Counts from all other areas used in the SCR Census were conducted in 1985–88. Operation Seafarer (1969–70) did not attempt to locate all inland nesting skuas so will have underestimated numbers (Cramp *et al.*, 1974). However, the proportion of Great Skuas nesting 'inland' is small, and major colonies in Shetland such as Foula, Hermaness (Unst), Fetlar and Noss were all surveyed completely in 1969. Small numbers nesting inland on mainland Shetland would have been overlooked. In addition, detailed counts of skuas were organised by the RSPB and others in 1974–75 (Everett, 1982) and in 1992 (Meek *et al.*, 1994; Sears *et al.*, 1995), whilst many major skua colonies have been censused regularly outwith these national surveys, so that trends are very clearly documented. Not all colonies were counted in the same year, but this should not cause problems, as Great Skuas that have nested in one colony have never been recorded moving to breed elsewhere in a subsequent year (Furness, 1987).

By comparison with most other seabird species, Great Skuas are relatively easy to census. Throughout the breeding season, but especially during incubation and early chick-rearing (early May–late June), they show very high territory attendance, with the territory hardly ever left unattended (Hamer & Furness, 1993; Caldow & Furness, 2000). Pairs that have lost eggs or young chicks almost invariably remain on territory and those that fail early (which is when most clutches are lost) will lay a replacement clutch. The aggressive defence of the territory against intruding humans is a well-known feature of skuas, but the assumption that all pairs show this behaviour can lead to inaccuracies in counting. In fact, some 10–40% of pairs do not attack human intruders (this proportion also varies between colonies and according to time in the breeding season and food availability), but will either circle above the territory or fly to a nearby lookout point outside the territory until the disturbance is over. Counting pairs by walking through Great Skua colonies and noting when birds attack tends to result in significant underestimates of numbers. The preferred census method is to observe undisturbed birds from a distance, preferably from a high vantage point. Thus counts tend to be of Apparently Occupied Territories (AOT). An AOT can be a pair with a nest, a pair, or a single bird in apparently suitable nesting habitat and showing signs of holding territory. Counts based on finding all nests are much more labour intensive, and even these may undercount numbers as nests are usually fairly well hidden and some late-laying birds are likely to be unavailable until a date by which early breeders may have lost clutches. Counts of Great Skuas are more difficult where there are no suitable high vantage points, or where the topography is dissected so that birds might incubate in hollows and not readily be seen from a distance. For example, the island of Foula provides easy counting conditions with high hills and generally even ground. Counting is more difficult at sites such as Yell (Shetland) or Hermaness where it is not easy to gain a clear view of large areas of the colony from a distance, and the terrain is dissected by gullies and ridges. In colonies where counting from a viewpoint is not practical, surveys tend to be undertaken along transects. These surveys are probably less accurate, especially in dense colonies, but use the same criteria for recognising AOTs as counts from a vantage point, and should generally produce similar results.

Weather conditions can affect count accuracy. In areas frequented by Great Skuas foggy conditions are common in summer, and some AOTs may have been missed during counts made in foggy

Great Skuas actively defend their territories against all intruders, which helps surveyors identify apparently occupied territories (AOT) (Pep Arcos)

weather. Some of the counts in 1999–2002, especially those in large areas with low densities of Great Skuas, were made in relatively poor weather.

Colony density will affect count accuracy. AOT counts are more difficult in dense colonies, and especially in colonies where non-breeders gather in clubs. Great Skuas tend to return to the exact part of the colony in which they were born, and there they congregate in clubs with other immatures. They usually return to the colony first when they are three or four years old, tending to return a little earlier in each subsequent season until they recruit at 5–12 years old (Klomp & Furness, 1992). Most birds take up territory near the club they frequented as non-breeders. Some first breed on the edge of a club, where such breeding attempts are usually unsuccessful. However, this can make counting AOTs rather difficult as it is not easy to distinguish between club birds, territory-holding club birds, and actual breeders.

Once a bird has recruited, it almost invariably returns to the same breeding territory every year. Divorces are relatively infrequent, and birds that do divorce rarely move more than 150 m and usually pair with a near neighbour (Catry & Furness, 1997). No breeding bird has ever been found to move to a new breeding site more than 1 km from its previous territory, so that local changes in numbers cannot be ascribed to redistribution of established breeding adults.

Great Skuas return to Scottish breeding sites in April, most lay during mid to late May, and chicks fledge in the latter half of July. The numbers of occupied territories are fairly stable from mid-May to late July. Whilst there can be late breeding attempts continuing into September or even October, most breeders leave their colonies during August. In some seasons when feeding conditions are poor, numbers begin to fall quite fast even during July. These seasonal patterns should not greatly affect the census datasets as almost all counts were made during the optimal period from mid-May to mid-July.

No formal measurements of Great Skua census accuracy have been made, but it is possible to gain an impression of the accuracy of counts by comparing independent counts made in one colony in the same or adjacent years. Breeding Great Skuas have a survival rate close to 90% per annum and it is extremely uncommon for a bird to take a year off and subsequently return to breed in later years (Catry *et al.*, 1998; Ratcliffe *et al.*, 2002). So the change in breeding numbers from one year to the next tends to be very small. The exception to this occurs in a small number of colonies where many birds may be shot over a short period of time. For example, this is suggested to be the reason for strong fluctuations in numbers on Fair Isle (Shetland), where periods of increasing numbers have often been followed by illegal persecution, reducing breeding numbers considerably (see below).

Independent counts made in the same year on Foula differed by 15% in 1974 (Furness, Ph.D. thesis; Everett; 1982), 0.2% in 1986 (Furness, unpubl.; Ewins *et al.*, 1987) and 5% in 1991 (Furness, unpubl.; Sears *et al.*, 1995). Similarly, counts made at other colonies in adjacent years have differed by 19% on Noss in 1969 and 1970 (Cramp *et al.*, 1974; Harris, 1976), by 14% on Handa in 2000 and 2001 (Mavor *et al.*, 2002), by 28% on Fair Isle in 1991 and 1992, and by 16% at Hermaness in 1974 and 1976 (Albon *et al.*, 1976). At St Kilda (Western Isles), the Seabird 2000 surveyors reported 168 AOT in 1999, but in 1996 there were 229 AOT and in 1997 there were 271 AOT (Phillips *et al.*, 1999a), while in 2000 there were 240 AOT (R. A. Phillips, *in litt.*). At Hermaness in 1974, a census by the reserve warden found 660 pairs, whereas Albon *et al.* (1976) found 786 pairs. The close agreement in most pairs of counts at Foula probably reflects the relatively easy counting conditions there, whilst the larger discrepancy at Hermaness is understandable given the much more dissected terrain and lack of vantage points to enable counting of undisturbed birds from a distance. The inconsistent counts from St Kilda are rather more difficult to explain, as counting conditions there are good. Perhaps the low counts by the Seabird 2000 team reflect their inexperience of Great Skuas and their focus of effort on cliff-nesting species. These comparisons suggest that differences in counts of up to at least 40% may result from counting errors rather than from change in numbers, especially in colonies where topography makes viewing difficult. Such large errors for a species thought to be rather easy to census demonstrate the need for great caution in interpretation of apparent trends when only a few counts have been made across a period of years.

CURRENT STATUS AND TRENDS

Most Great Skuas breeding in Britain and Ireland (71%) were in Shetland (Fig. 1). Shetland has always been the stronghold of the British and Irish population, but the proportion breeding there decreased from 96% in Operation Seafarer (1969–70) to 72% in the SCR Census (1985–88).

Table 1a   Numbers of breeding Great Skuas (AOT) in Scotland and Ireland 1969–2002.

Administrative area or country	Operation Seafarer (1969–70)	SCR Census (1985–88)	Seabird 2000 (1998–2002)	Percentage change since Seafarer	Percentage change since SCR
Shetland	2,968	5,447	6,846	131%	26%
Orkney	88	2,000[1]	2,209	2410%	10%
Western Isles–Comhairle nan eilean	19	113	345	1716%	205%
Caithness	0	2	5		150%
Sutherland	4	82	216	5300%	163%
Ross & Cromarty	0	1	8		700%
Lochaber	0	0	2		
Argyll & Bute	0	0	3		
Scotland Total	3,079	7,645	9,634	213%	26%
Co. Mayo	0	0	1		
Ireland Total	**0**	**0**	**1**		
Britain and Ireland Total	3,079	7,645	9,635	213%	26%

Note
[1] Extrapolated from a count of 1,652 AOT in 1982 (Meek *et al.*, 1985) using previous trend data (Furness, 1986) to estimate numbers in 1986 (see Lloyd *et al.*, 1991).

Table 1b: Numbers of breeding Great Skuas (AOT) in Orkney in 1982, 1992 and Seabird 2000 (1998–2002).
ID corresponds to areas shown in Fig. 1b.

ID	Local area	1982[1]	1992[2]	Seabird 2000 (1998–2002)	Percentage change since 1982	Percentage change since 1992
1	Auskerry	1	1	1	0%	0%
2	Burray (Hunda)	0	2	1		−50%
3	Calf of Eday	4	3	10	150%	233%
4	Cava	nc	1	1		0%
5	Eday	4	9	16	300%	78%
6	Eynhallow	1	3	4	300%	33%
7	Fara	6	7	5	−17%	−29%
8	Flotta	0	2	9		350%
9	Gairsay	3	2	2	−33%	0%
10	Hoy & South Walls	1,573	1,900	1,973	25%	4%
11	Mainland	24	25	50	108%	100%
12	Papa Westray	2	3	8	300%	167%
13	Rousay	13	31	81	523%	161%
14	Shapinsay	nc	1	2		100%
15	South Ronaldsay	2	2	5	150%	150%
16	Stronsay (Including Linga Holm)	8	15	22	175%	47%
17	Sule Skerry	nc	nc	1		
18	Swona	nc	nc	3		
19	Westray	6	12	15	150%	25%
	Total	1,647	2,019	2,209	34%	9%

Notes

[1] Totals derived from raw data held in Seabird Colony Register database. Meek *et al.* (1985) gave at total of 1,652 AOT.

[2] Totals derived from raw data held in Seabird Colony Register database except the count for Burray (Hunda), which is taken from Meek *et al.* (1994). Meek *et al.* (1994) gave a total of 2,018.

nc   not counted

Table 1c   Numbers of breeding Great Skuas (AOT) in Shetland in 1985–86, 1992 and Seabird 2000 (1998–2002).
ID corresponds to areas shown in Fig 1b.

ID	Local area	1985–86[1]	1992[2]	Seabird 2000 (1998–2002)	Percentage change since 1982	Percentage change since 1992
1	East Mainland	110	118	103	−6%	−13%
2	Fair Isle	84	110	143	70%	30%
3	Fetlar	291	523	593	104%	13%
4	Foula	2495	2174	2293	−8%	5%
5	North Mainland	348	218	293	−16%	34%
6	Papa Stour	14	24	48	243%	100%
7	South Mainland	421	1019	1454	245%	43%
8	Unst	1274	1567	1385	9%	−12%
9	West Mainland	96	73	135	41%	85%
10	Whalsay	1	2	15	1400%	650%
11	Yell	313	308	384	23%	25%
	Total	5447	6136	6846	26%	12%

Notes

[1] Data derived from raw data held on Seabird Colony Register database. Sears *et al.* (1992) gave a total of 5,647 AOT.

[2] Data taken from Sears *et al.* (1992).

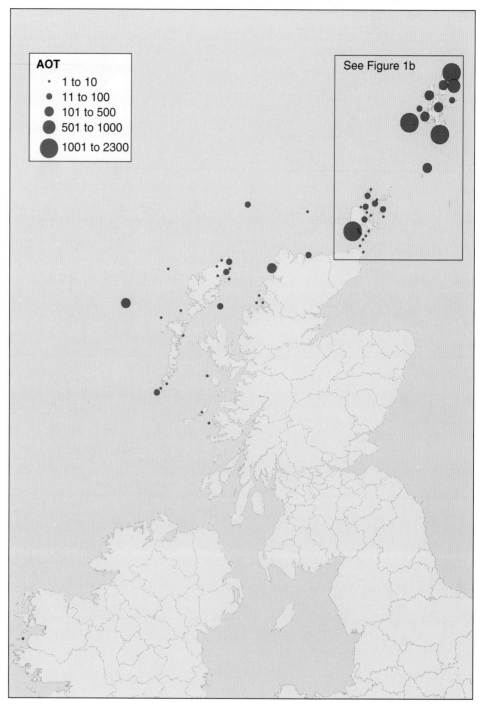

Figure 1a   Abundance and distribution of breeding Great Skuas in Britain and Ireland 1998–2002.

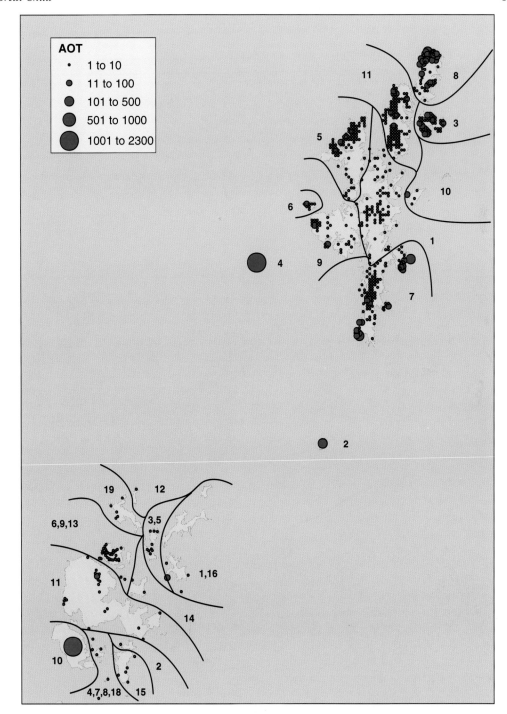

Figure 1b   Abundance and distribution of breeding Great Skuas (AOT) in Orkney and Shetland 1998–2002.
Numbers correspond to areas listed in Tables 1b, c; except Sule Skerry (no. 17, Orkney) that is situated 60km west of
Orkney (see fig 1a).

Table 2   Changes in the number of breeding Great Skuas (AOT) at major colonies or areas 1969–2002.

Colony/Area	AOT				Rank			
	Operation Seafarer (1969–70)	1982/85–86	1992	Seabird 2000 (1998–2002)	Seabird 2000 (1998–2002)	1992	1982/85–86	Operation Seafarer (1969–70)
Foula	1,786	2,495	2,174	2,293	1	1	1	1
Hoy	72	1,563	1,900	1,973	2	2	2	7
Unst	384	1,508	1,569	1,385	3	3	3	2
Fetlar	275	291	523	593	4	4	6	3
Noss	210	378	424	432	5	5	4	4
Yell	125	313	308	384	6	6	5	5
Fitful Head	13	c.200	c.300	327	7	7	7	9
North Roe	62	140	133	299	8	9	8	8
Bressay	92	115	248	275	9	8	9	6
St Kilda	10[1]	54	112	240[2]	10	10	12	10
Handa	3	66	103	195	11	12	11	12
Fair Isle	8[3]	84	110	143	12	11	10	11

Notes
[1] 1971
[2] 2000, Phillips (unpubl.)
[3] Fair Isle bird report

Orkney has become increasingly important and now holds 23% of breeding Great Skuas in Britain and Ireland, with 4% in the Western Isles (Table 1a).

Numbers increased on Shetland by 84% between Operation Seafarer (1969–70) and the SCR Census (1985–88), but by only 26% since (Table 1a). Growth rates in the smaller populations further south have been higher, so that the population in Scotland increased at higher rate than in Shetland, of 148% between 1969–70 and 1985–88, but at the same rate of 26% since. This suggests that the population in Scotland is approaching carrying capacity and may have reached it in some areas where population density is highest.

The largest colonies were similarly ranked in order of size during Seabird 2000 as they were in Operation Seafarer (1969–70) and the SCR Census (1985–88), with the exception of Hoy (Orkney) which now holds the second largest colony in Scotland, having been only the seventh largest in 1969–70 (Table 2). All major colonies increased in size between 1969–70 and 1985–88. But between the SCR Census and Seabird 2000 the size of the long-established colonies (e.g. on Foula, Unst, Fetlar, Noss) has tended to reach an equilibrium or decrease, whilst colonies established more recently have increased rapidly in size. In fact the net increase in population size in Shetland between the SCR Census (1985–88) and Seabird 2000 was entirely due to the growth of smaller existing colonies and the establishment of new ones.

It is unlikely that any Great Skua colony can sustain a rate of population growth in excess of c.7% per annum on the basis of local production of young (Phillips *et al.*, 1999a). On that basis, the rates of growth of several Great Skua colonies in the Western Isles, Caithness and Sutherland must be supported by a substantial immigration into these areas (presumably of birds born in Shetland and Orkney). Several new colonies have been founded in recent years in the west of Scotland and Western Isles, e.g., on Canna (Lochaber), the Flannan Isles (Western Isles), Barra (Western Isles), the Uists (Western Isles), the Treshnish Islands (Western Isles), Mull (Argyll & Bute), and Coll (Argyll & Bute), and some longer established colonies in these areas have grown rapidly (for example on Handa and St Kilda). However, some new, small, colonies in these areas have declined in numbers or disappeared completely. The single AOT in C. Mayo, Ireland (Fig. 1), represents the first breeding record from Britain and Ireland outside Scotland.

CAUSES OF CHANGE

Lloyd *et al.* (1991) identified human persecution and protection from it, together with changes in food availability caused by fisheries, as the main factors affecting Great Skua populations. These are probably still the most important influences. Great Skuas do accumulate high concentrations of contaminants, but there is no evidence that these affect survival rates, and any effect on breeding success is negligible. Loss of breeding habitat or disturbance can have local impacts, but these have been unimportant at the regional or national population scale. Ring recoveries show that some birds, especially juveniles, drown as a result of entanglement in fishing nets or on longlines, and some are shot on migration or in winter. Some birds die as a result of storms, and a few are killed in oil spills. However, none of these factors seems likely to determine breeding population size. As the numbers of Great Skuas have increased, they have also increased their geographical range through colonisation of new areas. However, the extent to which the range can spread south may be limited by temperature since these cold-adapted birds find direct sunshine and warm days stressful whilst incubating (Furness, 1987). In addition to temperature, the other main factors affecting their spread into new breeding areas and their rates of population growth may differ between administrative areas. For example, Great Skuas feed extensively on fisheries discards while breeding in Orkney and Shetland, but in the small colonies in west Scotland, and in Russia, nesting Great Skuas feed mainly on other seabirds. That the rates of increase in breeding numbers differ dramatically between regions implies either that there are major differences in demography between regions or that there are large net movements of birds born in one area and choosing to recruit in another. Probably both of these are true.

The initial growth in Great Skua numbers in Scotland during the 20th century can certainly be attributed to reduction in human persecution. With the advent of legal protection around 1900, large-scale shooting of Great Skuas ceased, and the current population increase in Scotland began at a rate of *c*.7% per annum. In recent years, licensed shooting has been carried out at a few colonies, including Foula and Noss, to remove Great Skuas from lambing parks (Furness, 1987), but numbers shot legally have been very small and inconsequential in terms of overall colony sizes. However, illegal shooting of breeding adults certainly still occurs at a few colonies, and occasionally by fishermen at sea. Some indirect evidence for the impact of shooting can be seen in the numbers of Great Skuas breeding on Fair Isle (Fig. 3). After a few years of growth in numbers, sharp decreases occurred in 1958, 1964–69, 1978, 1987, 1993 and 1998. At least in some of these years it is known that birds had been shot during the spring (e.g. Furness, 1987, Fair Isle Bird Observatory Rep. 1998). Ring recoveries also show that several ringed birds were found shot at the colony in many of these years. After 60 years of existence, the Fair Isle Great Skua colony had only increased to 143 AOT by 2001. Other colonies founded at a similar time have increased to much higher numbers, such as 210 AOT on Noss, 240 AOT at St Kilda, 270 AOT on Fetlar and 400 AOT on Hoy. It seems that shooting on Fair Isle has restricted the population size to less than half what it might now be without any persecution. There is also some, often circumstantial, evidence to suggest that breeding numbers at newly colonised sites failed to grow due to shooting, and this may apply to the small colonies in west Scotland where decreases occurred between the SCR Census (1985) and Seabird 2000 (Fig. 2). However, the numbers shot at large colonies (i.e. at Hermaness, Noss and Foula) have almost certainly been too few to cause reductions in growth or decreases in breeding numbers (Fig. 3; see also Furness, 1987). Clearly other processes that are strongly density-dependent have been acting.

The most likely density-dependent effects are related to food abundance and availability, and to the opportunity to recruit into densely occupied colonies. Great Skuas are highly opportunistic in diet and feeding methods, but also show a very high degree of individual specialisation. Within

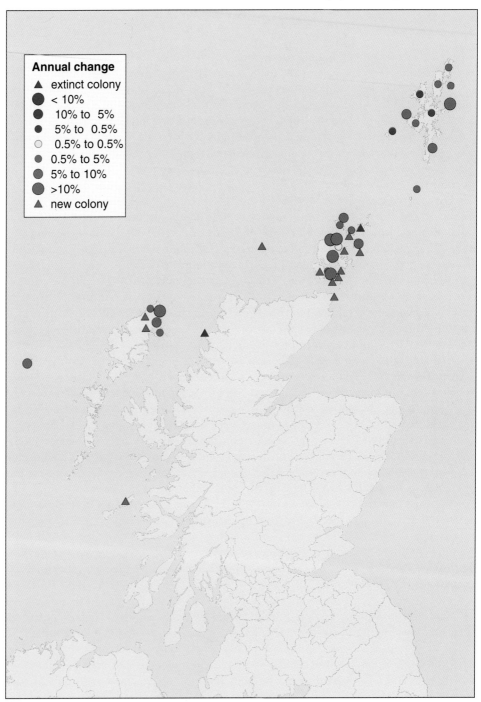

Figure 2   Changes in the number of breeding Great Skuas (AOT) at all colonies (except in Orkney and Shetland where change is denoted for each count area—see Fig. 1b and Tables 1b, c for definitions) from 1979–88 to 1998–2002.

Great Skua attempting to steal food from a Northern Gannet (Russell Wynn)

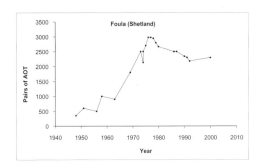
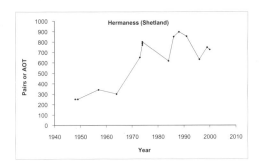

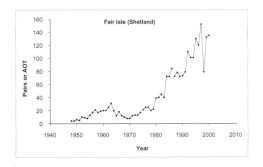
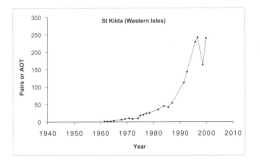

Figure 3   Numbers of breeding Great Skuas (AOT or pairs) at colonies where repeated counts have been conducted during 1948–2001.

breeding pairs, partners tend to share feeding specialisations. Diets also vary between colonies according to food availabilities. In Iceland and the Faeroes, Great Skuas kill large numbers of seabirds, scavenge on a wide range of foods including goose-barnacles and take fish, by catching them for themselves or by kleptoparasitising other seabirds (particularly gannets, gulls and auks) and by scavenging discards from fishing vessels. They also take a wide range of minor food items such as squid, rabbits, bird eggs, terrestrial invertebrates and berries. Around most Scottish colonies, they feed much less by killing birds, with a diet composed primarily of fish, many of which are taken as fishery discards. Predation on birds tends to be more widespread within the Great Skua population at colonies where their numbers are still small, and rapidly increasing, such as St Kilda (Phillips *et al.*, 1997). At the largest colonies, the diet is predominantly of fish, although predation on birds increases in periods when fish availability is reduced (Hamer *et al.*, 1991; Bearhop *et al.*, 2000, 2001). Some, but by no means all, bird specialists will establish a feeding territory on a nearby area of cliff where they will exclude conspecifics from hunting on the seabirds living in that area. This behaviour is much more commonly seen in subantarctic and Antarctic populations of skuas (Young, 1963, 1978).

Availability of sandeels, discards and seabird prey all increased in the northwest North Sea during the 1960s and 1970s. This trend may have allowed the Great Skua population in Shetland and Orkney to grow to higher levels than might have been sustainable in earlier decades. However, in the 1980s the local Shetland stock of sandeels decreased in abundance, as did stocks of gadoids such as cod, haddock and whiting. The reduction in those stocks led to a decrease in amounts of fish discarded, so that the increasing numbers of Great Skuas were subjected to reduced food supply from the 1980s. During the mid-1980s the breeding success of Great Skuas at Shetland was severely reduced (Hamer *et al.*, 1991), as was adult survival rate at Foula (Ratcliffe *et al.*, 2002). As Great Skuas do not breed until about 5–12 years old, any reduction in breeding success would not directly affect breeding numbers until at least 5–10 years later. Therefore, the immediate changes in breeding numbers of Great Skuas at Foula can be attributed to changes in adult survival rates and levels of recruitment, including the balance between immigration and emigration (Ratcliffe *et al.*, 2002). Numbers of non-breeders attending clubs at Foula fell dramatically, and numbers of AOTs declined (though less than expected given the severe drop in numbers of non-breeders and the increased adult mortality), suggesting that recruitment continued despite these adverse conditions (Klomp & Furness, 1992). These changes can all be related to the approximate 80% decrease in the sandeel stock at Shetland during the period 1985–1990 (Furness, 2002; Furness & Tasker, 2000), together with a progressive decrease in amounts of haddock and whiting discards, and an increased reproductive effort by breeding Great Skuas attempting to compensate for reduced food abundance (Ratcliffe *et al.*, 1998b). In Shetland, Great Skuas feed very extensively on fishery discards throughout the breeding season, but particularly when sandeel availability decreases (usually in June; Hudson & Furness, 1988, 1989). Subsequent analysis of the diet and breeding success of Great Skuas in Shetland suggests that the declining quantities of haddock and whiting being discarded by the whitefish fisheries in the northwest North Sea have also been contributing to the food shortages experienced by Great Skuas in recent years, especially where competition is high in the larger colonies, which is consistent with discards now forming the majority of the diet at colonies in Shetland (Furness, Votier and others; unpubl.). In contrast to the situation in Shetland, Great Skuas on Handa have maintained a high adult survival rate, and high breeding success, as well as a rapid growth in breeding numbers, but the diet at that colony consists more of seabirds than of fish (Furness, unpubl.).

In Shetland the fact that large and densely populated colonies of Great Skuas have decreased in size, whilst small colonies have continued to grow, suggests there may be a degree of density-dependent competition for food. However, the evidence for this is unclear. Great Skuas do not consume sufficiently large quantities of sandeels to deplete this food resource, but interference competition over sandeel balls probably does occur. There is also strong evidence of competition between Great Skuas scavenging discards behind fishing vessels (Hudson & Furness, 1988, 1989).

Aspects that seem likely to be important but remain unresolved include the importance of winter diet in Great Skua population dynamics, and the interactions during summer between Great Skuas and Great Black-backed Gulls. Migration studies and observations at sea in winter suggest that Great Skuas may feed predominantly by scavenging at fishing vessels in southern European and northwest African fisheries, and this food supply may affect the body condition of birds and so may influence survival and subsequent breeding. There is also a suggestion from the data on colony size and from observed behavioural interactions that Great Skuas and Great Black-backed Gulls conflict when breeding. The Great Black-backed Gulls that successfully dominate Great Skuas (by chasing any skuas that come near their nest or chicks, and breed successfully in isolated territories surrounded by breeding Great Skuas) are predominantly bird-specialists feeding mainly on Atlantic Puffins, whereas the Great Black-backed Gulls killed by Great Skuas appear to be those that feed on fish (especially discards) and breed colonially (see also Hudson, 1982). It is unclear from the national survey data whether the presence of an established population of Great Black-backed Gulls inhibits colonisation by Great Skuas.

Although birds form only a small part of the diet of Great Skuas in Shetland and Orkney, this predation can have a very pronounced impact on populations of their seabird prey, especially when periods of reduced sandeel stocks or reduced fishery discard rates can lead to high predation rates on birds such as Black-legged Kittiwakes, storm-petrels, auks, and even Northern Fulmars and Great Black-backed Gulls (see relevant species' chapters). The reductions in numbers of these major seabird prey populations may in the longer term influence the numbers of Great Skuas that can be sustained.

INTERNATIONAL CONTEXT

The Great Skua breeding population has now increased to *c*.16,000 pairs (Table 3). The accuracy of this total is constrained by the few counts made of the relatively large numbers in Iceland and by rapid growth of numbers in remote areas such as the Barents Sea, where populations may already be larger than indicated by the most recent published estimates. Nevertheless, 16,000 pairs represents an 18% increase over the previous estimate of 13,600 pairs (Lloyd *et al.*, 1991), and this is mostly due to the continued growth of breeding numbers in Scotland. Almost two-thirds of the entire world population of Great Skuas now breed in Shetland and Orkney. Iceland holds most of the rest (Table 3), although numbers in the far north (Barents Sea) are now growing rapidly and are becoming a significant part of the world population.

Although the population in Iceland appears to have remained fairly stable over many decades, numbers of Great Skuas elsewhere in the North Atlantic have increased dramatically. Around 1900, the species was close to extinction in the Faeroes and in Shetland, as large numbers of adults were shot in the 1880s and 1890s by Victorian collectors. In the Faeroes the population was reduced to just four pairs and by 1900 only two colonies remained in Shetland, on Foula and on Unst. Following protection, these numbers grew, and the species has slowly spread to other areas. The spread from Foula and Unst led to colonisation of most of Shetland and then Orkney, and eventually of the north and west of Scotland. The species then spread to areas further north, colonising north and west Norway, Bear Island, Svalbard, Jan Mayen and northern Russia. In all of these areas, birds that had been ringed in Foula as chicks or non-breeders have been found nesting. Rates of increase in Shetland began to fall from the 7% per annum during the period 1900–1950, whilst emigration has led to more rapid rates of increase in most of the newly colonised areas.

Curiously, there seems to be no evidence from the moderate amount of ringing of Great Skuas in Iceland to demonstrate that Icelandic Great Skuas have colonised any other country. The growth of the Great Skua population in the Faeroes appears to have ceased many decades ago, and only small numbers remain. Therefore, the growth of the world population of Great Skuas has been largely, or perhaps almost entirely, a consequence of the expansion of the British population. This might, however, simply reflect the relatively small numbers of Great Skuas ringed in Iceland compared with the much larger numbers ringed in Shetland. By contrast with the rapid expansion of range northwards, southward spread of breeding Great Skuas seems to have been inhibited. This may perhaps be related to the polar adaptations of skuas, making them able to tolerate low temperatures better than milder climates, and possibly also to persecution in some newly colonised areas of Scotland. Rates of population growth have been high in Svalbard, Bear Island and Norway, and it seems likely that numbers in these new, higher latitude, colonies will continue to increase. Hence, the centre of breeding distribution may shift northwards, particularly if numbers in Scotland decline due to reductions in discarding rates in the future. The Great Skuas colonising high latitudes appear to be feeding mainly on other birds, and this limited diet may only sustain relatively small numbers of skuas. This prediction is based on the observation that large colonies of Great Skuas in Scotland obtain most food from discards and sandeels, resources that are not generally available at high latitudes. Whether Great Skuas in the Arctic can adapt to feed on widely abundant fish such as capelin has yet to be seen.

Table 3   International context.

Country or region	Number of pairs	Year	Source
Great Britain (Scotland)	9,600	1999–2002	Seabird 2000
Republic of Ireland	1	1999–2000	Seabird 2000
Faeroes	270	1980s–1990s	del Hoyo *et al.* (1996); Hagemeijer & Blair (1997)
Iceland	5,400	1984–85	Lund-Hansen & Lange (1991)
Norway	80	1995	Anker-Nilssen *et al.* (2000); Vader (1994); R.T. Barrett (*in litt.*)
Norway (Bear Island)	50	1995	Anker-Nilssen *et al.* (2000)
Norway (Jan Mayen)	10	1995	Gabrielsen *et al.* (1997)
Norway (Svalbard)	300	1995	Anker-Nilssen *et al.* (2000)
Russia	10	1995	Hagemeijer & Blair (1997); Anker-Nilssen *et al.* (2000)

Biogeographic region	Number of pairs		% GB
World*	16,000		60.0%

* Stroud *et al.* (2001)

Mediterranean Gull *Larus melanocephalus*

Matthew Parsons

INTRODUCTION

The Mediterranean Gull is the most recent addition to the breeding seabirds of Britain and Ireland. Yet it is probably more familiar to birdwatchers as a passage migrant and winter visitor, because although breeding numbers have increased in recent decades, its population in these islands is little more than 100 pairs, mostly on the south and southeast coasts of England.

Almost entirely restricted to the West Palearctic, the centre of the Mediterranean Gull's breeding population is the northwest shores of the Black Sea, particularly in the Ukraine, where current estimates place the population as *c.*75,000 breeding pairs (Ardamatskaya, 1998). Elsewhere in Europe, the main colonies are in France, Greece, Belgium, The Netherlands and Italy. The species winters largely on coastal waters of the Black Sea and the Mediterranean, and on the Atlantic coast of southwest Europe.

The range of the Mediterranean Gull has expanded quite markedly over the last 50 years. Westward expansion commenced in Hungary, where it was regularly breeding by 1953, then into Germany (regular breeding by 1963), Belgium (by 1969) and The Netherlands by 1970 (Bekhuis *et al.*, 1997). Range expansion also occurred eastwards during the 1970s and 1980s.

The first breeding occurrence of Mediterranean Gull in Britain was in 1968, at Needs Ore Point in Hampshire (Taverner, 1970). Thereafter, a pair bred at Dungeness in Kent, in 1979, increasing to two pairs by 1985. A site in north Kent (which was later to become established as one of the major colonies in England) was colonised in 1983. Also during this period a handful of other breeding attempts was made, including pairings with Black-headed Gulls. The first breeding attempt in Ireland was in Antrim in 1995, followed in 1996 by a pair nesting in Co. Wexford.

The Mediterranean Gull nests in small to large colonies (up to several thousand pairs in the Ukraine), among other gulls or terns when relatively few pairs are present, as is the case in Britain and Ireland, where Black- headed Gulls are the usual associates. It favours sparsely vegetated, low-lying islands of coastal lagoons or estuaries, and breeding success is often reduced by tidal inundation of nests. The nest is a shallow depression lined with grass and a few feathers. Two or three eggs are laid, but replacement clutches are exceptional (Peter L. Meininger, pers. comm.). During breeding in northwest Europe, food appears to be chiefly terrestrial invertebrates, particularly earthworms but also insects (Meininger *et al.*, 1991; Chris Cockburn, pers. comm.); at other times marine fish and molluscs are usually taken.

CENSUS METHODS

The habit of Mediterranean Gulls of nesting within large colonies of other species, most usually Black-headed Gulls, may lead to some pairs being missed, and therefore to an underestimate of the population. Furthermore, it has been the experience of some observers that a small number of visible pairs of adult birds at a colony can belie a far larger number of actual nests (Peter L. Meininger, pers. comm.). An additional potential source of error may arise because of the habit of adults leaving the colony to feed, whilst the chicks remain (unobtrusively) in crèches (Peter L. Meininger, pers. comm.). Nevertheless, the degree to which any underestimates may have occurred is unlikely to have changed with time. Contrarily, the relative rarity of the Mediterranean Gull as a breeding species and birdwatchers' attention to rarities will have acted to reduce underestimates in Seabird 2000. This is also likely to be true for the SCR Census (1985–88), although it is conceivable that during that census observers were less familiar with the species than now and may have overlooked it.

Potentially more problematic is the gulls' tendency to move between breeding sites from one year to the next. This was minimised in Seabird 2000 by aiming to survey such species in the same year, although in practice some sites had to be counted in other years. There is therefore a possibility that a limited amount of 'double-counting' occurred, although all the larger colonies were counted in the same year, so the overall effect of this is likely to be small. Given the interest in the species, most colonies have been counted in most years. This has permitted a greater degree of temporal coordination of count data across the species' range, and has enabled us to analyse, to a fair degree of precision, the rate and spread of colonisation (Fig. 2).

This account includes information on numbers and distribution of breeding Mediterranean Gulls from the time of its colonisation in 1968 until 2002, but it should be noted that coverage was less complete in 2001–02 than in other years of the Seabird 2000 census. This was due to the restriction in access to the countryside that resulted from the outbreak of foot and mouth disease during 2001, and to the possibility that further records of breeding in most recent years will come to light after this text was prepared.

Around 65% of breeding records during Seabird 2000 were collected either during the ideal monitoring period of 15 May–30 June or when there was definite proof of breeding, such as eggs in a nest. Some 27% of records were from unknown dates, and 8% were from dates only marginally outside the recommended period. In total, 69% of records were of Apparently Occupied Nests, 12% of Apparently Occupied Territories (where actual nests or incubation behaviour could not be observed), and 19% not attributed to either of these categories, being simply recorded as 'proved breeding'. Therefore, we can have a fair degree of confidence that the majority of records represent actual breeding attempts and have expressed numbers as AONs, the prescribed count unit for gulls during Seabird 2000.

On the periphery of its breeding range, as is Britain and Ireland, it is not uncommon for Mediterranean Gull to hybridise with other species, most usually Black-headed Gulls (in colonies of which the Mediterranean Gull often nests). A few instances of this have been recorded in England, although none were during the Seabird 2000 census, and all figures presented refer to pairs in which both adults were Mediterranean Gulls.

In the text and analysis, the term 'colony' is defined, for this species, as an agglomeration of AONs within a particular location. In some cases a few sites in close proximity may hold one or a few breeding pairs and they will have been defined as a single 'colony', particularly where it is judged that annual movement between sites is probable.

CURRENT STATUS AND TRENDS

The results indicate that there were 113 pairs of Mediterranean Gull breeding in Britain and Ireland during the Seabird 2000 census, with 108 AON present in Great Britain, and five AON in Ireland (Table 1, Fig. 1). This represents a dramatic increase since the SCR Census (1985–88), when just one pair bred (Lloyd *et al.*, 1991).

New sites were colonised at an increasing rate from the late 1980s (Fig. 2), and today the population is distributed across some 26 separate colonies in 13 administrative areas (Table 1, Fig. 1). Most colonies were on the south and southeast coasts of England (from Dorset, east and north to Norfolk), accounting for 103 AON within 19 colonies. The remaining pairs occur in Cambridgeshire, Lancashire and West Yorkshire, in England, and Co. Wexford and Co. Down in Ireland.

It is evident that the colonisation of Britain and Ireland by the Mediterranean Gull has occurred along a 'frontline' across southern and southeast England, and whilst the centre of the population has not moved from there, the most recent areas to be colonised include those further west and north, with the first breeding in Lancashire in 1990 (followed by another new site there in 1998), Co. Antrim in 1995, Co. Wexford in 1996, West Yorkshire in 1999, Cambridgeshire in 2001 and Co. Down in 2002. It therefore appears that there is limited continued expansion in range within Britain and Ireland, although the potential for further expansion is unknown.

The size of the largest colony in any year initially ranged 1–3 AON from 1979 to 1989, rising to 5–6 AON in 1990–95. From 1996, however, there was a marked increase in the population, with a colony in Kent holding 16 AON in 1997, and a colony in Hampshire holding 38 AON in 2000 and 47 in 2001. In 1985–2000 the population increased nearly five fold, whereas the number of colonies only doubled, indicating that the increase in population over that time was largely accounted for by the increasing size of existing colonies, rather than by colonisation of new sites or expansion in range (Fig. 2). Indeed, between 1999 and 2000 the population rose from 61 to 93 AON, whilst the number of colonies actually decreased slightly, from 16 to 14.

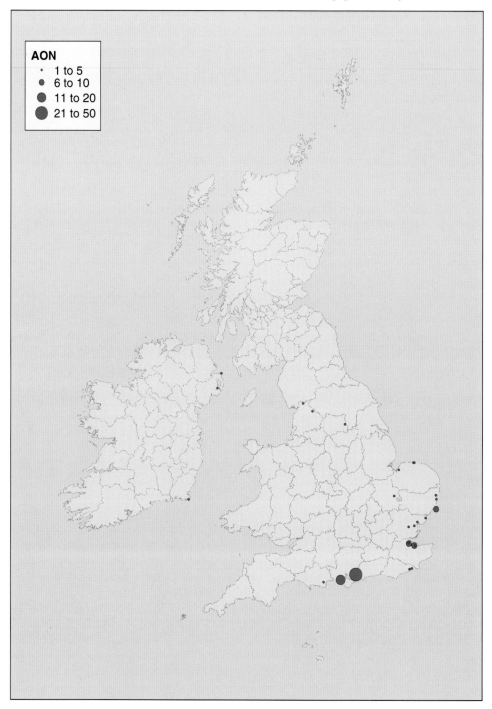

Figure 1   Abundance and distribution of breeding Mediterranean Gulls in Britain and Ireland 1999–2002.

Table 1   Numbers of breeding Mediterranean Gulls (AON) in Britain and Ireland 1969–2002.

Administrative area or country	SCR Census (1985–88)	Seabird 2000 AON	Year
Norfolk	0	3	1999–2000
Suffolk	0	8	1999–2001
Cambridgeshire	0	1	2001
Essex	0	9	2000
Kent	1	23	2000
East Sussex	0	6	2000–01
Hampshire	0	43	2000, 2002
Isle of Wight	0	6	2000
Dorset	0	5	2000
West Yorkshire	0	1	1999
Lancashire	0	3	1999, 2001
England Total	**1**	**108**	**1999–2002**
Co. Down	0	2	2002
Co. Wexford		3	2002
All-Ireland Total	**0**	**5**	**2002**
Britain and Ireland Total	**1**	**113**	**1999–2002**

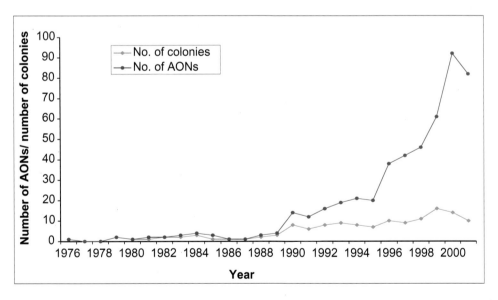

Figure 2   Number of colonies and total number of breeding pairs (AON) of Mediterranean Gull in Britain and Ireland, 1976–2001.

CAUSES OF CHANGE

The initial colonisation of Britain and Ireland by the Mediterranean Gull was part of a wider range expansion of the species west into Europe from its core on the shores of the Black Sea (Meininger & Bekhuis, 1990; Bekhuis *et al.*, 1997). Having expanded from its centre of population into Hungary and Germany during the 1950s and 1960s, regular breeding became established in Belgium by 1969 and in The Netherlands by 1970 (Bekhuis *et al.*, 1997), in southern France by 1981 and northern and western France by the mid-1980s (Yésou, 1997). Clearly, the first occurrence of breeding in Britain and Ireland, in Hampshire in 1968, and the establishment of regular breeding in the British Isles by 1979, coincided with this westward expansion through Europe. The expansion of the breeding population in Britain (and, to a lesser extent, Ireland) more or less coincided with an apparent increase in the overwintering population of the species there (Britton, 1986) and the breeding range and non-breeding aggregations are broadly similar, concentrated along the south and southeast coasts of England, and along the east coast of Ireland. A corresponding increase in the non-breeding population in other northwest European countries started in the 1960s and 1970s (Cramp & Simmons, 1983), and intensified during the 1980s and particularly the 1990s. (e.g. Meininger *et al.*, 1993).

The core breeding population of the Mediterranean Gull, around the shores of the Black Sea, has undergone periodic and sometimes dramatic fluctuations in size (Chernichko, 1993). It increased from fewer than 40,000 pairs in 1953 to around 155,000 pairs in 1966, then declined, to 17,000 pairs in 1974, increased markedly in 1975–83 (to 335,000 pairs), then declined such that in 1993 fewer than 20,000 pairs bred. By 1995, however, the population had risen to 70,000 pairs and the most recent estimate, in 1998, puts the population at around 75,000 pairs (Ardamatskaya, 1998). The colonisation of Britain and Ireland may be a consequence of the cyclic fluctuations of the Black Sea population and subsequent spread into northwest Europe. The exact relationship between the fluctuations of the Black Sea population and the colonisation of western Europe is a matter for speculation. It has been suggested (Isenmann *et al.*, in press) that the initial spread westward, in the 1950s and 1960s, was a result of high productivity (and consequent population increase) of the Black Sea colonies, but since then the increases in western Europe may in part have been a consequence of deteriorating conditions, due to pollution and disturbance, around the Black Sea colonies, forcing birds to move farther afield for suitable sites.

Information from ringing (and more usefully colour-ringing, since the recovery rate for the species is very low) has helped to shed light on the origins of the population change. Data from ringing on the origins of birds that breed in Britain and Ireland are scarce, but interestingly the first Mediterranean Gull to breed in Britain, in Hampshire in 1968, was ringed as a chick in the then East Germany, in 1966 (Taverner, 1970). Sightings of colour-ringed birds breeding in England show that they include birds hatched from colonies in The Netherlands and Belgium, and one bird that bred in Belgium and moved to breed on the Isle of Wight three years later (Peter L. Meininger, *in litt.*). Sightings of non-breeding colour-ringed birds and ringing recoveries in Britain and Ireland show that they originate from breeding colonies in The Netherlands and Belgium (involving 291 individual birds up to February 2002; Peter L. Meininger, *in litt.*), Germany (five records; Toms, 2002), Hungary (30 records; Varga, *et al.*, 1999), the former Yugoslavia (one record; Toms, 2002) and Italy (one record; Baccetti *et al.*, 1999). In turn, movements of birds hatched in the Black Sea colonies to northwest Europe have been demonstrated from ringing (Cramp & Simmons, 1983; Tekke, 1976). The extent to which the rapid expansion of the British population be attributed to immigration from nearby breeding colonies (particularly The Netherlands and Belgium) or to immigration directly from the Black Sea population is open to question, but evidence exists only for the former.

Another important parameter in determining population change is the breeding success of individuals and subsequent survival of progeny to breeding age and beyond. Too few data exist to tell us much about survival. Information on the number of chicks fledged by British and Irish Mediterranean Gulls is limited, due to various logistical difficulties involved in its collection. Without further data it is impossible to determine whether productivity in the British colonies has been sufficient to cause the increases in breeding numbers seen over the last decade or so. However, the limited information available suggests that at the main colonies productivity can be relatively high, with the large Hampshire colony recording a mean 0.86 chicks per nest in 1998, 1.1 in 2000 and 0.5 in 2001. Unfortunately, insufficient information on inter-colony movements from ringed birds has emerged to further illuminate the dynamics of the population. A factor that was suggested to contribute to the Mediterranean Gull's rapid population increase in France was the high proportion of young birds breeding (Yésou, 1997); that is birds in their second summer, the youngest age at which the species breeds (Cramp & Simmons, 1983). Data on the proportion of young breeders in British and Irish colonies is incomplete, but this phenomenon may help to explain the species' rapid expansion in these isles.

As with other ground-nesting species of seabirds that locate their nests close to the high-tide mark, Mediterranean Gulls are susceptible to nest failure due to tidal inundation, particularly during unusually high spring tides. This is, of course, a natural phenomenon and probably the major cause of nest failure. It is tempting to speculate whether colonies along coasts with smaller tidal ranges, such as those on the Mediterranean or Black Seas, suffer as much from tidal inundation as do those along Atlantic coasts, and to what extent this affects the overall dynamics of population change. Other threats to breeding success include loss of eggs (and chicks) to natural predators (e.g. crows, foxes) and to egg collectors.

Several questions remain concerning the Mediterranean Gull population in Britain and Ireland that merit further study and analysis. Perhaps foremost among these is the degree of potential for further expansion of the species within Britain and Ireland, both in terms of numbers and range. Further information is required on inter-colony movements, productivity, recruitment and survival, in order to attain a better understanding of population dynamics and to predict future trends. The possible effects of climate change pose interesting questions: if the predicted increased storminess of our coastal waters becomes a reality, how will species that nest close to the water's edge be affected? Will a rising sea level cover existing nest sites; are there alternative nest sites? Given the widespread colonisation of the species across Europe during recent decades, and the observed complex pattern of movements between colonies and during the non-breeding season, it is perhaps time to undertake a comprehensive analysis of ringing and population data to better understand the past and possible future changes in the world population of the Mediterranean Gull.

INTERNATIONAL CONTEXT

Despite the impressive expansion in range and development of breeding colonies in Britain and Ireland (and elsewhere in northwest Europe) over recent decades, the breeding population is but a tiny fraction of the Atlantic biogeographic population (Table 2). The latter is estimated at 184,000 pairs, whereas the British total is 108 AON and the all-Ireland total is 5 AON. The vast majority of the European breeding population remains in its traditional location, on the Ukranian shores of the Black Sea (Bekhuis *et al.*, 1997).

Adult Mediterranean Gull breeding at Lady's Island Lake, Wexford (Dave Daly)

Table 2   International context.

Country or region	Number of pairs			
	Min	Max	Year	Source
Great Britain, Isle of Man and Channel Isles	108	108	1999–2002	Seabird 2000
All Ireland	5	5	2002	Seabird 2000
Albania	0	1,000	1962	BirdLife International / EBCC (2000)
Austria	12	21	1995–97	BirdLife International / EBCC (2000)
Belarus	0	20	1988–98	BirdLife International / EBCC (2000)
Belgium	300	300	2001	Vermeersch *et al.* (2002)
Czech Republic	13	15	1998	Chytil (1999)
Denmark	1	1	1998	Fritze (1999)
France	2218	2228	2000	Isenmann *et al.* (in press)
Germany	66	66	1998	Boschert (1999)
Greece	1,350	1,350	1998	Goutner *et al.* (1999)
Hungary	185	185	1998	Varga *et al.* (1999)
Italy	900	900	1992	Boldreghini *et al.* (1992)
Netherlands	1,150	1,150	2001	Meininger (2002)
Poland	1	1	1989	Meininger & Bekhuis 1990)
Romania	100	100	1994	Ceico & Tanase (1994)
Russia	3,530	13,236	1970s–1980s	Ardamatskaya (1999)
Slovakia	78	78	1998	Chytil (1999)
Spain	1	1	1988	Meininger & Bekhuis (1990)
Switzerland	0	2	1993–96	BirdLife International / EBCC (2000)
Turkey	4,900	5,500	1991–98	Karauz & Kiraç (1999)
Ukraine	75,000	75,000	1998	Ardamatskaya (1999)
Biogeographic region	**Min**	**Max**	**Min % GB**	**Max % GB**
Europe (excl. Russia & Turkey)*	81,000	81,000	0.1%	0.1%
World	90,000	100,000	0.1%	0.1%

*Stroud *et al.* (2001)

Mediterranean Gull chick hatched at Lady's Island Lake, Wexford (Steve Newton)

Black-headed Gull *Larus ridibundus*

Timothy E. Dunn

INTRODUCTION

The Black-headed Gull is the most widespread seabird breeding in Britain and Ireland, with similar numbers breeding inland as on the coast. The majority of the breeding population is resident, with numbers being greatly bolstered during winter by birds from northern and eastern Europe, especially in east and southeast England (Wernham *et al.*, 2002). Black-headed Gulls breed throughout the middle latitudes of the Palearctic and have recently formed a breeding outpost in northeastern North America (Montevecchi *et al.*, 1987). Britain and Ireland hold approximately 6% of the world breeding population.

Black-headed Gulls tend to nest on open ground and occasionally in low trees and bushes, in colonies from a few to over 10,000 apparently occupied nests (AON) (Baxter & Rintoul, 1953; Vine & Sergeant, 1948). Habitats such as wetlands, bogs, marshes and artificial ponds are favoured breeding sites, but dry areas adjacent to water are also used (Hagemeijer & Blair, 1997).

During the 20th century, Black-headed Gulls have exploited the products of a burgeoning human population. Flooded gravel pits, reservoirs and sewage farms have provided additional habitat for feeding, nesting and loafing, but most importantly they were able to exploit the wide range of human-based food resources such as fishery discards and domestic waste. During winter, in areas of intense farming such as southeast England, wide-scale tillage has provided a readily available source of invertebrate prey.

These increases in food availability probably fuelled the increase in the breeding population in England and Wales, witnessed by successive surveys of Black-headed Gulls breeding inland and on the coast, in 1938 (Hollom, 1940), 1958 (Gribble, 1962) and 1973 (Gribble, 1976). The total population of England and Wales increased by 38% in 1938–58 and by 52% between 1958 and 1973 (Fig. 3). The total of 105,200 AON in 1973 was more than double the number found in the 1938 survey. An influx of birds from continental Europe may have helped boost the population during this period, especially in southern England (Aspinall, 1993). Subsequently, the population in England and Wales declined by a maximum of 20% between 1973 and the SCR Census (1985–88). Changes in the population of England and Wales mirrored those in other northern European countries during the latter half of the 20th century (Fredriksson, 1979; Risberg *et al.*, 1990; Hagemeijer & Blair, 1997; Vermeersch *et al.*, 2002).

Prior to Seabird 2000, the population of Black-headed Gulls in Britain and Ireland had only ever been incompletely surveyed. During Operation Seafarer, in 1969–70 (Cramp *et al.*, 1974), complete coverage of coastal colonies was achieved, but no inland colonies were counted, and these hold just under half of the Black-headed Gulls breeding in Britain and Ireland (see below). Both coastal and inland colonies were surveyed during the SCR Census (1985–88: Lloyd *et al.*, 1991), but inland coverage was incomplete, and so only provided a minimum estimate of the number of Black-headed Gulls nesting away from the coast. The number of Black-headed Gulls breeding on the coasts of Britain and Ireland increased by just 4% between Operation Seafarer (1969–70) and the SCR Census (1985–88), from 74,927 AON to 77,573 AON. However, this apparent stability masked considerable geographic variation in trends, with numbers in Scotland falling by half, whilst concurrently increasing by 17% in England and 25% in Wales, and almost doubling in Ireland. Over a similar period (1968–71 to 1988–91), the breeding distribution of Black-headed Gulls (measured as the number of 10-km squares occupied by breeding birds) decreased by 19% in Britain and 48% in Ireland (Sharrock, 1976; Gibbons *et al.*, 1993; Table 3).

CENSUS METHODS

During Seabird 2000 the recommended census unit for Black-headed Gulls was the Apparently Occupied Nest (AON). Counts of AONs were conducted from either within the colony or from a suitable vantage point. Black-headed Gulls nesting at Britain's largest colony, on the marshes of the Ribble Estuary (Lancashire), were surveyed using sample quadrat counts of AONs, by entering accessible areas of the colony and using remote counts from vantage points, where the saltmarshes and mudflats were too dangerous to access. When counting from a vantage point, surveyors can usually only identify nests that are attended by an incubating or brooding adult, thus temporarily unattended nests will be missed. In order to avoid underestimating the number of AONs from vantage point counts, nests in a sample of accessible sub-colonies were counted from both within the colony and a vantage point outside the colony. A correction factor derived from the average ratio of the two counts within each sub-colony was used to correct vantage point counts of AONs from inaccessible areas of the colony. However, despite the survey of the Ribble Estuary being comprehensive, it may have slightly underestimated the colony size, as some areas were surveyed in June 1999 after flooding by spring tides caused major redistribution and loss of nesting pairs. The colonies at Insh Marshes (Badenoch & Strathspey) and Loch of Kinnordy (Perth & Kinross) were surveyed from the air, as they are located on low-lying marshy areas, which are unsuitable to walk on

Black-headed Gull with chick at an 'apparently occupied nest' (AON) (Ernie James)

and contain few suitable vantage points. Aerial surveys and counts from vantage points have the added benefit of causing little or no disturbance to the colony.

The ideal period to survey Black-headed Gull colonies is from mid-May to early June, when most pairs are incubating and when the number of AONs can be estimated from a distance by counting apparently incubating adults. Spread of laying, and repeat laying after the loss of first clutches, can lead to an underestimate of colony size. It is, therefore, beneficial to conduct repeated counts of AONs at a colony (Walsh *et al.*, 1995). In such cases the highest count of AONs was used as the estimate of colony size.

At colonies that could not be accessed (e.g. on marshy ground or on islands) and where there was no suitable vantage point, flush counts of individuals attending the colony were made. Counts of individuals were divided by two to provide a rough approximation of the number of AONs present (Lloyd *et al.*, 1991). This is the least accurate method for censusing breeding gulls, as such counts will include an unknown percentage of non-breeders and attendance at the colony by both breeders in a pair is highly variable throughout the day and throughout the breeding season. During Seabird 2000 only 13% of the total population estimate of AONs for Britain and Ireland was determined from flush counts of individuals, which compares favourably to 18% during the SCR Census (1985–88).

Survey coverage was based on a list of colonies extracted from the SCR Database, that were known to have existed at some time between 1969 and 1998. In Britain, this list was amended, by BTO County Bird Recorders, with records of new colonies and of those that had ceased to exist (see chapter on Census Methods). Administrative areas bordering the Firth of Forth were surveyed by searching all 10-km squares containing waterbodies. Coverage of Black-headed Gull colonies in Britain during Seabird 2000 was comprehensive, with the exception of inland colonies in Durham and in western North Yorkshire, where some colonies may have been missed, but numbers involved are not thought to be large. In Ireland, the only colonies not surveyed were those on the islands of

Lough Derg (Co. Clare, Co. Tipperary and Co. Galway), which held a total of 1,400 AON during the SCR Census (1985–88); however, it is thought that numbers there have declined markedly since then (S. F. Newton pers comm.).

CURRENT STATUS AND TRENDS

During Seabird 2000, the total population of Black-headed Gulls breeding in Britain and Ireland was 141,890 AON (Table 1b), of which 58% were in England, the Isle of Man and the Channel Isles, 30% in Scotland, 9% in Ireland and 1% in Wales.

The breeding range in Britain and Ireland stretched from Uyea (north Shetland) to Bodmin Moor (Cornwall), and from Minsmere (east Suffolk) to Spanish Island (Co. Kerry), and the species was present in 60% of all administrative areas, compared to 70% in the SCR Census (1985–88; Fig. 1). Just over half of the population (56%) nested on the coast. Inland colonies were widespread and by no means restricted by proximity to the sea, reaching as far inland as the Upper Spey Valley (Badenoch & Strathspey) and Ofally Bogs (Co. Offaly). Over the last 15 years, since the SCR Census (1985–88), there have been some pronounced changes in both the size and distribution of inland and coastal nesting populations of Black-headed Gulls in Britain and Ireland (Figs. 1–2).

The number of 10-km OS grid squares occupied by breeding Black-headed Gulls was compared between Seabird 2000 and *The New Atlas of Breeding Birds in Britain and Ireland* conducted in 1988–91 (Gibbons *et al.*, 1993: Fig. 2). Between 1988–91 and Seabird 2000, the number of occupied 10-km squares decreased by 50% in Britain and by 77% in Ireland (Table 3, Fig. 2). This continued the constriction of the breeding range which was observed between the two successive breeding bird atlases of Britain and Ireland, in 1968–71 (Sharrock, 1976) and 1988–91 (Gibbons *et al.*, 1993). Since 1968–71 the range of breeding Black-headed Gulls has decreased by 60% in Britain and by 95% in Ireland. The proportional reduction in range was similar in Scotland, England, Wales and Northern Ireland, but was much greater in the Republic of Ireland (Table 3). However, some caution should be exercised when comparing these data, as unlike the Atlas surveys, 10-km squares were not systematically surveyed during Seabird 2000, and it is therefore possible that smaller colonies were occasionally missed.

The size of the Black-headed Gull breeding population in Britain and Ireland has declined by at least 16% since the SCR Census (1985–88), which reported a minimum of 168,093 AON (Table 1b), as not all inland colonies were surveyed. During the same period, the total number of Black-headed Gulls nesting in Scotland increased by a maximum of 25%, England's population remained relatively stable and there were declines of at least 34% in Wales and 70% in Ireland. That coverage of inland areas was less during the SCR Census (1985–88) than during Seabird 2000 has meant that declines presented here are likely to be underestimates, and conversely, increases are likely to be overestimates.

The number of Black-headed Gulls breeding in coastal colonies in Britain and Ireland has increased by 2% since the SCR Census (1985–88) and 6% since Operation Seafarer (1969–70). However, there have been some marked regional differences in population trends on the coast since the last two censuses (see below). The inland population of Britain and Ireland has declined by at least 30% from a minimum count of 90,520 AON during the SCR Census (1985–88) to 62,498 AON during Seabird 2000. Numbers inland declined in Ireland by 81%, in Wales by 43% and in England by 14%, but apparently increased in Scotland by 45%.

In 1938, 42% of the Black-headed Gull population in England and Wales nested on the coast (Hollom, 1940), but, by 1958, after the population had increased, the majority (71%) were coastal

Table 1a   Numbers of coastal-breeding Black-headed Gulls (AON) in Britain and Ireland 1969–2002.

Administrative area or country	Operation Seafarer (1969–70)	SCR Census (1985–88)[1]	Seabird 2000 (1998–2002)	Percentage change since Seafarer	Percentage change since SCR	Annual percentage change since SCR
Shetland	502	318	586	17%	84%	4.0%
Orkney	4656	2710	2854	−39%	5%	0.4%
North coast Caithness		99	184		86%	4.7%
East coast Caithness		250	27		−89%	−14.7%
Caithness total	*86*	*349*	*211*	*145%*	*−40%*	*−3.6%*
Northwest coast Sutherland		169		−100%	−100%	
East coast Sutherland		155	0		−100%	
Sutherland total	*27*	*324*		*−100%*	*−100%*	
West coast Ross & Cromarty		7			−100%	
East coast Ross & Cromarty			4			
Ross & Cromarty total	*55*	*7*	*4*	*−93%*	*−43%*	
Inverness		150			−100%	
Nairn		10	300		2900%	33.0%
Moray		40			−100%	
Banff & Buchan	33	1654	430	1203%	−74%	−9.1%
Gordon	2220	305	194	−91%	−36%	−3.2%
City of Aberdeen			68			
Angus		400	19		−95%	−19.6%
Northeast Fife	8000			−100%		
Berwickshire		238	90		−62%	−8.0%
Nithsdale		20	40		100%	5.3%
Stewartry	92	60	26	−72%	−57%	−5.5%
Wigtown	260	509	52	−80%	−90%	−16.9%
Kyle & Carrick	882	30	13	−99%	−57%	−5.4%
Cunninghame	73	300	50	−32%	−83%	−12.0%
Renfrew		520	250		−52%	−5.9%
Inverclyde		5			−100%	
Clydebank		5			−100%	
Dumbarton			5			
Argyll & Bute	428	1121	679	59%	−39%	−3.8%
Lochaber	1	70	5	400%	−93%	−19.6%
Skye & Lochalsh	96	4		−100%	−100%	
Western Isles–Comhairle nan eilean	815	405	1012	24%	150%	6.9%
Scotland Total	**18226**	**9554**	**6888**	**−62%**	**−28%**	**−2.4%**
Northumberland	3313	4988	2794	−16%	−44%	−4.3%
Humberside		1	2		100%	4.7%
Lincolnshire	4050	1765	38	−99%	−98%	−22.3%
Norfolk	1313	4296	4906	274%	14%	0.9%

Administrative area or country	Operation Seafarer (1969–70)	SCR Census (1985–88)	Seabird 2000 (1998–2002)	Percentage change since Seafarer	Percentage change since SCR	Annual percentage change since SCR
Suffolk	2153	2596	2767	29%	7%	0.4%
Essex	3824	6194	14561	281%	135%	5.9%
Kent	3778	7168	11091	194%	55%	3.2%
East Sussex	260	1175	33	−87%	−97%	−23.4%
West Sussex	1	891	31	3000%	−97%	−20.0%
Hampshire	22058	7303	9304	−58%	27%	1.8%
Isle of Wight	283	105	786	178%	649%	14.4%
Dorset	21	2820	1801	8476%	−36%	−3.2%
Merseyside			37			
Lancashire	1708	21093	16881	888%	−20%	−1.8%
Cumbria	10380	1573	517	−95%	−67%	−8.4%
Isle of Man		78	2		−97%	−25.5%
England and Isle of Man Total	53142	62046	65551	23%	6%	0.4%
Dyfed			10			
Gwynedd	700	950	840	20%	−12%	−0.9%
Clwyd	100	52		−100%	−100%	
Wales Total	800	1002	850	6%	−15%	−1.2%
Great Britain and Isle of Man Total	72168	72602	73289	2%	1%	0.1%
Co. Antrim	33	109	1834	5458%	1583%	25.3%
Co. Down	1361	4486	2203	62%	−51%	−5.2%
Co. Fermanagh	45			−100%		
Co. Wexford	500	200	949	90%	375%	11.0%
Co. Cork		7			−100%	
Co. Kerry	4		39	875%		
Co. Clare		168			−100%	
Co. Galway	286		208	−27%		
Co. Sligo	4			−100%		
Co. Donegal	526	1	870	65%	86900%	68.4%
All−Ireland Total	2759	4971	6103	121%	23%	1.5%
Britain and Ireland Total	74927	77573	79392	6%	2%	0.2%

Note

[1] The figures for the SCR are actual counts and do not include adjustments to totals made in order to account for unsurveyed colonies (see Lloyd *et al.*, 1991)

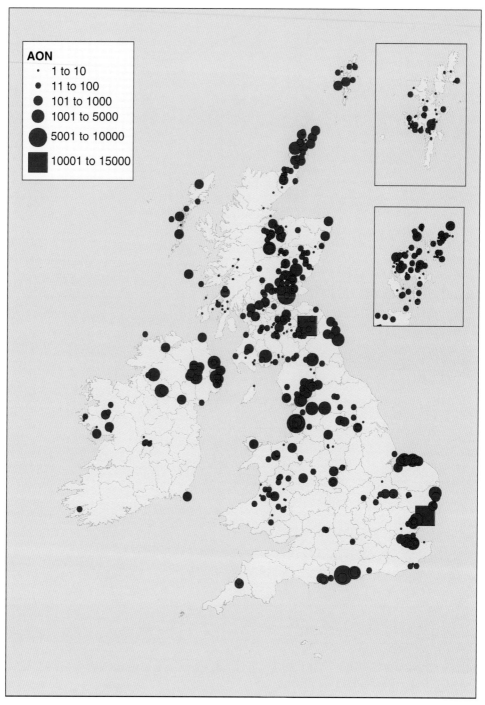

Figure 1   Abundance and distribution of breeding Black-headed Gulls in Britain and Ireland 1998–2002.

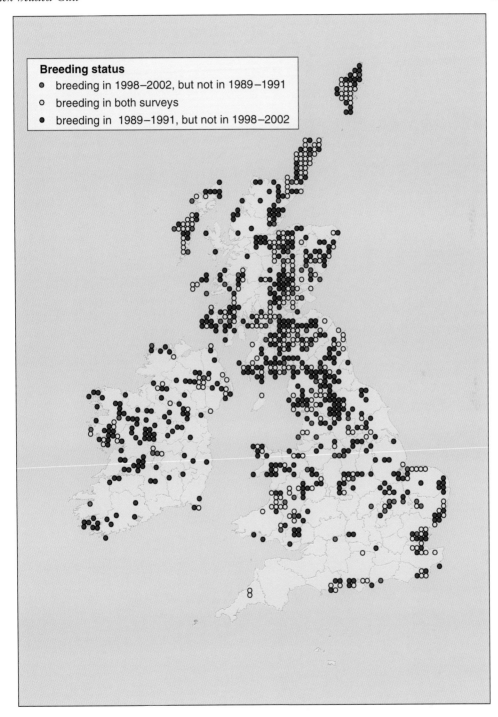

Figure 2   Comparison of Black-headed Gull breeding occurence in OS 10-km squares in Britain and Ireland during Seabird 2000 (1998–2002) and the New Atlas of Breeding Birds (1989–91; Gibbons et al., 1993).

Table 1b   Numbers of inland and coastal-breeding Black-headed Gulls (AON) in Britain and Ireland 1985–2002. Coverage of inland colonies during the SCR Census (1985–88) was incomplete.

Administrative area or country	Inland colonies only			Inland and coastal		
	SCR Census (1985–88)	Seabird 2000 (1998–2002)	Percentage change since SCR	SCR Census (1985–88)	Seabird 2000 (1998–2002)	Percentage change since SCR
Shetland				318	586	84%
Orkney				2710	2854	5%
North coast Caithness				99	184	86%
Inland Caithness	712	324	−54%	712	324	−55%
East coast Caithness				250	27	−89%
Caithness total	*712*	*324*	*−54%*	*1061*	*535*	*−50%*
Northwest coast Sutherland				169		−100%
Inland Sutherland		1			1	
East coast Sutherland				155		−100%
Sutherland total		*1*		*324*	*1*	*−100%*
West coast Ross & Cromarty				7		−100%
Inland Ross & Cromarty	73		−100%	73		−100%
East coast Ross & Cromarty					4	
Ross & Cromarty total	*73*		*−100%*	*80*	*4*	*−95%*
Inverness		414		150	414	176%
Nairn	140	91	−35%	150	391	161%
Badenoch & Strathspey		1902			1902	
Moray	723	174	−76%	763	174	−77%
Banff & Buchan				1654	430	−74%
Gordon		2		305	196	−36%
City of Aberdeen					68	
Kincardine & Deeside		246			246	
Angus	5250	2484	−53%	5650	2503	−56%
Perth & Kinross	1	9554	955300%	1	9554	955300%
City of Dundee		495			495	
Northeast Fife		152			152	
Falkirk		11			11	
West Lothian	120		−100%	120		−100%
City of Edinburgh	1154		−100%	1154		−100%
East Lothian	15		−100%	15		−100%
Midlothian	862	725	−16%	862	725	−16%
Tweedale	955	85	−91%	955	85	−91%
Ettrick & Lauderdale	10562	14724	39%	10562	14724	39%
Berwickshire		23		238	113	−53%
Roxburgh	26	247	850%	26	247	850%
Nithsdale	1000		−100%	1020	40	−96%
Stewartry	157	1145	629%	217	1171	440%
Wigtown	247	551	123%	756	603	−20%
Kyle & Carrick		55		30	68	127%
Cumnock & Doon Valley	152	178	17%	152	178	17%
Clydesdale	2044	1385	−32%	2044	1385	−32%
Cunninghame		0		300	50	−83%
Kilmarnock & Loudoun	1		−100%	1		−100%
Eastwood	350	448	28%	350	448	28%
Motherwell	3		−100%	3		−100%
Monklands	21		−100%	21		−100%
City of Glasgow		1			1	
Renfrew	205	25	−88%	725	275	−62%
Inverclyde				5		−100%
Clydebank				5		−100%
Bearsden & Milngavie	40	42	5%	40	42	5%
Strathkelvin	8	2	−75%	8	2	−75%
Cumbernauld & Kilsyth	2	1	−50%	2	1	−50%
Dumbarton					5	
Stirling	282	816	**189%**	282	816	189%

Administrative area or country	Inland colonies only			Inland and coastal		
	SCR Census (1985–88)	Seabird 2000 (1998–2002)	Percentage change since SCR	SCR Census (1985–88)	Seabird 2000 (1998–2002)	Percentage change since SCR
Argyll & Bute				1121	679	−39%
Lochaber				70	5	−93%
Skye & Lochalsh				4		−100%
Western Isles–Comhairle nan eilean				405	1012	150%
Scotland Total	25105	36303	45%	34659	43191	25%
Northumberland	2510	1464	−42%	7498	4258	−43%
Durham	1085		−100%	1085		−100%
North Yorkshire	1180	4252	260%	1180	4252	260%
Humberside	250		−100%	251	2	−99%
West Yorkshire	270	372	38%	270	372	38%
South Yorkshire	315	565	79%	315	565	79%
Lincolnshire				1765	38	−98%
Cambridgeshire	816	604	−26%	816	604	−26%
Northamptonshire		31			31	
Bedfordshire	100	21	−79%	100	21	−79%
Berkshire		22			22	
Norfolk				4296	4906	14%
Suffolk		31		2596	2798	8%
Essex	30	6	−80%	6224	14567	134%
Kent				7168	11091	55%
East Sussex				1175	33	−97%
West Sussex				891	31	−97%
Hampshire	2		−100%	7305	9304	27%
Isle of Wight				105	786	649%
Dorset				2820	1801	−36%
Cornwall	110	256	133%	110	256	133%
Gloucestershire		18			18	
Wiltshire		50			50	
Warwickshire	2	445	22150%	2	445	22150%
Hereford & Worcester		0			0	
Shropshire	90	200	122%	90	200	122%
Staffordshire	194	132	−32%	194	132	−32%
Derbyshire	259	370	43%	259	370	43%
Cheshire	1000	30	−97%	1000	30	−97%
Merseyside					37	
Greater Manchester	2		−100%	2		−100%
Lancashire		1770		21093	18651	−12%
Cumbria	12948	6540	−49%	14521	7057	−51%
Isle of Man				78	2	−97%
England, Isle of Man and Channel Isles Total	21163	17179	−14%	83209	82730	−1%
West Glamorgan		75			75	
Dyfed		203			213	
Powys		410			410	
Gwynedd	1993	46	−98%	2943	886	−70%
Clwyd	15	402	2580%	67	402	500%
Wales total	2008	1136	−43%	3010	1986	−34%
Great Britain, Isle of Man & Channel Islands Total	48276	54618	15%	120878	127907	6%
Co. Londonderry		100			100	
Co. Antrim	6851	2050	−70%	6960	3884	−44%
Co. Down				4486	2203	−51%
Co. Armagh	4200	50	−99%	4200	50	−99%
Co. Fermanagh	800	2800	250%	800	2800	250%
Co. Tyrone	22000	1070	−95%	22000	1070	−95%

Table 1b   continued.

	Inland colonies only			Inland and coastal		
Administrative area or country	SCR Census (1985–88)	Seabird 2000 (1998–2002)	Percentage change since SCR	SCR Census (1985–88)	Seabird 2000 (1998–2002)	Percentage change since SCR
Co. Monaghan		800			800	
Co. Offaly		113			113	
Co. Wicklow	14		−100%	14		−100%
Co. Wexford				200	949	375%
Table 1b continued.						
Co. Cork	15		−100%	22		−100%
Co. Kerry					39	
Co. Tipperary	832		−100%	832		−100%
Co. Clare	770		−100%	938		−100%
Co. Galway	4381	431	−90%	4381	639	−85%
Co. Mayo	2381	466	−80%	2381	466	−80%
Co. Donegal				1	870	86900%
All–Ireland Total	42244	7880	−81%	47215	13983	−70%
Britain and Ireland Total	90520	62498	−30%	168093	141890	−16%

nesters (Gribble, 1962). There was little change in distribution when the population peaked in 1973 (Gribble, 1976), but since then the proportion nesting on the coast has risen again, with 78% of the population during Seabird 2000 breeding in coastal colonies (Fig. 3). Scotland provides stark contrast to this trend, with a large decline in coastal breeding Black-headed Gulls over the last 30 years. Between Operation Seafarer (1969–70) and the SCR Census (1985–88), coastal breeding numbers declined by almost 50%. Over the last 15 years this rate has slowed slightly, with a further 28% decrease, representing a decline of 62% over the last 30 years.

Numbers of Black-headed Gulls breeding on the west coast of Scotland have declined markedly in the last 30 years, with the coasts of Sutherland, west coast Ross & Cromarty, and Skye & Lochalsh, now being devoid of breeders. The coastal population in Argyll & Bute has declined by 39% in the last 15 years and a decrease of 70% has occurred over the same period on the southwest coast, between Dumbarton and Nithsdale (including the Firth of Clyde and north Solway Firth). The total decline for colonies on the west coast of Scotland, excluding the Western Isles, has been about 60% in the last 15 years and 39% over the last 30 years since Operation Seafarer (1969–70). However, the actual number of birds nesting is quite low, with the west coast holding just 1.5% of the British population and inland areas 8%. The inland west of Scotland population has remained stable over the last 15 years, so there does not appear to have been a substantial influx of coastal nesting birds.

There has also been a 60% decline in the Scottish east coast mainland population since the SCR Census (1985–88) and by an order of magnitude since Operation Seafarer, from approximately 10,000 to just over 1,000 AON, representing a decline of 87%. However, over the last 15 years, inland eastern populations have increased by a maximum of 54% and it is possible that this increase has been brought about by relocation of coastal-nesting Black-headed Gulls. The colony at Bemersyde Moss (Perth & Kinross) has increased by 40% since the SCR Census (1985–88) and is now the largest inland colony in Britain and Ireland, holding 14,575 AON in 2000 (Table 2). However, more recent surveys suggest that this colony may be in substantial decline. Perth & Kinross also holds the second-largest inland colony, with 6,832 AON, at St Serf's Island, Loch Leven NNR.

Populations in the outer island groups showed a different pattern of change to those in the rest of Scotland, with total populations (all colonies surveyed on the Western and Northern Isles during the SCR Census (1985–88) and Seabird 2000 are considered coastal here) in the Western Isles and

Table 2 Changes in the number of breeding Black-headed Gulls (AON) at major coastal and inland colonies in Britain and Ireland between the SCR Census (1985–88) and Seabird 2000 (1998–2002). Major coastal colonies are those which contained the top 70% of the British coastal population or the top 80% of the Irish coastal population during the SCR Census and during Seabird 2000. Major inland colonies are those that contained the top 70% of the British inland population or the top 80% of the Irish inland population.

Colony	SCR Census (1985–88)	Seabird 2000 (1998–2002)	Percentage change since SCR	Annual percentage change since SCR	Pecentage of British or Irish population 1998–2002
Coastal					
Ribble Estuary (NNR)	20000	14851	−26%	−2.8%	20%
North Solent Nature Reserve (Needs Ore Point)	7250	6125	−16%	−1.3%	8%
Coquet Island	4047	2210	−45%	−4.6%	3%
Flanders Mere	3990	3725	−7%	−0.5%	5%
Hamford Water	3000	11000	267%	10.5%	15%
Garnhams Island	2000		−100%		0%
Round & Long Islands	2000		−100%		0%
Loch of Strathbeg	1610	430	−73%	−8.9%	1%
Burntwick	1400	4375	213%	9.1%	6%
Rye Harbour	1150	33	−97%	−24.0%	0%
Blakeney Point	1100	200	−82%	−10.7%	0%
Outer Trial Bank	910		−100%		0%
Chichester Harbour	891	1	−100%	−36.3%	0%
Dungeness RSPB Reserve	850	100	−88%	−13.4%	0%
Kirton Marsh	800	0	−100%		0%
Rat Island (River Colne)	500	2300	360%	10.7%	3%
Greenborough	60	2500	4067%	33.1%	3%
Langstone Harbour	53	3179	5898%	34.1%	4%
Blythburgh		2000			3%
Strangford Lough: Jackdaw Island	2500		−100%		0%
Strangford Lough: Ogilby Island	750	1182	58%	3.6%	19%
Strangford Lough: Lythe Rock	544		−100%		0%
Strangford Lough: Craigaveach Rock	254	4	−98%	−27.3%	0%
Lady's Island Lake	200	949	375%	11.0%	16%
Larne Lough: Blue Circle Island		1398			23%
Inch Island		800			13%
Big Copeland Island		372			6%
Rathlin Island: Brookley		300			5%
Inland					
Sunbiggin Tarn	12500	1200	−90%	−19.4%	2%
Bemersyde	10375	14575	40%	2.5%	26%
Loch of Kinnordy	5250	2299	−56%	−5.7%	4%
Llyn Trwsfynydd Rese	1330	0	−100%		0%
Holburn Moss	1300	0	−100%		0%
Caistron	1200	0	−100%		0%
Bavelaw	1150	0	−100%		0%
Woolston	1000	0	−100%		0%
Upper Barden Reservoir	500	4000	700%	14.9%	7%
Loch Ken	115	1145	896%	18.0%	2%
Loch Leven: St. Serfs Island		6832			12%
Killington Reservoir		3100			6%
Stocks Reservoir		1680			3%
Insh Marshes		1644			3%
Plenmeller Common		1185			2%
Fisher Tarn and Fisher Tarn Reservoir		1150			2%
Lough Neagh: Scaddy Island	20000	800	−96%	−21.9%	10%
Lough Neagh: Padgin Island	5000	1212	−76%	−10.3%	15%
Lough Corrib (Total)	4342	431	−90%	−17.6%	5%
Lough Neagh: Shallow Flat Islands	3000		−100%		0%
Lough Neagh: Brockish Bay Islands	1400	400	−71%	−9.2%	5%
Lough Neagh: Blackers Rock Island/River Rock	2000	270	−87%	−14.2%	3%
Lough Erne (Total)	800	2800	250%	8.4%	36%
Lough Egish		800			10%

Table 3   Comparison of Black-headed Gull breeding occurrence in OS 10-km squares in Britain and Ireland during Seabird 2000 (1998–2002) and the Atlas surveys in 1968–71 (Sharrock, 1976) and 1988–91 (Gibbons et al., 1993).

Country	Number of occupied OS 10–km squares					Seabird 2000 (1998–2002)	
	Atlas (1968–72)	New Atlas (1988–91)	Seabird 2000 (1998–2002)	Percentage change since 1968–72	Percentage change since 1988–91	Number of 10-km squares occupied in 1998–2002 but unoccupied in 1988–91	Number of 10-km squares occupied in 1988–91 but unoccupied in 1998–2002
Scotland	498	379	206	−59%	−46%	44	217
England	260	237	100	−62%	−58%	24	162
Wales	69	55	27	−61%	−51%	5	32
Nortehrn Ireland	50	29	14	−72%	−52%	1	17
Republic of Ireland	231	116	20	−91%	−83%	6	101
Britain	827	671	333	−60%	−50%	73	411
All Ireland	281	145	34	−95%	−77%	7	118
Britain and Ireland total	1498	816	367	−76%	−55%	80	529

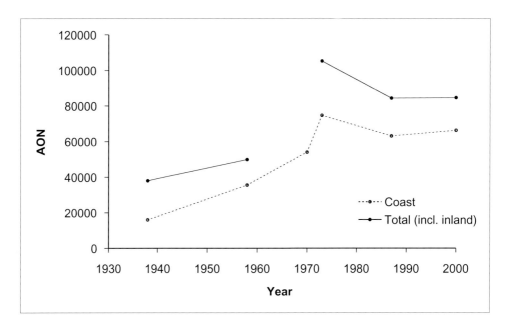

Figure 3   Number of Black-headed Gulls (pairs) breeding in coastal and inland colonies in England and Wales 1938–88.

Shetland returning to the levels identified during Operation Seafarer (1969–70), with respective increases of 84% and 150% since the SCR Census (1985–88). The Orkney population has changed little since 1985–88, and so remained 40% lower than during Operation Seafarer (1969–70).

England holds 89% of the British coastal-nesting Black-headed Gull population and has not suffered the declines seen in Scotland, with respective increases of 6% and 23% since the SCR Census (1985–88) and Operation Seafarer (1969–70: Table 1a). The Ribble Estuary NNR (Lancashire), held 14,851 AON (Table 2), making it the largest colony in Britain and Ireland, but had decreased by 26% since 1986, contributing greatly to the 20% decline observed in Lancashire over the last 15 years. The next largest colonies, at Hamford Water (Essex) and Needs Ore Point (Hampshire), held 11,000 AON and 6,125 AON respectively. The English coastal population has probably been bolstered by birds relocating from inland colonies in England and Wales, which have fared less favourably, with respective declines of at least 14% and 43% since the SCR Census (1985–88).

The east–west cline apparent in the Scottish inland nesting population was also evident in England, with a maximum increase of 30% in the east and a decline of at least 33% in the west since the SCR Census (1985–88). However, actual increases in the east are likely to be even higher, as inland Durham was not surveyed during Seabird 2000 and contained over 1,000 AON in the SCR Census (1985–88). The two largest inland colonies in England were at Barden (North Yorkshire) and Killington (Cumbria) reservoirs, holding 4,000 AON and 3,100 AON respectively (Table 2).

Northumberland's Black-headed Gull population decreased by 44% on the coast and 42% inland since the SCR Census (1985–88). All the colonies on the Lincolnshire side of the Wash had been abandoned by the time of Seabird 2000, but birds from these colonies may have simply moved across the border to Norfolk and perhaps into Suffolk, Essex and Kent, where the stronghold of Britain's Black-headed Gull population remains. Since 1938, colonies in southeast England have been increasing (Gribble, 1976) and this trend continued up to Seabird 2000. This, largely coastal-nesting, population has increased by 65% since the SCR Census (1985–88) and by 201% since Operation Seafarer (1969–70), and held 45% of the British coastal population during Seabird 2000. Within southeast England, the largest increases occurred in colonies on the Blackwater Estuary (Essex), the Medway Estuary (Kent) and Hamford Water (Essex: Table 2).

On the south coast of England numbers remained almost the same as those recorded during the SCR Census (1985–88). There was, however, a decline of 97% in East and West Sussex and it is possible that some of these birds may have relocated to neighbouring Hampshire, where numbers increased by a similar amount over the same period. The huge increase in colony size at Langstone Harbour (Hampshire), from 53 AON in 1987 to 3,078 AON in 2001, may have been a result of immigration from Sussex.

Black-headed Gulls were absent from the southwest coasts of England and Wales, from Furzey Island (Dorset) to Cors Fochno (Dyfed), but there were some small colonies further inland. The combined coastal breeding population of Wales and northwest England has declined by 23% since the SCR Census (1985–88).

Ireland held approximately 8% of the British and Irish coastal population, and the number of coastal nesters has increased by 23% since the SCR Census (1985–88) and 121% since Operation Seafarer (1969–70). The colony on Blue Circle Island in Larne Lough (Co. Down) became established in the late 1990s and has become the largest coastal colony in Ireland, with 1,398 AON (Table 2). The distribution of breeding sites has changed little in the last 15 years, with the main coastal population still located on islands in Strangford Lough (Co. Down), and smaller populations in southeast and west Ireland (Fig. 2). The number of Black-headed Gulls nesting on the coasts of Co. Wexford and Co. Donegal has increased markedly in the last 15 years, with the colony at Lady's Island Lake (Co. Wexford) almost quadrupling in size to 949 AON and a new colony of 800 AON becoming established on Inch Island (Co. Donegal).

Of great conservation concern is the dramatic decline in numbers of breeding Black-headed Gulls in Ireland's interior. In the last 15 years, the inland population decreased by at least 81% (Table 1b). In 1987, Davidson (1987) undertook a complete census of the islands in Lough Neagh, the stronghold of the Irish population in the mid-1980s, and found a total of 33,051 AON. In 2000, a survey of the same islands found just 3,269 AON, a decline of 90%. The number of Black-headed Gulls nesting on Lough Neagh's Scaddy Island, Ireland's largest colony during the SCR Census (1985–88), had decreased by 96%, from 20,000 AON to just 800 AON. The disappearance of birds from Lough Neagh has accounted for 87% of the decline in numbers of Black-headed Gulls breeding at inland colonies in Ireland. Inland colonies in the west of Ireland have also undergone dramatic declines, with previously healthy populations in Co. Mayo and Co. Galway decreasing by at least 80% and 90% since the SCR Census (1985–88). The complete survey of inland gull colonies in Co. Galway, Co. Mayo, Co. Sligo and Co. Donegal in 1977–78 (Whilde, 1978) found a total of 16,414 AON. The Seabird 2000 census found just 897 AON, a decline of almost 95%.

CAUSES OF CHANGE

The distribution and abundance of breeding Black-headed Gulls over the last 15 years has, according to the results of Seabird 2000, varied greatly in Britain and Ireland. However, the lack of historical information on the size of inland populations and the limited research conducted on Black-headed Gull populations in Britain and Ireland, and elsewhere, has meant that factors contributing to these changes remain unclear and the evidence presented here is largely circumstantial.

With a 25% increase in breeding numbers since the SCR Census (1985–88), Scotland was the only country in Britain and Ireland to have an apparently increasing Black-headed Gull population. The largest increases have apparently occurred inland; however, this may have been exaggerated by underestimates of population size in some areas during the SCR Census (1985–88) due to incomplete coverage. The continued growth of the colony at Bemersyde Moss, coupled with the establishment of the large colony on St Serf's Island, Loch Leven (Table 2), have been the main contributors to this increase. Since the early 1980s, the inland colony at Bemersyde has been expanding and is now the largest in Britain and Ireland. The establishment of a nature reserve at this site has probably greatly contributed to its success. This previously drained wetland has been left to refill, and now affords some protection to nesting Black-headed Gulls from predators such as foxes and rats. However, since the Seabird 2000 survey was conducted, a decrease has been noted and studies into the causes of the decline are currently underway. One notable impact on the Bemersyde colony is licensed egg collecting (quota 10,000 eggs per annum), although historically this seems to have had little effect on population size. It seems more likely that predation may have caused recent declines. St Serf's Island is also part of a nature reserve and therefore benefits from similar protection. It is likely that breeding numbers at these two protected sites have been swollen by birds emigrating from other colonies where site quality has diminished in some way. One such site is Loch of Kinnordy (Perth & Kinross), which in 1992 held a colony of 7,000 AON of Black-headed Gulls nesting on islets of bogbean, growing in shallow areas of the loch. In the last few years these islets have grown sufficiently large to form a peninsular, linking them to the shore. It is thought this peninsular now forms a corridor, along which land predators, such as rats, can gain access to the colony. Between 1992 and 2000 the colony declined by almost 70%, with emigration of birds to a safer nesting site nearby (A. Leitch, pers. comm.).

The decrease in breeding numbers and distribution in many coastal and inland areas of Scotland, may well be due to increased predation at existing colonies, coupled with the loss of alternative safe nesting sites elsewhere. One of the biggest threats to ground-nesting bird species in Britain and Ireland in recent years has come from an introduced predator, the American Mink. Originally escapees from fur farms, feral mink are now widespread in much of Britain and Ireland, and have undoubtedly had an effect on Black-headed Gull populations. These expert swimmers can reach island colonies, which were previously safe from most predators (e.g. foxes and rats), and by taking eggs and killing adults and young can severely reduce colony size. Otters are also known to predate such colonies, but unlike mink, they do not engage in surplus killing and tend to have a less devastating effect on the population (Craik, 1995). This, coupled with the fact that mink can inhabit coastal areas at much higher densities than otters (up to 1–2 mink/km of coast), has exacerbated the problem (Birks, 1986). The impact of mink on gull colonies on the west coast of Scotland has been particularly well documented. Craik (1998) showed that the removal of mink from the vicinity of gull colonies led to a significant decrease in predation and subsequent increase in productivity.

The huge decline in inland-nesting Black-headed Gulls in Ireland over the last 15 years could also be attributed to increased predation from mink. In recent years an increase in the mobility of Irish Black-headed Gull colonies has been noted, suggesting that colonies relocate annually in an attempt to avoid predation (S. F. Newton, pers. comm.). In 1989, the Irish Mammal Review undertook a comprehensive survey of Ireland and found that mink had spread to nearly all of the 20-km squares surveyed (Hayden, 2000). It is highly probable that declines observed on inland loughs in areas such as Co. Antrim, Co. Armagh, Co. Galway and Co. Mayo have been due to increased predation by mink. Declines in large gull species in Ireland have been attributed to botulism, i.e. poisoning through ingestion of botulinum toxin, produced by the bacterium *Clostridium botulinum* growing anaerobically in meat. However, there is little evidence to suggest that botulism has affected Black-headed Gulls in Ireland.

Over the last 30 years there have been some major changes in agricultural management, which have resulted in more intensive farming practices. Intensification was particularly pronounced in 1970–88, and changes included increased crop production, a shift from spring to autumn-sown cereals, and the increased usage of inorganic fertilizers and biocides. Analyses of data from the Common Bird Census for England and Wales have shown that populations of many farmland bird species, and overall abundance of farmland birds, decreased markedly in 1974–91, strongly suggesting the two were linked (Chamberlain *et al.*, 2000). It is widely thought that a reduction in the quality or abundance of food available to birds, a result of agricultural intensification, is the main reason for this decline (e.g. Benton *et al.*, 2000). It is possible that increased agricultural intensity was also responsible for the declines seen in the inland-breeding Black-headed Gull population in England and Wales over the same period (Fig. 3). Invertebrates form the mainstay of the Black-headed Gull's diet (Cramp & Simmons, 1983), and a decline in such prey items through increased pesticide usage may well have occurred (Benton *et al.*, 2002). Decreases in spring-sown cereals would also have meant a reduction in tillage during this season and the valuable invertebrate food source this uncovers. A drop in availability of a high-quality food source such as this, prior to the breeding season, coupled with a general decline in insect abundance, may have affected the condition of breeding Black-headed Gulls and reduced their productivity. Destruction of wetland habitat for agricultural and urban development may have also negatively affected Black-headed Gulls in inland areas.

Immigration of Black-headed Gulls from areas affected by predation, food depletion and habitat loss may have contributed, at least in part, to the continued increase of numbers at breeding colonies on the southeast coast of England. This region has extensive areas of saltmarsh and intertidal mudflats that provide safe nesting sites and high-quality feeding areas in estuaries such as the Wash, the Medway, Thames, Swale and Blackwater.

Comparisons between the two breeding bird atlases (1968–72 and 1988–91) and Seabird 2000 have shown that there has been an ongoing reduction in range and that the breeding population is concentrated into a diminishing number of high-quality sites.

The Black-headed Gull has historically been given relatively little attention by conservationists. However, the stark declines seen in breeding numbers in Ireland and many parts of Britain should stimulate future interest in this species. It is important that we assess the effect of factors such as predation, food availability and habitat change in areas where the most significant declines are occurring.

INTERNATIONAL CONTEXT

The global breeding population of Black-headed Gulls is estimated at 2,100,000–2,800,000 pairs, with most of these in Europe. However, little is known about the status of the Asian population, especially those breeding in Siberia. The British breeding population is estimated to contain 5–6% of the world breeding population and the Irish 0.5–0.7% (Table 4).

Black-headed Gulls breed throughout middle latitudes of the Palearctic, with their main population cutting a broad swathe across Europe and Asia, from the east Atlantic seaboard to the western shores of the Kamchatka. Their northern range stretches from Iceland, to north of the Arctic Circle in Norway and to the upper Kolyma River basin in Siberia, and they breed south, from southwest Spain, across Central Asia, to Vladivostok on the Sea of Japan (Cramp & Simmons, 1983). The stronghold lies in northern Europe, where the largest breeding populations occur in Britain and The Netherlands, and in the countries surrounding the Baltic Sea, namely Denmark, Sweden, Finland, Estonia and Lithuania (Hagemeijer & Blair, 1997). In the last 20 years Black-headed Gulls have also become established in Labrador and Newfoundland, with the first documented breeding attempt in 1977 (Montevecchi *et al.*, 1987). Since then, the population may have undergone some expansion, especially on the west coast of Newfoundland and in Labrador, but accurate breeding population data is limited. The current breeding population is estimated to be 10–100 AON (W. A. Montevecchi, pers. comm.).

In the late-19th and early-20th centuries, the Black-headed Gull population in Europe began to expand in both range and size. Colonies became established in the Faeroes, Norway and Finland in the late 1800s, and in Greenland, Iceland, Germany, Spain, and Italy between 1910 and 1960. From 1950 to 1980, there was widespread population increase and further expansion of range in northern Europe, whilst the much smaller Mediterranean population remained relatively stable. An exception to this was in Demark, where coastal numbers halved during the same period, whilst increasing inland. It is thought that this coastal population was affected by an increase in Herring Gull numbers, hunting, persecution and nest site predation by rats (Moller, 1978).

The Black-headed Gull population, from the first comprehensive survey of Europe and the Baltic States (1971–81), including European Russia and Turkey, but excluding the Ukraine, was estimated at 1,573,000–1,873,000 AON (Glutz von Blotzheim & Bauer, 1982). However, analysis of more recent breeding census data, collected in 1985–89, from a number of European countries, including The Netherlands and Finland, put this figure at 1,782,000–2,082,000 AON (Isenmann *et al.*, 1991). The current European breeding population, including the Ukraine, is estimated at 2,100,000–2,800,000 AON (Table 4).

In the late 1970s there was evidence that the northern European Black-headed Gull population was beginning to stabilise, with Sweden's population levelling at less than 20% of the peak in the early 1970s (Fredriksson, 1979). During the 1980s and 1990s there was further proof that the growth of the northern European population was waning, with parts of Finland experiencing a steady decline in breeding numbers (Risberg *et al.*, 1990), and numbers in central France declining then stabilising (Hagemeijer & Blair 1997) and Flanders (Belgium) stabilising (Vermeersch *et al.*, 2002). In 1992–1997 the breeding population of The Netherlands was estimated to be 132,000–170,000 AON, representing a decline of 25–40% since the 1980 peak (Bijlsma *et al.*, 2001). It thought that coastal areas of The Netherlands have been affected by increased fox predation (foxes colonised the area approximately 30 years ago) and that inland areas are more likely to have been affected by food shortages (van Dijk, 1998, 2002). It is possible that, as in England and Wales (see above), reduced food availability (through increased agricultural intensity), increased predation and reduction in breeding habitat, may be the main reasons behind the declines seen in northern Europe.

Table 4 International context.

Country or region	Number of pairs		Year	Source
	Min	Max		
Great Britain, Isle of Man and Channel Isles	130,000	130,000	1999–2002	Seabird 2000
All Ireland	14,000	14,000	1999–2002	Seabird 2000
Austria	7,000	9,000		BirdLife International/EBCC (2000)
Belarus	180,000	220,000	1988–98	BirdLife International/EBCC (2000)
Belgium	20,000	25,000	1981–90	BirdLife International/EBCC (2000)
Bulgaria	500	700	1990–97	BirdLife International/EBCC (2000)
Croatia	3,000	4,000		BirdLife International/EBCC (2000)
Czech Republic	80,000	150,000	1985–95	BirdLife International/EBCC (2000)
Denmark	150,000	150,000	1993–96	BirdLife International/EBCC (2000)
Faeroe Islands	250	250	1995	BirdLife International/EBCC (2000)
Greenland	5	50	1983	BirdLife International/EBCC (2000)
Estonia	50,000	100,000		BirdLife International/EBCC (2000)
Finland	80,000	130,000	1990–95	BirdLife International/EBCC (2000)
France	38,945	38,945	1997–2001	Cadiou *et al.* (in press)
Germany	280,000	350,000	1990–94	BirdLife International/EBCC (2000)
Greece	0	5		BirdLife International/EBCC (2000)
Hungary	10,000	12,000	1998	BirdLife International/EBCC (2000)
Iceland	25,000	30,000	1990	BirdLife International/EBCC (2000)
Italy	500	1,000	1988–97	BirdLife International/EBCC (2000)
Latvia	100,000	110,000	1986	BirdLife International/EBCC (2000)
Lithuania	30,000	60,000	1996–98	BirdLife International/EBCC (2000)
Moldova	700	900	1989	BirdLife International/EBCC (2000)
Netherlands	132,000	170,000	1992–97	Bijlsma *et al.* (2001)
Norway	20,000	30,000	1990	BirdLife International/EBCC (2000)
Poland	200,000	300,000		BirdLife International/EBCC (2000)
Romania	2,000	10,000		BirdLife International/EBCC (2000)
Russia (European)	400,000	500,000	1984–88	BirdLife International/EBCC (2000)
Slovakia	9,000	16,000		BirdLife International/EBCC (2000)
Slovenia	200	200		BirdLife International/EBCC (2000)
Spain	1,100	1,400	1988	BirdLife International/EBCC (2000)
Sweden	100,000	150,000	1990	BirdLife International/EBCC (2000)
Switzerland	1,300	1,800	1993–96	BirdLife International/EBCC (2000)
Turkey	2,000	10,000		BirdLife International/EBCC (2000)
Ukraine	80,000	110,000	1988	BirdLife International/EBCC (2000)
Canada (East)	14	14	1985	Montevecchi *et al.* (1987)
Russia (Asiatic)[1]	?	?		Kondratiev & Litvinenko (1991)
China[2]	?	?		Melville (1984)

Biogeographic region	min	max	min % GB	max % GB	min % Ireland	max % Ireland
World*	2,100,000	2,800,000	4.6%	6.2%	0.5%	0.7%

*Stroud *et al.* (2001)

Notes

[1] Unknown numbers breed at the mouth of the Amur River and in northeast of Sakhalin Island. Also breeds in small numbers on Apuka River delta.

[2] Unknown numbers breed in west Xinjiang, Jilin and Heilongjiang provinces

Common Gull *Larus canus*

Mark L. Tasker

INTRODUCTION

The Common Gull breeds across the Palearctic and in North America, on coasts and at inland sites, and spends the winter inland, on estuaries and at sea. Terrestrial foods include earthworms, beetles and other insects, whilst discarded fishery wastes supplement natural food at sea. In Britain and Ireland the breeding distribution is virtually confined to Scotland and northwest Ireland (Fig. 1).

Common Gull is a colonial breeder, but can also breed solitarily. During Seabird 2000 over half (57%) of the total population in Britain and Ireland bred inland. Despite the inland bias in distribution, only coastal-nesting Common Gulls were counted during both Operation Seafarer (1969–70) and the SCR Census (1985–88), so comparison between Seabird 2000 population estimates and the previous censuses is based only on coastal colonies (see below). Lloyd *et al.* (1991) estimated the total inland population during the SCR Census (1985–88) at 60,000 pairs. This was based largely on the fact that in 1988–89 some 40,000 pairs were nesting at just a few colonies in the Mortlach Hills (Moray) and Correen Hills (Gordon) in northeast Scotland.

The coastal-nesting population of Common Gulls in Britain and Ireland increased from around 13,000 pairs in Operation Seafarer (1969–70) to around 15,500 pairs in the SCR Census

(1985–88). There was little change in distribution between the two censuses (Cramp *et al.*, 1974; Lloyd *et al.*, 1991). In 1985–88, 98% of the British and Irish coastal population were breeding in Scotland, of which over half were in Orkney (where all breeding seabirds were considered 'coastal'), where numbers had increased by 66% since Operation Seafarer (1960–70). The only other large concentrations of coastal-breeding Common Gulls, in Shetland and in Argyll & Bute had shown contrasting trends between 1969–70 and 1985–88, increasing by 86% to 2,487 pairs and decreasing by 17% to 2,200 pairs respectively. In Ireland, numbers on the coast had apparently decreased from 744 pairs in 1969–70 to 301 pairs in 1985–88. However, some colonies in west-coast Ireland were not surveyed during the SCR Census (1985–88) and Lloyd *et al.* (1991) estimated that the population had in fact increased to around 900 pairs.

There is no reason to suggest that coastal and inland-nesting Common Gull populations are in anyway separate. Therefore, it is essential that inland colonies are surveyed as thoroughly as those on the coast if an accurate assessment of the current status of Common Gulls in Britain and Ireland is to be made.

CENSUS METHODS

Common Gulls nest in many inland areas of Scotland and remoter areas of England and Ireland. Coverage of such areas during Seabird 2000, by the relatively small number of observers involved, is difficult to assess but it is likely that all areas were covered at least once during the period of the survey. If however the species is mobile between sites within this count period, some breeding sites

Common Gull colony in the Mortlach Hills, Banff and Buchan—the largest in Britain and Ireland (Matt Parsons)

could have been missed and other groups of birds double-counted. There has never been a census of this species over one year that would enable this possibility to be assessed.

The recommended count unit for Common Gulls in Seabird 2000 was Apparently Occupied Nests (AON). Counts of 'pairs' given for Operation Seafarer and the SCR Census in Cramp *et al.* (1974) and Lloyd *et al.* (1991) equated to counts of AONs. In areas where Common Gulls nest at low density in small colonies, it is comparatively easy to either enter the colony to count nests or to observe nests from a distance. However, only a small proportion of Common Gulls nest in such situations (and a few may be overlooked in colonies of larger gulls). In Orkney and Shetland, Common Gulls tend to nest in larger groups on relatively inaccessible terrain (e.g. marshes and reedbeds), which makes access either impossible or would cause too much disturbance to the colony. In such areas, counts of nests are not possible and counts of individuals were made. The same difficulty occurred in Operation Seafarer (1969–70: Cramp *et al.*, 1974) and in the SCR Census (1985–88: Lloyd *et al.*, 1991). Counts of individuals that were submitted were divided by two to estimate pairs. It is likely that this provides a low estimate of the actual number of pairs at each site. The accuracy of counts of individuals is difficult to assess. However, during both the SCR Census (1985–88) and Seabird 2000, similar proportions of the total number of AONs counted were derived from counts of individuals, i.e. 30% and 38% respectively.

Counts of AONs in towns and cities, and in small rural colonies, may also be made by observation from a distance (e.g. Monaghan & Coulson, 1977; Raven & Coulson, 1997). The larger rural colonies in northeast Scotland have been counted by sampling (Tasker *et al.*, 1991; White *et al.*, 1996; Mitchell & Thompson, 1998). In these counts, a regular grid was laid out across the breeding colonies using bamboo poles at 100-m intervals and then the number of nests within a circle of 300 m^2 centred on each pole was counted. Each nest was assessed to decide whether it was active or not: an active nest had eggs, freshly disturbed soil or nest material in it. The grid was also used to map the extent of each colony surveyed. The largest colonies often had a high-density core; this too was mapped. A combination of colony area and mean count density for those colonies was then used to estimate total numbers. Mitchell & Thompson (1998) re-analysed counts made by Tasker *et al.* (1991) and White *et al.* (1996) in order to improve the precision of these estimates. The largest remaining problem of these inland counts is in the interpretation of 'inactive nests'. It may be that these represent late and incomplete breeding attempts that may subsequently become 'active' (in which case they are AON), or maybe a failed breeding attempt by a pair for reasons including death of an adult, disturbance or a decision to move breeding site (in which case they might not be an AON). There is evidence that the proportion of active nests is lower in those colonies that have declined compared with those colonies that have increased or remained stable. Thus, even a study at one colony of the significance of inactive nests would not necessarily be transferable to another colony with a different history of occupancy.

In the context of this survey, coastal colonies were regarded as those being within 5 km of the high-water mark; inland colonies were further from the sea than this. All colonies in the Orkney, Shetland and the Western Isles were regarded as coastal (see chapter on Data Processing and Analysis).

CURRENT STATUS AND TRENDS

There was a total of 49,780 AON of Common Gulls at inland and coastal colonies in Britain and Ireland during Seabird 2000. Of these, 97% were in Scotland, with 1,617 AON in Ireland, 50 AON in England and the Isle of Man, and none in Wales (Table 1). In both Scotland and Ireland, around 43% were nesting on the coast.

As in the previous two censuses, the main coastal concentration of breeding Common Gulls was in Orkney. This island group alone held more than half of the total number breeding on the coasts of Britain and Ireland. Shetland, the Western Isles and Argyll & Bute all held numbers in excess of 1,500 AON. Numbers in Orkney increased by 37% since the SCR Census (1985–88) and have more than doubled in the 30 years since Operation Seafarer (1969–70). The population in Shetland has remained constant since 1985–88, but had previously almost doubled in size since 1969–70. Coastal numbers in Argyll & Bute (only 3 AON were inland) have remained more or less constant over the 30 years, whilst those in the Western Isles increased dramatically by three to four times since both Operation Seafarer (1969–70) and the SCR Census (1985–88). This apparent increase in the Western Isles may, at least in part, be due to improved coverage of colonies during Seabird 2000. Coverage of many moorland and sea loch colonies in Lewis was poor during Operation Seafarer (Bourne & Currie, 1983). Numbers nesting elsewhere on Scottish coasts were relatively small.

Whilst the main coastal concentrations were in north and west Scotland, most of the inland colonies were in a broad swathe across Scotland, north of the central valley and mainly southeast of the Great Glen, though notable concentrations were in southeast Sutherland and in Caithness (Fig. 1). Relatively few nested in the western Highlands and there were a few smaller colonies in the southern uplands (Ettrick and Lauderdale). Tasker & Walsh (1993) noted that while there had been little change in overall distribution of breeding Common Gulls between the surveys conducted for the *Atlases of Breeding Birds of Britain and Ireland* conducted in 1968–1972 (Sharrock, 1976) and 1988–91 (Gibbons *et al.*, 1993), there had been a 17% decline in the number of OS 10-km squares occupied in Scotland and Ireland. Although the method of coverage during the atlases was different to that in Seabird 2000, comparisons of breeding distribution within 10-km squares during Seabird 2000 and the atlases, show that this trend of disappearance from 10-km squares has continued up to Seabird 2000 (Table 3). In Britain and Ireland the range of breeding Common Gulls (measured as the number of occupied 10-km squares) has diminished by 44% since 1968–72 (Table 3). The disappearance of breeding Common Gulls from 10-km squares has been particularly pronounced in northeast Scotland (i.e. Kincardine and Deeside, City of Aberdeen, Gordon, Banff & Buchan and Moray as defined in Buckland *et al.*, 1990). In total the number of 10-km squares in northeast Scotland occupied by breeding Common Gulls has declined from 49 in 1968–72 (Sharrock, 1976), to 38 in 1981–84 (Buckland *et al.*, 1990), to 30 in 1988–91 (Gibbons *et al.*, 1993) and was only 20 in 1999–2002 (Fig. 2).

The first systematic census of the largest inland colonies in Britain at the Correen (Gordon) and the Mortlach Hills (Moray) in northeast Scotland was in 1988–89 and found 24,500 and 16,200 AON respectively (Tasker *et al.*, 1991). The size of the Correen Hills colony had shrunk to 6,400 AON by 1995 (Walsh *et al.*, 1996) and become extinct just three years later (Mitchell & Thompson, 1999). At the same time the Mortlach Hills colony increased to 21,700 AON in 1995 (Walsh *et al.*, 1995) and then decreased to 17,900 AON in 1998 (Mitchell & Thompson, 1998). Some of the birds from the Correen Hills may have moved to the nearby Bluemills colony (Gordon), which formed sometime between 1989 and 1995 and numbered 3,200 AON in 1998 (Mitchell & Thompson, 1998), and is currently the largest colony outside the Mortlach Hills. However, the current whereabouts of the majority of the birds that formally bred at the Correen Hills is a mystery.

The habit of nesting in or on man-made structures appears to be spreading (Table 2). Sullivan (1982) and Stewart (1986) noted Common Gulls nesting on roofs in Aberdeen (the site of the world's largest urban Herring Gull colony). Since then numbers of Common Gulls nesting in Aberdeen have risen from 142 AON in 1993–95 (Raven & Coulson, 1997) to 280 AON in 2001, making it the largest known urban concentration of this species. The next largest roof-nesting colony is at Heiligenhafen, Germany (Kubetzki, 2001). Roof-nesting Common Gulls in Britain are confined

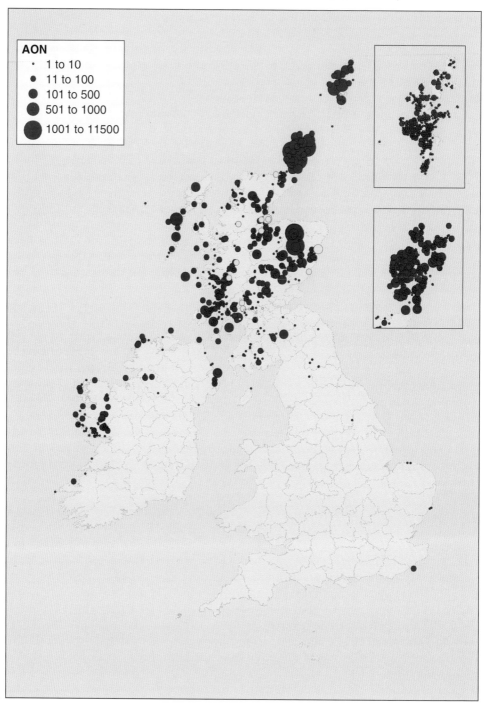

Figure 1   Abundance and distribution of breeding Common Gulls in Britain and Ireland 1998–2002. Natural sites are shown in red and man-made sites (e.g. rooftops) are in yellow (the scale is the same for both types of site).

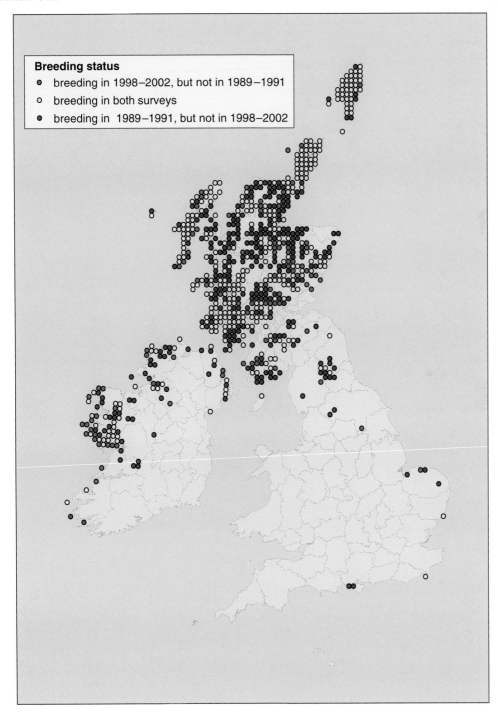

Figure 2   Comparison of Common Gull breeding occurrence in OS 10-km squares in Britain and Ireland during Seabird 2000 (1998–2002) and the New Atlas of Breeding Birds (1989–1991; Gibbons et al., 1993).

Table 1 *Numbers of coastal-breeding Common Gulls (AON) in Britain and Ireland 1969–2002. Numbers breeding inland and on the coast during Seabird 2000 (1998–2002) are also given.*

Administrative area or country	Coastal colonies only[1]						Seabird 2000 inland and coastal
	Operation Seafarer (1969–70)	SCR Census (1985–88)[2]	Seabird 2000 (1998–2002)	Percentage change since Seafarer	Percentage change since SCR	Annual percentage change since SCR	
Shetland	1,336	2,487	2,424	81%	−3%	−0.2%	2,424
Orkney	4,895	8,132	11,141	128%	37%	2.3%	11,141
North coast Caithness		136	453		233%	9.7%	453
Inland Caithness							91
East coast Caithness		16	15		−6%	−0.4%	15
Caithness total	*36*	*152*	*468*	*1200%*	*208%*	*8.4%*	*559*
Northwest coast		83	87		5%	0.4%	87
Inland Sutherland							447
East coast Sutherland		113	124		10%	0.7%	164
Sutherland total	*380*	*196*	*211*	*−44%*	*8%*	*0.6%*	*698*
West coast Ross &		116	51		−56%	−5.8%	51
Inland Ross & Cromarty							38
East coast Ross &		2	297		14750%	45.3%	297
Ross & Cromarty total	*403*	*118*	*348*	*−14%*	*195%*	*8.3%*	*386*
Inverness	10	37	135	1250%	265%	10.1%	1,007
Nairn	12			−100%			40
Badenoch & Strathspey							167
Moray	67	23		−100%	−100%		18,845
Banff & Buchan	16	13		−100%	−100%		
Gordon							3,625
City of Aberdeen		47	280		496%	14.4%	280
Kincardine & Deeside	43		22	−49%			965
Angus			19				541
Perth & Kinross							1,465
City of Dundee							7
Midlothian							2
Ettrick & Lauderdale							108
Roxburgh							1
Nithsdale	1			−100%			
Stewartry	96	11	14	−85%	27%	1.6%	40
Wigtown		1	5		400%	11.4%	13
Kyle and Carrick	48		2	−96%			26
Cumnock & Doon Valley							13
Clydesdale							72
Cunninghame	495	197	330	−33%	68%	4.1%	330
Eastwood							39
East Kilbride							1
Renfrew							8
Inverclyde		352	25		−93%	−17.5%	27
Clydebank			1				4
Cumbernauld & Kilsyth							3
Dumbarton		4	50		1150%	20.1%	80
Stirling							169
Argyll & Bute	2,661	2,200	2,683	1%	22%	1.5%	2,686
Lochaber	541	407	367	−32%	−10%	−0.8%	367
Syke & Lochalsh	530	271	235	−56%	−13%	−1.1%	267
nan eilean	659	486	1,707	159%	251%	9.6%	1,707
Scotland Total	**12,229**	**15,134**	**20,467**	**67%**	**35%**	**2.2%**	**48,113**
Northumberland							9
North Yorkshire							1
Norfolk	2	3	6	200%	100%	4.9%	6
Suffolk		20	16		−20%	−1.6%	16
Kent	4	8	11	175%	38%	2.3%	11
East Sussex	1			−100%			

Administrative area or country	Operation Seafarer (1969–70)	SCR Census (1985–88)[2]	Coastal colonies only[1] Seabird 2000 (1998–2002)	Percentage change since Seafarer	Percentage change since SCR	Annual percentage change since SCR	Seabird 2000 inland and coastal
Cumbria	1	0	0	−100%			1
Isle of Man		5	6		20%	1.5%	6
England and Isle of Man Total	8	36	39	388%	8%	0.6%	50
Gwynedd	2			−100%			
Wales Total	2	0	0	−100%			0
Great Britain, Isle of Man and Channel Islands Total	12,239	15,170	20,506	68%	35%	2.2%	48,163
Co. Antrim	12	64	107	792%	67%	3.4%	107
Co. Down	44	128	276	527%	116%	5.7%	276
Co. Fermanagh							174
Co. Cork	4	4		−100%			
Co. Kerry	64	30	47	−27%	57%	3.8%	47
Co. Clare			10				10
Co. Galway	57		155	172%			333
Co. Mayo	178	47	210	18%	347%	12.4%	506
Co. Sligo	3	12	11	267%	−8%	−0.6%	11
Co. Donegal	382	16	153	−60%	856%	19.0%	153
All-Ireland Total	744	301	969	30%	222%	9.1%	1,617
Britain and Ireland Total	12,983	15,471	21,475	65%	39%	2.5%	49,780

Notes

[1] Operation Seafarer and the SCR Census did not survey inland.

[2] The figures for the SCR are actual counts and do not include adjustments to totals made in order to account for unsurveyed colonies (see Lloyd *et al.*, 1991)

to Scotland (there are none in Ireland) and the total number has increased from 236 AON in 1993–95 to 621 AON during Seabird 2000 (Table 2). The countryside west and southwest of Aberdeen also has several small colonies of Common Gulls nesting inside enclosures established to protect gas pipeline facilities (Fig. 1). A colony of 101 AON was also present inside the protection afforded by the Nigg oil terminal (Ross & Cromarty). In the Clyde Valley, Common Gulls nest around reservoirs enclosed by predator-proof fences.

The majority of the Irish Common Gull population breeds in the north and west (in Co. Galway, Co. Mayo and Co. Donegal). Changes in numbers here are difficult to assess due to variation in coverage. The total coastal count for Ireland during Seabird 2000 was 969 AON, which apparently represents a three-fold increase since the SCR Census (1985–88; Table 1). However, coverage in 1985–88 was incomplete in western Ireland and Lloyd *et al.* (1991) estimated that the total was nearer 900 AON. Hence there may in fact have been little change in the coastal-breeding numbers in Ireland since the SCR Census (1985–88). About half of all Common Gulls nesting in Ireland were found inland during Seabird 2000. They were breeding on islands in just seven loughs: 186 AON at Lough Corrib (Co. Galway), 169 AON at Lower Lough Erne, 5 AON at Lough Vearty (both in Co. Fermanagh), 124 AON at Lough Mask, 65 AON at Lough Carra, 59 at Lough Carrowmore and 40 AON at Lough Conn (all in Co. Mayo). The was no systematic census of inland sites during the SCR Census, but Common Gulls nesting at Loughs Corrib, Mask and Carra were counted in 1988. Numbers at Loughs Corrib and Mask had each declined by 79%

Table 2 Numbers of roof-nesting Common Gulls (AON) in Scotland 1976–2002.

Administrative area or country	1976[1]		1993–95[2]		1999–2002		Percentage change since 1976	Percentage change since 1993–95
	AON	Colonies[3]	AON	Colonies[3]	AON	Colonies		
Shetland					1	1		
North coast Caithness			12	1	86	1		617%
Caithness total			*12*	*1*	*86*	*1*		*617%*
East coast Sutherland					13	1		
Sutherland total					*13*	*1*		
East coast Ross & Cromarty			34	4				
Ross & Cromarty total			*34*	*4*				*–100%*
Inverness	1[4]	1	20	1	96	2	9500%	380%
City of Aberdeen			142	1	280	1		97%
Angus					19	1		
Cunninghame					4	1		
Inverclyde			2	1	19	2		850%
Cumbernauld & Kilsyth					3	1		
Dumbarton					40	1		
Argyll & Bute			1	1	40	1		3900%
Lochaber			25	1	20	1		–20%
Scotland total	**1**	**1**	**236**	**10**	**621**	**14**	**62000%**	**163%**

Notes
[1] Source data: Monaghan & Coulson (1977)
[2] Source data: Raven & Coulson (1997)
[3] The numbers of colonies do not include those in 1976 and 1993–95 that were not counted
[4] One pair nested on a shed at Dalcross Airport, Inverness, in 1971.

Table 3 Comparison of Common Gull breeding occurrence in OS 10-km squares in Britain and Ireland during Seabird 2000 (1998–2002) and the Atlas surveys in 1968–71 (Sharrock, 1976) and 1988–91 (Gibbons et al. 1993).

Country	Number of occupied OS 10-km squares					Seabird 2000 (1998–2002)	
	Atlas (1968–72)	New Atlas (1988–91)	Seabird 2000 (1998–2002)	Percentage change since 1968–72	Percentage change since 1988–91	Number of 10-km squares occupied in 1998–2002 but unoccupied in 1988–91	Number of 10-km squares occupied in 1988–91 but unoccupied in 1998–2002
Scotland	643	554	378	–41%	–32%	68	244
England	14	23	9	–36%	–61%	3	17
Wales	5	0	0	–100%		0	5
Northern Ireland	19	16	9	–53%	–44%	2	9
Republic of Ireland	124	71	55	–56%	–23%	23	39
Britain	662	577	387	–42%	–33%	71	261
All Ireland	143	87	64	–55%	–26%	25	48
Britain and Ireland total	805	664	451	–44%	–32%	96	309

between 1988 and 1999–2002 and were also down by 35% at Lough Carra. Common Gulls were not counted at Lough Derg (Co. Clare, Co. Galway and Co. Tipperary) during Seabird 2000, but only 14 AON were found there in 1988.

CAUSES OF CHANGE

The uncertainty that there has been change in the Common Gull population (varying count units and the first inland survey), coupled with the limited research in Britain and Ireland on the species, make describing causes of change speculative. Two changes seem relatively certain and some pressures on the Common Gull population are known.

The loss of what was possibly one of the world's largest Common Gull colonies from the Correen Hills in about a decade was most likely caused by local factors. There was no a major decline at the other large colony in northeast Scotland, on the Mortlach Hills. Forestry encroached on part of the eastern section of the Correen Hills colony following planting with Sitka spruce in 1981. There was also some indication that the colony once spread into other areas that had been planted earlier (Tasker *et al.*, 1991). Forestry will have reduced available nesting area, but there still appeared to be plenty of suitable ground left on the hills. Both the Correen Hills and the Mortlach Hills colonies are predominantly in heather moorland that is used for grouse shooting. Management activities undertaken for grouse shooting include predator control and muirburn. The former will incidentally reduce the number of predators of gulls (e.g. fox), whilst the latter may improve habitat for nesting. There are no records of the scale of predator control on either hills, but large declines in numbers of Common Gulls at some sub-colonies in the Mortlach Hills coincide with areas of heather that have become deep and old due to lack of recent burning (Mitchell & Thompson, 1998). It may be that

Common Gulls nesting at one of the many gas pipeline installations in NE Scotland. The fence provides protection against ground predators (Matt Parsons)

the loss of the Correen Hills colony was due to a combination of these factors. High vegetation does not appear to be preferred by gulls in this location, possibly due to the extra cover given to predators, but nevertheless extensive areas of low grassland remain within the area of the former colony. Numbers of predators and vegetation growth may both have changed due to changes in land management.

Elsewhere, predators have been proved to have an effect at a local level. Craik (1990, 1995, 1997, 1998) has described the affects of escaped and now feral American Mink on the seabirds of Argyll. Seabirds affected by American Mink included Common Gulls, although overall numbers in Argyll have not changed (assisted, no doubt, by a mink control programme that started in the early 1990s). Breeding success in areas affected by American Mink was usually zero. Kilpi (1995) and Keijl & Arts (1998) noted that predation at a Common Gull colony tended to disperse surviving adults into smaller colonies. Craik (1997) noted a movement from islands and areas affected by American Mink to islands further offshore. The recent growth of small colonies of Common Gulls in pipeline enclosures west and south of Aberdeen, and the rising numbers of urban roof-nesting Common Gulls have both surely resulted from predator avoidance behaviour by the gulls. It may be that the largely unrecorded spread of American Mink in mainland Scotland has had a much wider effect than previously realised.

The decline of Common Gull numbers breeding on inland loughs in Ireland is consistent with major declines in populations of Black-headed Gulls nesting throughout Ireland's interior, which have been attributed to the recent spread of mink within both the Republic and Northern Ireland. In west Cork, mass mortality of gulls (mostly Black-headed Gulls, but some Common Gulls) was attributed to botulism (Buckley & O'Halloran, 1986), a factor mentioned also by Whilde *et al.* (1993) in considering changes in gull population in northwest Ireland. In contrast to effects on larger gulls, botulism or large-scale deaths do not appear to have affected Common Gull populations in Great Britain and Ireland.

INTERNATIONAL CONTEXT

The problem with estimating numbers of breeding Common Gulls is the same throughout their range; most nest in relatively small, dispersed colonies away from the coast. All estimates from other countries with larger populations are thus relatively uncertain. The largest numbers breed in Norway, Sweden, Finland and Britain (Table 4), with substantial numbers in other countries around the Baltic. The range of the Common Gull extends through northern and central Europe, across Russia and to Alaska and northwest Canada. The combined European and Russian population is estimated at 400,000–650,000, of which Britain holds around 7–12% and Ireland just 0.3% (Table 4).

Table 4 *International context.*

Country or region	Subspecies	Min	Max	Year	Source
Great Britain, Isle of Man	*canus*	48,000	48,000	1999–2002	Seabird 2000
All Ireland	*canus*	1,600	1,600	1999–2002	Seabird 2000
Austria	*canus*	2	6	early 1990s	Géroudet (1995)
Belarus	*canus*	500	1,200	1988–98	BirdLife International/EBCC (2000)
Belgium	*canus*	6	7	mid 1990s	Seys *et al.* (1998)
Czech Republic	*canus*	3	7	1985–1995	BirdLife International/EBCC (2000)
Denmark	*canus*	25,000	25,000	mid-1990s	Bukaciski & Bukaciski (2003)
Estonia	*canus*	10,000	15,000		BirdLife International/EBCC (2000)
Faroes	*canus*	1,000	1,000	1995	BirdLife International/EBCC (2000)
Finland	*canus*	50,000	70,000	1990–95	BirdLife International/EBCC (2000)
France	*canus*	30	30	1997–2001	Cadiou *et al.* (in press)
Germany	*canus*	18,000	21,000	1990–94	BirdLife International/EBCC (2000)
Hungary	*canus*	2	4	1998	BirdLife International/EBCC (2000)
Iceland	*canus*	350	450	1990	BirdLife International/EBCC (2000)
Latvia	*canus*	500	600	1986	BirdLife International/EBCC (2000)
Lithuania	*canus*	100	150	1996–98	BirdLife International/EBCC (2000)
Moldova	*canus*	0	10	1988	BirdLife International/EBCC (2000)
Netherlands	*canus*	6,000	6,000	1996	Keijl & Arts (1998)
Norway	*canus*	100,000	200,000	1990	BirdLife International/EBCC (2000)
Poland	*canus*	1,800	1,900	late 1990s	Bukaciski & Bukaciski (2003)
Russian Federation*	*canus, heinei, kamtschatschensis*	40,000	60,000	1984–88	BirdLife International/EBCC (2000)
Slovakia	*canus*	5	10		BirdLife International/EBCC (2000)
Sweden	*canus*	100,000	200,000	1990	Birdlife International/EBCC (2000)
Switzerland	*canus*	2	5	early 1990s	Géroudet (1995)
Ukraine	*canus*	50	50	1990s	Bukaciski & Bukaciski (2003)
USA (Alaska)	*brachyrhychus*	10,000	10,000	1990s	Burger & Gochfeld (1996)
Canada (northwest)	*brachyrhychus*	?			

Country	Subspecies	Min	Max	Min % GB	Max % GB	Min % Ireland	Max % Ireland
NW & C Europe/ Atlantic/ Mediterranean**	*canus, heinei, kamtschatschensis*	400,000	650,000	7.4%	12.0%	0.2%	0.4%
World	all	410,000	660,000	7.3%	11.7%	0.2%	0.4%

* mostly *canus*, total numbers of other subspecies unknown

** Stroud et al. (2001)

Lesser Black-backed Gull *Larus fuscus*

John Calladine

INTRODUCTION

The Lesser Black-backed Gull has increased in numbers throughout its range during much of the 20th century. It breeds in north and west Europe, from the Taimyr Peninsular (Siberia), through Fenno-Scandinavia, the North Sea littoral, Britain, Ireland, the Faeroe Islands to Iceland and northwest Spain and Portugal in the west (Pons & Yésou, 1997). Post-breeding, birds from colonies in Britain and Ireland, along with those from southern Scandinavia, Germany and the Netherlands, generally migrate along the western seaboard of Europe to spend at least some of the non-breeding season in Iberia or western North Africa with some reaching the Gulf of Guinea (Rock, 2002). During the 20th century they have become less migratory and can now be found within much of their breeding range throughout the year (Baker, 1980; Hickling, 1986; Rock, 2002)

Lesser Black-backed Gulls nest colonially, often with other gull species, especially Herring Gull. Colonies occur on offshore islands and inland freshwater bodies, coastal cliffs, sand dunes, saltmarshes, moorland and on the roofs of buildings. Seemingly, many sites that are either inaccessible to ground predators (e.g. islands and urban roofs) or where the latter are particularly scarce (e.g. narrow peninsulas or on moorland managed as sporting estate) can prove attractive to nesting Lesser Black-backed Gulls. Though often sharing breeding areas with Herring Gulls, their nest sites and feeding strategies generally differ; Lesser Black-backed Gulls forage over larger distances (Verbeek, 1977; Mudge & Ferns, 1982; Garthe *et al.*, 1999) and they tend to nest within more vegetated areas (Harris, 1964; Calladine, 1997). A greater proportion of Lesser Black-backed Gulls also breed inland.

National surveys since the 1960s have all shown the Lesser Black-backed Gull to breed widely around the coasts of Britain and Ireland. In common with many other seabirds, it benefited from reduced exploitation and the introduction of bird protection legislation in the 20th century. As a generalist and opportunist feeder, it was apparently able to capitalise on increased food availability through fishery discards and at garbage tips (Furness & Monaghan, 1987). Exceptions to the generally increasing population through much of the 20th century are found in the Northern Isles, where some major declines have been reported (Thom, 1986). In common with the Herring Gull, the Lesser Black-backed has been subject to culling and clutch destruction, especially during the 1970s and 1980s (Duncan, 1981a; Coulson, 1991; Wanless *et al.*, 1996). In some instances, Lesser Black-backeds have been incidental victims of more directed efforts to reduce numbers of the, then more abundant, Herring Gull. Despite such localised efforts to restrict Lesser Black-backed numbers, the coastal population of Britain and Ireland increased from *c.*50,000 Apparently Occupied Nests (AON) in Operation Seafarer (1969–70) to just over 64,000 AON in the SCR Census (1985–88).

CENSUS METHODS

The nests of Lesser Black-backed Gulls are normally on the ground or another solid surface, occasionally in bushes, and can vary from insignificant scrapes to fairly substantial constructions. The locations of nests range from open flat rocks, roofs or bare peat hags to being concealed within rank vegetation. Accordingly, the visibility of nests and even birds sitting on them is highly variable. The differing accessibility to and visibility of colonies as a whole also limits attempts to adopt a common approach to counting all colonies. For example, landing on some islands is impractical and access to some roofs impossible. Accordingly, five counting methods, all variations on either direct nest counts or counts of birds, were recommended. The methods used at different colonies depended not only on some of the factors above, but also on colony size and available manpower (see Appendix I). Each method inevitably has associated biases that remain largely unquantified. Even where accessibility, topography and manpower are all sufficiently favourable to permit direct counting of nests, accurate counting can be difficult, as even experienced counters miss nests (Ferns & Mudge, 1981; Wanless & Harris, 1984), and in not all instances have appropriate correction factors, to account for the missed proportions, been determined. For Seabird 2000, 91% of counts were of nests, the rest were derived from counts of birds, apparently occupied sites or territories.

Not all adult Lesser Black-backed Gulls breed each year and nests that are built will not necessarily have eggs laid in them (Calladine & Harris, 1997; O'Connell *et al.*, 1997). As some birds construct several nests, laying in just one, and some pairs hold territories and construct nests but do not lay eggs, nest counts may actually overestimate the breeding population. A correction factor of 0.61 has been suggested (O'Connell *et al.* 1997), but this proportion can vary between years (Perrins & Smith, 2000), and doubtless varies between sites. When estimates of colony size are determined by bird counts (either of individuals or of Apparently Occupied Territories), a proportion of non-breeding adults present can lead to the number of active nests being overestimated. Where counts were of individuals, these were systematically divided by two to estimate the number of AONs. As it is unlikely that both members of all pairs would be present, this correction would to some unknown degree counter the possible overestimate due to the presence of non-breeders.

In common with the two earlier censuses, counts between mid-May and early June were recommended. This coincides with the peak of incubation at most colonies in Britain and Ireland, that is when most birds will have laid, but relatively few will have hatched and thus the maximum number of nests is expected to be occupied (Wanless & Harris, 1984). On the Isle of May (Fife), the timing of breeding appears to vary little between years or with colony size; with median clutch completion dates of 22 and 23 May in 1974 and 1975 respectively, when there were approximately 700 AON (Duncan, 1981b) and 21 May in 1993 and 1994 when there were over 1,200 AON (pers. obs.). Therefore, the assumption that the timing of breeding remains reasonably constant is likely to be valid. Some 60% of the AONs counted during Seabird 2000, where the date was known, were made on the recommended dates, compared with just 25% during the SCR Census (1985–88). In Seabird 2000, 10% of counts did not include a recorded date, whilst 26% did not for the SCR Census (1985–88).

In mixed colonies, more often than not shared with Herring Gulls, determination of the proportion of a count to assign to a particular species provides a further potential source of error, as eggs of the two species can not be readily distinguished during counts. In all but the smallest colonies, where individual nests may be attributed to any given species, it was recommended that the proportion of Lesser Black-backed Gulls be determined from sample head counts representative of the colony as a whole. The frequency of attendance at nests did not differ between Herring and Lesser Black-backed Gulls during incubation, but did so during chick-rearing at both a colony on the German North Sea coast (Garthe *et al.*, 1999) and on the Isle of May (pers. obs.). Thus, head counts of mixed colonies made outside of the recommended count dates could lead to an inaccurate estimate of species composition. The difference in nest attendance between the two species, during chick-rearing, were in opposing directions at the two study sites, with Lesser Black-backed Gulls more frequently attending nests at the German colony, but less frequently on the Isle of May. Whether a late count will overestimate or underestimate the proportion of Lesser Black-backed Gulls will likely depend on the foraging behaviour of the birds of both species at the individual colony.

Clearly, counting gulls is difficult, especially at mixed colonies. In assessing trends at an individual colony level, biases introduced by counting methods must be carefully considered. However, the two earlier national censuses also used a number of similar techniques, and there is little reason to suppose that the wider scale, long-term patterns shown for coastal sites are not real. Seabird 2000 represents the first attempt to census all inland breeding colonies of Lesser Black-backed Gulls in Britain and Ireland. Whilst coverage was good in most areas, inland Durham was not surveyed, but only 2 AON were recorded there in 1987.

CURRENT STATUS AND TRENDS

Seabird 2000 estimated the total British and Irish Lesser Black-backed Gull population at 116,684 AON, with 57% in England, the Isle of Man and the Channel Islands, 21% in Scotland, 18% in Wales and 4% in Ireland.

Lesser Black-backed Gulls are now widespread around the coasts of Britain and Ireland; indeed few coastal counties lack breeding birds (Fig. 1). The only major change in their coastal distribution since Operation Seafarer (1969–70) has been the establishment of breeding birds along the east coast of England. During Operation Seafarer (1969–70) the coast between the Farne Islands (Northumberland) and Orford Ness (Suffolk) was unoccupied. Even during Seabird 2000, only very small numbers nested between the Tees Estuary (Cleveland) and The Wash (Lincolnshire and Norfolk). There has also been considerable infilling of sites along the south coast of England.

Neither of the two previous censuses included inland gulls, but Sharrock (1976) and Gibbons *et al.* (1993) summarised their distribution in comparable periods. Some 22% of breeding Lesser Black-backed Gulls in Seabird 2000 were inland, but very few were in excess of 20 km from either the coast or an estuary. The inland distribution of breeding Lesser Black-backed Gulls has been variable during the latter half of the 20th century. Increased occurrence in central Scotland, the Lake District, West Midlands and Greater London has been offset by apparent decreases in northeast Scotland and North Yorkshire. Within North Yorkshire (and Durham, which was not surveyed inland during Seabird 2000) a small number of Lesser Black-backed Gulls appeared to try to establish territories on moors during Seabird 2000, but in many instances their attempts did not persist (pers. obs.). Approximately 50 pairs may have attempted to nest on moorland within the boundaries of the Yorkshire Dales National Park (North Yorkshire) in any one of the years covered by Seabird 2000, but the presence of non-breeding summering birds makes any assessment difficult (I. Court, pers. comm.).

Although widespread in Britain and Ireland, there are significant concentrations from the Forth to the Clyde in central Scotland, around Morecambe Bay in northwest England, in west Wales, the Severn Estuary, and East Anglia. In Seabird 2000, these five broad areas held over 80% of the estimated total population of Britain and Ireland.

The three censuses of coastal-breeding in Britain and Ireland gave estimates of 50,035 AON Lesser Black-backed Gulls in Operation Seafarer (1969–70), 64,417 AON in the SCR Census (1985–88) and 91,323 AON in Seabird 2000 (Table 1). In addition to the range expansions already described, numbers breeding at many established colonies have also increased. Of the major coastal colonies in Britain and Ireland most increased between the SCR Census (1985–88) and Seabird 2000, and in many instances markedly (Table 2, Fig. 2). Notable exceptions were declines at some (though not all) island colonies in the Firth of Clyde (Cunninghame and Kyle & Carrick) and on Skomer and Skokholm (both Dyfed). The colony on Skomer, formerly the largest in Britain and Ireland, is now exceeded in size by colonies at South Walney (Cumbria) and Tarnbrook Fell (Lancashire) where both populations at least doubled since 1985–88 (Table 2). For sites counted annually as part of the Seabird Monitoring Programme (SMP), it is apparent that the broad changes between the SCR Census (1985–88) and Seabird 2000 have not necessarily been constant throughout the period. Numbers on the Isle of May increased from a little over 600 AON in 1989–90, peaked at just over 1,600 AON in 1995–96 and subsequently declined to 1,200 in 2001. The combined population of several colonies in west Wales peaked in the early 1990s with a subsequent steady decline, specifically on Skomer (Dyfed), where numbers peaked at 20,200 AON in 1993, decreasing to 10,007 AON in 2000 (Perrins & Smith, 2000). In contrast, colonies in Norfolk and Suffolk increased throughout the period. Long-term declines in the Northern Isles (Thom, 1986) have continued, a trend that also appears to have spread to many of the small colonies around the north and west coasts of Scotland.

Inland-nesting Lesser Black-backed Gulls in Britain have received somewhat less attention from those monitoring seabird populations, although it appears that their distribution and numbers have fluctuated markedly. The largest inland colony was at Tarnbrook Fell (Lancashire), with 18,518 AON in 2001, but the count of that colony in 2002 was down to 12,088 AON (Sowter, 2002). The Lesser Black-backed Gulls nesting furthest from the coast were on the roof-tops of Birmingham, perhaps the most unlikely site for a seabird colony where the 40 AON found in 2001. Roof-nesting by Lesser Black-backed Gulls was first recorded in 1945, and by 1993–95 over 2,500 nests were known from 64 sites in Britain and Ireland (Raven & Coulson, 1997). In Seabird 2000, some 10% (10,790 AON at 125 sites) of nesting Lesser Black-backed Gulls in Britain were on roof-tops, frequently in urban areas (Fig. 1, Table 3). The roof-nesting habit has become reasonably widespread in many seaside towns, but truly marked concentrations occur across central Scotland and in Avon and Gloucestershire, where large industrial buildings are favoured. Seabird 2000 recorded five roof-top colonies that exceeded 500 AON: in Lowestoft (Suffolk), Bristol (Avon) and at three sites around

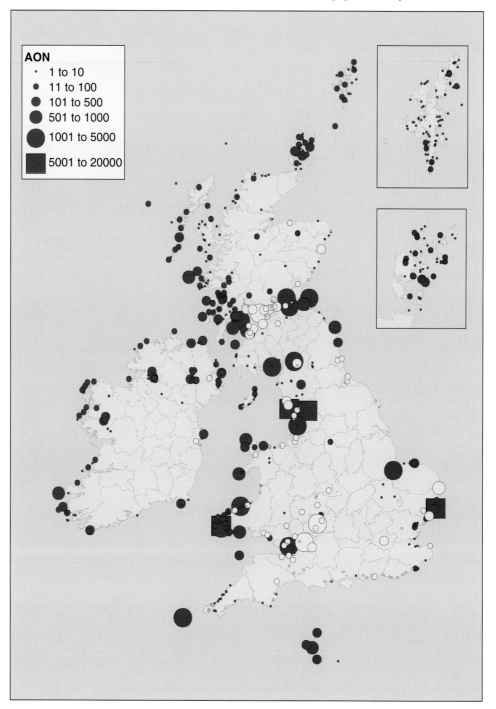

Figure 1   Abundance and distribution of breeding Lesser Black-backed Gulls in Britain and Ireland 1998–2002.
Natural sites are shown in red and man-made site (e.g. rooftops) are in yellow (the scale is the same for both types of site).

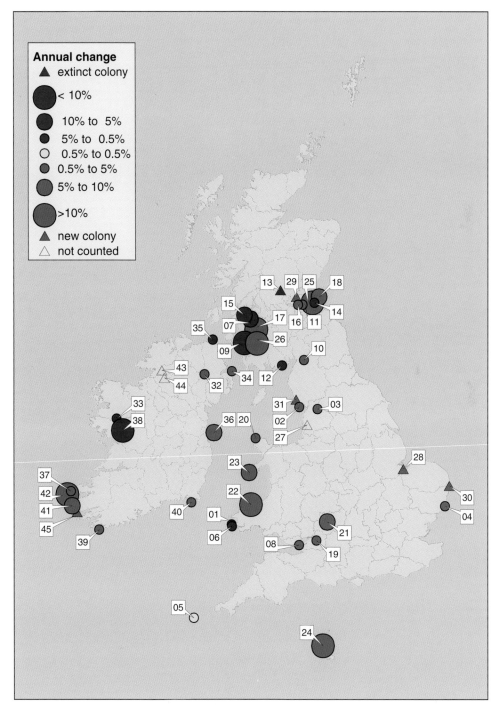

Figure 2   Changes in the number of breeding Lesser Black-backed Gulls (AON) at major colonies in Britain and Ireland between the SCR Census (1985–88) and Seabird 2000 (1998–2002). Major colonies are those that contained the top 75% of the British population during the SCR and/or Seabird 2000 or the top 50% of the Irish population during the SCR and/or Seabird 2000. Numbers correspond to colonies listed in Table 2.

Table 1   Numbers of coastal-breeding Lesser Black-backed Gulls (AON) in Britain and Ireland 1969–2002. Numbers breeding inland and on the coast during Seabird 2000 (1998–2002) are also given.

Administrative area or country	Coastal colonies only[1]						Seabird 2000 inland and coastal
	Operation Seafarer (1969–70)	SCR Census (1985–88)[3]	Seabird 2000 (1998–2002)	Percentage change since Seafarer	Percentage change since SCR	Annual percentage change since SCR	
Shetland	541	488	341	−37%	−30%	−2.4%	341
Orkney	910	1,714	1,045	15%	−39%	−3.6%	1,045
North coast Caithness		5	2		−60%	−6.3%	2
East coast Caithness		11		−100%	−100%		
Caithness total	*16*	*16*	*2*	*−88%*	*−88%*	*−13.8%*	*2*
Northwest coast Sutherland		73	44		−40%	−3.8%	44
East coast Sutherland		250	1		−100%	−33.6%	1
Sutherland total	*373*	*323*	*45*	*−88%*	*−86%*	*−13.7%*	*45*
West coast Ross & Cromarty		176	41		−77%	−9.8%	41
East coast Ross & Cromarty			7				7
Ross & Cromarty total	*258*	*176*	*48*	*−81%*	*−73%*	*−8.8%*	*48*
Inverness			6				18
Nairn	6			−100%			
Badenoch & Strathspey							1
Moray	42	10		−100%	−100%		129
Banff & Buchan	15	23	10	−33%	−57%	−5.5%	10
Gordon	1	45	6	500%	−87%	−12.6%	6
City of Aberdeen			154				154
Kincardine & Deeside	3	27	8	167%	−70%	−8.7%	8
Angus		16	7		−56%	−5.5%	7
Perth & Kinross							1,120
City of Dundee			65				65
North East Fife	300	520	1,203	301%	131%	6.2%	1,203
Kirkcaldy	2,000	1,753	3,282	64%	87%	4.8%	3,282
Dunfermline	10	730	1,262	12520%	73%	4.3%	1,262
Clackmannan							88
Falkirk			113				179
City of Edinburgh	2	70	323	16050%	361%	13.7%	323
East Lothian	335	1,130	1,470	339%	30%	2.0%	1,470
Midlothian							1
Berwickshire	7	5	1	−86%	−80%	−11.4%	1
Nithsdale			2				2
Stewartry	645	1,523	1,025	59%	−33%	−3.5%	1,025
Wigtown	6	4	10	67%	150%	6.8%	11
Kyle & Carrick	434	1,925	1,721	297%	−11%	−0.8%	1,721
Cumnock & Doon Valley							4
Clydesdale							40
Cunninghame	1,045	4,573	4,588	83%	0%	0.0%	4,588
Kilmarnock & Loudoun							134
Eastwood							40
East Kilbride							250
Motherwell							34
City of Glasgow			209				640
Renfrew			340				518
Inverclyde		31	190		513%	15.8%	190
Clydebank			30				31
Bearsden & Milngavie							118
Strathkelvin							329
Cumbernauld & Kilsyth							449
Dumbarton		119	143		20%	1.5%	209
Argyll & Bute	4,191	3,203	3,235	−23%	1%	0.1%	3,235
Lochaber	152	165	88	−42%	−47%	−4.7%	88
Skye & Lochalsh	47	351	41	−13%	−88%	−14.7%	41

Administrative area or country	Coastal colonies only[1]						Seabird 2000 inland and coastal
	Operation Seafarer (1969–70)	SCR Census (1985–88)[3]	Seabird 2000 (1998–2002)	Percentage change since Seafarer	Percentage change since SCR	Annual percentage change since SCR	
Western Isles–Comhairle nan eilean	692	584	552	−20%	−5%	−0.4%	552
Scotland Total	**12,031**	**19,524**	**21,565**	**57%**	**10%**		**25,057**
Northumberland	1,583	1,035	850	−46%	−18%	−1.4%	858
Tyne and Wear		3	4		33%	2.0%	11
Cleveland		9	90		900%	20.4%	90
North Yorkshire			1				1
Humberside			1				1
Cambridgeshire							5
Norfolk		22	1,605		7195%	34.5%	1,605
Suffolk	150	5,000	6,956	4537%	39%	2.4%	6,956
Essex		3	155		5067%	28.5%	157
Greater London		1	195		19400%	47.5%	257
Kent			75				75
East Sussex	2	1	38	1800%	3700%	32.1%	38
West Sussex		1	36		3500%	30.5%	36
Hampshire			2				2
Isle of Wight	1	2	1	0%	−50%	−4.5%	1
Dorset	1	2	10	900%	400%	12.8%	10
Channel Islands	304	778	1,734	470%	123%	6.7%	1,734
Cornwall	13	11	39	200%	255%	10.0%	39
Isles of Scilly	2,500	3,762	3,603	44%	−4%	−0.4%	3,603
Devon	101	180	426	322%	137%	6.4%	426
Somerset	171	1	64	−63%	6300%	43.3%	74
Avon	1,730	350	768	−56%	119%	6.7%	1,823
Gloucestershire		115	2,224		1834%	23.7%	2,350
Hereford & Worcester							79
West Midlands							40
Derbyshire							30
Merseyside			51				51
Lancashire	7	2[2]	4,167	59429%	208250%	69.9%	22,685
Cumbria	18,175	11,806	22,772	25%	93%	5.2%	22,905
Isle of Man	54	99	114	111%	15%	1.1%	114
England, Isle of Man and Channel Islands Total	**24,792**	**23,183**	**45,981**	**85%**	**98%**	**5.2%**	**66,056**
Gwent	10	50	36	260%	−28%	−2.2%	65
South Glamorgan		2,096	3,381		61%	3.1%	3,381
Mid Glamorgan			0				0
West Glamorgan	1		94	9300%			94
Dyfed	7,782	16,007	15,588	100%	−3%	−0.2%	15,588
Powys							1
Gwynedd	3,727	1,883	1,556	−58%	−17%	−1.3%	1566
Clwyd	9	7	27	200%	286%	8.8%	27
Wales Total	**11,529**	**20,043**	**20,682**	**79%**	**3%**	**0.2%**	**20,722**
Great Britain, Isle of Man and Channel Islands total	**48,352**	**62,750**	**88,228**	**77%**	**41%**		**111,835**
Co. Londonderry							42
Co. Antrim	64	160	485	658%	203%	7.7%	647
Co. Down	159	288	548	245%	90%	4.9%	548
Co. Armagh							164
Co. Fermanagh							447
Co. Tyrone							125
Co. Monaghan							6
Co. Dublin	45	158	334	642%	111%	5.9%	334
Co. Wexford	468	126	165	−65%	31%	2.1%	165

Table 1   continued

Administrative area or country	Coastal colonies only[1]						Seabird 2000 inland and coastal
	Operation Seafarer (1969–70)	SCR Census (1985–88)[3]	Seabird 2000 (1998–2002)	Percentage change since Seafarer	Percentage change since SCR	Annual percentage change since SCR	
Co. Waterford	25			−100%			
Co. Cork	132	339	227	72%	−33%	−2.8%	227
Co. Kerry	587	519	792	35%	53%	3.4%	792
Co. Clare	24		66	175%			66
Co. Galway	68	5	37	−46%	640%	18.9%	43
Co. Mayo	60	39	237	295%	508%	15.0%	539
Co. Sligo	16	23	36	125%	57%	3.3%	36
Co. Donegal	35	10	168	380%	1580%	24.0%	668
All-Ireland Total	1,683	1,667	3,095	84%	86%	4.8%	4,849
Britain and Ireland Total	50,035	64,417	91,323	77%	42%		116,684

Notes

[1] Operation Seafarer and the SCR Census did not survey inland.

[2] The Ribble Estuary (Lancashire) colony was not counted during the SCR.

[3] The figures for the SCR are actual counts and do not include adjustments to totals made in order to account for unsurveyed colonies (see Lloyd *et al.*, 1991)

Table 2   Changes in the number of breeding Lesser Black-backed Gulls (AON) at major colonies in Britain and Ireland between the SCR Census (1985–88) and Seabird 2000 (1998–2002). Major colonies are those that contained the top 75% of the British population during the SCR and/or Seabird 2000 or the top 50% of the Irish population during the SCR and/or Seabird 2000. ID corresponds to colony symbols in Fig. 2.

ID	Colony	SCR Census (1985–88)	Seabird 2000 (1998–2002)	Percentage change since SCR	Annual percentage change since SCR	Percentage of population in Britain or Ireland (1998–2002)
1	Skomer	11,760	10,007	−15%	−1.2%	9.2%
2	South Walney	10,000	19,487	95%	5.3%	17.9%
3	Tarnbrook Fell[1]	7,984	18,518	132%	5.4%	17.0%
4	Orfordness	5,000	5,500	10%	0.7%	5.0%
5	Isles of Scilly	3,762	3,603	−4%	−0.4%	3.3%
6	Skokholm	3,531	2,419	−31%	−2.9%	2.2%
7	Little Cumbrae Island	3,000	1,200	−60%	−6.8%	1.1%
8	Flat Holm	1,800	3,309	84%	4.5%	3.0%
9	Ailsa Craig	1,800	400	−78%	−10.2%	0.4%
10	Rockcliffe Marsh[3]	1,791	2,400	34%	2.7%	2.2%
11	Inchkeith	1,753	3,276	87%	4.3%	3.0%
12	Almorness	1,500	1,023	−32%	−3.8%	0.9%
13	Meall A'choire Odhair	1,200	0	−100%		0.0%
14	Craigleith	930	782	−16%	−1.3%	0.7%
15	Inchmarnock Island	825	200	−76%	−8.5%	0.2%
16	Inchcolm	730	1,221	67%	3.5%	1.1%
17	Horse Island	641	2,677	318%	10.7%	2.5%
18	Isle of May	520	1,203	131%	6.2%	1.1%
19	Bristol[2]	518	850	64%	3.5%	0.8%
20	The Skerries	453	574	27%	1.7%	0.5%
21	Gloucester (incl. RAF Quedgeley)[1,2]	450	2,250	400%	10.4%	2.1%
22	Cardigan Island	375	1,648	339%	11.1%	1.5%

ID	Colony	SCR Census (1985–88)	Seabird 2000 (1998–2002)	Percentage change since SCR	Annual percentage change since SCR	Percentage of population in Britain or Ireland (1998–2002)
23	Bardsey Island	225	634	182%	7.7%	0.6%
24	Sark	154	555	260%	10.8%	0.5%
25	Fidra	140	599	328%	12.8%	0.5%
26	Lady Isle	125	1,000	700%	12.3%	0.9%
27	Hesketh and Banks Marshes, Ribble Estuary	nc	4,100			3.8%
28	Outer Trial Bank		1,378			1.3%
29	St Serfs Island, Loch Leven[1]		1,103			1.0%
30	Lowestoft[2]		750			0.7%
31	Haverigg Prison[1,2]		430			0.4%
32	Lough Neagh (SPA)[1]	449	494	10%	0.7%	10.2%
33	Lough Mask[1]	447	286	−36%	−4.0%	5.9%
34	Old Lighthouse Island and Mew Island	200	240	20%	1.1%	4.9%
35	Rathlin Island	155	127	−18%	−1.4%	2.6%
36	Lambay Island	150	309	106%	6.2%	6.4%
37	Blasket Sound Islands (Beginish Island, Young's Island)	148	162	9%	0.8%	3.3%
38	Lough Corrib[1]	123	6	−95%	−22.3%	0.1%
39	Cape Clear Island	103	204	98%	5.4%	4.2%
40	Great Saltee	80	144	80%	4.7%	3.0%
41	Puffin Island	55	139	153%	6.4%	2.9%
42	Inishvickillane	30	156	420%	14.6%	3.2%
43	Inishgoosk	nc	500			10.3%
44	Lower Lough Erne[1]	nc	444			9.2%
45	Scariff Island		97			2.0%

Notes

[1] Inland

[2] Roof-nesting

[3] SCR 1988 count estimated from a mixed count of 2,500 AON of Herring Gulls and Lesser Black-backed Gulls using a ratio of 2.53LBBG:1HG measured in 1990.

nc   not counted

Gloucester (Gloucestershire). Unfortunately, a survey of roof-nesting Lesser Black-backed Gulls in Edinburgh was practically impossible, but subjective estimates suggest that this population has increased substantially in the last ten years and probably numbers several hundred pairs (A. Leitch pers. comm). The only roof-nesting Lesser Black-backed Gulls reported from Ireland were of 21 AON in Dublin (Co. Dublin) and 63 in Belfast (Co. Antrim).

The status of breeding Lesser Black-backed Gulls in Ireland contrasts with that in Britain. Some 36% were found breeding inland (21% in Britain) and the largest colony, on Inishgoosk on the inland Lough Derg (Co. Donegal), held just 500 AON. Although the Irish population has shown a similar proportional increase to that in Britain between Seabird 2000 and the SCR Census (1985–88), curiously no larger colonies, comparable to those in Britain (many of which are in the west and geographically close to the Irish coast), have developed. Most of the recent increases in Ireland have been at coastal colonies, with decreases reported at some inland sites (Fig. 2). Between 1969 and 1983, the proportion of Lesser Black-backed Gulls nesting inland in Ireland was estimated at 81%, compared with 52% in 1984–95 (Creme *et al.*, 1997).

Seabird populations of Britain and Ireland

Table 3   Numbers of roof-nesting Lesser Black-backed Gulls (AON) in Britain and Ireland 1976–2002.

Administrative area or country	1976[1]		1993–95[2]		1999–2002		Percentage change since 1976	Percentage change since 1993–95
	AON	Colonies[3]	AON	Colonies[3]	AON	Colonies		
East coast Sutherland					*1*	*1*		
Sutherland total					1	1		
Inverness					6	1		
Moray					28	1		
Banff & Buchan			5	2	4	1		−20%
City of Aberdeen			50	1	154	1		208%
Angus					7	2		
City of Dundee			7	1	65	1		829%
Kirkcaldy					6	1		
Dunfermline					38	1		
Clackmannan					88	2		
Falkirk			4	1	179	5		4375%
West Lothian			15	2	nc			
City of Edinburgh			107	3	nc			
East Lothian			1	1	nc			
Kyle & Carrick			120	2	311	4		159%
Cunninghame			20	1	97	1		385%
Kilmarnock & Loudoun					134	1		
East Kilbride					250	1		
Motherwell					28	2		
Monklands					6	1		
City of Glasgow			349	1	1,553	1		345%
Inverclyde			141	1	189	2		34%
Strathkelvin			2	1	119	1		5850%
Cumbernauld & Kilsyth			350	1	449	2		28%
Dumbarton			175	1	134	2		−23%
Scotland Total			1,346	19	3,846	35		186%
Northumberland			4	1	6	1		50%
Tyne & Wear	8	2	46	2	11	1	38%	−76%
Cleveland			9	2	90	3		900%
North Yorkshire			4	2	1	1		−75%
Humberside					1	1		
Suffolk			1	1	1,149	3		114800%
Essex					5	2		
Greater London			11	1	204	1		1755%
Kent			25	2	50	3		100%
East Sussex	1	1	2	1	18	6	1700%	800%
West Sussex					29	4		
Hampshire					1	1		
Dorset			1	1	5	2		400%
Channel Islands			2	1				
Cornwall					14	6		
Devon			6	3	17	3		183%
Somerset			6	1	47	7		683%
Avon	38	2	420	2	1,421	3	3639%	238%
Gloucestershire	80	1	255	1	2,350	4	2838%	822%
Wiltshire			5	1				
Hereford & Worcester			28	2	77	4		175%
West Midlands					40	1		
Derbyshire					30	1		
Merseyside			18	1	51	2		183%
Lancashire			7	2	56	4		700%
Cumbria			104	4	877	5		743%
England, Isle of Man and Channel Islands Total	127	6	954	31	6,550	69	5057%	587%

Administrative area or country	1976[1] AON	Colonies[3]	1993–95[2] AON	Colonies[3]	1999–2002 AON	Colonies	Percentage change since 1976	Percentage change since 1993–95
Gwent	9	1	14	4	65	2	622%	364%
South Glamorgan	170	2	101	3	72	3	−58%	−29%
Mid Glamorgan	19	2						
West Glamorgan			71	2	94	2		32%
Dyfed					112	5		
Gwynedd			9	3	25	6		178%
Clwyd			6	1	26	3		333%
Wales Total	198	5	201	13	394	21	99%	96%
Great Britain, Isle of Man and Channel Islands total	325	11	2,501	63	10,790	125	3220%	331%
Co. Antrim			8	1	63	1		688%
Co. Dublin					21	1		
All-Ireland Total			8	1	84	2		950%
Britain and Ireland Total	325	11	2,509	64	10,874	127	3246%	333%

Notes

[1] Source data: Monaghan & Coulson (1977)

[2] Source data: Raven & Coulson (1997)

[3] The numbers of colonies do not include those in 1976 and 1993–95 that were not counted.

nc   not counted

CAUSES OF CHANGE

In common with other *Larus* gulls, the increase in numbers of breeding Lesser Black-backed Gulls in Britain and Ireland through much of the 20th century is believed to have been initiated by increased protective legislation and reduced exploitation, which was subsequently favoured by increased feeding opportunities. The latter were largely man-made, notably the development of landfill sites with an abundance of edible garbage and the increased availability of discards from sea fisheries (Cramp & Simmons, 1983; Furness *et al.*, 1992). The reduced tendency for Lesser Black-backed Gulls to migrate from their breeding range in winter since the 1960s (Baker, 1980) could well have reduced the risks and expenses associated with migrating, and had further positive effects on the species' fecundity. Seabird 2000 identified some regional declines, whilst more intensive local monitoring suggests that the long-term increases may well have halted or even reversed during the 1990s at some sites. Potential reasons for these changes include culling, reduced food availability from changes in refuse disposal and fisheries practices, predation, competition from other seabirds (for food and for sites) and habitat changes.

Breeding Lesser Black-backed Gulls, along with sympatric Herring Gulls, have been culled at a number of colonies on nature reserves, where the principal aims were to reduce the impact of the gulls (predation and competition) on other breeding birds, usually terns (Thomas, 1972). Although this will have reduced local, even regional populations, or at least reduced their growth rates (e.g. Coulson, 1991), the achievement of target (lower) populations on some of those nature reserves and a reduced enthusiasm for such intervention ended many such culling and control programmes during the 1980s and 1990s. Increases following the cessation of culls (e.g. Wanless *et al.*, 1996) will have contributed to some of those reported in the period between the SCR Census (1985–88) and Seabird 2000, for example on some of the islands in the Firth of Forth, the Clyde and Loch Leven (Perth & Kinross). Outside of nature reserves, some culling programmes have been more thorough

A colony of Lesser Black-backed Gulls, safe from ground predators on Inchkeith, Firth of Forth (John C. Davies)

and resulted in the eradication of colonies. For example, the large inland colony at Flanders Moss (Stirling) was all but extirpated by the time of the SCR Census (1985–88), although disturbance and predation are also thought to have played a role. The nearby colony of Meall A'choire Odhair (Perth & Kinross), which subsequently became established and held some 1,200 pairs in 1989–90, had also disappeared by the time of Seabird 2000 (Table 2, Fig. 2). Persistent disturbance and clutch destruction at another inland colony on a Wharfedale grouse moor (North Yorkshire), which was estimated by some to hold as many as 3,000 pairs in 1990–91, reduced it to just 12 pairs (mostly unsuccessful), by 2000 (D. Sowter, pers. comm.). In common with Flanders Moss, the disturbance was likely to have contributed to the establishment of other 'satellite' colonies up to 20 km distant, but these too were systematically disturbed. The largest cull of breeding Lesser Black-backed Gulls undertaken at the time of Seabird 2000 was at the inland colony on moorland in the Bowland Fells including that at Tarnbrook Fell (Lancashire), where over 29,000 gulls, mostly Lesser Black-backed, were culled in 1999–2002 (Sowter, 2002). This cull aimed to reduce the risks of contaminating public water supplies and the impacts of gulls on the commercially managed grouse moors that parts of the colony occupy. An unknown number of colonies have been removed and potential colonists deterred from managed grouse moors as part of the gull control measures. It is ironic that it is perhaps such actions, for example through the removal of mammalian predators, which make such areas attractive to nesting gulls in the first place. Increased abundance of mammalian predators was probably responsible for reduced numbers of breeding Lesser Black-backed Gulls in parts of western Scotland, in those instances notably American Mink (Craik & Campbell, 2000). It is, perhaps, of note that the largest colony of Lesser Black-backed Gulls at the time of Seabird 2000, at South Walney (Cumbria), is probably also the only large gull colony in Britain where no culling has occurred.

Reductions in food available to breeding Lesser Black-backed Gulls as a result of changes in refuse disposal and fisheries practices are also suspected to have contributed to population declines. This is essentially a reversal of the process that is widely accepted as a major factor that contributed to their increase. The closure of some landfill sites and the practice of covering dumped waste have reduced that food source. Such measures have been linked to declines in Herring Gull populations in Brittany, France (Pons, 1992). A reduction in the practice of continuous gutting on fishing vessels, which can be especially important for breeding Lesser Black-backed Gulls (Noordhuis & Spaans, 1992; Garthe *et al.*, 1999), may have also reduced the food available to gulls breeding at some colonies; discards may become more concentrated and not necessarily within foraging range of suitable breeding locations (Perrins & Smith, 2000). On Skomer, chicks tended to be fed on terrestrial invertebrates when fishing discards became unavailable, with a concurrent marked reduction in breeding success (Perrins & Smith, 2000).

Whilst scavenging for discards behind fishing vessels, Lesser Black-backed Gulls can be out-competed by some larger seabirds, e.g. Northern Gannets, Great Black-backed Gulls and Great Skuas (Furness *et al.*, 1992). The greater mobility of Lesser Black-backed Gulls, on the other hand, perhaps gives them a competitive advantage over Herring Gulls in such situations (Noordhuis & Spaans, 1992), although Camphuysen (1994) found no competitive advantage for either species scavenging on flatfish discards. Increasing populations of the larger, competitively more successful species has been suggested, but not proven, as a cause of the long-term decline of breeding Lesser Black-backed Gulls in northern Scotland (Thom, 1986). Similarly, competition for fishery discards, in favour of Lesser Black-backed Gulls against Herring Gulls has been suggested as a cause for the reduced breeding success and declining numbers of the latter in The Netherlands (Noordhuis & Spaans, 1992). A comparison of trends in breeding numbers of the two species in Britain and Ireland show that the Lesser Black-backed Gull has increased whilst Herring Gull has declined in many areas (see Herring Gull chapter), implying that there may be competition for some common resource. Herring Gulls have continued to decline at some sites where numbers of breeding Lesser Black-backed Gulls have more recently started to decline. There has, however, probably been insufficient time to detect the effect of reduced competition, if indeed there ever has been any. Recent studies on the German North Sea coast suggest that competition between the species is unlikely, and that the Lesser Black-backed Gulls' ability to forage at greater distances from the breeding colony permits them to breed more successfully and increase independently of any inter-specific interactions. To date, there is no evidence to suggest that competition for nest sites between colony-sharing species has exerted an influence on population changes of Lesser Black-backed Gulls. Indeed, the distribution of nests in an increasing population of Lesser Black-backed Gulls on Cape Clear Island (Co. Cork) did not correspond to areas previously occupied by Herring Gulls, implying that relaxation of inter-specific competition for nest sites was unlikely to have been a factor in the increase of the former species at that site (Creme *et al.*, 1997).

Changes in the habitats in which Lesser Black-backed Gulls nest influences their distribution within a colony; for example, they avoid areas with dense nettles and ragwort at South Walney (Sowter, 2002), whilst encroachment by bracken probably provided adequate cover to permit some colony expansion on Skomer in the 1960s (Perrins & Smith, 2000). However, there is little evidence to suggest that habitat changes have had a significant effect on population change, except perhaps at the extremely localised, intra-colony level. One possible exception is the island of Craigleith (East Lothian) in the Firth of Forth, where encroachment by tree-mallow may have reduced the area available for nesting gulls (A. Leitch, pers. comm.); it is the only island in the Firth of Forth where numbers of nesting Lesser Black-backed Gulls apparently declined between the SCR Census (1985–88) and Seabird 2000 (Fig. 2).

Botulism, a condition whereby birds are poisoned by toxins produced by the bacterium *Clostridium botulinum*, is often associated with rubbish tips during warm weather, and has been recorded amongst Lesser Black-backed Gulls at a number of breeding colonies (e.g. Sowter, 2002).

Although botulism poisoning is considered to have influenced local Herring Gull populations (see Herring Gull chapter), quantitative evidence of any influence at the population level is lacking for Lesser Black-backed Gulls.

The two over-riding factors that are likely to have most influenced the population and distribution of breeding Lesser Black-backed Gulls in recent years, are, the availability of food (household waste and fishery discards) and the security of breeding sites (culling and its cessation). The availability of sufficient food, especially during the chick-rearing period, within an acceptable foraging range of secure nesting sites appears critical.

Although the Lesser Black-backed Gull is as numerous as it ever has been in Britain and Ireland, there have been some regional declines and suggestions that the increase in some areas has recently halted or perhaps even reversed. The current large population is arguably a result of unwise, often wasteful, environmental management. Declining populations, therefore, need not necessarily be cause for concern. However, in view of the international importance of the British population of Lesser Black-backed Gulls (see below), continued monitoring of its demography and assessing causes of change are high priorities. A conservation strategy based on regional minimum populations that are acceptable and sustainable is perhaps a more sensible way forward for the Lesser Black-backed Gull rather than maintenance of its current status.

INTERNATIONAL CONTEXT

The difficulties of counting breeding Lesser Black-backed Gulls for Seabird 2000 (see above) will be common to all countries and so population estimates from outside Britain and Ireland (Table 4) should be treated with similar caution. Within their global range, five subspecies have been recognised, for which there are varying opinions on several by at least some authorities (Cramp & Simmons, 1983). All Lesser Black-backed Gulls breeding in Britain and Ireland are of the subspecies *L. f. graellsii*, which also breeds in France, Iberia, the Faeroe Islands, Iceland and very locally in southwest Norway and Greenland (Snow & Perrins, 1998). However, it is clear that *L. f. graellsii* and the closely related *L. f. intermedius* have expanded their breeding range during the 20th century. As a breeder, they have colonised, or recolonised, Iceland, The Netherlands, Belgium, Germany, France, Spain and Portugal (Pons & Yésou 1997; Snow & Perrins, 1998). Recent breeding in the Canary Islands and Greenland, with increasingly frequent occurrences in North America (Post & Lewis, 1995; Grande & Palacios, 2002), suggests that range expansion is continuing. A possible mixed pairing with a Kelp Gull *L. dominicanus* in Senegal, in 1980, where both species are well outside their established breeding ranges, provides an intriguing record (Keijl *et al.*, 2001).

The total world population of the Lesser Black-backed Gull is estimated at 267,000–316,000 pairs, of which *L. f. graellsii* is estimated at *c.*179,000 pairs. Britain, along with the Isle of Man and Channel Islands holds *c.*65% of the world's breeding *L. f. graellsii*, whilst Ireland supports about 3% (Table 4).

Most populations of *L. f. graellsii* and *intermedius* appear to have recently increased, in common with those in Britain and Ireland, and have been subject to similar management strategies and changes in food availability. Other races have fared somewhat differently, for example, *L. f. fuscus* in northern Scandinavia, with some significant declines recorded. They have different feeding and migration strategies (Cramp & Simmons, 1983; Straan & Vader, 1992), and therefore the causal factors may well differ markedly.

Table 4 International context.

Country or region	Subspecies	Number of pairs		Year	Source
		Min	Max		
Great Britain, Isle of Man and Channel Isles	*graellsii*	117,000	117,000	1999–2002	Seabird 2000
All Ireland	*graellsii*	4,800	4,800	1999–2002	Seabird 2000
Belgium	*intermedius*	180	180	1996	BirdLife International /EBCC (2000)
Denmark	*intermedius*	4,400	4,400	1993–96	BirdLife International /EBCC (2000)
Estonia	*fuscus*	250	300		BirdLife International /EBCC (2000)
Faeroes	*graellsii*	9,000	9,000	1995	BirdLife International /EBCC (2000)
Finland	*fuscus*	6,000	8,000	1990–95	BirdLife International /EBCC (2000)
France	*graellsii*	22,655	22,655	1997–2001	Cadiou *et al.* (in press)
Germany	*intermedius*	3,700	9,300	1993	BirdLife International /EBCC (2000)
Greenland	*graellsii*	10	20	1996	BirdLife International /EBCC (2000)
Iceland	*graellsii*	25,000	25,000	1990	BirdLife International /EBCC (2000)
Netherlands	*intermedius*	32,000	57,000	1992–97	Bijlsma *et al.* (2001)
Norway	*fuscus & intermedius*	25,000	36,000	1990	BirdLife International /EBCC (2000)
Poland	*fuscus*	0	10		BirdLife International /EBCC (2000)
Portugal	*graellsii*	5	10	1989	BirdLife International /EBCC (2000)
Russia	*fuscus*	2,120	2,300	1998	BirdLife International /EBCC (2000)
Spain	*graellsii*	240	300	1990	BirdLife International /EBCC (2000)
Sweden	*fuscus & intermedius*	15,000	20,000	1990	BirdLife International /EBCC (2000)

Biogeographic region		Min	Max	Min % GB	Max % GB	Min % Ireland	Max % Ireland
Greenland, Iceland, Faeroes, Britain, Ireland, France, Spain and Portugal*	*graellsii*	179,000	179,000	65.4%	65.4%	2.7%	2.7%
World	all	267,000	316,000	37.0%	43.8%	1.5%	1.8%

*Stroud *et al.* (2001)

Herring Gull *Larus argentatus*

Brian Madden and Stephen F. Newton

INTRODUCTION

The Herring Gull has a near-Holarctic distribution, breeding mainly at middle and high latitudes, except in Siberia, where it is replaced by other related taxa. It is also absent from high-arctic areas. Most Herring Gulls breeding in northwest Europe are of the nominate race *L. a. argentatus*, with the race *argenteus* breeding in Britain and Ireland, where it is largely resident (movements tend to be within that region or to neighbouring coastal countries) and can show a high degree of philopatry (Calladine, 2002).

Herring Gulls are widespread around the coasts of Britain and Ireland, with the largest concentrations in northern and western Scotland and northwest England. Rocky coastline, with cliffs, islets and offshore islands, is the preferred breeding habitat, although a range of other habitats are used, including sand dunes, shingle banks and, increasingly, buildings in urban areas. A small proportion nests inland, mainly on lake islands and moorland.

It is an opportunist feeder, being both predator and scavenger. Whilst primarily a coastal feeder, mainly in the littoral and shallow sub-littoral zones (Cramp & Simmons, 1983), it readily avails of the often abundant food supplies available indirectly from man, especially waste from the fishing industry (Furness *et al.*, 1992) and landfill sites. Outside the breeding season, Herring Gulls are common along most of the coastline and inshore waters of Britain and Ireland, and also occur inland (Lack, 1986).

The Herring Gull population experienced a marked increase in all parts of its west European range through much of the 20th century, especially from about the 1930s to at least the 1970s (Cramp & Simmons, 1983). For Britain, Chabrzyk & Coulson (1976) estimated a rate of increase of *c*.13% per annum from the 1930s until the 1970s. The main reasons for the increase are considered to be increased protection, especially from egg collecting and shooting, and the species' ability to exploit new food resources derived from the activities of man, notably discards and waste from the fishing industry, refuse tips and sewage outlets. In the last decades of the 20th century, however, populations stabilised or even declined in parts of the species' range (del Hoyo *et al.*, 1996; Snow & Perrins, 1998). In Britain and Ireland, the population breeding on the coast almost halved in numbers between Operation Seafarer (1969–70: Cramp *et al.*, 1974) and the Seabird Colony Register (SCR) Census (1985–88), from 343,586 to 177,065 AON (Lloyd *et al.* 1991). Since the late 1980s, the overall population in Britain and Ireland has continued to decline, although local increases have occurred, especially in England.

CENSUS METHODS

Census methods for Herring Gulls followed the generic guidelines issued by Seabird 2000 for all *Larus* gulls (see Appendix I). Five methods were prescribed for counting gulls: 1. counts from vantage points, 2. sample quadrat counts, 3. transect counts, 4. aerial counts, and 5. flush counts of individuals. Surveyors were asked to use the most appropriate for each colony. Counts from vantage points and aerial surveys, do not require disruptive entry to the colony, but the others do. The first four methods were preferred, since these use the prescribed count units for Herring Gulls, i.e. the Apparently Occupied Nest (AON) or Apparently Occupied Territory (AOT) when there was evidence of a breeding pair holding a territory, but the nest was either not visible or could not be found. Estimates of breeding numbers are expressed as AONs, which approximate to a breeding pair or AOT. Counts of individuals attending a colony were divided by two in order to provide a rough estimate of the number of AONs (Lloyd *et al.*, 1991). Only 4% of the Seabird 2000 population estimate for Britain and Ireland was obtained from flush counts, compared to 6% during the SCR Census (1985–88), hence estimates from the two censuses are comparable in terms of methods used.

Most counts (73%) were conducted from vantage points, whilst 18% were transect counts of nests made within the colony and only 0.5% were extrapolated from sample counts of nests. Seabird 2000, more so than its predecessors, advocated aerial counts, with 4% of AONs counted in this way. These proved to be essential for surveying some urban, roof-nesting colonies (Durham, 2002) and also the most cost-effective approach for some large dense colonies on offshore islands (Davies, 2002). The most significant drawback to the method is that Herring and Lesser Black-backed Gulls tend to manifest themselves on transparencies as white dots, not separable to species, and thus some ground fieldwork is required. This is easy enough for an urban colony, but it can be more difficult to reach an offshore island sufficiently close in time to the aerial survey.

In common with other large gulls, most Herring Gull clutches are laid in May, usually during the first half of the month. Counts were thus timed for the middle to late incubation period when the maximum number of adults can be expected to be on eggs, i.e. late May–early June. In some years, nesting can be earlier and many pairs will have chicks in early June, making a May count preferable. Flush counts should be undertaken between 09.00 and 16.00 hours (BST) when they appear to be most consistent from day to day (Walsh *et al.*, 1995). Flush counts and other types of surveys

244

Seabird populations of Britain and Ireland

Table 1 Numbers of coastal-breeding Herring Gulls (AON) in Britain and Ireland 1969–2002. Numbers breeding inland and on the coast during Seabird 2000 (1998–2002) are also given.

Administrative area or country	Coastal colonies only[1]						Seabird 2000 inland and coastal
	Operation Seafarer (1969–70)	SCR Census (1985–88)[2]	Seabird 2000 (1998–2002)	Percentage change since Seafarer	Percentage change since SCR	Annual percentage change since SCR	
Shetland	9,273	4,944	4,027	−57%	−19%	−1.4%	4027
Orkney	7,831	2,726	1,933	−75%	−29%	−2.5%	1933
North coast Caithness		374	240		−36%	−3.3%	240
East coast Caithness		9,659	3,503		−64%	−7.5%	3503
Caithness total	22,483	10,033	3,743	−83%	−63%	−7.2%	3743
Northwest coast Sutherland		2309	544		−76%	−10.3%	544
Inland Sutherland							3
East coast Sutherland		450	33		−93%	−17.6%	33
Sutherland total	7,035	2,759	577	−92%	−79%	−11.0%	580
West coast Ross & Cromarty		1,033	634		−39%	−3.5%	634
Inland Ross & Cromarty							1
East coast Ross & Cromarty		97	1,345		1287%	22.2%	1345
Ross & Cromarty total	12,983	1,130	1,979	−85%	75%	4.2%	1980
Inverness	3	137	356	11767%	160%	7.1%	356
Nairn	300		80	−73%			80
Moray	1,043	539	581	−44%	8%	0.6%	709
Banff & Buchan	27,748	6,689	6671	−76%	−0%	−0.0%	6671
Gordon	4,037	3,330	853	−79%	−74%	−8.7%	853
City of Aberdeen	130	259	3,522	2609%	1260%	22.4%	3522
Kincardine & Deeside	10,682	8,217	4,226	−60%	−49%	−4.9%	4227
Angus	1,571	5,576	1,060	−33%	−81%	−11.0%	1064
Perth & Kinross							126
City of Dundee		150	296		97%	5.2%	296
Northeast Fife	15,808	2,101	2,846	−82%	35%	2.4%	2846
Kirkcaldy		4,091	3,590		−12%	−1.0%	3590
Dunfermline	55	1,090	700	1173%	−36%	−3.5%	700
Clackmannan							35
Falkirk			19				24
City of Edinburgh	10	160	424	4140%	165%	8.5%	424
East Lothian	7,371	3,593	3,553	−52%	−1%	−0.1%	3553
Berwickshire	1,516	1,852	945	−38%	−49%	−5.0%	945
Nithsdale			11				11
Stewartry	5,305	624	748	−86%	20%	1.6%	748
Wigtown	1,523	539	487	−68%	−10%	−0.7%	487
Kyle & Carrick	1,909	3,285	3,615	89%	10%	0.7%	3615
Cumnock & Doon Valley							15
Cunninghame	1,250	4,773	2,561	105%	−46%	−4.8%	2561
Kilmarnock & Loudoun							15
Eastwood							1
East Kilbride							20
Motherwell							1
City of Glasgow		3	7		133%	6.6%	19
Renfrew			1				1
Inverclyde		22	102		364%	13.2%	102
Clydebank			0				0
Bearsden & Milngavie							6
Strathkelvin							5
Cumbernauld & Kilsyth							17
Dumbarton		3	30		900%	19.9%	106
Argyll & Bute	11,004	14,946	15,370	40%	3%	0.2%	15370
Lochaber	3,150	3,109	2,798	−11%	−10%	−0.8%	2798
Skye & Lochalsh	1,427	2,934	1,283	−10%	−56%	−6.1%	1283
Western Isles–Comhairle nan eilean	3,790	3,336	2,665	−30%	−20%	−1.6%	2665
Scotland Total	159,237	92,950	71,659	−55%	−23%	−1.9%	72130
Northumberland	452	327	999	121%	206%	8.8%	1,040
Tyne & Wear	80	350	262	228%	−25%	−2.2%	273
Durham	11			−100%			
Cleveland	1,016	647	1,140	12%	76%	4.1%	1,175
North Yorkshire	1,059	907	2,299	117%	153%	6.4%	2,299

Administrative area or country	Coastal colonies only[1]						Seabird 2000 inland and coastal
	Operation Seafarer (1969–70)	SCR Census (1985–88)[2]	Seabird 2000 (1998–2002)	Percentage change since Seafarer	Percentage change since SCR	Annual percentage change since SCR	
Humberside	1,265	901	659	−48%	−27%	−2.3%	659
Bedfordshire							1
Norfolk		28	1,311		4582%	33.6%	1,311
Suffolk	151	3,393	1,248	726%	−63%	−6.5%	1,248
Essex			167				175
Greater London		3	76		2433%	22.7%	79
Kent	663	1,249	770	16%	38%	−3.1%	780
East Sussex	857	67	1,459	70%	2078%	25.8%	1,459
West Sussex	1	43	684	68300%	1491%	22.4%	685
Hampshire	3	1	59	1867%	5800%	33.9%	59
Isle of Wight	1,221	174	244	−80%	40%	2.1%	244
Dorset	2,125	200	606	−71%	203%	8.2%	606
Channel Islands	3,970	3,551	4,347	9%	22%	1.6%	4,347
Cornwall	9,630	2,589	4,940	−49%	91%	5.0%	4,979
Isles of Scilly	1,000	1,278	900	−10%	−30%	−2.9%	900
Devon	12,752	3,193	4,035	−68%	26%	1.7%	4,037
Somerset	3,207	92	286	−91%	211%	9.3%	531
Avon	5,990	800	1,164	−81%	46%	3.1%	1,578
Gloucestershire	49	10	85	73%	750%	16.6%	107
Hereford & Worcester							3
West Midlands							6
Derbyshire							3
Merseyside			59				59
Lancashire	2	1	939	46850%	93800%	58.6%	1,415
Cumbria	20,580	11,344	19,541	−5%	72%	4.0%	19,654
Isle of Man	9,977	9,062	7,126	−29%	−21%	−1.8%	7,126
England, Isle of Man and Channel Islands Total	**76,061**	**40,210**	**55,405**	**−27%**	**38%**	**2.4%**	**56,838**
Gwent	199	25	68	−66%	172%	6.9%	76
South Glamorgan	211	638	294	39%	−54%	−5.0%	294
Mid Glamorgan	196		3	−98%			3
West Glamorgan	189	13	519	175%	3892%	26.6%	519
Dyfed	15,394	5,242	8,424	−45%	61%	3.6%	8,424
Gwynedd	31,660	5,060	4,424	−86%	−13%	−0.9%	4,460
Clwyd	727	111	198	−73%	78%	3.7%	198
Wales Total	**48,576**	**11,089**	**13,930**	**−71%**	**26%**	**1.6%**	**13,974**
Great Britain, Isle of Man and Channel Islands Total	**283,874**	**144,249**	**140,994**	**−50%**	**−2%**	**−0.2%**	**142,942**
Co. Londonderry		17			−100%		
Co. Antrim	9,245	5,843	101	−99%	−98%	−24.5%	101
Co. Down	6,757	11,701	608	−91%	−95%	−19.5%	608
Co. Fermanagh							5
Co. Monaghan							7
Co. Dublin	13,407	6684	2,905	−78%	−57%	−6.0%	2,905
Co. Wicklow	374	150	29	−92%	−81%	−11.9%	29
Co. Wexford	6,590	1770	75	−99%	−96%	−20.2%	75
Co. Waterford	4,060	1654	409	−90%	−75%	−10.2%	409
Co. Cork	3,511	1,990	300	−91%	−85%	−12.2%	300
Co. Kerry	4,458	428	276	−94%	−36%	−3.5%	276
Co. Clare	1,426	36	69	−95%	92%	5.2%	69
Co. Galway	1,844	75	46	−98%	−39%	−4.2%	49
Co. Mayo	2,078	186	369	−82%	98%	5.5%	369
Co. Sligo	611	214	123	−80%	−43%	−4.4%	123
Co. Donegal	5,351	2,068	810	−85%	−61%	−7.2%	910
All–Ireland Total	**59,712**	**32,816**	**6,120**	**−90%**	**−81%**	**−12.0%**	**6,235**
Britain and Ireland Total	**343,586**	**177,065**	**147,114**	**−57%**	**−17%**	**−1.4%**	**149,177**

Notes

[1] Operation Seafarer and the SCR Census did not survey inland.

[2] The figures for the SCR are actual counts and do not include adjustments to totals made in order to account for unsurveyed colonies (see Lloyd *et al.*, 1991)

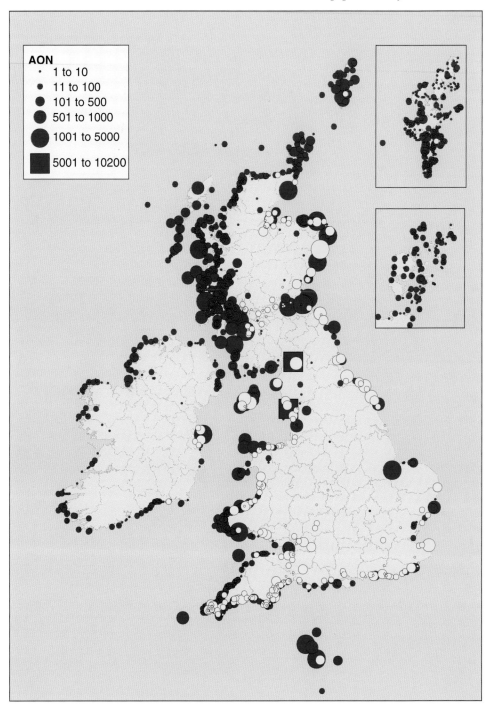

Figure 1   Abundance and distribution of breeding Herring Gulls in Britain and Ireland 1998–2002. Natural sites are shown in red and man-made sites (e.g. rooftops) are in yellow (the scale is the same for both types of sites).

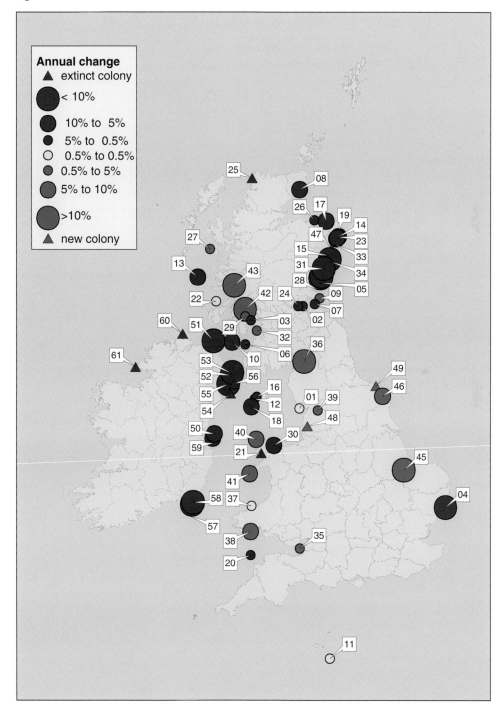

Figure 2   Changes in the number of breeding Herring Gulls (AON) at major coastal colonies in Britain and Ireland between the SCR Census (1985–88) and Seabird 2000 (1998–2002). Major coastal colonies are those that contained the top 40% of the British population during the SCR and/or Seabird 2000 or the top 75% of the Irish population during the SCR and/or Seabird 2000. Numbers correspond to colonies listed in Table 2.

involving disturbance to the colony should be undertaken in dry conditions, to avoid eggs and chicks becoming chilled.

Herring Gulls frequently nest in association with Lesser Black-backed and Great Black-backed Gulls, and less commonly with the smaller Black-headed and Common Gulls, and such colonies pose challenges for surveyors. Counting mixed colonies is better done by remote methods, especially from vantage points, as untended clutches can be difficult to allocate to the different species. A composite approach was sometimes used, whereby adults attending clutches or small chicks are flushed and the overall number of breeding adults counted, followed by a fairly thorough nest search. The number of AONs allocated to each species is derived from the relative proportion of adults flushed.

Seabird 2000 differed from Operation Seafarer (1969–70) and the Seabird Colony Register Census (1985–88), in that the overall strategy was to cover *all* breeding seabirds in Britain and Ireland. Thus, coverage was planned for coastal sites and islands, and with particular relevance to Herring Gulls, inland areas such as moorland and reservoirs and urban areas where roof-nesting was known to occur. Previously, roof-nesting gulls were counted separately, with the most recent previous survey in 1993–95 (Raven & Coulson, 1997). Given the substantial decline in numbers of coastal breeding Herring Gulls in Britain and Ireland between 1969–70 and 1985–88 (Lloyd *et al.*, 1991), it was considered important that Seabird 2000 should concurrently count roof-nesting and inland colonies.

Eventual coverage in Seabird 2000, although not complete, was comprehensive across the different colony types, and all major colonies and breeding areas were censused. The largest gaps were in western and southern Ireland, particularly the islands off Connemara (Co. Galway) and the mainland coast of west Co. Cork. However, the former were covered systematically during the 1995 All-Ireland tern survey, which indicated that very few significant Herring Gull colonies were present in the area (Hannon *et al.*, 1997).

CURRENT STATUS AND TRENDS

Seabird 2000 estimated the total British and Irish Herring Gull population at 149,177 AON, with 49% in Scotland, 38% in England, the Isle of Man and the Channel Islands, 9% in Wales and 4% in Ireland (Table 1). In Britain, the Herring Gull was widely distributed around the coastline (Fig. 1). The largest continuous gap in distribution was in east England, between Flamborough Head (Humberside) and The Wash (Lincolnshire and Norfolk), and the species was only intermittently present as far south as Kent. In Ireland, it was fairly widely distributed along southern, western and northwest coasts but, apart from localised concentrations in Co. Antrim, Co. Down, Co. Dublin and Co. Wicklow, was absent from much of the coast between Co. Londonderry to south Co. Wexford (Fig. 1). Its apparent absence from much of the Co. Galway coast in the west was due to poor coverage of the Connemara islands. The absence or intermittent presence in both eastern England and eastern Ireland appears to be largely due to the lack of suitable natural nesting habitat. The species was scarce inland.

The establishment of colonies on artificial surfaces, mainly roofs of buildings, has extended the overall distribution of the species in Britain since Operation Seafarer (1969–70), although the habit is still very localised in northern and western Scotland (other than the Forth–Clyde region) and in Ireland (Cramp, 1971; Monaghan & Coulson, 1977; Raven & Coulson, 1997; Madden, 2001). Between 1976 and 1994, the number of sites colonised by roof-nesters increased by 5% per annum (Raven & Coulson, 1997). Since 1993–95 (Raven & Coulson, 1997) the number of colonies on buildings in Britain and Ireland has increased from 125 to 220 (Table 3). Roof-nesting colonies were

Table 2 Changes in the number of breeding Herring Gulls (AON) at major colonies in Britain and Ireland between SCR Census (1985–88) and Seabird 2000 (1998–2002). Major colonies are those that contained the top 40% of the British population during the SCR and/or Seabird 2000 or the top 75% of the Irish population during the SCR and/or Seabird 2000. ID number corresponds to colony symbols in Fig. 2.

ID	Colony	SCR Census (1985–88)	Seabird 2000 (1998–2002)	Percentage change since SCR	Annual percentage change since SCR	Percentage of population in Britain or Ireland 1998–2002
1	South Walney	10,000	10,129	1%	0.1%	7.1%
2	Inchkeith	4,091	3,580	−12%	−0.9%	2.5%
3	Little Cumbrae Island	3,500	2,000	−43%	−4.2%	1.4%
4	Orfordness	3,390	700	−79%	−10.0%	0.5%
5	Ethie Cliffs, including Red Head Cliffs	2,875	118	−96%	−20.5%	0.1%
6	Ailsa Craig (SPA)	2,350	1,450	−38%	−3.4%	1.0%
7	Craigleith	2,280	1,969	−14%	−1.1%	1.4%
8	Stack of Occumster to Uamh Ron	2,222	690	−69%	−8.3%	0.5%
9	Isle of May (SPA)	2,100	2,845	35%	2.2%	2.0%
10	Sanda Islands (SSSI)	1,900	700	−63%	−7.4%	0.5%
11	Jersey	1,500	1,546	3%	0.2%	1.1%
12	Isle of Man: Glen Maye to Peel	1,475	957	−35%	−3.0%	0.7%
13	Tiree	1,430	787	−45%	−4.5%	0.6%
14	Whinnyfold Cliffs	1,304	365	−72%	−8.1%	0.3%
15	Tremuda Bay to Old Hall Bay	1,297	112	−91%	−17.1%	0.1%
16	Isle of Man: Peel to Glen Mooar	1,276	707	−45%	−4.4%	0.5%
17	Gardenstown to Collie Head	1,236	614	−50%	−4.6%	0.4%
18	Calf of Man	1,200	670	−44%	−4.8%	0.5%
19	Grey Mare to Slains Castle	1,153	826	−28%	−2.2%	0.6%
20	Lundy	1,117	777	−30%	−2.5%	0.5%
21	Bodorgan Head	1,110	0	−100%		0.0%
22	Colonsay and Oransay	1,079	1,121	4%	0.3%	0.8%
23	Sands of Forvie (SPA)	1,048	272	−74%	−8.6%	0.2%
24	Inchcolm	1,040	621	−40%	−3.4%	0.4%
25	Eilean an Roin	993	0	−100%		0.0%
26	Logie Head to Sandend	989	837	−15%	−1.1%	0.6%
27	Canna and Sanday (SPA)	977	1,138	16%	1.2%	0.8%
28	Meg's Craig to Deils Heid North	975	127	−87%	−13.6%	0.1%
29	Inchmarnock Island	950	1,550	63%	3.1%	1.1%
30	Puffin Island (SSSI)	919	400	−56%	−5.4%	0.3%
31	St Cyrus	909	2	−100%	−35.4%	0.0%
32	Lady Isle	900	1,500	67%	2.9%	1.0%
33	Old Slains to Collieston	884	216	−76%	−9.0%	0.2%
34	Trelong Bay	802	665	−17%	−1.3%	0.5%
35	Steep Holm Island	750	956	27%	2.1%	0.7%
36	Rockcliffe Marsh[1]	708	7,200	917%	23.5%	5.0%
37	Cardigan Island	700	746	7%	0.4%	0.5%
38	Caldey Island	684	2,134	212%	7.9%	1.5%
39	Tarnbrook Fell[2]	420	475	13%	0.8%	0.3%
40	The Skerries (SPA)	361	840	133%	6.2%	0.6%
41	Bardsey Island (SPA)	205	663	223%	8.7%	0.5%
42	Burnt Islands	190	659	247%	11.0%	0.5%
43	Bach Island	100	810	710%	19.2%	0.6%
44	Birchington[3]	20	575	2775%	25.1%	0.4%
45	Outer Trial Bank, The Wash	10	1,003	9930%	43.0%	0.7%
46	Scarborough[3]	1	870	86900%	49.1%	0.6%

Table 2   continued

ID	Colony	SCR Census (1985–88)	Seabird 2000 (1998–2002)	Percentage change since SCR	Annual percentage change since SCR	Percentage of population in Britain or Ireland 1998–2002
47	Aberdeen City[3]	nc	3350			2.3%
48	Hesketh and Banks Marshes, Ribble Estuary (part of SPA)	nc	750			0.5%
49	Whitby[3]	nc	528			0.4%
50	Lambay Island	5,500	1,806	−67%	−8.9%	29.0%
51	Rathlin Island (SPA)	4,037	14	−100%	−33.3%	0.2%
52	Old Lighthouse Island and Mew Island	4,000	97	−98%	−20.8%	1.6%
53	Big Copeland Island	3,000	258	−91%	−13.4%	4.1%
54	Gun's and Sandy Islands	1,665	0	−100%		0.0%
55	Strangford Lough (SPA)	1,736	253	−85%	−13.6%	4.1%
56	Burial Island	1,250	0	−100%		0.0%
57	Great Saltee	825	43	−95%	−20.2%	0.7%
58	Little Saltee	600	30	−95%	−22.1%	0.5%
59	Ireland's Eye	540	246	−54%	−5.9%	3.9%
60	Garvan Isles	531	nc			
61	Rathlin O'Birne	505	nc			

Notes

[1] SCR 1988 count estimated from a mixed count of 2,500 AON of Herring Gulls and Lesser Black-backed Gulls using a ratio of 2.53LBBG:1HG measured in 1990.

[2] Inland

[3] Roof-nesting

[4] The colony on Lambay Island was reduced by culling from 20,000 AON in 1985

nc   not counted

concentrated along southern and northeast coasts of England, the Bristol Channel, the Forth–Clyde region and northeast Scotland (Fig. 1). Administrative areas that have been colonised by roof-nesters since 1993–95 include Sutherland, Clackmannan, Falkirk, Essex, Suffolk and West Sussex. Herring Gull has established a substantial presence in The Wash, where it was unknown as a breeder at the time of Operation Seafarer, by utilising an artificial island known as the Outer Trial Bank (Smith, 2001).

Whilst Herring Gulls have not been lost from any substantial stretch of coast in either Britain or Ireland since the SCR Census, a number of large colonies have been totally or virtually abandoned, notably in Co. Down (Gun's & Sandy Islands, Burial Island) and in Gwynedd (Bodorgan Head), Sutherland (Eilean An Roin) and Kincardine & Deeside (St Cyrus).

Seven sites held 2,000 or more AON: South Walney (Cumbria), Rockcliffe Marsh (Cumbria), Inchkeith (Kirkcaldy), Aberdeen City, the Isle of May (Fife), Caldey Island (Dyfed) and Little Cumbrae Island (Cunninghame). A further nine sites held 1,000–2,000 AON (Table 2). Only 2,074 AON, or 1.4% of the total population, occurred inland, with the moorland site at Tarnbrook Fell in the Pennines being the largest colony (475 AON). A significant proportion of the population, 20,170 AON or 13.5% of the total, now nest on buildings (Fig. 1, Table 3). In addition to the large roof-nesting colony in Aberdeen City, a further five sites support more than 500 AON: Scarborough, North Yorkshire (870 AON), RAF Carlisle, Cumbria (750 AON), Birchington, Kent (575 AON), Whitby, North Yorkshire (528 AON) and Hartlepool, Teesside (532 AON). Colonies also occur on other man-made structures, such as at Hinckley Power Station, Somerset (107 AON).

The total of 147,114 AON in coastal areas in Seabird 2000 compares to 177,065 AON in the SCR Census (1985–88), or a decline of 16.9%, and to 343,586 in Operation Seafarer (1969–70), a

Table 3   Numbers of roof-nesting Herring Gulls (AON) in Britain and Ireland 1976–2002.

Administrative area or country	1976[1]		1993–95[2]		1999–2002		Percentage change since 1976	Percentage change since 1993–95
	AON	Colonies[3]	AON	Colonies[3]	AON	Colonies		
Shetland	6	1	59	1	21	1	250%	−64%
North coast Caithness			58	1	50	1		−14%
East coast Caithness			73	1				
Caithness total			*131*	*2*	*50*	*1*		*−62%*
East coast Sutherland					33	1		
Sutherland total					*33*	*1*		
East coast Ross & Cromarty	1	1	35	5	83	7	8200%	137%
Ross & Cromarty total	*1*	*1*	*35*	*5*	*83*	*7*	*8200%*	*137%*
Inverness	3	1	150	1	356	1	11767%	137%
Nairn	9	1			80	1	789%	
Moray	1	1	32	1	153	2	15200%	378%
Banff & Buchan			322	6	444	4		38%
City of Aberdeen	1	1	2,000	1	3,350	1	334900%	68%
Angus			448	2	398	2		−11%
Perth & Kinross					1	1		
City of Dundee	9	1			296	1	3189%	
Northeast Fife			1	1				
Kirkcaldy					10	1		
Dunfermline					18	3		
Clackmannan					35	1		
Falkirk					24	2		
West Lothian			5	2	nc			
City of Edinburgh			42	3	nc			
East Lothian			23	2	nc			
Berwickshire	22	2	125	2	194	1	782%	55%
Kyle & Carrick			133	2	144	4		8%
Cunninghame			3	1	19	1		533%
Kilmarnock & Loudoun	3	1			15	1	400%	
East Kilbride					20	1		
Motherwell					1	1		
City of Glasgow			6	1	26	1		333%
Inverclyde			35	1	40	3		14%
Strathkelvin					5	1		
Cumbernauld & Kilsyth			13	1	17	1		31%
Dumbarton			5	1	10	1		100%
Scotland Total	**55**	**10**	**3,568**	**36**	**5,843**	**46**	**10524%**	**64%**
Northumberland	33	1	216	1	252	2	664%	17%
Tyne & Wear	459	2	1,236	2	125	1	−73%	−90%
Durham			1	1				
Cleveland	27	1	422	5	604	2	2137%	43%
North Yorkshire	434	5	556	6	1,749	6	303%	215%
Humberside			1	1	17	2		1600%
Suffolk					421	3		
Essex					28	2		
Greater London	5	1	5	1	77	1	1440%	1440%
Kent	301	4	1,491	11	696[4]	6	131%	−53%
East Sussex	244	4	nc		1,033	11	323%	
West Sussex			nc		510	6		
Hampshire			20	3	48	2		140%
Dorset	29	3	47	2	201	4	593%	328%
Channel Islands	1	1	129	1	190	1	18900%	47%
Cornwall	152	4	647	9	1,487	35	878%	130%
Devon	141	7	1,040	16	1838	34	1204%	77%
Somerset	2	1	19	1	411	8	20450%	2063%
Avon	69	2	183	2	622	4	801%	240%
Gloucestershire	60	1	46	2	107	2	78%	133%
Hereford & Worcester					3	1		

Table 3   continued.

Administrative area or country	1976[1]		1993–95[2]		1999–2002		Percentage change since 1976	Percentage change since 1993–95
	AON	Colonies[3]	AON	Colonies[3]	AON	Colonies		
West Midlands					6	1		
Derbyshire					3	1		
Merseyside	1	1	20	1	59	2	5800%	195%
Lancashire			11	2	185	4		1582%
Cumbria	3	1	422	6	1,606	4	53433%	281%
Isle of Man	1	1	13	3	6	1	500%	−54%
England, Isle of Man and Channel Isles Total	1,962	40	6,525	76	12,284	146	526%	88%
Gwent	69	2	19	3	76	2	10%	300%
South Glamorgan	435	3	148	2				
Mid Glamorgan	74	2	1	1				
West Glamorgan	82	1	161	2	472	3	476%	193%
Dyfed			31	2	434	6		1300%
Gwynedd	260	4	289	5	674	10	159%	133%
Clwyd	7	1	123	1	170	5	2329%	38%
Wales Total	927	13	772	16	1,826	26	97%	137%
Great Britain, Isle of Man and Channel Islands Total	2,944	63	10,865	128	19,953	218	578%	84%
Co. Antrim			1	1	8	1		700%
Co. Dublin	2	1	121	4	180	5	8900%	49%
Co. Waterford	12	1	24	1	29	1	142%	21%
All-Ireland Total	14	2	146	6	217	7	1450%	49%
Britain and Ireland Total	2,958	65	11,011	134	20,170	225	582%	83%

Notes

[1] Source data: Monaghan & Coulson (1997)

[2] Source data: Raven & Coulson (1997)

[3] The numbers of colonies do not include those in 1976 and 1993–95 that were not counted.

[4] Colonies were not surveyed at Dover and Folkestone, which held a combined total of 900 AON in 1983–85.

nc   not counted

decline of 57.2%. Whilst virtually all areas experienced declines between Operation Seafarer and the SCR Census, there have been quite different regional population trends across Britain and Ireland between the SCR and Seabird 2000.

Ireland experienced a dramatic population collapse (26,696 AON or 85.8% decline) since the SCR Census. This was a considerably higher proportional decline than in the period between Operation Seafarer and the SCR Census (45.0% decline). Declines were registered at virtually all sites in Ireland, although the largest losses (in terms of absolute numbers) were in the former strongholds in the northeast and southeast, namely Rathlin Island (Co. Antrim), the Copeland Islands (Co. Down), Burial Island, Gun's & Sandy Islands (all Strangford Lough; Co. Down), Lambay (Co. Dublin) and the Saltee Islands (Co. Wexford). Long-term monitoring at Lighthouse and Mew Islands in the Copeland Islands (Fig. 3) showed that the population peaked at 7,000 AON in 1982, fell sharply to 1,850 AON in 1987, and reached the low hundreds by 1992, with no subsequent recovery (90 pairs 2000–2002: Stewart, 1991; J. Stewart, pers. comm.). At Lambay (Fig. 3) a population peak of 20,000 AON in 1984 was followed by a sharp decline to 5,000–6,000 AON, due mainly to intensive culling over several seasons. The population has been in gradual decline since, with 2,485 AON in 1995 and a low of 358 AON by 2002 (Merne & Madden, 1999; Madden & Newton, 2002). At Clare Island in western Ireland, the Herring Gull population dropped from

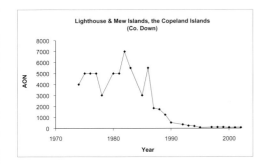

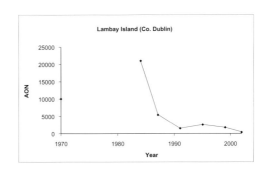

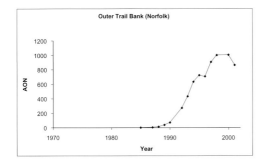

Figure 3   Numbers of breeding Herring Gulls (AON) at colonies where repeated counts have been conducted 1970–2002. Data for the Copeland Islands from Stewart (1991) and J. Stewart (pers. comm.) data for Lambay Island from Merne & Madden (1999) and Madden & Newton (2002); data for Outer Trial Bank from Smith (2001).

460 AON in 1982 to only 23 AON in 1999 (Cussen *et al.*, 1999), whilst on Cape Clear Island in the extreme southwest, the population fall from 568 AON in 1983 to 46 AON in 1999. At inland gull colonies in western Ireland, the Herring Gull population almost collapsed between 1977–78 and 1992–93, from 752 to 50 individuals respectively (Whilde *et al.*, 1993).

In Scotland, the major decline which took place between Operation Seafarer (1969–70) and the SCR Census (1985–88) of 66,287 AON or 41.6% continued into Seabird 2000 but at a slower rate (21,291 AON or 22.9%). Whilst each region in Scotland experienced an overall decline since the SCR Census (1985–88), some sites have remained stable or have increased. The largest losses occurred in Caithness, where for instance the colony at the Stack of Occumster-Uamh Ron declined from 2,222 to 690 AON, whilst in Sutherland the colony at Eilean An Roin has been abandoned (it held 993 AON in 1985–88). In the southwest, the situation is less clear. Substantial increases occurred at several sites, including Bach Island (100 to 810 AON), Inchmarnock Island (950 to 1,550 AON) and Lady Island (900 to 1,500 AON), whilst substantial declines occurred on the Sanda Islands (1,900 to 700 AON) in Argyll & Bute, and at Little Cumbrae Island, in the Firth of Clyde (3,500 to 2,000 AON). Numbers on Colonsay and Oronsay, also in Argyll & Bute, remained remarkably stable between 1986 (1,160 AON) and 1999–2000 (1,121 AON: Jardine *et al.*, 2002). In eastern Scotland, losses were registered at practically all of the main colonies between Banff & Buchan and East Lothian. These included almost the total extirpation of a substantial colony at St Cyrus (Kincardine & Deeside) between 1985–88 and 1994 (909 to 2 AON: Walsh *et al.*, 1995). Large declines were also registered at Ethie Cliffs (2,875 to 118 AON) and Meg's Craig (975 to 127 AON) in Angus. The Herring Gull population on the Isle of May had declined dramatically from 15,000 to 2,100 AON between Operation Seafarer (1969–70) and the SCR Census (1985–1988). This was partly due to a culling programme which ceased in 1986. Numbers rose from 1992, to reach 2,970 AON in 1996 (Thompson *et al.*, 1997) and have fluctuated at around this level since.

The thriving roof-nesting colony in Aberdeen City, now the fifth-largest Herring Gull colony in Britain and Ireland and the largest urban gull colony in the world, increased by 68% (2,000 to 3,350 AON) between 1993–95 and 2000.

In contrast to Scotland and Ireland, populations in England and Wales increased since the SCR Census, although a decline was registered in the Isle of Man. The increase in England (excluding the Isle of Man and Channel Islands) of 40.6% or 16,335 AON, follows the earlier loss of 34,517 AON between Operation Seafarer and the SCR Census. Whilst a substantial part of the increase can be attributed to continued growth in the number of roof-nesting pairs, there have also been significant increases in several large colonies at natural sites. South Walney, which has the largest Herring Gull colony in Britain and Ireland, has remained stable since the 1985–88 period. This colony, however, had been considerably larger in the 1970s with an estimated 43,852 individuals in May 1978 (Hosey & Goodridge, 1980). Further north, at Rockcliffe Marsh on the Solway Firth, the Herring Gull colony has increased almost ten-fold since 1985 (708 to 7,200 AON). In east England, the colony on the Outer Trial Bank in the Wash, which had only 10 AON in 1987, increased to a peak of 1,003 AON (minimum count) in 2001 (Fig. 3; Smith, 2001). In Suffolk, the colony at Orford Ness, which was one of the few that grew significantly between Operation Seafarer and the SCR Census, declined since with numbers varying between 700 and 1,450 AON in 1999–2002 (M. Wright, pers. comm.). Roof-nesting Herring Gulls now account for 26.6% of the total population in England. Since the survey in 1993–95 by Raven & Coulson (1997) the number of roof-nesting pairs in England has increased from 6,523 to 12,088 (Table 1b). Raven & Coulson (1997) estimated that the number of roof-nesting Herring Gulls in Britain and Ireland increased at a rate of 10% per annum in 1976–94. This rate of increase was sustained in England in 1994–2001.

The Herring Gull population on the Isle of Man fell by a relatively low level between Operation Seafarer and the SCR Census (9,977 to 9,062 AON), although Slinn (1971) considered that the total Manx population in 1969 was actually nearer 12,000 AON. The population has declined at a faster rate (21.4%) since the SCR, with the decline most evident along the west coast and especially on the Calf of Man, which experienced a drop from 1,200 to 670 AON (Sharpe & Sapsford, 1999). Roof-nesting is rare in the Isle of Man, with only 6 AON in one colony in Castletown.

The population in the Channel Islands has shown more long-term stability than most other areas in Britain and Ireland. After a drop in numbers of 10.5% between Operation Seafarer and the SCR Census, numbers increased by 22.4% between the SCR and Seabird 2000 to reach 4,347 AON. One substantial roof-nesting colony (190 AON) exists in St Helier.

A moderate increase in the Herring Gull population in Wales has occurred since the SCR Census (2,841 AON or 25.6%), although this follows heavy losses between Operation Seafarer and the SCR Census (37,487 AON or 77.2% decline). Almost half the recent increase, however, is due to a very substantial rise on Caldey Island (Dyfed) (684 to 2,134 AON). Significant increases also occurred on Bardsey Island (Gwynedd) and the Skerries (Gwynedd). Losses occurred at some sites, with the colony at Bodorgan Head (Gwynedd) being completely abandoned, whilst that at Puffin Island (Gwynedd) declining by 56.5%. On Skomer Island, numbers increased through the 1960s to 2,200 AON in 1969 and then remained fairly stable through the 1970s. A dramatic decrease occurred in the early 1980s to 645 AON by 1984. Numbers fluctuated at this level in the following years but then declined to reach 299 AON in 1998 (Perrins & Smith, 2000). Since then, there has been an increase to 505 AON in 2001 (Mavor *et al.*, 2002). Roof-nesting birds have also contributed to the rise in the Welsh population, now accounting for 13.0% of the total, the largest colony is at Port Talbot in West Glamorgan (265 AON).

Since the SCR Census (1985–88), a small number of yellow-legged gulls (*L. a. michahellis* / *L. a. cachinnans*) have appeared in Britain and have frequented some English coastal and inland sites. The first bird involved in a nesting attempt was in 1992 on Coquet Island (Northumberland), but in this case and in several other attempts, the yellow-legged gull formed a 'hybrid' pair, usually with a Lesser Black-backed Gull. A pure pair of yellow-legged gulls attempted to breed at a site in Dorset in 1995, in a mixed colony of Black-headed Gulls, Common Terns, Herring Gulls and Great Black-backed Gulls. In each year during 1999 to 2001, one or two pure pairs have nested at the site and five young have fledged during this period (M. Ogilvie & Rare Breeding Birds Panel, pers. comm.). In 2001 a third pure pair of yellow-legged gulls nested at another site in Dorset.

CAUSES OF CHANGE

The Herring Gull population in Britain and Ireland was probably at an all-time high during the 1960s and early 1970s (Harris, 1970; Cramp *et al.*, 1974; Cramp & Simmons, 1983). The period between Operation Seafarer (1969–70) and the SCR Census (1985–88) saw dramatic declines in the breeding population throughout all regions in Britain and Ireland. Seabird 2000 found continued declines in the populations in some regions, whilst in other regions populations had stabilised or increased since the SCR Census.

In considering the decline in the Herring Gull population in Britain and Ireland between the 1969–70 and 1985–88 censuses, Lloyd *et al.* (1991) highlighted that since 1975 avian botulism had been proved or strongly suspected to have caused mortality incidents among gulls both on and off the breeding colonies throughout Britain and Ireland. Avian botulism is a paralytic, often fatal, disease of birds that results when they ingest toxin produced by the bacterium *Clostridium botulinum* (Friend & Franson, 1999). *C. botulinum* is an anaerobic bacterium that exists in the form of dormant spores when environmental conditions are adverse. Spores of type C botulism, the main strain which causes mortality in waterbirds, are widespread in wetland sediments. Botulinum toxin is produced only after the spores germinate, when the organism is actively growing and multiplying. As with other bacteria, temperature plays a critical role in the multiplication of *C. botulinum*. Conditions that elevate sediment temperatures and decrease dissolved oxygen, including the presence of decaying organic matter and shallow water, may increase the risk of botulism outbreaks. Decomposing carcasses, both vertebrate and invertebrate, are well known to support toxin production. Refuse tips which receive organic waste are likely to provide favourable conditions for botulism outbreaks. Although many substances are suitable for botulinum toxin production, in order for a botulism outbreak to occur the toxin must be in a form that is available to birds. In some cases decaying organic matter may be directly ingested or infection can occur via maggots picked from carcasses that are infected with the disease. In this way botulism outbreaks often become self-perpetuating. Botulism typically occurs in waves during the breeding season, although outbreaks can occur in winter (Buckley & O'Halloran, 1986). Healthy birds, sick, and recently dead birds will commonly be found together during a botulism outbreak, along with carcasses in various stages of post-mortem decay. Whilst laboratory confirmation of the disease is usually not feasible, the clinical symptoms consistent with botulism are easily recognisable. Inability to sustain flight is seen early in botulism and is followed by paralysis of the inner eyelid and neck muscles, resulting in inability to hold the head erect. There are no diagnostic lesions associated with botulism (Friend & Franson, 1999).

Since the SCR Census, it is evident that botulism has continued to affect birds in most regions, but particularly in Ireland and western Britain. As the disease affects all age classes of birds, it not only removes existing breeders from the population but also potential recruits. At most of the former large colonies in Ireland, botulism is suspected to be the principal, or at least a significant, cause of the recent declines. At Lambay, botulism has had a continuous presence in the gull population since at least the mid-1980s, with regular losses occurring throughout the year. For instance, in excess of

200 dying or recently dead birds, including fledged young, were counted in July 2001 (Merne & Madden, 1999; Madden & Newton, 2002). Lambay is located 5 km from a major municipal landfill situated on an enclosed estuary and, prior to the collapse of the breeding population, birds regularly commuted between the two sites. Botulism has also been suspected as the main cause for the large losses at Rathlin Island (L. McFaul, pers. comm.), the Copeland Islands (Stewart, 1991; J. Stewart, pers. comm.), Strangford Lough (Upton *et al.*, 2000) and Great Saltee (O. J. Merne, pers. comm.), and is considered the most likely cause for the demise of the Herring Gull at inland sites in western Ireland (Whilde *et al.*, 1993). In Scotland, substantial population declines at Ailsa Craig and the Sanda Isles are considered to be due mainly to botulism, which has been almost an annual occurrence in recent years (B. Zonfrillo & R. Morton, pers. comm.). Whilst losses due to botulism are annual in the large gull colonies at South Walney (Dean, 1990; Mavor *et al.*, 2001; K. Milligan, pers. comm.) and Rockcliffe Marsh (K. Milligan, pers. comm.) these sites have not declined since the SCR Census. Botulism is present in the Herring Gull population in the Isle of Man and is suspected to be a contributing factor for recent losses (C. Sharpe, pers. comm.). Perrins & Smith (2000) note that the major decline in the Herring Gull population on Skomer Island coincided with the introduction of botulism into the population. The source of the botulism was considered to be local rubbish tips, as many of the Skomer gulls had switched to feeding at these following the closure of the fish docks at Milford Haven. As avian botulism appears to be now endemic in many Herring Gull populations in Britain and Ireland, study into the sources for the outbreaks is required, as well as procedures for the prevention and control of outbreaks.

Whilst the increase in the Herring Gull population through much of the 20th century is attributable, at least in part, to the availability of plentiful and easily accessible food supplies from artificial sources, especially refuse tips, fishery operations and sewage outlets, the decline in recent decades in the amount of food from these same sources is suspected to have contributed to the population declines witnessed since the SCR Census.

The trend away from the use of refuse tips for waste disposal and the improved management of existing landfill sites, which includes use of small active work areas, rapid covering of dumped material and bird control procedures, means that there are now fewer scavenging opportunities for gulls. The dependence that some populations of Herring Gulls have had on refuse tips has been shown in several studies. For instance, in the Bristol Channel Mudge (1978) showed that nearly 70% of food taken during the breeding season was obtained from refuse tips, while in a colony of Herring Gulls in Brittany it was demonstrated that the proportion of refuse in the gulls' diet was 61–85% (Pons, 1992). Some studies have indicated that the breeding success of Herring Gulls may be higher in populations nesting close to refuse tips than those further away. In a population of Herring Gulls in The Netherlands, Spaans (1971) observed a positive relationship between brood size and the amount of human refuse in the chick's diet. In a study of breeding parameters in a population situated 12 km from a landfill site in Brittany, Pons (1992) showed that when the amount of refuse dumped was reduced by 80%, significantly fewer gulls visited the tip than before and that the decreased food availability affected all breeding parameters, with overall breeding success decreasing from a mean of 1.3 to 0.5 young per breeding pair.

In recent decades, the amount of fisheries waste available to gulls has decreased considerably, as a result of declines in the total catch and reduction of dumping of waste, both at sea and in ports. In eastern North America, Nisbet (1978) noted that areas where the Herring Gull population has been in decline are those where total fish landings have declined most markedly. Perrins & Smith (2000) considered that the closure of the Milford Haven fish docks must have had a serious effect on the availability of food for Herring Gulls which visited the docks regularly. On Canna (Lochaber), poor breeding performance was detected in 2001 (only 10% of 704 checked nests produced young) and the situation worsened in 2002 when 800 pairs fledged only 60 young (Mavor *et al.*, 2002; Swann,

2003). Nest failure mostly occurred at the egg or very small chick stage. Poor productivity was attributed to the decline in the local prawn fishing industry, given a large part of the Herring Gulls' diet comprises discards. Adults have attempted to switch to a diet of shellfish and European Shag eggs to meet the shortfall in food for chicks (Swann, 2003).

Herring Gulls also feed on offal and undersized fish discarded at sea from trawlers (Furness *et al.*, 1988), but their success in obtaining such food is dependent on discard size, other scavenging species present and on geographical location. In Shetland waters, Herring Gulls were unable to swallow larger discards, which were taken quickly by Northern Gannets, Great Black-backed Gulls and Great Skuas (Hudson & Furness, 1988, 1989). However, in the Clyde area and wider Irish Sea, Herring Gulls were more numerous and had a better relative foraging success (Furness *et al.* 1988, 1992). More recent work in the Celtic Sea (Berrow, 1998) has demonstrated the importance of discards to Herring Gulls in winter. However, this has apparently not benefited local breeders, since some nearby colonies have collapsed since the Seabird Colony Register (e.g. Great Saltee, Co. Wexford).

Restrictions imposed on the fishing industry by the EU Common Fisheries Policy have become more severe in recent years, particularly since 2000. This has included cuts in overall catch, a reduction in the time vessels are permitted at sea, closures of certain geographical areas (e.g. parts of the Irish Sea for cod) and concomitant increases in mesh size. However, such measures were introduced too recently for them to be responsible for any population changes between the SCR Census (1985–88) and Seabird 2000. There is a great need for more work to be done on Herring Gull diet, especially in areas like the Irish Sea where the declines in the breeding population recorded by Seabird 2000 were greatest. However, the effort by the EU to restore sustainability to the fishing industry is unlikely to have any beneficial effect on seabirds, including breeding Herring Gulls (see Dunn, 1997).

Untreated sewage is utilised as food by many gull species and can be a locally important food resource (Cramp & Simmons, 1983). Until recently, untreated or partially treated sewage was routinely discharged into estuaries and shallow coastal waters throughout much of Britain and Ireland. With the disposal of untreated sewage being phased out due to various EU legislation, another food resource for gulls is being gradually removed. Whilst data are lacking to show that the closure of any sewage outlet has caused population declines at nearby Herring Gull colonies, it is reasonable to assume that populations in close proximity to sewage outlets would benefit to some extent from a readily available food supply. The effect of changing sewage levels on gull numbers has been studied in the River Tyne, northeast England (Raven & Coulson, 2001). Total gull numbers using the river throughout the year declined significantly by 37% between 1969/70 and 1993/94 when the new sewage scheme had become fully operational.

Mammalian predation can have severe localised effects on nesting colonies of gulls and may be more widespread than generally thought, as proof of predation can be difficult to determine. Two predators in particular, Red Fox and American Mink, have been identified as causing serious losses at individual sites or over larger areas. Both species are considered to have increased in numbers since the 1970s and 1980s (Corbett & Harris, 1990), whilst the mink has also extended its range in Ireland (Hayden & Harrington, 2000) and parts of Britain (Clode & Macdonald, 2002). The increase in the Red Fox population would be expected due to the recovery of rabbits from myxomatosis, as rabbits are the main prey of foxes in many areas (C. Webbon, pers. comm.). As both predators, but especially mink, are strong swimmers, small inshore islands or sand banks with gull colonies are particularly vulnerable, though islands up to 2 km or more from the mainland have also been reached by mink (Craik, 1997).

The mixed gull colony at Orford Ness in Suffolk is an example of a site where fox predation has seriously affected breeding success, with 75% of nests suffering predation in 1999 (Mavor *et al.*, 2001), whilst at Gun's Island (Co. Down), which is an inshore island connected to the mainland at

A dead Herring Gull on its nest in Ireland, where Botulism is thought to have been a major cause of the dramatic decline in both Northern Ireland and the Republic of Ireland (Alyn Walsh)

low tide, fox predation is considered a factor in reducing a colony of nearly 2,000 AON in 1990 to just 55 AON in 1997 (Thompson *et al.*, 1998) and subsequent total abandonment. Craik (1995, 1997, 1998) has shown that mink have been causing widespread breeding failure in gull and tern colonies in west Scotland since the late 1980s. This is believed to have corresponded with an increase in mink numbers and their resulting spread and occupation of much of the coast. In a study area along the mainland coast between Mallaig (Lochaber) and West Loch Tarbert (Argyll & Bute), the Herring Gull population showed an overall decrease of *c.*37% between 1989 and 1998, which was largely attributed to predation by mink (Craik, 1998). By 2002, a total of 32 former colonies had become extinct and a further 11 were in long-term decline, with low or zero productivity due to near-annual mink predation (J. C. A. Craik, pers. comm.). Ground-nesting seabirds respond to repeated mink-related breeding failure by abandoning affected breeding sites, especially at smaller colonies of under *c.*250 pairs (J. C. A. Craik, pers. comm.). Since 1995, the mink–seabird project has removed mink from selected colonies on an annual basis, and at most sites, ground-nesting seabirds such as Herring Gulls have returned to breed (Craik, 2001).

Changes in breeding populations of gulls in a region may result from control measures at specific colonies, which can cause redistribution of the population (see discussion in Lloyd *et al.*, 1991, and the Lesser Black-backed Gull chapter). Culling can be carried out for a number of reasons, principally nature conservation (Thomas, 1972) and public health (Hatch, 1996), although sometimes for other reasons such as safety at airports (Horton *et al.*, 1983; Macdonald & Goodwillie, 1984). In the well-documented culling programme on the Isle of May (Fife) where almost 44,000 gulls, mostly Herring Gulls, were killed in the first five years of the scheme, it was estimated that a further 27,000 birds were deterred from joining the colony during this period and that many of these moved to other breeding colonies, mostly in east Scotland and northeast England (Duncan & Monaghan, 1977; Duncan, 1978; Parsons & Duncan, 1978). No large-scale culls of Herring Gulls were known to be in operation at the time of Seabird 2000, and nowadays control of gull populations is mainly carried out to benefit tern conservation, such as at Blakeney Point (Norfolk) and Havergate Island (Suffolk) (Mavor *et al.*, 2002), at Rockabill (Co. Dublin) (Crowe *et al.*, 2000) and at Coquet Island (Northumberland) (Morrison *et al.*, 2002). Such schemes usually involve non-lethal methods.

What little growth occurred in some Herring Gull populations between the SCR Census and Seabird 2000 was mostly attributable to the continued increase in the habit of roof-nesting. Herring Gulls nesting on buildings accounted for 13.5% of the total population in Britain and Ireland in Seabird 2000, and this is likely to be a minimum estimate owing to the difficulty of counting roof-nesting gulls at some sites. Furthermore, two large colonies at Dover and Folkestone (both in Kent), which held a total of almost 900 AONs in 1994 (Raven & Coulson, 1997), were not surveyed during Seabird 2000. Raven & Coulson (1997) noted that the increase had taken place in two ways: first by the expansion of existing colonies and secondly by the progressive colonisation of towns previously without nesting gulls. Small colonies increase rapidly and once established are very unlikely to disappear without concerted action by the human population. The source of many of the roof-nesters is undoubtedly from natural sites and it has been shown that many young gulls reared on the Isle of May in the Firth of Forth have been found breeding on buildings in northeast England (Monaghan & Coulson, 1977). The reason for the continued upward trend in the population of roof-nesting gulls compared to those nesting on natural sites is unknown. Raven & Coulson (1997) suggested that man-made sites are either more attractive to recruits or the survival rates of adults nesting on buildings are higher than those breeding on cliffs or islands. They considered that it probable that the same factor, food, contributes to both possibilities. In urban areas there are additional sources of food to avail of, such as discarded material from 'fast-food' outlets and garbage from restaurants. Herring Gulls nesting in urban areas appear to have higher breeding success compared with those elsewhere. Monaghan (1979) reported that Herring Gulls on roof-tops in South Shields (Tyne & Wear) reared 1.2–1.6 chicks per pair in the 1970s, compared to 0.6–1.2 chicks per pair recorded by various studies in natural coastal colonies elsewhere. A further advantage of roof-nesting is that birds have fewer predators to contend with than those nesting in many natural sites. Whilst human disturbance is usually low, the increasing numbers in towns is bringing roof-nesting birds into

Urban waste provides a convenient food source close to safe roof-top breeding sites, contributing to the continued success of Herring Gulls breeding in towns throughout Britain (Bill Paton)

conflict with residents, as well as commercial and industrial interests, due to problems such as noise and fouling of buildings. Raven & Coulson (1997) point out that no satisfactory method has been developed for managing and eliminating gulls from towns. In a survey of roof-nesting gulls in 1976, ten towns were reported to be undertaking extensive gull control measures (Monaghan & Coulson, 1977) but in 1994 all of these towns still had roof-nesting gulls and, in all cases, the numbers present were greater than in 1976.

It is assumed that the rapid growth seen in some Herring Gull colonies since the SCR Census (1985–88), such as at Rockcliffe Marsh on the Solway, must be fuelled by immigration from other colonies. Ringing recovery data show that inter-colonial movements do occur and also that Herring Gulls appear to readily cross the Irish and Celtic Seas, as well as the North Sea (Wernham *et al.*, 2002). Rapid growth of a colony can sometimes be linked to a new local food source. At Orford Ness (Suffolk) the change from battery to free-range pig-rearing is thought to have contributed to the increase in the number of nesting birds as the gulls feed regularly on easily available food around the troughs. The recent fall in the numbers of breeding birds at this site may reflect the decline in this industry (Orford Ness warden, pers. comm.). Craik & Campbell (2000) suggest that a recent increase in the number of Herring Gulls breeding at Sligneach Mor in Loch Sunart (Lochaber) is due, at least partially, to excess fish feed from the large salmon farms in the loch. Given the large spread in salmon farming on the west coast of Scotland and the Northern Isles, as well as in western Ireland, this could be an important alternative food source for local Herring Gull populations.

In the past, detailed survey and research efforts on Herring Gull ecology and population dynamics have tended to be associated with control programmes. The recent population crash in Ireland, and declines in some parts of Britain are at such a scale that the species now easily meets the requirements for addition to the Red List in Ireland (Newton *et al.*, 1999), and at least to the Amber List of Birds of Conservation Concern in the UK (Gregory *et al.*, 2002). Given it remains a potential problem species in some towns and cities, and on tern reserves, adequate resources should be given to monitoring populations in the future and to determining the reasons for population changes, particularly in Ireland.

INTERNATIONAL CONTEXT

'Herring Gull' taxonomy is complex (see Chylarecki, 1993; Yésou *et al.*, 1994) and until recently the pale grey-mantled and pink-legged subspecies of northwest Europe were treated by all sources as conspecific with the yellow-legged gulls, i.e. *L. a. cachinnans* and *L. a. michahellis*, which breed from western France east through the Mediterranean to Central Asia (del Hoyo *et al.*, 1996; Merne, 1997a; Snow & Perrins, 1998). Recently, several authorities have classified 'Yellow-legged Gulls' as separate species to Herring Gulls, i.e. *L. michahellis* and *L. cachinnans* (Clements, 2000; Malling Olsen & Larsson, 2003). However, we have used the same nomenclature as the British Ornithologists' Union, and have considered Herring Gulls and Yellow-legged Gulls to be conspecific.

About 1,000,000 pairs of Herring Gulls breed in the Palearctic and North America, including over 150,000 in the USA and Canada (Table 4; del Hoyo *et al.*, 1996; Malling Olsen & Larsson, 2003). The biogeographic population that breeds in northwest Europe comprises the races *L. a. argentatus* and *L. a. argenteus* and their intergrades. Breeding occurs in at least 22 European countries, with the 'centre of gravity' of the population lying in Great Britain, Norway, Sweden, Denmark, Germany, The Netherlands and France. Breeding also occurs in European Russia. The estimated total European population size (excluding Russia) is 757,945–830,567 pairs, with a mean of 789,940 pairs (Hagemeijer & Blair, 1997). This estimate relates mainly to the mid- and late 1980s.

Most European populations were considered to be still increasing or stable up to the early 1990s (Hagemeijer & Blair, 1997; Snow & Perrins, 1998; Malling Olsen & Larsson, 2003). Norway has the largest population, estimated at 150,000–200,000 pairs in 1970–90. Sweden held 50,000–100,000 pairs in the late 1980s and the population was considered stable. In The Netherlands, the population increased markedly to 89,000 pairs in 1984 when it stabilised. A decline occurred in the early 1990s, with the population falling to 68,000 in 1996 (Spaans, 1998). The fall in the Dutch population was largely responsible for an overall decline in the Herring Gull breeding population in the Wadden Sea, which fell from 89,577 pairs in 1991 to 77,250 pairs in 1996 (Rasmussen *et al.*, 2000). Although overall numbers are small, the Belgian population has risen dramatically since the early 1990s and the roof-nesting habit is now established (Seys *et al.*, 1998). An estimated 85,000–90,000 pairs occur in France where the population was considered stable in the early 1990s. The Danish population was considered stable in the early 1990s at *c.*57,000 pairs. The German population had peaked in 1974 and a total of 46,000 pairs was estimated in the mid-1980s. Between 30,000 and 40,000 pairs occurred in Estonia in 1991 where an explosive increase had occurred in previous decades. In Russia, the total European population is unknown but is considered to be increasing inland and decreasing on the Kola Peninsula, with 9,600 pairs in the main colonies in 1991.

Britain held approximately 18.0% of the European population (i.e. *L. a. argentatus* and *L. a. argenteus*) in the late 1980s and Ireland held 4.7% (Lloyd *et al.*, 1991). At the present, Britain still supports 18–20% of the European population but Ireland now supports only 0.8–0.9% of the total. In a global context, Britain supports 12–13% of Herring/Yellow-legged Gulls and Ireland about 0.5–0.6%.

Table 4   International context.

Country or region	Subspecies	Number of pairs		Source
		Min	Max	
Great Britain, Isle of Man and Channel Isles	*argenteus*	143,000	143,000	Seabird 2000
All-Ireland	*argenteus*	6,500	6,500	Seabird 2000
Belarus	*argentatus*	100	200	Malling Olsen & Larsson (2003)
Belgium	*argentatus/argenteus*	683	683	Malling Olsen & Larsson (2003)
Denmark	*argentatus*	55,000	58,000	Malling Olsen & Larsson (2003)
Estonia	*argentatus*	40,000	40,000	Malling Olsen & Larsson (2003)
Faeroe Islands	*argenteus*	1,500	1,500	Malling Olsen & Larsson (2003)
Finland	*argentatus*	28,300	28,300	Malling Olsen & Larsson (2003)
France (Brittany)	*argenteus*	60,300	60,300	Malling Olsen & Larsson (2003)
France (excluding Brittany)	*argentatus/argenteus*	27,800	27,800	Malling Olsen & Larsson (2003)
Germany (western)	*argentatus/argenteus*	50,000	50,000	Malling Olsen & Larsson (2003)
Germany (eastern)	*argentatus*	1,500	1,700	Malling Olsen & Larsson (2003)
Iceland	*argenteus*	2,500	2,500	Malling Olsen & Larsson (2003)
Latvia	*argentatus*	550	600	Malling Olsen & Larsson (2003)
Lithuania	*argentatus*	300	350	Malling Olsen & Larsson (2003)
Netherlands	*argentatus/argenteus*	67,000	67,000	Malling Olsen & Larsson (2003)
Norway	*argentatus*	150,000	200,000	Malling Olsen & Larsson (2003)
Poland	*argentatus*	2,200	2,200	Malling Olsen & Larsson (2003)
Russia	*argentatus*	8,000	8,000	Malling Olsen & Larsson (2003)
Sweden	*argentatus*	60,000	100,000	Malling Olsen & Larsson (2003)
Switzerland	*argentatus?*	5	6	Malling Olsen & Larsson (2003)
Mediterranean/ Western France/Iberia	*michahellis*	158,000	208,000	Malling Olsen & Larsson (2003)
Russia/Ukraine	*cachinnans*	25,000	30,000	Malling Olsen & Larsson (2003)
Armenia/Turkey	*armenicus*	20,000	20,000	Malling Olsen & Larsson (2003)
North America (Canada/USA)	*smithsonianus*	150,000	150,000	Malling Olsen & Larsson (2003)

Biogeographic region		Min	Max	Min % GB	Max % GB	Min % Ireland	Max % Ireland
NW Europe & Iceland/W Europe*	*argentatus & argenteus*	705,000	799,000	17.9%	20.3%	0.8%	0.9%
World	all	1,100,000	1,200,000	11.9%	13.0%	0.5%	0.6%

* Stroud *et al.* (2001)

Great Black-backed Gull *Larus marinus*

James B. Reid

INTRODUCTION

Despite an extensive breeding range across the North Atlantic and adjacent seas, from Baffin Island and the Foxe Channel in the west to Novaya Zemlya and Ostrov Vaygach in the east, the Great Black-backed Gull is considered monotypic. Historically, Britain and Ireland have hosted most of the world population, after Iceland and Norway. However, there have been few breeding censuses of the species here, at least in part because nesting occurs primarily on sparsely populated islands and other locations that are difficult of access.

Great Black-backs breed mainly in the Outer and Inner Hebrides and the Northern Isles of Scotland. These regions offer extensive areas of the preferred breeding habitat of well-vegetated rocky coastline with stacks and cliffs. The species is also common in other western areas where the scene is similar, including further south in Scotland, western Ireland, the Irish Sea, and the coastal fringes of the Celtic Sea. It breeds in only small numbers in eastern Scotland and the English Channel, and is mostly absent as a breeder from eastern England.

The 20th century saw widespread expansion of the Great Black-backed Gull breeding range and numbers on both sides of the Atlantic (Cramp & Simmons, 1983; Good, 1998). In Britain at least, population increase was remarkable given that a period of decline rendered the species virtually extinct as a breeder towards the end of the previous century. Population growth seems to date from *c.*1880 (Alexander & Lack, 1944), although only about 20 pairs bred in six counties of England and Wales in 1893 (Harrison & Hurrell, 1933). The first complete census of the species in England and Wales in 1930 revealed that the population had grown to 1,000–1,200 breeding pairs, mostly on the Isles of Scilly and Pembrokeshire (Harrison & Hurrell, 1933). Continued growth up to 1956, including a slight range extension east to Hampshire and the Isle of Wight, resulted in an estimated breeding population of 1,770–1,860 pairs; this was accounted for by increases in island populations, mostly those in the Irish Sea but also in the Channel Islands (Davis, 1958). In the latter half of the 20th century, further growth in England, Wales and the Channel Islands saw the population rise to more than 3,000 pairs in 1969–70 (Cramp *et al.*, 1974). However, there was a subsequent decline, principally at the Welsh colonies, and also on the Isles of Scilly, to an estimated 2,500 pairs in 1985–87 (Lloyd *et al.*, 1991).

The decline of the Great Black-backed Gull in the 19th century in England and Wales appears not to have been mirrored in Scotland; however, the same significant population growth occurred in the 20th century, seemingly from about 1920 (Parslow, 1973). Whilst there are reports of localised increases in the main northern and western breeding areas in the early 20th century (Baxter & Rintoul, 1953), the first complete census of the Great Black-back in Scotland was not until 1969–1970, when *c.*70% of the total British and Irish population bred there (Cramp *et al.*, 1974). This followed breeding range expansion, albeit involving small numbers, on the east coast of the country from Aberdeenshire south in the 1960s, and consolidated in the 1970s and 1980s as far as East Lothian (Thom, 1986; Lloyd *et al.*, 1991). Between the only previous Scottish censuses of Great Black-backed Gulls, Operation Seafarer (1969–70) and the SCR Census (1985–88), population size in Scotland changed very little. In the latter census, an estimated 15,300 pairs bred, ostensibly 600 fewer than in 1969–70 (Table 1).

Despite few surveys of the species, especially on the west coast, the Great Black-backed Gull population in Ireland also clearly increased in the 20th century. Five counties in the northeast and west were colonised for the first time between 1900 and 1951 (Hutchison, 1989) and population growth continued up to 1969–70, when an estimated 3,400 pairs bred (Cramp *et al.*, 1974). Breeding numbers at selected colonies all around the coast, with the exception of those in Co. Antrim and Co. Down, increased during this period (Hutchison, 1989). Further increase took place up to 1985–88, perhaps by more than 30% (Lloyd *et al.*, 1991).

In Britain and Ireland as a whole, there was little change in the size of the coastal breeding population of the Great Black-backed Gull between 1969–70 and 1985–88 (Table 1); in the former period, a total of 22,412 Apparently Occupied Nests (AON) was counted, whereas in the latter, 20,892 AON were counted, an indication that the overall population was relatively stable in the intervening period, notwithstanding some localised and marked declines (and increases).

Great Black-backs nest almost exclusively in coastal habitats, but they also nest inland at freshwater sites as well as on the roofs of buildings. Davis (1958) reported that in the first half of the 20th century all the traditional inland breeding sites in England and Wales were abandoned, although the species still bred at some localities. Inland sites were not surveyed during Operation Seafarer (1969–70) or the SCR Census (1985–88), so longer term trends in inland nesting are unknown; however, the number of birds doing so has always been very small. Similarly, very few Great Black-backs nest on buildings; in 1976, seven pairs did so at three sites, and in 1994 this had risen only to 11 pairs at ten sites, although there was a suggestion that the habit had become more widespread (Monaghan & Coulson, 1977; Raven & Coulson, 1997).

CENSUS METHODS

In common with other *Larus* gulls, the recommended census unit for the Great Black-backed Gull is the Apparently Occupied Nest (AON) or, when actual nests cannot be discerned, the Apparently Occupied Territory (AOT). Clearly, each of these equates to one breeding pair. When colonies or the nests within them are difficult of access, or time is limited, then flush counts of individuals may be made. In order to aid comparison between the various surveys all counts were converted into AONs, either from pairs (as reported in Operation Seafarer) or from individuals (dividing by two) where appropriate in the SCR Census and Seabird 2000.

Several methods permit the estimation of AONs in colonies, be they of single or mixed species (see Appendix I), but the likely errors associated with each have not been adequately quantified, certainly for the Great Black-backed Gull. Great Black-backs are visually conspicuous with distinctively deep vocalisations, so perhaps fewer might be overlooked in mixed colonies with Herring and/or Lesser Black-backed Gulls. However, solitary nests or pairs, especially those in remote areas, might easily be missed. Wide margins of error, dependent on colony size, may be associated with flush counts, irrespective of the disturbance they cause. Errors arise from not counting birds accurately, as well as converting numbers of individuals into pairs. Similarly, the degree of precision achieved in counts of AONs in large colonies is unknown. Estimates from single counts in colonies that have an extended breeding season, perhaps as a consequence of re-laying after egg loss, are also likely to have wide confidence intervals. Clearly, repeat counts are advisable, although they are rarely conducted.

The precise methods used to census Great Blacked Gulls in the SCR Census (1985–88) are largely unknown (>70% of all count records and AONs). However, only 29% of AONs were derived from counts of individuals on land. In contrast, a variety of methods were deployed and recorded in Seabird 2000 (see Appendix I). Most (82%) AONs were counted directly, either from land-based vantage points (51%) or from boats (26%), or from within the colony (7%). Only 18% of AONs were estimated from flush counts of individuals. Thus, suitable methodology was applied in capturing Great Black-back population data in the great majority of cases.

However, relatively few AONs (29%) were counted in Seabird 2000 within the ideal period, i.e. 15 May–5 June to coincide with the peak incubation period when sitting adults are conspicuous. The extent to which this has resulted in inaccurate estimates is unknown. There is probably a high degree of tolerance outside the ideal period, however, and occasionally censusing might be advisable beyond it if, for example, breeding is delayed for some reason. In any case, this would certainly appear to represent an improvement over the SCR Census (1985–88) when only 15% of AONs were counted within the ideal census period.

Of all recorded/derived AONs in Seabird 2000, 80% were believed by the recorders to be accurate counts in areas where all birds were visible, the remaining 20% deriving from an estimate of the whole colony based on accurate counts of samples of the colony. This is similar to the accuracy achieved in the SCR Census.

Notwithstanding the precise census methods used in SCR being mostly unrecorded, the two surveys, SCR and Seabird 2000 remain comparable; no major gaps in survey coverage are known for Seabird 2000, certainly in Britain (see Census Methods chapter).

CURRENT STATUS AND TRENDS

Table 1 indicates breeding population sizes of the Great Black-backed Gull in the three surveys. As inland breeders were not censused in 1969–70 or 1985–88 comparisons are valid only for coastal

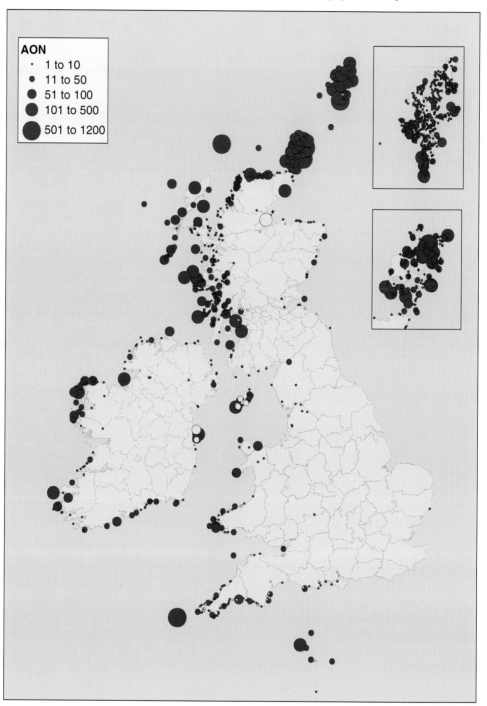

Figure 1   Abundance and distribution of breeding Great Black-backed Gulls in Britain and Ireland 1998–2002. Natural sites are shown in red and human-made sites (e.g. rooftops) are in yellow (the scale is the same for both types of site).

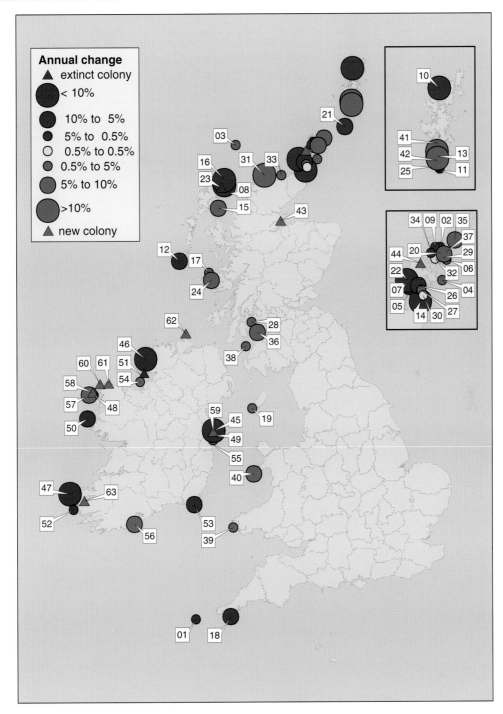

Figure 2   Changes in the number of breeding Great Black-backed Gulls (AON) at major colonies in Britain and Ireland between the SCR Census (1985–88) and Seabird 2000 (1998–2002). Major colonies are those that contained the top 40% of the British population during the SCR and/or Seabird 2000 or the top 50% of the Irish population during the SCR and/or Seabird 2000. Numbers correspond to colonies listed in Table 2.

Table 1   Numbers of coastal-breeding Great Black-backed Gulls (AON) in Britain and Ireland 1969–2002. Numbers breeding inland and on the coast during Seabird 2000 (1998–2002) are also given.

Administrative area or country	Coastal colonies only[1]						Seabird 2000 inland and coastal
	Operation Seafarer (1969–70)[2]	SCR Census (1985–88)[2]	Seabird 2000 (1998–2002)	Percentage change since Seafarer	Percentage change since SCR	Annual percentage change since SCR	
Shetland	2,674	3,094	2,875	8%	−7%	−0.5%	2,875
Orkney	5,999	5,657	5,505	−8%	−3%	−0.2%	5,505
North coast Caithness		171	30		−82%	−12.4%	30
East coast Caithness		842	181		−79%	−11.1%	181
Caithness total	*1,048*	*1,013*	*211*	*−80%*	*−79%*	*−11.3%*	*211*
Northwest coast Sutherland		805	1,058		31%	2.1%	1,058
East coast Sutherland		16	1		−94%	−18.6%	1
Sutherland total	*1,360*	*821*	*1,059*	*−22%*	*29%*	*1.9%*	*1,059*
West coast Ross & Cromarty		197	159		−19%	−1.5%	159
East coast Ross & Cromarty		9	220		2344%	27.6%	220
Ross & Cromarty total	*660*	*206*	*379*	*−43%*	*84%*	*4.6%*	*379*
Inverness	1	47	5	400%	−89%	−14.9%	5
Nairn	20			−100%			
Moray	4	12	10	150%	−17%	−1.4%	11
Banff & Buchan	16	15	37	131%	147%	6.3%	37
Gordon	2	12	5	150%	−58%	−5.7%	5
City of Aberdeen			9				9
Kincardine & Deeside	23	4	21	−9%	425%	13.5%	21
Angus	1		8	700%			8
Perth & Kinross							2
Northeast Fife	4	2	27	575%	1250%	20.4%	27
Dunfermline			1				1
City of Edinburgh			2				2
East Lothian	1	7	11	1000%	57%	3.6%	11
Berwickshire			1				1
Stewartry	55	10	7	−87%	−30%	−3.1%	7
Wigtown	14	9	7	−50%	−22%	−1.8%	7
Kyle & Carrick	30	97	298	893%	207%	7.8%	298
Cunninghame	82	135	133	62%	−1%	−0.1%	133
Inverclyde		2	18		800%	17.9%	18
Dumbarton		1	3		200%		3
Argyll & Bute	586	988	1,736	196%	76%	4.5%	1,736
Lochaber	157	245	247	57%	1%	0.1%	247
Skye & Lochalsh	218	342	151	−31%	−56%	−6.1%	151
Western Isles–Comhairle nan eilean	2,995	2,596	2,007	−33%	−23%	−1.9%	2,007
Scotland Total	**15,950**	**15,315**	**14,773**	**−7%**	**−4%**	**−0.3%**	**14,776**
Northumberland		0	2				2
Suffolk			4				4
Hampshire		1	2		100%	5.9%	2
Isle of Wight	6	9	10	67%	11%	0.7%	10
Dorset	16	10	74	363%	640%	14.2%	74
Channel Islands	200	180	310	55%	72%	4.4%	310
Cornwall	262	278	322	23%	16%	1.1%	322
Isles of Scilly	1200	999	807	−33%	−19%	−1.8%	807
Devon	106	165	166	57%	1%	0.0%	166
Somerset	17		1	−94%			1
Avon	42	13	18	−57%	38%	2.5%	18
Hereford & Worcester							1
Lancashire	1	1	9	800%	800%	23.3%	16
Cumbria	26	58	51	96%	−12%	−1.0%	53

Administrative area or country	Coastal colonies only[1]						Seabird 2000 inland and coastal
	Operation Seafarer (1969–70)[2]	SCR Census (1985–88)[2]	Seabird 2000 (1998–2002)	Percentage change since Seafarer	Percentage change since SCR	Annual percentage change since SCR	
Isle of Man	275	376	405	47%	8%	0.6%	405
England, Isle of Man and Channel Islands Total	2,151	2,090	2,181	1%	4%	0.3%	2,191
Gwent	33	10		−100%	−100%		
South Glamorgan			2				2
Dyfed	700	189	322	−54%	70%	4.1%	322
Gwynedd	172	90	101	−41%	12%	0.8%	103
Wales Total	905	289	425	−53%	47%	2.9%	427
Great Britain, Isle of Man and Channel Islands Total	19,006	17,694	17,379	−9%	−2%	−0.1%	17,394
Co. Antrim	91	114	16	−82%	−86%	−12.8%	16
Co. Down	149	163	55	−63%	−66%	−7.7%	55
Co. Armagh							1
Co. Fermanagh							4
Co. Dublin	230	538	486	111%	−10%	−0.8%	486
Co. Wicklow	7	2	2	−71%	0%	0.0%	2
Co. Wexford	505	204	76	−85%	−63%	−7.0%	76
Co. Waterford	75	101	62	−17%	−39%	−3.6%	62
Co. Cork	381	272	201	−47%	−26%	−2.1%	201
Co. Kerry	527	625	291	−45%	−53%	−5.9%	291
Co. Clare	135	9	28	−79%	211%	8.9%	28
Co. Galway	485	137	146	−70%	7%	0.5%	147
Co. Mayo	416	461	652	57%	41%	2.8%	653
Co. Sligo	82	81	133	62%	64%	3.7%	133
Co. Donegal	323	491	164	−49%	−67%	−8.3%	164
All-Ireland Total	3,406	3,198	2,312	−32%	−28%	−2.4%	2,319
Britain and Ireland Total	22,412	20,892	19,691	−12%	−6%	−0.4%	19,713

Notes

[1] Operation Seafarer and the SCR Census did not survey inland.

[2] The figures for Operation Seafarer and the SCR are actual counts and do not include adjustments to totals made in order to account for unsurveyed or incompletely surveyed colonies (see Lloyd *et al.*, 1991)

breeders (defined as those within 5 km of the mean high-water mark or within the Northern Isles—see Data Processing and Analysis chapter).

The coastal breeding population of Great Black-backs in Britain and Ireland during Seabird 2000 was estimated at 19,691 AON, plus 22 AON counted inland. Of this total, most (75%) were in Scotland, with 12% in Ireland, 11% in England, the Isle of Man and the Channel Islands, and 2% in Wales.

The main breeding concentrations of the Great Black-backed Gull remained in north and west Britain and Ireland (Fig. 1). The Northern Isles, western Scotland, including the Outer and Inner Hebrides, the Irish Sea, western Ireland and southwest England hold the great majority of the breeding population. The largest breeding populations were 983 AON on North Rona (Western Isles), 675 AON on the Calf of Eday (Orkney) and 415 AON at Rothiesholm Head on Stronsay (Orkney); barely more than 100 AON were recorded on the east coast of mainland Britain. Between the SCR Census (1985–88) and Seabird 2000, breeding occurred for the first time on the coasts of Berwickshire, Suffolk and South Glamorgan. The SCR Census did not record any Great Black-backs breeding in Northumberland, but the Seabird 2000 record of 2 AON on the Farne Islands is not the first, as 1–3 pairs bred there in 1975–83 and since 1992.

Table 2   Changes in the number of breeding Great Black-backed Gulls (AON) at major colonies in Britain and Ireland between the SCR Census (1985–88) and Seabird 2000 (1998–2002). Major colonies are those that contained the top 40% of the British population during the SCR and/or Seabird 2000 or the top 50% of the Irish population during the SCR and/or Seabird 2000. ID corresponds to colony symbols in Fig. 2.

ID	Colony	SCR Census (1985–88)	Seabird 2000 (1998–2002)	Percentage change since SCR	Annual percentage change since SCR	Percentage of population in Britain or Ireland 1998–2002
1	Isles of Scilly total	999	807	−19%	−1.8%	4.6%
2	Calf of Eday (SPA)	800	675	−16%	−1.2%	3.9%
3	North Rona (SPA)	733	983	34%	2.5%	5.7%
4	Copinsay	618	1189	92%	5.5%	6.8%
5	Hoy: Burn of Forse	613	207	−66%	−8.0%	1.2%
6	Stronsay and Papa Stronsay	504	595	18%	1.2%	3.4%
7	Hoy: Stourdale	450	176	−61%	−7.0%	1.0%
8	Lewis: Tolsta Head	258	2	−99%	−35.5%	0.0%
9	Holm of Faray	223	175	−22%	−1.8%	1.0%
10	Ramna Stacks and Gruney (SPA)	151	15	−90%	−14.3%	0.1%
11	Horse Island	150	80	−47%	−4.1%	0.5%
12	Mingulay (SPA)	150	44	−71%	−9.1%	0.3%
13	High Holm	145	5	−97%	−22.9%	0.0%
14	Stroma	134	18[1]	−87%	−13.4%	0.1%
15	Shiant Islands	126	310	146%	7.2%	1.8%
16	Lewis: Cellar Head	125	3	−98%	−24.8%	0.0%
17	Coll	120	177	48%	3.0%	1.0%
18	Mullion Island	117	49	−58%	−6.0%	0.3%
19	Calf of Man	116	146	26%	1.7%	0.8%
20	Muckle Green Holm	115	150	30%	1.9%	0.9%
21	Fair Isle	113	32	−72%	−8.1%	0.2%
22	Hoy: Lochs of Suifea	100	6	−94%	−18.3%	0.0%
23	Lewis: Druim Moor	100	0	−100%		0.0%
24	Treshnish Islands including Dutchman's Cap	99	342	245%	10.0%	2.0%
25	Lady's Holm	95	160	68%	3.5%	0.9%
26	Fara	94	48	−49%	−5.0%	0.3%
27	Switha (SPA)	90	120	33%	2.2%	0.7%
28	Little Cumbrae Island	80	120	50%	3.2%	0.7%
29	Linga Holm	79	94	19%	1.3%	0.5%
30	Swona	78	75	−4%	−0.3%	0.4%
31	Eilean Hoan	75	360	380%	14.0%	2.1%
32	Little Green Holm	75	75			0.4%
33	Strathy Point	72	86	19%	1.4%	0.5%
34	Kili Holm	70	60	−14%	−1.1%	0.3%
35	Sanday: Tafts Ness	60	181	202%	8.2%	1.0%
36	Lady Isle	55[2]	200	264%	7.5%	1.1%
37	Holm of Huip	45	150	233%	9.0%	0.9%
38	Ailsa Craig (SPA)	42	85	102%	5.2%	0.5%
39	Skomer	33	61	85%	4.9%	0.4%
40	Ynys Gwylan Fawr	17	61	259%	8.8%	0.4%
41	Little Havra	9	150	1567%	22.3%	0.9%
42	Colsay	4	80	1900%	23.8%	0.5%
43	Nigg Oil Terminal	0	149			0.9%
44	Orkney Mainland: Little Billia Fiold	0	61			0.4%
45	St Patrick's Island	285	100	−65%	−7.2%	4.3%
46	Roaninish	250	29	−88%	−14.3%	1.3%
47	Inishtooskert	225	3	−99%	−28.3%	0.1%
48	Duvillaun Islands	217	144	−34%	−3.1%	6.2%
49	Lambay Island	145	193	33%	2.4%	8.3%
50	Inishark	137	55	−60%	−7.9%	2.4%
51	Inishduff	135	nc			
52	Puffin Island	125	72	−42%	−3.6%	3.1%

ID	Colony	SCR Census (1985–88)	Seabird 2000 (1998–2002)	Percentage change since SCR	Annual percentage change since SCR	Percentage of population in Britain or Ireland 1998–2002
53	Little Saltee	100	45	−55%	−6.4%	1.9%
54	Inishmurray	81	117	44%	2.7%	5.0%
55	Ireland's Eye	65	90	38%	2.5%	3.9%
56	Sovereign Islands	19	75	295%	10.3%	3.2%
57	Black Rock	17	55	224%	10.2%	2.4%
58	Inishkea Islands	nc	100			4.3%
59	Shenicks Island	0	90			3.9%
60	Illandavuck	nc	75			3.2%
61	Pig Island	nc	62			2.7%
62	Inishtrahull	nc	61			2.6%
63	Kings Head	0	57			2.5%

Notes

[1] Count conducted from sea so may have been an under estimate

[2] Counted in 1982

nc   not counted

Table 3   Numbers of roof-nesting Great Black-backed Gulls (AON) in Britain 1976–2002.

Administrative area or country	1976[1]		1993–95[2]		1999–2002		Percentage change since 1976	Percentage change since 1993–95
	AON	Colonies[3]	AON	Colonies[3]	AON	Colonies		
East coast Sutherland					1	1		
Sutherland total					*1*	*1*		
Inverness					5	1		
Moray					1	1		
City of Aberdeen			2	1	9	1		350%
Angus					2	1		
City of Edinburgh			1	1				
Kyle & Carrick			1	1				
Cunninghame			1	1	1	1		0%
Inverclyde			1	1	2	1		100%
Scotland Total			6	5	21	7		250%
Hampshire			1	1	1	1		0%
Dorset			1	1	4	2		300%
Channel Islands					6	1		
Cornwall	7	3			24	6	243%	
Devon			2	2	22	6		1000%
Lancashire					1	1		
Cumbria			1	1	3	1		200%
England and Channel Islands Total	7	3	5	5	61	18	771%	1120%
Dyfed					1	1		
Wales Total					1	1		
Great Britain and Channel Islands Total	7	3	11	10	83	26	1086%	655%

Notes

[1] Source data: Monaghan & Coulson (1977)

[2] Source data: Raven & Coulson (1997)

[3] The numbers of colonies do not include those indicated in 1976 and 1993–95 that were not counted.

Ostensibly, the Seabird 2000 population estimates represent population decline in Scotland from 1985–88 to 1998–2002 of 3.5% (and of 7.4% since 1969–70); in England, the Isle of Man and the Channel Islands an increase of 4.4% (and of 1.4% since 1969–70); in Ireland, a decrease of 27.7% (and of 32.1% since 1969–70); and in Wales, an increase of 47.1% (but 53.0% decline since 1969–70). In Britain and Ireland as whole, there was a decrease of 5.7% (and of 12.1% since 1969–70). Lloyd *et al.* (1991) suggested that the difficulties in accurately counting gull colonies rendered it impossible to detect changes in the sizes of gull populations of less than 10%. If so, then it would appear that little change occurred in the Great Black-backed Gull population in Britain and Ireland between the SCR Census (1985–88) and Seabird 2000 or, indeed, since Operation Seafarer (1969–70).

Although the overall population of the Great Black-backed Gull in Britain and Ireland appeared to change little between 1985–88 and 1998–2002, some quite marked changes were noted in several areas and colonies (Tables 1, 2; Fig. 2). Very large proportional increases occurred in several regions, for example in northeast Fife (1250%), Inverclyde (800%) and Lancashire (800%). However, the magnitude of such changes is exaggerated given the low baseline numbers recorded in the SCR Census (1985–88). Changes in the absolute numbers of Great Black-backed Gulls breeding in several regions were quite marked. Thus, increases of more than 100 AON were recorded in Argyll & Bute, Kyle & Carrick, Sutherland, Co. Mayo, Ross & Cromarty, the Channel Islands, and Dyfed, while decreases of more than 100 AON occurred in Caithness, the Western Isles, Co. Kerry, Co. Donegal, Shetland, Orkney, the Isles of Scilly, Skye & Lochalsh, Co. Wexford and Co. Down (Table 1).

Similarly, some very large changes at Great Black-backed breeding sites occurred between the SCR Census (1985–88) and Seabird 2000. Of the most important sites in 1985–88, one of 100 AON at Druim Mor on Lewis (Western Isles) was abandoned. A large colony (149 AON in 2000) was established at the Nigg Oil Terminal (Ross & Cromarty) in 1990 (Swann, 2002b). Several other important colonies, at Little Billia Field (Orkney), Shenicks Island (Co. Dublin) and at King's Head (Co. Kerry), increased substantially from just a few pairs previously (Table 2, Figure 2)

Of the 14 sites at which decreases of more than 100 AON were recorded (in all cases representing change well in excess of 10%), four were in the Western Isles, three in Orkney, two in Shetland, and one each in Caithness, Co. Donegal, Co. Kerry and Co. Dublin, and the Isles of Scilly. However, of the ten sites at which increases of more than 100 AON were recorded (again, in all cases representing change well in excess of 10%), three were in Orkney, two in the Western Isles, and one each in Shetland, Sutherland, Ross & Cromarty, Kyle & Carrick, and Argyll & Bute (Table 2; Fig. 2).

While many important Great Black-backed Gull breeding sites in Shetland, Orkney, and the Western Isles declined significantly, notable increases at other sites in these regions were insufficient to offset the declines. There would appear to be little other evidence of marked geographical change in the distribution of Great Black-backs between 1985–88 and 1998–2002. The decline in the Northern and Western Isles in the context of no overall change in Britain and Ireland is also illustrated by the slightly different size distributions of colonies in the two survey periods; Table 2 indicates that in 1998–2002, there were a greater number of colonies of more than 100 AONs, the mean size of which was also greater, than in 1985–88. Lloyd *et al.* (1991) also noted that smaller colonies grew and larger ones decreased in size from 1969–70 to 1985–88.

Although an increase in the breeding population of Great Black-backs on the islands of the Clyde, and the Irish and Celtic Seas might be suggested by Fig. 2, overall breeding numbers here remained fairly similar between 1985–87 and 1998–2002, despite large absolute decreases at the Isles of Scilly and St Patrick's Island (Co. Dublin; Table 2). Some redistribution of breeders might be suggested here, as elsewhere throughout Britain and Ireland, although the species usually shows high breeding-site fidelity (Cramp *et al.*, 1974).

Notwithstanding the foregoing, regions where significant population decline has apparently continued from 1969–70 include the Western Isles, Caithness, the Isles of Scilly, Co. Wexford and

Co. Cork, whilst those in which continued population growth appeared to occur include Argyll & Bute, the Isle of Man and Co. Mayo (Table 1).

In common with the Herring Gull and the Lesser Black-backed Gull, but to a much lesser extent, the number of Great Black-backs nesting on the roofs of buildings in 1998–2002 greatly increased, thereby continuing the trend recorded from the 1970s to 1993–95 (Raven & Coulson, 1997; Table 3). By Seabird 2000, there were 83 AON at 26 sites, with more than half of the nests in Devon and Cornwall (Table 3, Fig. 1).

CAUSES OF CHANGE

Clearly, the sizes of Great Black-backed Gull populations depend on survival, productivity and recruitment rates. The environmental and ecological determinants of these parameters have been the focus of relatively few studies in this species, so the reasons for numerical fluctuations in local populations and colonies are for the most part unknown. That there is little geographic pattern to the population changes recorded between 1985–88 and 1998–2002 in Britain and Ireland suggests that no single mechanism of change was responsible.

Notwithstanding relatively little research on the ecology of Great Black-backed Gulls, several causes of change at the population or colony level are known to operate. Certainly, the significant increase on both sides of the Atlantic in the 20th century was almost certainly due to, or at least facilitated by, protection after long periods of persecution and exploitation (Lloyd *et al.*, 1991; Good, 1998). Protection at some colonies in the Barents Sea at which eggs were exploited also led to population increase after the 1930s and 1940s (Anker-Nilssen *et al.*, 2000). Similarly, on Skomer (Dyfed), Great Black-backs increased in numbers after the island was designated a NNR in 1959, an increase attributed to reduced human disturbance and the cessation of egg collecting.

Having grown to almost 300 pairs in the early 1960s, a culling programme over the following two decades reduced the Skomer population to fewer than 100 pairs; further decline occurred due to botulism, such that by 1984 only 25 pairs bred on the island. The increase since the botulism outbreaks of the 1980s, to 65 pairs in 1999 and 61 in 2000, has also been mirrored at other colonies in southwest Wales (Table 2; Perrins & Smith, 2000). Great Black-back numbers in northwest Ireland may also have been reduced by botulism between the mid-1980s and mid-1990s (Walsh *et al.*, 1995).

Although botulism affected Great Black-back populations in Wales (Sutcliffe, 1986, 1997), and possibly northern Ireland, there is no geographical pattern to the recoveries of ringed birds that have died of illness (Wernham *et al.*, 2002), and while more than one-third of ring recoveries result from deliberate persecution, there is no evidence that this has resulted in population decline in those areas where decreases have occurred.

Predation on eggs and young by mammals and other birds, including other gulls, is unlikely to be responsible for any of the major changes recorded within regions. However, introduced American Mink have been responsible for low productivity and even breeding failure at some sites. For example, in 1999, at 30 sites in Argyll and Lochaber at which complete breeding failure occurred, mink were responsible in at least 17 cases, and in 2000, of 18 failed sites mink were probably responsible at ten (Craik, 2000, 2001). In 2001, only seven young fledged at 53 sites where mink were active (Craik, 2002). However, there is no evidence for widespread extirpation of Great Black-backs from areas where mink are common; total breeding failure also occurred at sites in the Argyll and Lochaber study area at which mink were probably absent, and indeed, the population of Great Black-backs increased by more than 700 AON (69.5%) between 1985–87 and 1998–2000 (Table 1). The reasons for this large increase are unknown, although it has been suggested that it may have been at least partly due to the expansion of aquaculture on the west coast of Scotland; certainly few sea lochs here do not possess a fish farm (Craik, 2000). However, despite the enhanced feeding opportunities on, for example, salmon feed (Furness, 1996b; ICES, 2001), this is unlikely to account for such a large population increase.

The changes in some populations of seabirds between 1969–70, 1985–88, and 1998–2002 are certainly due to changes in food availability (Lloyd *et al.*, 1991; see Causes of Change). The same increased diversity and subsequent diminution of new food sources, mainly human-related, appears not to have resulted in widespread population change in Great Black-backed Gull numbers. Great Black-backs exploit a wide variety of food types. Of all the large gulls breeding in Britain and Ireland, it is the most marine and is one of the most common species at discarding trawlers, exploiting fisheries discards to a large degree (Furness *et al.*, 1992). However, although it is probable that productivity during the breeding season and increased winter survival both increased as a consequence of feeding on discards, the extent to which Great Black-back populations in Britain and Ireland have been sustained by fisheries waste is unknown; discarding studies have been undertaken mainly in the North Sea, and mostly outside the breeding season when large numbers of Scandinavian birds are present (e.g. Camphuysen *et al.*, 1995; Garthe *et al.*, 1996).

Although fish catches, and consequently the amount of fisheries waste discarded at sea, decreased over the period 1985–88 to the late 1990s (Reeves & Furness, 2002), this may not have affected Great Black-backs to the same extent as other gull species due to their competitive dominance. In addition to feeding extensively on discards during the breeding season, the Great Black-backed Gull, more than other gulls, also exploits more natural sources of food. Where present, a range of mammalian and avian prey are taken, including rabbits, puffins and Manx Shearwaters (e.g. Harris, 1964), and even at the same breeding location different breeding pairs may exploit different sources of food such as discards (by colonial breeders) and other birds (by solitary pairs; Hudson, 1982). When alternative, perhaps more easily exploitable, food sources become available, such as refuse tips, the species easily switches to these (Poole, 1995). The overall impression is of a very adaptable species whose populations are not limited by the availability of one or a small range of particular food sources.

Some areas where most change since 1985–88 appears to have occurred are notable in that they also host significant numbers of Great Skuas, for example the Northern Isles and Western Isles. Furness (1996) speculated that Great Black-back numbers on Hoy (Orkney) might have decreased through competition with Great Skuas. The Great Skua population here and elsewhere has increased significantly (see Great Skua chapter), perhaps as a consequence of feeding opportunities on fisheries discards at sea. Great Skuas and Great Black-backs compete for discards at sea and although the latter can swallow larger items, the skua is generally competitively dominant and has a higher success rate of capturing fisheries waste (Hudson & Furness, 1988; Furness *et al.*, 1992). Competition on the breeding grounds also occurs, and Great Skuas have been recorded as regularly killing Great Black-back chicks on Hoy (Furness, 1996). It might also be noteworthy that at Druim Mor (Western Isles), 100 Great Black-back AOTs were recorded in 1987 but the site was abandoned subsequently, coinciding with an increase in the local Great Skua population from 17 AOT in 1987 to 29 AOT in 2002. Of course, the reduction in the availability of discards generally (Reeves & Furness, 2002) might also have led to increased kleptoparasitism or predation on the gulls by the skuas.

Although a comparison of the changes in abundance and distribution of Great Black-backs (Fig. 2) and Great Skuas (see Great Skua chapter) in the Northern Isles might suggest some effect of Great Skua population growth on Great Black-back decline, numbers of the former species at some locations where large decreases of the latter have occurred are sometimes low. The Great Skua population increase has been widespread in the extreme north and west of Scotland, while there have been both increases and decreases at Great Black-backed Gull breeding locations in the Great Skua strongholds of Orkney and Shetland, as well as elsewhere where the two species co-occur. The large

Great Black-backed Gull apparently occupied nest (AON) on Puffin Island, Co. Kerry (NHPA/Jean-Louis Lemoigne)

growth of the Great Skua population on Handa Island (Sutherland), from 66 AOT in 1986 to 195 AOT in 2000, has not been accompanied by a reduction in the number of breeding Great Black-backs (31 AON in 1986 in and 36 AON in 2001), although it is always possible that such increase prevented growth of the gull population. Thus, it is impossible to determine whether the Great Black-backed Gull is being adversely affected by competition with the Great Skua without direct observation at the breeding sites. The Great Black-back population changes in areas where Great Skuas do not occur cannot, of course, be explained by such competition.

It is tempting to suggest that the various threats to Great Black-backed Gull populations have not greatly affected survival rates. Although the species generally shows high breeding-site fidelity (Cramp *et al.*, 1974; Wernham *et al.*, 2002), a redistribution of breeders, rather than population decline, might account for the changes recorded in Britain and Ireland between 1985–88 and 1998–2000. A partial redistribution of Russian colonies in the Barents Sea region resulted in response to food shortage in the late 1970s; as new colonies were established near human settlements, those on remoter islands declined (Anker-Nilssen *et al.*, 2000). This suggests that the species might at least retain a flexible strategy to deal with changing environmental conditions. Changes in the northern Scotland populations, such as within Orkney and Shetland, Caithness and Sutherland, Ross & Cromarty, Skye & Lochalsh and the Western Isles, especially might indicate this. Competition with Great Skuas might be the reason for redistribution, although again the evidence is circumstantial.

Clearly, the causes of change in Great Black-backed Gull numbers at particular sites or in particular areas are not well known. This highlights the fact that comparatively little research has been undertaken on the life history of this, perhaps unfashionable, species. Many unanswered questions might be addressed by ringing programmes at breeding sites, aimed at assessing adult survival, breeding site fidelity and recruitment.

INTERNATIONAL CONTEXT

Estimates of breeding populations of the Great Black-backed Gull elsewhere in the world are of variable accuracy and, especially in some more remote localities, subject to the same caveats as pertain to the complete Britain and Ireland surveys. Complete censuses of the species have been undertaken rarely; the estimates of some large populations have wide limits and some small populations may remain unrecorded. As far as possible, up-to-date information has been used in the following account.

The total number of breeding pairs of Great Black-backed Gulls in the world is 170,000–180,000, of which approximately 10% breeds in Britain and just over 1% in Ireland (Table 4).

The biogeographical population (Europe, excluding Russia); Stroud *et al.* (2001) numbers about 100,000–110,000 breeding pairs. These occur in 12 countries, and while Norway continues to host more than any other European country, Britain perhaps now holds more breeding Great Black-backs than does Iceland. More than 15% of the biogeographical population breeds in Britain and about 2% in Ireland. The biogeographical population appears to have decreased slightly from earlier estimates of 95,546–121,233 pairs (Hagemeijer & Blair, 1997) and 128,800–155,000 pairs (BirdLife International/EBCC, 2000). Populations in most countries seem to have been rather stable since the 1990s, although there have been some modest increases in parts of the southern North Sea and English Channel, for example in France (Monnat & Cadiou, in press), and in The Netherlands, which was colonised for the first time in 1993 (van der Weide, 2002). However, in Iceland the species has declined markedly over several years and was placed on that country's red list of threatened species in 2000. The decline is probably hunting-related; in 1995–99, an annual mean of more than 31,000 individuals were taken by hunters (A. Petersen, pers. comm.).

About 61,000 pairs of Great Black-backs breed in North America, and 3,000–5,000 in Greenland (Table 4). Over the latter part of the 20th century the Great Black-back population of North America increased both in size and in range, although the failure of capelin stocks, and the fishing moratorium and associated reduction in the availability of fisheries waste resulted in population decline in Newfoundland in the 1990s (Good, 1998).

Table 4   *International context.*

Country or region	Min	Max	Year	Source
Britain	17,000	17,000	2000	Seabird 2000
Ireland	2,300	2,300	2000	Seabird 2000
Estonia	2,000	5,000	?	BirdLife International/EBCC (2000)
Denmark	1,500	1,600	1996–1998	Grell *et al.* 1998
Faroe Islands	1,200	1,200	1995	BirdLife International/EBCC (2000)
Finland	2,800	2,800	2001	Hario & Rintala (2002)
France	4,079	4,141	1997–1999	Monnat & Cadiou (in press)
Germany	19	19	1999	Köppen (2001); Knief *et al.* (2001); Südbeck & Hälterlein (2001); Dierschke *et al.* (2000)
Iceland	15,000	20,000	1998	Petersen (2000)
Netherlands	15	15	2000	van der Weide (2002)
Norway	40,000	40,000	early 1990s	Lorentsen (1994)
Sweden	15,000	15,000	1990	SOF (2002)
Russia	3,000	4,000	mid-late 1990s	Krasnov *et al.* (1995); Krasnov & Nikolaeva (1998); Anon. (1999a); Anon. (1999b); Semashko and Cherenkov (in press)
Greenland	3,000	5,000	1996	Boertmann *et al.* (1996)
Canada	25,455	25,455	1980–1990	Good (1998)
USA	35,260	35,260	1975–1995	Good (1998)

Biogeographic region	Min	Max	Min % GB	Max % GB	Min % Ireland	Max % Ireland
Europe (excluding Russia)*	100,000	110,000	16.8	17.0	2.2	2.2
World	170,000	180,000	8.4	10.0	1.2	1.3

* Stroud *et al.* (2001)

Black-legged Kittiwake *Rissa tridactyla*

Martin Heubeck

INTRODUCTION

As well as being the most numerous species of gull in the world, the Black-legged Kittiwake is the most oceanic in its habits and the most adapted to nesting on vertical rocky sea cliffs. In Britain and Ireland, the largest and most numerous colonies are found along the North Sea coasts of northeast England, eastern Scotland, the northern isles of Orkney and Shetland, and northwest Scotland (Fig. 1). The largest gaps in their distribution are along the low coastlines of southeast and southern England, northwest England, and southwest Scotland. Colony size varies from less than ten pairs to several tens of thousands, but the locations of colonies tend to be traditional over many decades. Although most colonies are on sheer cliffs, in a few instances man-made structures such as buildings, bridges, seawalls and even offshore oil installations have been utilised.

During the breeding season Black-legged Kittiwakes feed mainly on small pelagic shoaling fish; around the British Isles, these are energy-rich species such as sandeels, sprats and young herring. However, birds will also scavenge for offal and discards around fishing boats, which can be an important food source in years when their preferred prey species are less abundant. Outside the breeding season the species is essentially oceanic, and it is probable that populations from many different breeding localities mix together in the North Atlantic and North Sea during winter, with some from British and Irish colonies (especially first-winters and immatures) spending time off the eastern seaboard of North America.

The British and Irish breeding population of Black-legged Kittiwakes increased considerably during the first half of the 20th century, at least partially in response to a lessening of human persecution for food and feathers, and sport shooting at colonies, which was widespread during the 19th century (Coulson, 1963). In reviewing the results of a national census in 1959, Coulson (1963) suggested that the population of England and Wales then numbered *c.*37,000 pairs and was increasing at *c.*3% per annum, but acknowledged there was insufficient information from much of Scotland or from Ireland to determine population trends there, where populations were estimated at *c.*100,000 and *c.*36,000 pairs, respectively. Although coverage of colonies improved during the Operation Seafarer census of 1969–70, breeding numbers had undoubtedly increased further with the British and Irish population estimated at 450,000–470,000 pairs (Cramp *et al.*, 1974, Lloyd *et al.*, 1991). A further partial census in 1979 found that some marked regional declines had occurred during the previous decade, mainly on the west coasts of Scotland, England and in Wales, and in southeast Ireland, but that numbers had continued to increase on North Sea coasts of England and mainland Scotland (Coulson, 1983). The SCR Census (1985–88) recorded a total of 539,645 AON in Britain and Ireland, 20% more than the Operation Seafarer total of 447,967. However, regional changes during this period were far from uniform. Numbers in northeast England and southeast Scotland increased by 164% and 125%, respectively, whereas those in Caithness and Orkney declined by 15% and 33%, respectively. Furthermore, in many regions coverage of colonies was more comprehensive in 1985–88 than in 1969–70, and a higher proportion of remote colonies were counted from the sea.

CENSUS METHODS

Coverage of known Black-legged Kittiwake colonies in Britain and Ireland was complete during both the SCR Census (1985–88) and Seabird 2000, with the exceptions of a colony in Co. Galway (Ireland) not counted during the former and one in Co. Sligo (Ireland) not counted during the latter survey.

Since Black-legged Kittiwakes are highly colonial at traditional sites on sea cliffs, build conspicuous nests on narrow ledges and have a relatively synchronised breeding season, they would appear to be an easy species to census. The count unit is the Apparently Occupied Nest (AON), defined as a well-built nest capable of holding eggs or young at which at least one adult is present (Walsh *et al.*, 1995). At some colonies, most nests are visible from clifftop vantage points and can be easily counted using binoculars or a telescope, with larger colonies being divided into sections using physical features of the cliff to aid counting. The main difficulty lies in the visibility of colonies on offshore stacks or inaccessible islands, those in and around cave entrances, or on long linear stretches of cliff. These are best counted from the sea, although the instability of a boat as a viewing platform can create problems at larger colonies (which may need to be counted from both land and sea), or where colonies are situated near persistent tide rips or exposed to Atlantic swell.

The recommended count period is during the late incubation period, in Britain and Ireland from late May to mid-June, although in some years nest building can be delayed by 2–3 weeks due to a scarcity of food in spring. In such years, a high proportion of pairs (up to 40%) may begin nest building but not complete a structure qualifying as an AON or progress to laying. This phenomenon was noted in Shetland in 1990 and 2002 (Heubeck, 2003), on the Isle of May in 1994 (Harris & Wanless, 1997a), and at St Abb's Head, Berwickshire in 1998 (Thompson *et al.*, 1999). However, since no such events were documented during Seabird 2000 counts this is unlikely to have caused a serious bias. Counts late in the season, when breeding failures may have resulted in the partial or complete disintegration of some nests, are likely to underestimate breeding numbers. During Seabird 2000, approximately 5% of the British and Irish total of AONs were counted in either late May or in early July; 60% of these (12,624 AON) were along the cliffs of Caithness during the first week of July 1999. Overall, however, it is unlikely that such 'out of season' counts had much influence on gross estimates of population change.

CURRENT STATUS AND TRENDS

The Seabird 2000 total for Britain and Ireland was 415,995 AON, a 23% decline since (1985–88) (Table 1). Although this decline occurred throughout most of the British Isles, there was substantial regional variation in trends.

The breeding distribution of Black-legged Kittiwakes has changed little since the mid-1980s or since 1969–70. The Seabird 2000 survey found that 68% bred in Scotland (67% in 1985–88), 19% in England, the Isle of Man and the Channel Isles (24%), 2% in Wales (2%) and 11% in Ireland (8%). The main change in these percentages over the past 30 years has occurred in England, which held only 11% of the British and Irish population in 1969–70; this proportion more than doubled during the 1970s and early 1980s, largely due to spectacular increases at colonies in northeast England.

Between the SCR Census (1985–88) and Seabird 2000, a substantial decrease of 69% occurred in Shetland with the loss of 36,800 AON, equivalent to 10% of the Scottish population in 1985–88. There was a 20% decrease in Orkney, which brought the population there down to just over half the level in 1969–70, although changes at the three largest colonies varied from an increase of 12% at West Westray, Noup Head, no change (+1%) at Marwick Head and a 54% decrease on Copinsay (Table 2). Numbers fell by 22% along the north coast of Caithness, whilst in Sutherland a 35% decline on Handa Island, the seventh-largest colony in Britain in the mid-1980s, was similar to decreases of 29–37% in other regions of northwest Scotland. The pattern was less uniform in southwest Scotland, with an increase of 20% in Argyll & Bute, a 45% decrease at Ailsa Craig, the only colony in Kyle & Carrick, and a decrease of 20% at the small colonies in Wigtown and Stewartry.

Black-legged Kittiwakes nesting on a gas platform in Morecambe Bay, 19km off the Lancashire coast (Graham Brown)

Table 1   Numbers of breeding Black-legged Kittiwakes (AON) in Britain and Ireland 1969–2002.

Administrative area or country	Operation Seafarer (1969–70)	SCR Census (1985–88)[4]	Seabird 2000 (1998–2002)	Percentage change since Seafarer	Percentage change since SCR	Annual percentage change since SCR
Shetland	43,475	53,571	16,732	−62%	−69%	−8.3%
Orkney	107,177	72,217	57,668	−46%	−20%	−1.6%
North coast Caithness		7,278	5,694		−22%	−1.8%
East coast Caithness		39,282	43,839		12%	0.8%
Caithness total	54,771	46,560	49,533	−10%	6%	0.5%
Northwest coast Sutherland		24,791	21,775		−12%	−1.0%
Sutherland total	16,234	24,791	21,775	34%	−12%	−1.0%
West coast Ross & Cromarty			195			
East coast Ross & Cromarty		329	749		128%	5.6%
Ross & Cromarty total	400	329	944	136%	187%	7.3%
Moray	600	249	488	−19%	96%	5.1%
Banff & Buchan	21,677	27,391	30,599	41%	12%	0.7%
Gordon	6,701	6,284	3,560	−47%	−43%	−3.7%
City of Aberdeen		1,502	1,695		13%	0.9%
Kincardine & Deeside	37,932	45,099	34,501	−9%	−23%	−2.0%
Angus	1,713	1,410	2,926	71%	108%	5.8%
North East Fife	3,282	6,765	3,639	11%	−46%	−4.3%
Kirkcaldy		483	349		−28%	−2.7%
Dunfermline			116			
East Lothian	2,820	4,413	3,349	19%	−24%	−2.1%
Berwickshire	9,951	21,977	18,739	88%	−15%	−1.2%
Stewartry	27	76	7	−74%	−91%	−15.6%
Wigtown	672	400	374	−44%	−7%	−0.5%
Kyle & Carrick	7,742	3,063	1,675	−78%	−45%	−4.2%
Argyll & Bute	3,983	7,509	8,976	125%	20%	1.4%
Lochaber	1,299	3,287	2,107	62%	−36%	−3.4%
Skye & Lochalsh	883	2,074	1,309	48%	−37%	−3.5%
Western Isles–Comhairle nan eilean	24,758	29,975	21,152	−15%	−29%	−2.9%
Scotland Total	**346,097**	**359,425**	**282,213**	**−18%**	**−21%**	**−1.8%**
Northumberland	2,935	6,638	8,621	194%	30%	2.0%
Tyne & Wear	3,559	4,074	2,628	−26%	−35%	−2.9%
Durham	10			−100%		
Cleveland	1,809	12,725	7,101	293%	−44%	−4.0%
North Yorkshire	4,276	7,451	8,616	101%	16%	1.0%
Humberside	30,797	83,694	41,971	36%	−50%	−5.0%
Norfolk	3			−100%		
Suffolk	32	93	369	1053%	297%	10.3%
Kent	50	2,450	1,229	2358%	−50%	−4.5%
East Sussex		972	1,002		3%	0.3%
Isle of Wight	8			−100%		
Dorset	262	375	115	−56%	−69%	−8.3%
Channel Islands	12	34	3	−75%	−91%	−17.6%
Cornwall	839	3,429	1,853	121%	−46%	−4.3%
Isles of Scilly	1,400	1,210	281	−80%	−77%	−11.5%
Devon	2,228	1,713	1,204	−46%	−30%	−2.6%
Lancashire			22[1]			
Cumbria	1,468	995	1,269	−14%	28%	1.9%
Isle of Man	908	1376	1,045	15%	−24%	−2.1%
England, Isle of Man and Channel Islands Total	**50,596**	**127,229**	**77,329**	**53%**	**−39%**	**−3.6%**
West Glamorgan	560	335	225	−60%	−33%	−2.7%
Dyfed	3,078	4,177	3,188	4%	−24%	−1.9%
Gwynedd	3253	4259	3,880	19%	−9%	−0.7%
Wales Total	**6,891**	**8,771**	**7,293**	**6%**	**−17%**	**−1.3%**

Administrative area or country	Operation Seafarer (1969–70)	SCR Census (1985–88)[4]	Seabird 2000 (1998–2002)	Percentage change since Seafarer	Percentage change since SCR	Annual percentage change since SCR
Great Britain, Isle of Man and Channel Islands Total	403,584	495,425	366,835	−9%	−26%	−2.2%
Co. Londonderry			498			
Co. Antrim	4,750	9,980	12,109	155%	21%	1.4%
Co. Down	3	60	453	15000%	655%	16.0%
Co. Dublin	3,853	5,400	7,049	83%	31%	2.2%
Co. Wicklow	21	1,575	1,832	8624%	16%	1.2%
Co. Wexford	3,759	2,912	2,125	−43%	−27%	−2.5%
Co. Waterford	3,417	3,876	2,557	−25%	−34%	−3.4%
Co. Cork	3,025	2,794	1,320	−56%	−53%	−4.6%
Co. Kerry	5,041	2,397	2,455	−51%	2%	0.2%
Co. Clare	4,380	5,003	7,958	82%	59%	4.0%
Co. Galway[3]	820		817	0%		
Co. Mayo	3,454	2,777	4,258	23%	53%	3.4%
Co. Sligo[2]	1,000	678				
Co. Donegal	10,860	6,768	5,729	−47%	−15%	−1.4%
All-Ireland Total	44,383	44,220	49,160	11%	11%	1.0%
Britain and Ireland Total	447,967	539,645	415,995	−7%	−23%	−2.3%

Notes
[1] Morecambe Bay gas platform
[2] Aughris Head not counted in Seabird 2000
[3] Inishmore, Aran Isles not counted in 1985–88 (552 AON in 1990)
[4] The figures for the SCR are actual counts and do not include adjustments to totals made in order to account for unsurveyed colonies (see Lloyd et al., 1991)

Along the east coast of Scotland the pattern of change also varied. Numbers generally increased around the Moray Firth; by 12% along the east Caithness coast, 128% at the North and South Sutor colonies in Ross & Cromarty, 96% in Moray, but only by 1% in Banff Buchan and Gordon. Further south along the east coast of Scotland, numbers decreased by 20% (16,335 AON) overall, with declines of 10% at Fowlsheugh and 45% at nearby Turturra Heughs in Kincardine & Deeside, 46% on the Isle of May (North East Fife), and 19% at St Abb's Head (Berwickshire). However, within southeast Scotland numbers doubled at the small colonies in Angus (2,926 AON in 2000).

Numbers in northeast England experienced an overall decline of 40%, a loss of 45,600 AON. Exceptions were increases of 30% in Northumberland (but a decrease of 14% on the Farne Islands) and of 16% in North Yorkshire. In Tyne & Wear and Cleveland, numbers fell by 36% and 44%, respectively, whilst in Humberside 41,700 fewer AONs were counted at the Bempton/Flamborough Head cliffs (−50%), this being by far the largest colony in Britain and Ireland in the mid-1980s. At the much smaller colonies in southeast England overall numbers decreased by 26%, although there was a 297% increase in Suffolk, where birds nest on man-made structures at Lowestoft and Sizewell. In southwest England, including the Isles of Scilly and the Channel Islands, numbers fell by 49%.

Welsh colonies experienced an overall decline of 17%, with the greatest change (−33%) at the small, southernmost colonies in West Glamorgan, a 24% decrease in Dyfed, but a decline of only 9% at colonies in Gwynedd in northwest Wales. In the north Irish Sea, there was a 24% decrease at the four colonies in the Isle of Man, whereas numbers increased by 28% at the only cliff colony in northwest England, at St Bees Head in Cumbria; 22 pairs had established a colony on an offshore gas platform in Morecambe Bay (Lancashire).

In Ireland, the totals for 1969–70 (44,383 AON), 1985–88 (44,220) and Seabird 2000 (49,160) were similar, but some marked regional changes have occurred since the mid-1980s. In Northern

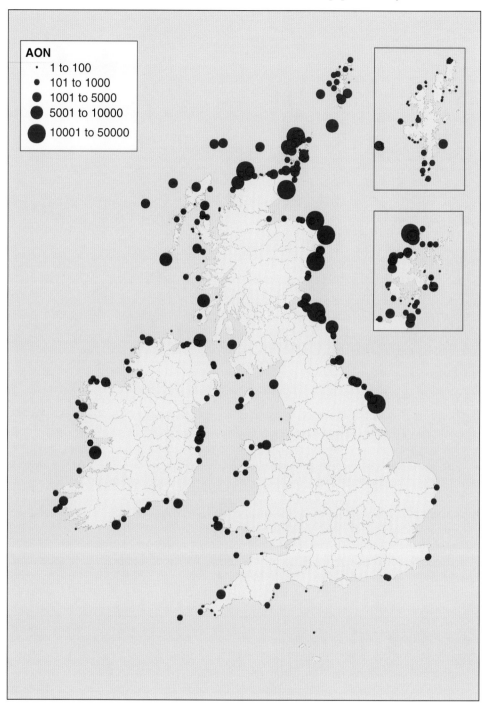

Figure 1   Abundance and distribution of breeding Black-legged Kittiwakes in Britain and Ireland 1998–2002.

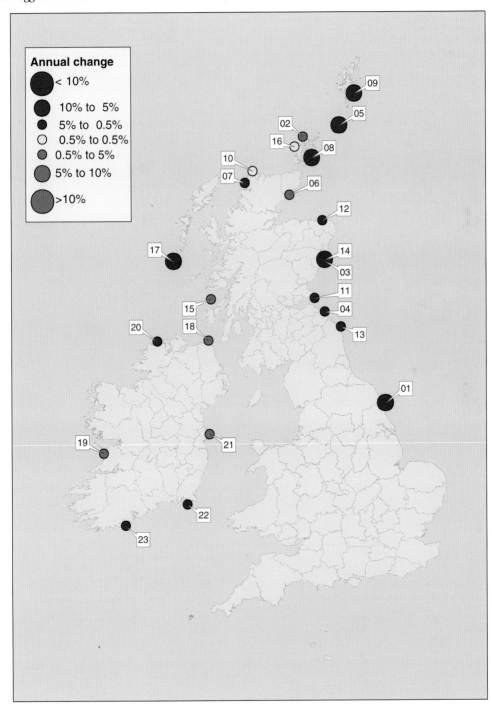

Figure 2 Changes in the number of breeding Black-legged Kittiwakes (AON) at major colonies in Britain and Ireland between the SCR Census (1985–88) and Seabird 2000 (1999–2002). Major colonies are those that contained the top 50% of the populations in Britain and in Ireland during the SCR Census. Numbers correspond to colonies in Table 2.

Table 2   Changes in the number of breeding Black-legged Kittiwakes (AON) at major colonies in Britain and Ireland between the SCR Census (1985–88) and Seabird 2000 (1999–2002). Major colonies are those that contained the top 50% of the national populations of either Britain or Ireland during the SCR Census. Numbers correspond to colony symbols in Fig. 2.

ID	Colony	SCR Census (1985–88)	Seabird 2000 (1998–2002)	Percentage change since SCR	Annual percentage change since SCR	Percentage of population in Britain or Ireland 1998–2002
1	Bempton Cliffs (incl. N. Flamborough Head)	85,095	42,659	−50%	−5.2%	11.6%
2	West Westray (SSSI)	31,085	34,864	12%	1.0%	9.5%
3	Fowlsheugh (SSSI)	22,051	19,842	−10%	−0.8%	5.4%
4	St Abb's Head to Fast Castle Head (SSSI)	20,132	16,223	−19%	−1.6%	4.4%
5	Fair Isle	19,072	8,204	−57%	−5.5%	2.2%
6	Berriedale Cliffs (SSSI)	13,847	24,427	76%	4.5%	6.7%
7	Handa	10,732	7,013	−35%	−3.5%	1.9%
8	Copinsay	9,550	4,364	−54%	−5.9%	1.2%
9	Noss	9,438	2,395	−75%	−8.2%	0.7%
10	Clo Mor	9,020	9,475	5%	0.4%	2.6%
11	Isle of May	6,765	3,639	−46%	−4.3%	1.0%
12	Lion's Head	6,653	5,431	−18%	−1.3%	1.5%
13	Farne Islands	5,915	5,096	−14%	−1.1%	1.4%
14	Turturra Heughs	5,674	3,098	−45%	−4.5%	0.8%
15	Colonsay: NW Cliffs	5,646	6,485	15%	1.0%	1.8%
16	Marwick Head (SSSI)	5,509	5,573	1%	0.1%	1.5%
17	Berneray	5,114	2,613	−49%	−5.0%	0.7%
18	Rathlin Island	6,822	9,917	45%	2.7%	20.2%
19	Cliffs of Moher	4,313	7,698	78%	5.0%	15.7%
20	Horn Head	4,256	3,854	−9%	−0.8%	7.8%
21	Lambay Island	3,005	4,091	36%	2.6%	8.3%
22	Great Saltee	2,908	2,125	−27%	−2.2%	4.3%
23	Old Head of Kinsale	2,059	1,188	−42%	−3.4%	2.4%

Table 3   Comparison of regional trends in numbers of Black-legged Kittiwakes estimated from monitoring plots at sample colonies in the Seabird Monitoring Programme (SMP) (Mavor et al., 2002, 2003) and from changes in total counts between the SCR Census (1985–88) and Seabird 2000 (1998–2002). See Mavor et al. (2002, 2003) for definitions of regions.

Region	SMP Annual percentage change	Change between SCR Census (1985–88) and Seabird 2000 Annual percentage change	Overall
Shetland[1]	−9.9% p.a.**	−7.5% p.a.	−68.8%
Northwest Scotland[1]	−1.6% p.a.**	−1.9% p.a.	−24.8%
Southwest Scotland[2]	+3.5% p.a.**	0% p.a	−0.1%
Northeast Scotland[1]	−1.5% p.a. ns	−0.9% p.a.	−12.0%
Southeast Scotland[1]	−3.3% p.a.***	−1.2% p.a.	−16.9%
Northeast England[1]	−1.1% p.a. ns	−3.3% p.a.	−39.8%
Southeast England[2]	−4.5% p.a.***	−2.8% p.a.	−34.8%
Wales[1]	−2.1% p.a.***	−1.7% p.a.	−16.9%
Southeast Ireland[2]	+0.6% p.a. ns	−0.1% p.a.	−1.5%

Notes

[1] 1986–2001

[2] 1986–2002

ns   non-significant trend

**   significant trend, P < 0.01

***   significant trend, P < 0.001

Ireland, there was an overall increase of 30% in Co. Down, Co. Antrim and Co. Londonderry, including a 45% increase from 6,822 to 9,917 AON at the largest colony, on Rathlin Island (Co. Antrim), which contrasted with the marked decrease on Ailsa Craig (Kyle & Carrick) just 70 km east of Rathlin. In northwest Ireland, a 15% decrease at colonies in Co. Donegal (5,726 AON counted) was a continuation of that documented between Operation Seafarer (1969–70) and the SCR Census (1985–88). In contrast, along the west coast of Ireland there were increases of 53% at colonies in Co. Mayo, of 82% at the Cliffs of Moher and Loop Head in Co. Clare, and of 2% in Co. Kerry. However, there was an overall decline of 37% along the south coast of Ireland, in Co. Cork, Co. Waterford and Co. Wexford, but increases of 16% in Co. Wicklow and 31% in Co. Dublin, both on the east coast of Ireland.

In summary, although there are many local variations, comparison of the SCR (1985–88) and Seabird 2000 counts suggest gross population changes within broad geographic zones. Such zones are perhaps arbitrary, but less so than borders between administrative areas or countries. The greatest proportional decline occurred in Shetland (69%), yet in the region encompassing Orkney, Caithness and the Moray Firth overall numbers fell by only 7%. From Aberdeen south to Yorkshire the decline was 32%, and 26% at the outlying colonies in southeast England. Southwest England, south Wales and the south coast of Ireland all showed similar changes, with an overall decline of 38%. Within the north-central Irish sea, Northern Ireland and southwest Scotland, there was an overall increase of 13%, and an increase of 20% along the west coast of Ireland. In northwest Scotland, the overall decline was 23%.

Since 1986, regional population indices for breeding Black-legged Kittiwakes have been calculated from annual counts at sample colonies as part of the Seabird Monitoring Programme (SMP) (Mavor *et al.*, 2002, 2003). For regions where declines have been gradual and rather consistent there is a reasonable match between trends in 1986–2001/02, as recorded by the SMP and changes between the SCR Census (1985–88) and Seabird 2000 (Table 3), i.e. in Shetland, northwest and northeast Scotland, Wales and southeast Ireland. In northeast and southeast Scotland and northeast England, the SMP data suggest increases during the late 1980s and decreases from the early to mid-1990s (Mavor *et al.*, 2002), whilst in southeast England a steep decline (−11.2% per annum) has more clearly occurred from the mid-1990s. In other areas there was little agreement between the two sets of data, e.g. an increase of 3.5% per annum (SMP) in southwest Scotland compared to no change between the SCR Census and Seabird 2000. Such discrepancies probably arise from the choice of colonies used in the SMP analyses, since trends at colonies counted by wardens of nature reserves or interested individuals may differ from other, perhaps larger colonies within the same region.

CAUSES OF CHANGE

By the time of Operation Seafarer (1969–70) there was no sign of a halt to the increase in the British and Irish breeding population of Black-legged Kittiwakes, and it was suspected then that the availability of nest sites was more likely to be a future limiting factor than food supplies (Cramp *et al.*, 1974). However, by 1979 a survey of Black-legged Kittiwakes in Britain and Ireland found that numbers had continued to increase on North Sea coasts, but had declined in southern and western Britain and southern Ireland, and food shortage during the breeding season was considered to be the most likely explanation (Coulson, 1983). Results from the SCR Census (1985–88) suggested that the total breeding population of Britain and Ireland had increased by *c.*20% since 1969–70, although some regional decreases had occurred (Lloyd *et al.*, 1991).

In long-lived seabirds such as Black-legged Kittiwakes, the most sensitive demographic parameter in relation to population change is adult survival (see chapter on Causes of Seabird Population Change). Other important factors are emigration and immigration of adults, recruitment and breeding success. All four factors may be interrelated. For instance, successful colonies with a high level of activity attract more prospecting birds than unsuccessful ones (Cadiou, 1999). This may account for opposite population trends in adjacent regions, such as Shetland and Orkney in the late 1980s when breeding success was low in Shetland but high in Orkney, and numbers were declining in Shetland but increasing (at least temporarily) in Orkney (Heubeck *et al.*, 1999). However, whilst persistent low breeding success may have contributed to some local and regional population declines, more complex demographic processes are also likely to have been involved; for example, breeding numbers at Handa declined by 35% since the mid-1980s despite 15 years of consistently high breeding success.

Since 1986, monitoring of breeding success has been undertaken throughout Britain & Ireland as part of the SMP (monitoring commenced prior to 1986 at some colonies). Adult survival has also been monitored over a similar period on the Isle of May, Fair Isle and Skomer. However, little is known of the survival of young Black-legged Kittiwakes between fledging and the time of first breeding 4–5 years later. Mass mortality of newly fledged juveniles in the vicinity of colonies can occur in some years due to food shortage, poor weather or a combination of the two. This was particularly evident in Shetland in 1987 and in such years measures of breeding success alone will give an over-optimistic impression of breeding performance (Heubeck, 1989; Riddiford, 1988). Such mass mortality has been reported previously from Orkney and Shetland (McCartan, 1958) and may be under-recorded elsewhere.

Data from 1986 to 1988 showed that low breeding success, observed in Shetland in 1985, gradually spread south among colonies on the North Sea coast over the three years, but that whilst success was variable and sometimes very low at west-coast colonies, no such latitudinal trend existed there (Harris & Wanless, 1990b). During 1986 to 2000, breeding success at monitored colonies in Britain and Ireland averaged 0.72 young fledged per AON, but with some distinct regional differences (Mavor *et al.*, 2002). Mean success in Shetland was 0.49 with almost no chicks fledged in some years, whereas it was consistently higher in Orkney, averaging 1.00. In eastern Scotland success was high during the late 1980s but fell markedly in the 1990s, whereas with the exceptions of 1997–98, it has remained high in eastern England. In southwest England and around the Irish Sea, success has mostly been moderately low (*c.*0.3–0.6). In western Scotland, there have been marked fluctuations in success, and some distinct long-term differences between colonies, e.g. a mean of only 0.49 over 15 years at St Kilda but a remarkably high mean of 1.31 at Handa.

Adult survival rates of Black-legged Kittiwakes on the Isle of May declined significantly between 1986 (99%) and 1996 (83%), during which time breeding success also declined, although the main decline in breeding numbers occurred after 1997 (Harris & Wanless, 1997a, Harris *et al.*, 2000a,b). On Fair Isle (Shetland), there was no significant trend in adult survival in 1986–96, which averaged 83.2%, during which time the colony was declining by 5% per annum, yet breeding success averaged a relatively high 0.81; it was suggested that either low immature survival rates were limiting recruitment to the colony, or immatures were recruiting into other colonies (Rothery *et al.*, 2002). On Foula (Shetland), adult survival averaged 80.1% in 1986–97 but with high variation, ranging from 53–98% (Oro & Furness, 2002). Low survival was associated with low abundance of 0-group sandeels and increased levels of predation by Great Skuas. On Skomer (Dyfed) adult survival averaged 89.8% in 1978–91, but then decreased to a mean of 79.4% in 1992–2000 (Perrins, 2002); overall breeding numbers in Dyfed increased by 36% between Operation Seafarer (1969–70) and the SCR Census (1985–88), but then decreased by 24%.

Two crucial environmental factors driving demographic changes in Black-legged Kittiwakes are food supply and predation. Black-legged Kittiwakes feed on a range of small shoaling fish, as well as planktonic crustaceans and fisheries discards or waste (Cramp & Simmons, 1983). Around Britain and Ireland the main fish prey are lesser sandeels, and the younger age classes of herring and sprat (Coulson & Thomas, 1985; Galbraith, 1983; Wanless & Harris, 1992; Lewis *et al.*, 2001b), and the distribution and abundance of these fish have varied both regionally and temporally over the past 30 years (Corten, 1990; Wright & Bailey, 1993). Being small-bodied surface feeders, with a relatively restricted foraging range from the breeding colony, Black-legged Kittiwakes are more affected by local changes in prey abundance or availability (i.e. swimming depth) than species that dive for the same prey or can range much further from the colony (Hamer *et al.*, 1993; Regehr & Montevecchi, 1997).

In Britain, studies of Black-legged Kittiwake feeding ecology during the breeding season have mostly been conducted at colonies in northeast England, southeast Scotland, and Shetland. These show that planktonic crustaceans are an important component of the diet in late winter and early spring, but adults mainly consume 1-group or older sandeels during the nest-building and incubation period, and tend to feed their chicks juvenile (0-group) sandeels (Pearson, 1968; Harris & Riddiford, 1989; Rindorf *et al.*, 2000; Lewis *et al.* 2001b). Thus, the abundance of 1-group or older sandeels in spring may influence both the timing of laying and the proportion of the population that decides to breed in a given year. Larval sandeels do not metamorphose into free-swimming 0-group fish until late May or June and the timing of their appearance and availability, as well as their abundance and nutritional quality is important for the survival of chicks and possibly also for post-breeding survival of adults (Wright & Bailey, 1993; Lewis *et al.*, 2001b; Oro & Furness, 2002). At least in the northwestern North Sea, the abundance and seasonal availability of sandeels of all age classes are therefore important to the breeding success of Black-legged Kittiwakes, even when alternative prey species such as clupeids are available to the diving auks (Lewis *et al.*, 2001a). Much less is known of the diet of breeding adults and their chicks in southern and western Britain, or in Ireland, and it may be the case that fish species other than sandeels are of more importance there.

In Shetland, very low breeding success of Black-legged Kittiwakes and other surface-feeding seabirds in the late 1980s and a rapidly declining catch in the local but unregulated fishery for sandeels prompted a multi-disciplinary investigation of sandeel biology, distribution and abundance and seabird feeding ecology (Wright & Bailey, 1993; Hamer *et al.*, 1993). Although it could not be proved that the fishery had not caused a reduction in sandeel abundance, it was considered more likely that changes in sea currents had affected the dispersal and survivorship of larval fish. Breeding success recovered somewhat during the early and mid-1990s but declined again during the late 1990s, by which time the fishery had first been closed and then reopened under tight restrictions (Mavor *et al.*, 2003).

Another sandeel fishery commenced in 1990 around the Wee Bankie off the Firth of Forth with a peak catch of 115,000 tonnes in 1993, double that of the Shetland fishery in the early 1980s. After catches declined in the late 1990s the Wee Bankie fishery was closed in 2000. The breeding success of Black-legged Kittiwakes and some other seabird species at colonies in the Firth of Forth was declining during the 1990s and studies were again initiated into the possible links between the fishery and seabird breeding performance (Rindorf *et al.*, 2000; Lewis *et al.* 2001a). These concluded that natural changes in the behaviour and abundance of older sandeels, and the timing of arrival of 0-group fish in the area were the main determinants of the breeding performance of Black-legged Kittiwakes. However, in years when older sandeels were less available early in the breeding season the fishery could have exacerbated a difficult situation for seabirds. Improved breeding success on the Isle of May in 2000 (0.97 fledged/AON), the year the fishery was closed, was probably due to an early appearance and rapid growth of 0-group sandeels, but success declined again there in 2001 (0.61) and 2002 (0.47: Mavor *et al.*, 2003), despite the continued closure of the fishery.

Great Skuas are important predators of adult Black-legged Kittiwakes and their chicks in Shetland. Levels of predation increased during the 1980s as the abundance of sandeels, an important natural prey for Great Skuas, declined (Hamer *et al.*, 1991). Predation by skuas is believed to have contributed significantly to the overall population decline in Shetland (Furness, 1997b; Heubcck *et al.*, 1997, 1999; Votier, 2001). Elsewhere, breeding numbers of Great Skuas have increased dramatically at St Kilda since the mid-1980s (Phillips *et al.*, 1999c), where they are known to depredate significant numbers of Black-legged Kittiwakes among other seabird species (Phillips *et al.*, 1997). Whilst Black-legged Kittiwake breeding success at St Kilda averaged only 0.47 in 1987–2001, and there was a 50% decline in the breeding population in 1987–99 (Murray, 2002), the contribution of predation by skuas to these figures is uncertain. Although gulls and corvids also predate nests of Black-legged Kittiwakes and the disturbance caused may prompt breeding adults to move to other colonies (Danchin & Monnat, 1993), such effects tend to be localised and are unlikely to contribute to regional population change.

In northeast England another significant cause of adult mortality has been highlighted. During the 1960s and 1970s, declines in adult survival were thought to have been a response to a reduction in food (young herring) during the pre-breeding period (Coulson & Thomas, 1985; Aebischer *et al.*, 1990), with further declines there during the mid-1980s; exceptionally high but localised mortality during the spring and summers of 1996–97 was thought to have been due to toxin-producing algal blooms (Coulson & Strowger, 1999). It was estimated that 15,000 birds may have died in the area during these two years, and the largest colony in the area (Marsden) declined by 72% in 1992–98. With hindsight, it was also believed that unusually high mortality and low survival rates in the mid-1980s may have been due to the same cause. It is unknown what effect these 'red tides' have on Black-legged Kittiwakes and other seabirds throughout the rest of Britain and Ireland, as so far the only records of these events have been from northeast England.

Oil pollution is unlikely to have contributed significantly to the population decline over the past 15 years. Although 136 Black-legged Kittiwakes were found oiled during the *Braer* oil spill in Shetland, during January 1993, severe weather at the time had prompted a wreck of birds thought to originate from a wide geographic range of colonies in the northeast Atlantic. Whilst there was evidence of increased non-breeding in 1993 at a colony close to the wreck site, most of those birds bred again the following year and little change could be detected in long-term trends at Shetland colonies (Weir *et al.*, 1996; Heubeck, 1997; Monaghan *et al.*, 1997). Black-legged Kittiwakes also featured prominently in the 1999/2000 *Erika* oil spill off Brittany, with 557 found oiled (Cadiou *et al.*, 2003). Again, however, such spills in midwinter probably kill birds breeding over a wide area and whilst undoubtedly having a detrimental effect, it is unlikely they could be linked to any regional population decline. On the positive side, the oiling rate of Black-legged Kittiwakes from chronic oil pollution in the North Sea has declined in recent years rather than increased, in common with other pelagic seabird species (Camphuysen, 1998).

In summary, it is most likely that the main determinant of population trends in Black-legged Kittiwakes in Britain and Ireland over the past 30 years has been oceanographic changes in the marine environment which affect stocks of key prey fish, with consequences for breeding success, body condition and survival rates of adults, and possibly also for survival rates of immatures. Whether these changes have been entirely natural, or whether they are also being influenced by man's activities (e.g. fisheries, climate change, or pollution) is unclear.

INTERNATIONAL CONTEXT

Black-legged Kittiwakes breed along coastlines of the North Atlantic, North Pacific and Arctic Oceans and their adjacent seas. Two subspecies are recognised, *R. t. tridactyla* in the North Atlantic and *R. t. pollicaris* in the North Pacific, but the separation zone between these subspecies along the arctic coast of Russia is uncertain Chardine, 2002, Chu, 1998. The Black-legged Kittiwake is the most abundant gull in the world, with a global population of *c.*4,300,000–5,200,000 breeding pairs (Table 4). This estimate is substantially less than the 6–8 million pairs given by Lloyd *et al.*, (1991), but many new survey data have been gathered in recent years, previous broad population estimates have been refined, and some populations have undoubtedly declined. At present, Britain and Ireland probably hold 12–15% and 2%, respectively, of the North Atlantic population of *R. t. tridactyla*, and 7–9% and 1%, respectively, of the world population of the species.

Three small colonies in Portugal and Spain delimit the southern edge of the species' range in the northeast Atlantic. Numbers at the few colonies in France, Germany (Helgoland) and Denmark increased in 1970–90. The large population in the Faeroe Islands is thought to have remained stable,

Table 4   International context.

Country or region	Subspecies	Number of pairs Min	Number of pairs Max	Year	Source
Great Britain, Isle of Man and Channel Isles	*tridactyla*	370,000	370,000	1999–2002	Seabird 2000
All Ireland	*tridactyla*	49,000	49,000	1998–2002	Seabird 2000
Denmark	*tridactyla*	625	625	1993–96	BirdLife International/EBCC 2000
Faeroe Islands	*tridactyla*	230,000	230,000	1995	BirdLife International/EBCC 2000
France	*tridactyla*	4,690	4,690	1997–2001	Cadiou *et al.* (in press)
Germany	*tridactyla*	6,500	6,500	1996	BirdLife International/EBCC 2000
Iceland	*tridactyla*	600,000	800,000	1990	BirdLife International/EBCC 2000
Norway	*tridactyla*	500,000	700,000	1990	BirdLife International/EBCC 2000
Norway (Svalbard and Bear Island)	*tridactyla*	270,000	270,000		Mehlum & Bakken (1994)
Portugal	*tridactyla*	3	10		BirdLife International/EBCC 2000
Russia (Barents Sea east to Novaya Zemlya)	*tridactyla*	136,900	146,900		Barrett & Tertitski 2000
Spain	*tridactyla*	200	200		BirdLife International/EBCC 2000
Sweden	*tridactyla*	30	30	1990	BirdLife International/EBCC 2000
Greenland	*tridactyla*	100,000	200,000	1996	BirdLife International/EBCC 2000
Canada (East)	*tridactyla*	224,500	224,500		ICES (2003)
Canada (northwest)	*tridactyla*	32,000	32,000[1]		Baird (1994)
Russia (Laptev Sea)	*pollicaris/tridactyla*	44,000	44,000[1]		Golovkin (1984)
Russia (East Siberian and Chukchi Seas)	*pollicaris*	25,000	150,000		Kondratyev *et al.* (2000)
Russia (north Bering Sea)	*pollicaris*	450,000	550,000		Kondratyev *et al.* (2000)
Russia (Kamchatka south to Kuril Islands)	*pollicaris*	517,000	617,000		Kondratyev *et al.* (2000)
USA (Alaska)	*pollicaris*	770,000	770,000		Lensink (1984)

Biogeographic region	Sub-species	Min	Max	Min % GB	Max % GB	Min % Ireland	Max % Ireland
North Atlantic*	*tridactyla*	2,500,000	3,000,000	12.3%	14.8%	1.6%	2.0%
World	*pollicaris/tridactyla*	4,300,000	5,200,000	7.1%	8.6%	0.9%	1.1%

* Stroud *et al.* (2001) took the eastern limit of the North Atlantic as Novaya Zemlya

Note

[1] figures represent a minimum, no maximum given.

whilst increases have occurred at colonies in Iceland. Although numbers in western Norway have declined since the 1970s, little is known of recent changes in the small (*c.*10,000 pairs) population on Jan Mayen, whilst those on Bear Island have seemingly remained stable since 1970 (Gabrielsen *et al.* 1997; Barrett & Tertitski, 2000). In the southern Barents Sea (including western Novaya Zemlya) breeding numbers increased during the 1960s and 1970s, but then declined from the mid- to late 1980s, probably due to reduced availability of capelin in the region (Krasnov & Barrett, 1995). Numbers in Svalbard continued to increase beyond the mid-1980s (Mehlum & Bakken, 1994), but there are few data on recent status at colonies in Franz Josef Land or east of Novaya Zemlya.

In the northwest Atlantic, breeding numbers have declined in Greenland (Boertmann *et al.*, 1996). The breeding distribution of Black-legged Kittiwakes in eastern Canada is disjunct, with a northern, arctic population, and a southern population centred around the Gulf of St Lawrence and Newfoundland. There is little evidence for change at arctic colonies since the mid-1970s (Chardine, 1999), but numbers increased markedly along the north shore of the Gulf of St Lawrence in 1974–85 (Chapdelaine & Brousseau, 1989), although with a subsequent decrease (Chardine, 1999). During the 1970s the breeding range expanded into Labrador, Nova Scotia and New Brunswick, and in the latter two regions this coincided with large increases in sandeel abundance (Lock, 1987; Birkhead & Nettleship, 1988; Baird, 1994).

Little is known of recent population changes of *R. t. pollicaris* breeding in the Russian far east, although Kondratyev *et al.* (2000) reported numbers to be generally stable along the eastern Kamchatka coast. In Alaska, there has been no evidence of recent overall change (Hatch *et al.*, 1993), but local decreases and increases have been linked to the influence of oceanographic change on the relative abundance of different prey species since the 1970s (Hatch *et al.*, 1993, Baird, 1994; Suryan & Irons, 2001).

Sandwich Tern *Sterna sandvicensis*

Norman Ratcliffe

INTRODUCTION

Sandwich Terns exhibit the most erratic population trends and distribution of any seabird breeding in Britain and Ireland. The population fluctuates dramatically between years owing to large variations in the proportion of mature birds attempting to breed, and distribution varies owing to mass movements of birds among colony sites.

The population is widely but patchily distributed around the coasts of Britain and Ireland and broadly reflects the availability of suitable nesting habitat: low-lying offshore islands, islets in bays or brackish lagoons, spits or remote mainland dunes (Cramp, 1985). Despite frequent changes in the colony sites used, the broad distribution of Sandwich Terns in Britain and Ireland has remained remarkably similar over the last 30 years. Sandwich Terns are among the most strongly gregarious of all seabirds, with the population being distributed in a small number of relatively large colonies in which birds nest at extremely high densities (Langham, 1974; Veen, 1977).

Tern populations in northwest Europe were bought to the brink of extirpation at the end of the 19th century by egg collection for food and hunting of adults for the millinery trade, but recovered in response to protective legislation in the early-20th century (Parslow, 1967; Bijlsma *et al.*, 2001). The Sandwich Tern population in Britain and Ireland increased from the 1920s to the mid-1980s, with protection from increasing recreational disturbance on beaches as well as from persecution probably facilitating this recovery (Cramp *et al.*, 1974; Lloyd *et al.*, 1991). Annual counts of the main colonies demonstrated that there was a sustained increase between the two surveys, but that the population fluctuated erratically around this trend (Ratcliffe *et al.*, 2000).

The population declined between the SCR census and Seabird 2000, with annual monitoring showing a stepped decline linked to discrete events at individual colonies during the late 1980s and early 1990s (Ratcliffe *et al.*, 2000, this chapter). The population now appears to be in a recovery phase, and has returned to levels documented during the late 1970s and early 1980s (this chapter).

CENSUS METHODS

Survey coverage of Sandwich Tern colonies was comprehensive within their British and Irish range during all three of the national surveys, and so long-term trends will be real rather than artefacts of survey coverage.

Sandwich Terns are highly nomadic even compared to congeners, and entire colonies may move site within a year or two in response to changing conditions (Smith, 1974; Lloyd *et al.*, 1991; Ratcliffe *et al.*, 2000). Such movements have the potential to produce severe bias in national population estimates that rely on summing counts from colonies surveyed in different years. To minimise such bias, all Sandwich Tern colonies in Britain and Northern Ireland were surveyed in 2000. In the Republic of Ireland, the colony in Co. Wexford was surveyed in 1999 and all other counts were taken from the 1995 All Ireland Tern Survey (Hannon *et al.*, 1997). Inspection of annual monitoring data for sites in the Irish Sea suggest that no mass movements occurred that would cause severe bias of the population trends. Furthermore, the proportion of pairs nesting in the Republic of Ireland in both surveys is relatively small, and so biases arising from movements between here and the UK will be slight.

During the SCR census, counts of colonies within regions were often taken from different years, and counts for the west coast of Ireland from the 1983 All Ireland Tern Survey (Whilde, 1984). Some movements among sites probably occurred, so some pairs may have been double-counted while others were omitted altogether.

Sandwich Terns are generally counted in units of Apparently Occupied Nests (AONs). During the Seabird 2000 census, this count unit was employed at 93% of colonies and for 99% of pairs. During the SCR, these values were 87% and 98% respectively, and so changes in count units among surveys are unlikely to bias the trends. Counts of AONs were collected using transect counts of nests or counts of incubating adults from a vantage point. Transect counts were used to census 49% of AONs during the Seabird 2000 census. This method is suited to counting Sandwich Terns as they nest on bare ground in discrete, dense colonies, and the size and colour of the eggs are unique compared to other terns breeding in Britain and Ireland (Cramp, 1985). Counts of incubating adults from a vantage point were used to census 50% of AONs during Seabird 2000. The high density of nesting Sandwich Terns and their irregular distribution within large colonies can make it very hard to keep track of which birds have been counted, and so this method tends to be less accurate than transect counts of nests.

The remainder (7% of colonies and 1% of pairs) were surveyed in units of adult birds using flush counts, all of these being small colonies in Orkney. The number of birds counted were divided by 1.5 in order to convert them into AONs. This correction factor was estimated for Arctic Terns in the Northern Isles during 1980 and so will only be approximate for Sandwich Terns during the Seabird 2000 survey. This method is less accurate than AON counts, but since flush counts represent such a small proportion of records this has little effect on the accuracy of national population estimates and trends.

Counts of Sandwich Tern colonies need to be conducted between the peak of laying and the start of hatching. Sandwich Tern laying phenology is highly synchronised within sites and years (Langham, 1974; Veen, 1977) and, provided predation or tidal flooding does not cause significant losses, there is a period of a week or two when the vast majority of AONs are available for survey. This usually occurs in early to mid-June and this was the recommended count period for sites where only a single survey could be made. However, as laying phenology varies between years and sites (Langham, 1974), surveyors were encouraged to make repeated counts from mid-May to late June and report the highest of these. During the Seabird 2000 survey, 90% of colonies and 91% of AONs fell within the specified census period. At the remainder of sites, an accurate date was not reported. During the SCR survey, the census date was reported only in 47% of colonies, and some small colonies in Orkney were surveyed in early July. However, it is unlikely that differences in the timing of counts among surveys will be sufficiently severe to affect the estimation of trends.

The size of the Sandwich Tern breeding population fluctuates erratically from year to year (Ratcliffe *et al.*, 2000). Trends based on comparison of two widely spaced surveys must therefore be viewed with caution, since one of them may have coincided with a year of temporarily depressed population size. Fortunately, all the key colonies in the UK and Ireland have been surveyed annually since 1969 (Lloyd *et al.*, 1975; Thomas, 1982, Thomas *et al.*, 1989; Ratcliffe *et al.*, 2000), allowing long-term population trends to be discriminated from background levels of fluctuation with greater confidence.

CURRENT STATUS AND TRENDS

Seabird 2000 estimated the total British and Irish population of Sandwich Terns at 14,252 AON (Table 1), making it the third-most abundant tern species breeding in Britain and Ireland. Of these, 63% were in England, 26% in Ireland, 7% in Scotland and 3% in Wales (Table 1). None occurred in the Isle of Man or Channel Isles.

Sandwich Tern colonies in Britain and Ireland are almost exclusively coastal, with the exception of two small inland colonies in Ireland (Hannon *et al.*, 1997). Colonies are widely distributed around most of the British and Irish coasts but, within this broad range, the distribution of sites is extremely patchy (Fig. 1). Sandwich Terns require extensive, sheltered, shallow waters that provide abundant sandeel and clupeid prey within foraging range of suitable nesting habitat on low-lying islands, sandy eminences or remote beaches (Cramp, 1985; Shealer, 1999). Therefore, the majority of the population occurs along the British North Sea coast and in the Irish Sea. Breeding Sandwich Terns are scarce along the exposed Atlantic coasts of Britain and Ireland, possibly owing to foraging activity being severely hampered by strong winds and rough seas (Dunn, 1973; Taylor, 1983; Stienen *et al.*, 2000).

The broad distribution of Sandwich Terns has remained stable at a regional level, although there have been losses of colonies from the periphery of the range since the mid-1980s (Shetland, the Monach Islands (Western Isles), Isles of Scilly (Cornwall) and Channel Islands), but these were small and of negligible national importance. Although the broad distribution patterns have not altered, the colony sites used within most regions has changed dramatically due to abandonment and colonisation events. Examples include the Firth of Forth, where Inchmickery was abandoned and the Isle of May colonised, Cumbria where South Walney and Foulney were abandoned in favour of Hodbarrow Lagoon, and southeast England where the Medway was occupied following

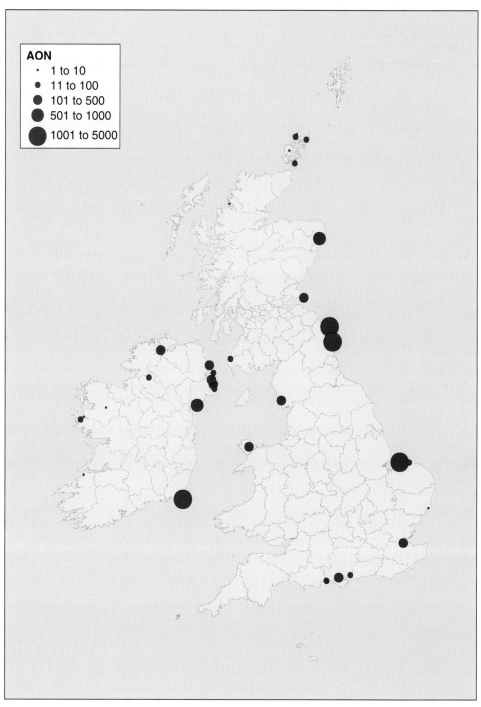

Figure 1   Abundance and distribution of breeding Sandwich Terns in Britain and Ireland 1998–2002.

Table 1   Numbers of breeding Sandwich Terns (AON) in Britain and Ireland 1969–2002.

Administrative area or country	Operation Seafarer (1969–70)	SCR Census (1985–88)/ All Ireland Tern Survey (1984)[1]	Seabird 2000 (1998–2002)/ All Ireland Tern Survey (1995)	Percentage change since Seafarer	Percentage change since SCR/AITS 1984	Annual percentage change since SCR/AITS 1984
Shetland		2			−100%	
Orkney	293	289	173	−41%	−40%	−3.8%
West coast Ross & Cromarty			1			
East coast Ross & Cromarty		43			−100%	
Ross & Cromarty total	*1,000*	*43*	*1*	*−100%*	*−98%*	
Banff & Buchan		130			−100%	
Gordon	740	1,082	524	−29%	−52%	−5.4%
North East Fife			300			
Dunfermline		6	0		−100%	
City of Edinburgh	270	656		−100%	−100%	
Wigtown		2	70		3400%	31.3%
Kyle & Carrick	162	3		−100%	−100%	
Cunninghame		1			−100%	
Western Isles–Comhairle nan eilean		72				
Scotland Total	**2,465**	**2,286**	**1,068**	**−57%**	**−53%**	**−5.7%**
Northumberland	2,428	4,505	3,676	51%	−18%	−1.6%
Norfolk	3,947	3,564	4,275	8%	20%	1.4%
Suffolk	163	201	7	−96%	−97%	−21.3%
Essex	17	99	0	−100%	−100%	
Kent		350	333		−5%	−0.4%
East Sussex		155			−100%	
West Sussex		27			−100%	
Hampshire	228	299	356	56%	19%	1.4%
Isle of Wight		2			−100%	
Dorset		25	31		24%	1.5%
Channel Islands	609	2		−100%	−100%	
Isles of Scilly		20			−100%	
Cumbria		595	340		−43%	−4.2%
England, Isle of Man and Channel Isles Total	**7,392**	**9,844**	**9,018**	**22%**	**−8%**	**−0.6%**
Gwynedd		450	450		0%	0.0%
Wales Total	**0**	**450**	**450**	**0%**	**0%**	**0.0%**
Great Britain, Isle of Man and Channel Islands Total	**9,857**	**12,580**	**10,536**	**7%**	**−16%**	**−1.3%**
Co. Antrim		149	348		134%	5.4
Co. Down	1,211	1,959	1,555	28%	−21%	−1.4
Co. Fermanagh		78	51		−35%	−2.6
Co. Wexford	475	241	1,048	121%	335%	9.6
Co. Kerry	63			−100%		
Co. Clare		7	34[2]		386%	15.5
Co. Galway	210	443	304[2]	45%	−31%	−3.4
Co. Mayo	56	385	151[2]	170%	−61%	−8.2
Co. Donegal	201	205	225[2]	12%	10%	0.8
All–Ireland Total	**2,216**	**3,467**	**3,716**	**68%**	**7%**	
Britain and Ireland Total	**12,073**	**16,047**	**14,252**	**18%**	**−11%**	

Notes

[1] All SCR counts in Ireland were conducted during the All Ireland Tern Survey in 1984 (Whilde, 1985)

[2] All counts in this administrative area were conducted during the All Ireland Tern Survey in 1995 (Hannon *et al.*, 1997)

abandonment of Dungeness, Foulness and Maplin Sands. Overall, the number of colonies has declined from 58 to 34, with 33 sites being abandoned since the mid-1980s and nine being colonised.

The five largest colonies were Scolt Head (Norfolk: 4,200 pairs), the Farne Isles and Coquet Island (Northumberland: 1,950 and 1,726 respectively), Inish Island in Lady's Island Lake (Co. Wexford: 1,048) and the islets in Strangford Lough (Co. Down: 894). Other important colonies during the Seabird 2000 census included the Sands of Forvie (Gordon: 524), Cemlyn Bay (Gwynedd: 450), Blue Circle Island in Larne Lough (Co. Antrim: 348), Hodbarrow Lagoon (Cumbria: 340), Isle of May (North East Fife: 300), North Solent (Hampshire: 268) and Inch Island in Loch Swilly (Co. Donegal: 258). The remaining 26 colonies recorded during Seabird 2000 each hosted fewer than 100 breeding pairs.

The total number of breeding Sandwich Terns in Britain and Ireland declined by 11% since the SCR census (Table 1). However, the population is still higher than the 12,073 pairs counted during Operation Seafarer in 1969–70. The declines since the mid-1980s were spread throughout the Sandwich Tern's British and Irish range, although patterns of change varied between regions with little evidence of any broad spatial pattern. Numbers declined alarmingly in southeast England (−48%), Scotland (−53%), northwest England (−42%) and western Ireland (−36%). Moderate declines occurred in the Solent and south coast harbours (−29%), Northern Ireland (−28%) and Northumberland (−18%). Numbers in southeast Ireland increased by 76%, those on the north Norfolk coast by 20%, whilst those in Anglesey remained stable.

Since Operation Seafarer, key Sandwich Tern colonies, which host approximately 80% of the national population, have been counted annually (Ratcliffe *et al.*, 2000) and these provide an index of the annual patterns of population change over the last 33 years. The population has fluctuated erratically over the study period, with sharp declines and rapid recoveries (Fig. 2). Since 1969, there was a general pattern of population increase with a peak occurring in 1988, but subsequently there

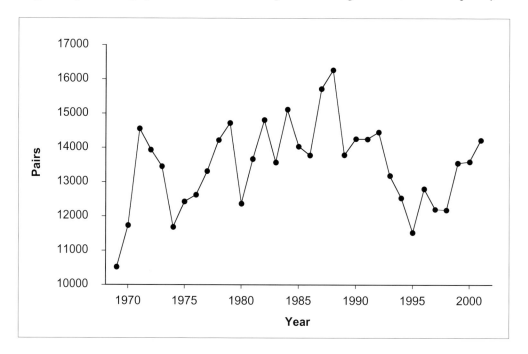

Figure 2. Population trends of breeding Sandwich Terns at key colonies monitored in Britain and Ireland 1969–2001.

was a stepped decline over a period of seven years reaching a nadir in 1994 (Fig. 2). This decline represented the loss of almost 5,000 pairs and was outside the range of the fluctuations that occurred in previous years in terms of both severity and duration. Subsequently, the population has undergone a halting recovery, and in 2001 was approaching levels found in the late 1970s and early 1980s (Fig. 2). As such, the moderate overall decline detected between the SCR and Seabird 2000 surveys appears to be a short-term perturbation in population status that, although outside the range of previous fluctuations, is not wholly atypical for the species.

CAUSES OF CHANGE

The decline of Sandwich Terns is linked to discrete events occurring at individual colonies rather than being spread across the range, and many declines are associated with predation. There is a scarcity of offshore islands within the Sandwich Tern's British and Irish breeding range, and so a large proportion of birds nest on mainland beaches, spits or near-shore islets where they are vulnerable to mammalian predation. A number of species have been documented preying on Sandwich Tern nests and chicks. Predation by Brown Rats has been reported in some years at Lady's Island Lake and Strangford Lough, by Stoats at Cemlyn Bay and Hodbarrow, and by American Mink at Dungeness, Rye Harbour and Mulroy Bay. However, Red Foxes are by far the most serious and widespread predator of Sandwich Tern colonies, and have caused periodic losses at most of the accessible sites.

Mammalian predation usually causes complete breeding failure and, once discovered, a colony will often be attacked on successive years until the terns abandon the site. There is usually a delay of a few years whilst a new site is colonised and, during this period, a large proportion of the adult birds in the population appear to defer breeding (Ratcliffe *et al.*, 2000). Predation therefore produces the characteristic fluctuations in Sandwich Tern population trends and also reduces future recruitment rates owing to breeding failure prior to the colony being abandoned and a reduced number of adults attempting to breed subsequently. Several colonies declined or were abandoned following mammalian predation (mainly by foxes) during the late 1980s and 1990s, including Sands of Forvie, Scolt Head, Hodbarrow, Foulness, Havergate, Foulney and Dungeness, and these were sufficient to explain a notable proportion of the national population decline (Ratcliffe *et al.*, 2000).

Fox predation also caused colony abandonment in previous decades (Lloyd *et al.*, 1975; Thomas, 1982; Thomas *et al.*, 1989), but the incidence of this in the 1990s was unprecedented. Fox populations and range in Britain have increased over the past few decades following a relaxation of management by gamekeepers (Tapper, 1992), such that fox predation of Sandwich Tern colonies is now more widespread and frequent than previously.

The Sandwich Tern population recovered rapidly between 1998 and 2001 as new sites were colonised, but many of these are also accessible to foxes and may be depredated and abandoned in the future. Electric fences are used at many colonies to exclude foxes (e.g. Patterson, 1974), but are not always completely effective. Only colonies on offshore islands are immune to attack, and these are scarce within the Sandwich Tern's British and Irish range. Restoration of existing offshore islands (Kress *et al.*, 1983; Kress, 1997) or creation of new islands from dredge-spoil (Burgess & Hirons, 1992) may be necessary to maintain Sandwich Tern populations into the 21st century.

Large gulls compete for breeding space with terns (Thomas, 1972; Kress, 1997), cause disturbance to nesting attempts and prey upon eggs and chicks (Fuchs, 1977; Yorio & Quintana, 1997), such that tern colonies decline and are ultimately abandoned (Thomas, 1972; Kress, 1997). Gulls prefer to nest on offshore islands and displace terns to inshore habitats where they are more vulnerable to mammalian predation (Kress *et al.*, 1983; Kress, 1997). Gulls extirpated the Sandwich Tern colony on Inchmickery during the mid-1990s (D. Fairlamb, pers. comm.), and this contributed to the decline of the national population. After four years when virtually no breeding occurred in the Firth of Forth, Sandwich Terns colonised the Isle of May (where gull distribution is controlled) and have now recovered to levels recorded in the early 1990s. Gull predation has also been documented as causing significant losses in some years at the Farnes (Northumberland), Scolt Head and Blakeney Point (both Norfolk). Control of expanding gull populations on offshore islands such as those in Northumberland and the Firth of Forth is necessary to prevent Sandwich Terns abandoning these sites, and plays a pivotal role in restoring offshore sites previously abandoned by terns in the USA (Kress *et al.*, 1983; Kress, 1997).

Sandwich Tern nesting habitat is highly dynamic and rests on a knife-edge between erosion and succession. Nesting habitat or entire breeding sites can be lost to erosion by winter storms (Thomas, 1982; Brown & McAvoy, 1985; Visser & Peterson, 1994) or become overgrown with rank herbage or scrub (Brown & McAvoy, 1985). These factors have not played a role in the recent population declines of Sandwich Terns, but erosion of sites may become a greater problem in the future owing to sea-level rise (Norris & Buisson, 1994). Continual management of vegetation on islands is essential to maintain existing offshore colonies, such as Coquet, and to restore former colony sites that have been lost due to succession, such as Mew Island in the Copelands (Co. Down).

The interactions of nesting habitat availability, competition and predation are clearly important determinants of Sandwich Tern population trends, but factors beyond the colony boundary could also play a role. Sandwich Terns are specialist foragers (Stienen *et al.*, 2000), and are dependent on dense shoals of clupeids and sandeel within foraging range of their colonies in order to breed successfully. The population of Sandwich Terns in The Netherlands declines in years when clupeid prey is scarce (Stienen & Brenninkmeijer, 1998a), probably owing to intermittent breeding during periods of poor food availability. It is likely that the declines at the Farne Islands are due to local reductions in food supply causing emigration to Coquet Island (J. Walton, pers. comm.). Population size and distribution is also related to local prey availability in the closely related Swift Tern (Crawford, 2003) and Elegant Tern (Schaffner, 1986). Poor food availability also has the potential to reduce growth and survival of chicks, and this can be exacerbated by Black-headed Gull kleptoparasitism (Stienen & Brenninkmeijer, 2002a,b).

Survival in the West African wintering grounds also has the potential to affect Sandwich Tern population trends. Ringing recoveries show that adult survival is 82% and that of first-years is 45% (Green *et al.*, 1990), but there is little information on factors affecting this. Studies in Guinea-Bissau show that nutritional stress of Sandwich Terns during winter is low (Brenninkmeijer *et al.*, 2002) and so is unlikely to depress survival rates. However, stocks of sardine and anchovy in West Africa are highly variable between years owing to oceanographic effects on spawning and larval survival (Kwei 1964; Cury & Roy, 1987; Mendelssohn & Cury, 1987; Cury & Fontana, 1988), and Sandwich Terns may suffer mortality owing to starvation in some years. Preliminary analyses by Green *et al.* (1990) suggested that immature survival rates were low during years when landings by the Ghanaian sardine fishery were low. Recent over-fishing of West African fish stocks by EU trawlers (MacKenzie, 2002) has the potential to reduce food availability and immature survival of terns.

Deliberate trapping by children in West Africa for sport and food results in the death of large numbers of immature Sandwich Terns each year (Dunn & Mead, 1982; Ntiamoa-Baidu *et al.*, 1992; Stienen *et al.*, 1998) and may suppress future recruitment rates. Education programmes to reduce trapping activity have been successfully implemented in Ghana (Ntiamoa-Baidu, 1991), although the benefits of this for Sandwich Terns at the population scale are far from clear. Recent studies show a resurgence of trapping activity in coastal Ghana (Ghana Wildlife Society, unpubl.) and further studies are necessary to understand the implications of this for population trends and to target education work effectively.

Sandwich Terns brooding and feeding their chicks (Chris Gomersall)

INTERNATIONAL CONTEXT

The global population of Sandwich Tern is 160,000–170,000 pairs (Table 2), and the breeding distribution is highly fragmented around the coasts of the Atlantic Ocean and adjacent seas. The species is polytypic, with three recognised subspecies. Nominate *sandvicensis* breeds in Britain and Ireland, and along the coasts of the North, Baltic, Mediterranean, Black and Caspian Seas, with a total breeding population of 90,800–100,900 pairs (Table 2). The smaller *acuflavida* (Cabot's Tern) breeds along the southeast coast of the USA and has a total breeding population of 49,000–50,000 pairs. Yellow-billed *eurygnatha* (sometimes regarded as a separate species, Cayenne Tern; Shealer, 1999) breeds in the Caribbean and northern South America, east Brazil and Argentina, with a population of 15,000–17,000 pairs. This is likely to be an underestimate owing to poor coverage of its range in Brazil.

The European population is estimated at 69,000–79,000 breeding pairs, with Britain and Ireland hosting 14–16% and 5% respectively (Table 2). The remainder of the European population breeds along the coasts of The Netherlands, Germany, France, Denmark and Belgium, and in the Ukraine along the Azov and Black Sea coasts, with small colonies occurring through the Baltic and Mediterranean Seas.

Population trends in northwest Europe have been well documented, and considerable temporal and spatial variations are apparent. Colonies in The Netherlands experienced a catastrophic collapse (from 30,000–46,000 pairs in the 1930s and 1950s to 875 pairs in 1965) due to pesticide pollution (Bijlsma *et al.*, 2001). Numbers recovered during the 1970s and 1980s owing to the cessation of

Table 2   International context.

Country or region	Subspecies	Number of pairs		Year	Source
		Min	Max		
Great Britain, Isle of Man and Channel Isles	*sandvicensis*	11,000	11,000	2000	Seabird 2000
All-Ireland	*sandvicensis*	3,700	3,700	1995, 1999, 2000	Seabird 2000
Belguim	*sandvicensis*	1,550	1,550	2000	Stienen pers. comm.
Bulgaria	*sandvicensis*	100	1,500	1990–97	BirdLife International / EBCC (2000)
Denmark	*sandvicensis*	4,500	4,500	1993–96	Grell (1998)
Estonia	*sandvicensis*	800	800		BirdLife International / EBCC (2000)
Finland	*sandvicensis*	1,100	1,100		Lloyd *et al.* (1991)
France	*sandvicensis*	6,700	6,700	2000	Yésou & Sadou (2003)
Germany	*sandvicensis*	9,700	9,700	1998	Hälterlein et al. (2000)
Greece	*sandvicensis*	0	50		BirdLife International / EBCC (2000)
Italy	*sandvicensis*	138	696	1988–97	BirdLife International / EBCC (2000)
Netherlands	*sandvicensis*	14,500	14,500	1998–2000	Stienen (2002)
Norway	*sandvicensis*	0	5	1990	BirdLife International / EBCC (2000)
Poland	*sandvicensis*	0	300		BirdLife International / EBCC (2000)
Romania	*sandvicensis*	500	500	98	BirdLife International / EBCC (2000)
Russia	*sandvicensis*	4,000	6,000	1984–88	BirdLife International / EBCC (2000)
Spain	*sandvicensis*	755	755	1989	BirdLife International / EBCC (2000)
Sweden	*sandvicensis*	300	400	1989	BirdLife International / EBCC (2000)
Ukraine	*sandvicensis*	9,900	15,600	1998	BirdLife International / EBCC (2000)
Turkmenistan	*sandvicensis*	22,000	22,000	1976	Golovkin (1984)
USA	*acuflavidus*	46,945	46,945	1975–95	Shealer (1999)
Carribean	*acuflavidus*	2,100	3,000		Norton (2000)
Carribean	*eurygnatha*	9,100	9,100		Norton (2000)
Venezuela	*eurygnatha*	1,100	1,900		Norton (2000)
Guyana	*eurygnatha*	1,400	2,000		Norton (2000)
Brazil	*eurygnatha*	500	1,000	1988	Antas (1991)
Argentina	*eurygnatha*	2,800	2,800	1993–95	Yori *et al.* (1999)

Biogeographic region	Subspecies	Min	Max	Min % GB	Max % GB	Min % Ireland	Max % Ireland
Europe*	*sandvicensis*	69,000	79,000	13.9%	15.9%	4.7%	5.4%
World	All	160,000	170,000	6.5%	6.9%	2.2%	2.3%

*Stroud *et al.* (2000)

pollution, but numbers stabilised during the 1990s at a level approximately one-third of that recorded during the 1950s (Bijlsma *et al.*, 2001; Stienen, 2002), possibly owing to food limitation (Stienen & Brenninkmeijer, 1998a). In Germany, numbers increased from 4,000 pairs in the 1950s to 11,000 in the early 1990s (Südbeck & Hälterlein, 1997; Hälterlein *et al.*, 2000), but have since stabilised or declined slightly (Hälterlein *et al.*, 2000). The population in France increased from fewer than 500 pairs in the 1940s to around 6,500 by the 1980s, and has since fluctuated between 6,500 and 7,000 pairs (Yésou & Sadoul, in press). In Belgium, the sole Sandwich Tern colony at Zeebrugge was colonised in 1988 following immigration from The Netherlands and the UK (E. M. W. Stienen, pers. comm.). The population there has since fluctuated erratically, increasing rapidly to 1,650 pairs in 1993, declining to 73 pairs in 1998 and recovering to 1,550 pairs in 2000, before crashing to 47 pairs in 2002 (E. M. W. Stienen, pers. comm.).

Elsewhere in the world, population trends are less well documented. Populations in the Ukraine have declined catastrophically with a decrease of 20–49% between 1970 and 1993 (Tucker & Heath, 1994), with a further decline of 80% in 1993–98 (BirdLife International, 2000). This is probably due to vegetation succession at colony sites following a decline in pastoral agriculture and grazing pressure (Tucker & Heath, 1994). The population size and range in the USA are increasing, probably owing to colony protection, and creation and management of nesting habitat (Shealer, 1999), but there are concerns that declines could occur in the future owing to erosion of beach habitat and dredge-spoil islands in Louisiana where the majority of the population occurs (Visser & Peterson, 1994).

In the Caribbean and Brazil, the populations of *eurygnatha* are probably decreasing owing to egg collecting and disturbance (Antas, 1991; Norton, 2000). In Argentina, increased predation and competition for territory from the expanding Kelp Gull population may threaten the status of the *eurygnatha* population breeding there (Yorio & Quintana, 1997; Quintana & Yorio, 1998). Given the small size of the *eurygnatha* population and the likelihood that it is a separate species, these threats and trends are of global conservation concern.

Roseate Tern *Sterna dougallii*

Stephen F. Newton

INTRODUCTION

The Roseate Tern population in Britain and Ireland experienced the most dramatic decline of any seabird species between Operation Seafarer (1969–70) and the SCR Census (1985–88). It also has one of the most restricted ranges of any seabird in Britain and Ireland, with most of the population breeding in just three colonies. Consequently, Roseate Terns are of high conservation concern in both Britain and Ireland, and are the only Red-listed seabird species in both the United Kingdom and Republic of Ireland (Newton *et al.*, 1999; Gregory *et al.*, 2002).

Roseate Terns have probably always been rare and localised in Britain and Ireland owing to their specialised foraging and nesting habitat requirements. They were driven to the brink of extinction by exploitation for the millinery trade during the 19th century, but recovered through the early-20th century as a result of protective legislation and management (Cabot, 1996). Numbers peaked at 3,812 pairs in 1968, but declined rapidly to just 521 pairs in 1985 (Cabot, 1996). The decline during the 1970s and early 1980s was probably due to poor immature survival rates, and this may have been at least partially attributable to deliberate trapping in the Ghanaian wintering grounds. Factors such as predation and nesting habitat loss (due to erosion, competition with gulls and/or disturbance) may have also played a role (Cabot, 1996).

The population stabilised at around 500 pairs until 1992 when it staged a slow recovery. The population of at least 816 pairs in 2003 was the highest since 1980. Conservation efforts such as education programmes in the wintering areas in northwest Africa and site management at breeding colonies have probably contributed to the population recovery over the last decade (Avery *et al.*, 1995). The recovery has been manifest only at the three largest colonies, with smaller peripheral colonies declining to perilously low levels or being abandoned, despite intensive efforts to maintain them. Movements of birds among colonies within the meta-population has been an important determinant of regional population trends during the past three decades, and thus maintaining or enhancing the range of Roseate Terns will probably depend on active conservation efforts to promote growth of relict colonies, restore breeding at abandoned sites and create new breeding sites.

CENSUS METHODS

Roseate Terns are restricted to a small number of well-known colonies, with all of those in Britain and along the east coast of Ireland being counted annually since 1969, such that their populations are monitored in more detail than any other seabird species breeding here. The small colonies found along the west coast of Ireland during the All Ireland Tern Survey in 1984 (Whilde, 1985) were not counted in 2000, but a repeat census in 1995 found that all of these had been abandoned (Hannon *et al.*, 1997). The coverage of Roseate Tern colonies during Seabird 2000 is therefore likely to have been comprehensive, although any birds recolonising sites along the west coast of Ireland will have been overlooked.

Roseate Terns may move among colonies between years in response to predation or habitat change, and so a census of a population should ideally survey all colonies within a single year to avoid double-counting or missing some pairs. Therefore, for Seabird 2000, counts of Roseate Terns breeding in Britain, Northern Ireland and the Irish Sea coast of the Republic of Ireland were made in 2000, except for the colony at Lady's Island Lake (Co. Wexford), which was surveyed in 1999. Inspection of counts made at other large colonies in 1999 and 2000 suggest that no large inter-colony movements of birds occurred between these two years, and so the counts used for Seabird 2000 should provide a representative snapshot of the status of Roseate Terns in Britain and Ireland.

The size of tern breeding populations can fluctuate between years, probably owing to variations in the proportion of mature birds that attempt to nest. Numbers at most Roseate Tern colonies are relatively stable, but those at the colony at Lady's Island Lake (Co. Wexford) tend to be less so (Mavor *et al.*, 2003). Numbers at the colony between the mid-1990s and 2003 fluctuated between 50 and 120 pairs, and the upper limit probably affords the best estimate of the number of mature pairs associated with the colony, even though not all of these attempt to breed annually. As such, the count of 116 pairs in 1999 has been used for Seabird 2000, rather the count of 78 pairs made in 2000. There was no evidence to suggest that the pairs that bred at Lady's Island in 1999 moved to any other colonies in Britain and Ireland the following year.

To estimate the size of the British and Irish population during the SCR Census (1985–88), Lloyd *et al.* (1991) used counts conducted in different years at some colonies, but did not specify in which year each colony was surveyed. In order to be comparable with Seabird 2000, we only used counts for the SCR Census that were conducted in 1986, when the most comprehensive coverage of colonies during the period 1985–88 was achieved. The total number of breeding Roseate Terns in 1986 was 550 pairs, whereas Lloyd *et al.* (1991) estimated 470 pairs for 1985–87. The discrepancy is due to the fact that Lloyd *et al.* (1991) used a count of 69 pairs for the colonies on Anglesey (Gwynedd), which was conducted in 1987 after numbers there had fallen dramatically from 209 in 1986.

Roseate Terns habitually nest in association with congeners. In Britain and Ireland, these are usually Common Terns, although at some colonies they also associate with Sandwich and Arctic Terns. Adult Roseate Terns are easily distinguished from other tern species by their unique combination of pale plumage, elongate outer tail feathers, dark bill and, during courtship and incubation, a rosy flush on the breast (Malling Olsen & Larsson, 1995). They also have very distinctive calls that signal their presence in dense flocks of flushed terns (Malling Olsen & Larsson, 1995). Consequently, it is usually straightforward to recognise their presence and location within a mixed tern colony. Their nests are also readily identifiable, as they are placed in much denser cover, and the eggs are more elongate, pale and finely marked compared to those of other terns (Cramp, 1985; Gochfeld *et al.*, 1998). Given that coverage of other tern species was comprehensive during Seabird 2000, it is therefore unlikely that many breeding Roseate Terns will have been overlooked.

Roseate Terns were all counted in units of apparently occupied nests (AON) during Seabird 2000. Most AONs (i.e. 98%) were surveyed by systematically counting all nests situated along transect lines through the colony. The remaining AONs were surveyed by counting the number of apparently incubating adults (AIA) from a vantage point. Roseate Tern nests are usually hidden in long vegetation, among boulders, in rabbit burrows or in nest boxes, and so counts of AIAs from a vantage point will miss a large proportion of nesting pairs. In small colonies or where Roseate Terns nest at low densities it is often possible to map nest sites from observation of adult breeding activity (e.g. nest building, incubation changeovers or chick feeding) from a vantage point using methods akin to AIA counts, even though the nest may be obscured from view by cover. At large or dense colonies, observations of the activity of breeding adults are useful to identify the location of nesting Roseate Terns, but nest counts are the best method to obtain estimates of breeding numbers. Counts of AONs along transects through the colony were repeated several times to avoid the more concealed nests being overlooked.

Counts of AONs were conducted in the second or third week of June when the majority of birds were incubating. Counts conducted earlier in the year tend to omit pairs that have not yet laid, while those conducted later tend to miss AONs as chicks disperse from nests and hide a few days after hatching.

CURRENT STATUS AND TRENDS

Seabird 2000 estimated the total breeding population of Roseate Terns in Britain and Ireland to be 790 AON (Table 1), making it the rarest of our breeding terns and the second rarest breeding seabird after Mediterranean Gull. Of these, 92.9% occurred in the Republic of Ireland, 4.6% in England, 1.8% in Scotland, 0.5% in Northern Ireland and 0.2% in Wales. None were found breeding in the Channel Islands or on the Isle of Man.

Roseate Tern distribution was restricted to the Irish Sea and a small section of the North Sea, comprising northeast England and southeast Scotland, with outlying pairs in Norfolk and Hampshire (Fig. 1). Only 12 sites were occupied during Seabird 2000, compared to 14 in 1986 and 16 over the course of SCR Census, i.e. 1985–88 (Lloyd *et al.*, 1991; Avery *et al.*, 1995; Cabot, 1996). Colonies in Carlingford Lough and Strangford Lough (both in Co. Down) were abandoned in the late 1980s, whilst those colonies along the west coast of Ireland (Co. Galway and Co. Donegal) were abandoned between 1984 and 1995. Colonies in the Isles of Scilly were abandoned in 1995. One, occasionally more, pairs have occupied or recolonised some sites since the SCR Census (1985–88), in counties such as Angus, Norfolk and Hampshire, although these have only been occupied intermittently over the past decade.

Table 1   *Numbers of breeding Roseate Terns (AON) in Britain and Ireland 1969–2000.*

Administrative area or country	Operation Seafarer (1969–70)	SCR Census (1986)	Seabird 2000 (1999–2000)	Percentage change since Seafarer	Percentage change since SCR	Annual percentage change since SCR
Orkney	3			−100%		
Angus	1		1	0%		
Northeast Fife			2			
Dunfermline	5		11	120%		
City of Edinburgh		18			−100%	
East Lothian	107			−100%		
Argyll & Bute	3			−100%		
Kyle & Carrick	15			−100%		
Scotland Total	134	18	14	−90%	−28%	
Northumberland	332	31	34	−90%	10%	0.7%
Norfolk			1			
Hampshire	2		1	−50%		
Isles of Scilly	20	3		−100%	−100%	
Cumbria	1			−100%		
England Total	355	34	36	−90%	6%	0.4%
Gwynedd	202	209	2	−99%	−99%	−28.2%
Wales Total	202	209	2	−99%	−99%	−28.3%
Great Britain, Isle of Man & Channel Islands Total	691	261	52	−92%	−80%	
Co. Antrim	13	21	4	−69%	−81%	−11.2%
Co. Down	251	41		−100%	−100%	
Co. Dublin	60	227	618	930%	172%	7.4%
Co. Wexford	1,352		116	−91%		
Co. Cork	10			−100%		
Co. Kerry	1			−100%		
Co. Donegal	6			−100%		
All-Ireland Total	1,693	289	738	−56%	155%	14.3%
Britain and Ireland Total	2,384	550	790	−67%	44%	9.1%

During Seabird 2000, the Roseate Tern population of Britain and Ireland was concentrated in three large colonies: 78% (618 AON) on Rockabill (Co. Dublin), 15% (116 AON) at Lady's Island Lake (Co. Wexford) and 4% (35 AON) on Coquet Island (Northumberland). The remaining regularly occupied sites were the two colonies in the Firth of Forth (2 AON and 11 AON) and single colonies on Anglesey (2 AON) and at Larne Lough (4 AON), with a single AON on the Farne Islands (Northumberland). Single AONs were found in 2000 at sites in Norfolk, Hampshire and Angus.

The Roseate Tern population in Britain and Ireland increased in size by 44% between the SCR Census (1986) and Seabird 2000 (1999–2000). The increase commenced in the early 1990s and has continued since the Seabird 2000 survey work, and by 2003 the population had increased to at least 816 AON, the largest since 1980 (Fig. 2). However, the current population is still less than a third of its size during the late 1960s when there over 3,000 pairs in Britain and Ireland (Cabot, 1996).

Whilst there has been an overall increase in Britain and Ireland, considerable variation in trends amongst colonies is evident. The overall increase in numbers in Britain and Ireland is mainly due to the growth of two colonies in the Republic of Ireland. The colony at Rockabill increased steadily through the 1990s and has now stabilised at around 610 AON, representing a 172% increase compared to 1986 (Fig. 3). The re-establishment and subsequent growth of the colony on Inish Island, in Lady's Island Lake (Co. Wexford), during the 1990s also made a large contribution to the increase in total British and Irish population size. This site has been consistently occupied since 1989,

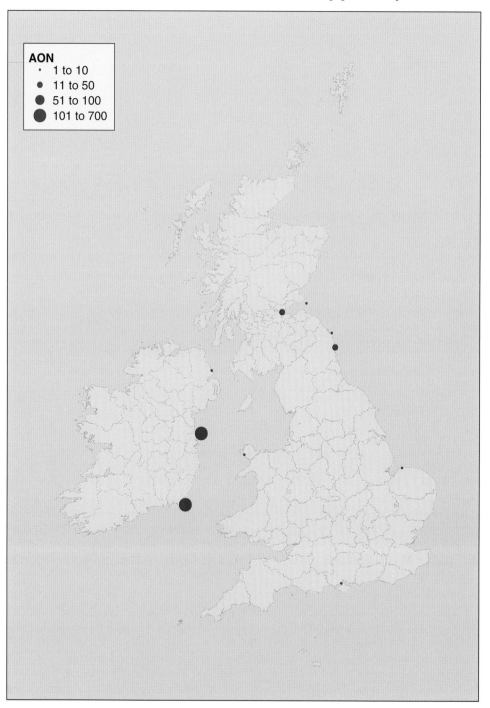

Figure 1   Abundance and distribution of breeding Roseate Terns in Britain and Ireland 1999–2000.

The tiny island of Rockabill, Dublin holds 78% of Roseate Terns breeding in Britain and Ireland (Alyn Walsh)

Roseate Terns courting by a nest box on Rockabill (Chris Gomersall)

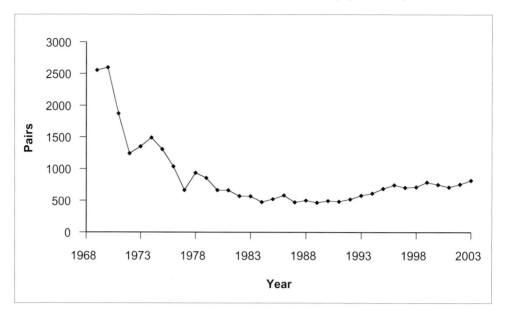

Figure 2   Numbers of breeding Roseate Terns in Britain and Ireland 1969–2003.

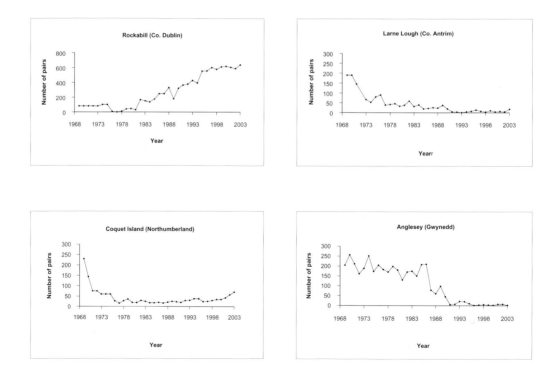

Figure 3   Numbers of breeding Roseate Terns at colonies where repeated counts have been conducted 1969–2003.

with numbers since fluctuating between 50 and 120 AON. A new colony of five pairs was also established on Dalkey Island (Co. Dublin) in 2003.

In Northern Ireland, the colonies have fared less well. In 1986 during SCR Census, a total of 62 AON were on islets in three sea loughs. The colonies at Strangford and Carlingford Loughs (Co. Down) have since been abandoned whilst the colony at Larne Lough remains, but with just 4 AON in 2000, compared to 190 in 1969. The size of the colony at Larne Lough decreased during the 1970s and 1980s, and has fluctuated between 3 and 13 AON since 1990 (Fig. 3; Cabot, 1996).

In England, the total numbers in Northumberland increased slightly from 31 to 34 pairs between 1986 and 2000. The main colony at Coquet Island held 33 AON in 2000 and has fluctuated between 17 and 38 AON since 1976 (Fig. 3). Prior to that, there were 230 AON on Coquet in 1969, before a sharp decline in 1970–76. Most recently, the size of the Coquet colony has been increasing and held 70 AON in 2003 (Fig. 3). In contrast, numbers on the Farne Islands have declined from 9 AON in 1986 to just 1 AON in 2000, and the colony at Holy Island was abandoned in 1988. Between 1995 and 1998, a maximum of 14 pairs colonised Sunderland Docks (Tyne & Wear), but subsequently abandoned the site following successive breeding failures.

In Wales, the three colonies on Anglesey (Gwynedd) experienced a catastrophic decline from a combined total 209 AON in 1986 to just 2 AON at a single site in 2000. The decline occurred rapidly between 1987 and 1991, with the population fluctuating between 2 AON and 20 AON since then (Fig. 3).

In Scotland, the only colony in 1986 of 18 AON on Inchmickery, Firth of Forth (City of Edinburgh) was abandoned in 1989, but most of these birds appear to have moved to two nearby islands, which held a combined total of 13 AON in 2000. However, since Seabird 2000, numbers in Scotland have declined to just a single pair, such that the persistence of the Roseate Tern as a breeding species in Scotland may be in jeopardy.

CAUSES OF CHANGE

The dramatic decline of the Roseate Tern population in Britain and Ireland during the 1970s and early 1980s occurred at all colonies, suggesting that the cause was wide ranging rather than localised to individual colonies. Productivity remained high at around 1.2 chicks per pair at most colonies during the period of decline (Cabot, 1996). Adult survival was low at around 81%, but this did not vary during the 1970s and is typical of stable populations elsewhere (Green, 1995; Spendelow *et al.*, 1995; Lebreton *et al.*, 2003). Ringing recoveries show that the number of immature birds reported in the wintering grounds increased during this period (Cabot, 1996), whilst the number of 3–5-year-old birds recovered in Britain and Ireland declined (Green, 1995). This suggests that immature survival is likely to have caused the decline by reducing the rate of recruitment into the breeding population, and so explanations for the population change must be sought in the wintering grounds.

Roseate Terns migrate along the Atlantic seaboard and winter almost exclusively in Ghana, and thus have a far more restricted wintering range than other terns (Ratcliffe & Merne, 2002). Ringing data show that large numbers of terns are deliberately trapped in Ghana, with most of these being first-year birds (Mead, 1978; Dunn & Mead, 1982; Ratcliffe & Merne, 2002). Studies in Ghana found that boys in fishing villages along the coast trap terns for sport, food and sale, with Roseate Terns being relatively vulnerable to capture (Ntiamoa-Badiu *et al.*, 1992). An education programme was implemented in the late 1980s and early 1990s (Everett *et al.*, 1987), and this appeared to be successful in reducing trapping rates in Ghana (Ntiamoa-Badiu, 1995). Ringing studies show that immature survival rates increased during the 1990s and consequential increases in recruitment rate

Roseate Terns breeding in Britain and Ireland are trapped by boys on their wintering grounds in Ghana (Chris Gomersall)

may have contributed to the population recovery (Ratcliffe *et al.*, 1998c). Recent studies in Ghana have found resurgence in trapping activity (Ghana Wildlife Society, unpubl.) and so further education programmes may be required to maintain the population recovery.

Food availability in Ghana is also likely to influence immature survival. Roseate Terns feed mainly on sardines and anchovies that occur in dense shoals along the Ghanaian coast (Dunn & Mead, 1982). The stocks fluctuate greatly among years owing to effects of oceanography on spawning and larval survival (Kwei, 1964; Cury & Fontana, 1988; Cury & Roy, 1989; Mendelssohn & Cury, 1987) and during years of low food availability immature survival could be depressed. Sustainable management of these fish stocks is necessary for the recovery of the Roseate Tern population in the future. The artisanal beach and canoe seine fisheries along the whole coast of Ghana are unlikely to cause severe stock depletion, but EU industrial fishing fleets that are now exploiting waters around West Africa have the potential to cause stock collapse through over-fishing (MacKenzie, 2002).

Whilst mortality in the wintering grounds is likely to partially explain population trends of Roseate Terns, the availability and quality of colony sites during the breeding season is also probably an important factor limiting population size and range. Roseate Terns must maintain exceptionally high productivity compared to other tern species in order to compensate for their comparatively low adult survival rates. In order to achieve this, Roseate Terns require high-quality sites characterised by an abundance of suitable nesting habitat that is above the level of tidal flooding and within foraging range (*c.*15 km) of dense shoals of herring, sprat or sandeels (Cramp, 1985; Gochfeld *et al.*, 1998). Furthermore, sites require the presence of congeners and absence or scarcity of mammalian predators and gull competitors. Sites exhibiting these characters are scarce within Britain and Ireland and this is likely to limit their distribution and population size.

Variations in quality of sites through time may influence rates of immigration, emigration, intermittent breeding and productivity, and these explain regional population trends. Within the Irish Sea, ringing studies demonstrated that the sudden decrease in size of colonies on Anglesey and in Northern Ireland resulted from birds emigrating to colonies in the Republic of Ireland, which experienced a simultaneous increase in size (Ratcliffe *et al.*, 1998c). It appears that these movements were caused by contrasting changes in quality between sites in the Republic of Ireland and elsewhere in the Irish Sea. For instance at the largest colony in the Republic, on Rockabill during the late 1980s and early 1990s, Herring Gulls were culled and gravel terraces were constructed on areas of bare rock and furnished with nest boxes to provide more nesting habitat for Roseate Terns (Casey *et al.*, 1995). At the same time, at Lady's Island Lake, in Co. Wexford, control of Brown Rats, provision of nest boxes and management of vegetation improved the availability of nest sites and breeding success (Avery *et al.*, 1995; Cabot, 1995). In contrast, colonies at other sites in the Irish Sea, such as at Strangford Lough, Larne Lough and Anglesey experienced increased levels of predation and disturbance by mammals or Peregrines, whilst on Green Island, in Carlingford Lough, nesting habitat was lost through erosion (Avery & Winder, 1990; Brown, 1992; Avery *et al.*, 1995). Such events probably encouraged birds to abandon the latter colonies and emigrate to the restored sites at Rockabill and Lady's Island Lake. The colony at Rockabill continued to grow through the 1990s, due to consistently high levels of productivity and natal recruitment (Newton & Crowe, 2000). Since the initial colonisation at Lady's Island Lake, numbers have fluctuated widely from year to year, probably due to a large proportion of the adult population not breeding in some years, since there is no evidence of birds moving to breed at other colonies during years when breeding numbers are low at Lady's Island.

On Rockabill, Roseate Terns are provided with nest boxes situated on purpose-built terraces (Steve Newton)

The colonies in the North Sea have been similarly affected by changes in site quality. Coquet Island has become increasingly important within the North Sea as numbers at other sites have dwindled or they have been abandoned. Active management at Coquet, including gull control, vegetation management and provision of nest boxes, has maintained suitable conditions for breeding Roseate Terns. Productivity at the site is usually below the level required to maintain a stable population, but immigration from Rockabill compensates for this (Ratcliffe *et al.*, 1998c). Construction of open gravel terraces furnished with nest boxes that mimic those on Rockabill have resulted in marked increases in numbers during 2002 and 2003 (P. Morrison, pers comm.), possibly owing to Rockabill birds being attracted to nesting habitat resembling that at their natal site. In contrast, colonies on the Farnes and Holy Island have declined or been abandoned, probably due to birds moving to Coquet. In the Firth of Forth, the colony on the large offshore islet of Inchmickery was abandoned during the 1990s owing to increasing competition for nesting habitat with Herring Gulls (D. Fairlamb, pers comm.). The birds moved to a tiny low-lying gravel islet that is susceptible to tidal flooding, predation and disturbance. Numbers in the Forth subsequently declined, probably owing to low productivity, intermittent breeding and emigration to other regions.

The overall recovery of the Roseate Tern population in Britain and Ireland is encouraging. In summer 2003 small numbers of Roseate Terns were seen at two sites in Co. Kerry and nesting was strongly suspected (M. O'Clery, pers. comm.; P. Smiddy, pers. comm.). Both islands were historical sites where birds had been present in one of the earlier censuses (1970 and 1988). This apparent re-occupation of former range in western Ireland follows a run of four highly productive years at the Rockabill colony, and stresses the importance of continuing to monitor former haunts. However, the concentration of birds at a small number of sites makes the population susceptible to localised catastrophic events. Reducing such risks depends on encouraging birds to emigrate from large colonies to alternative sites where they can breed successfully. Nesting habitat can be restored by control of gulls and predators, manipulation of nesting substrate, and using tern decoys and playback of vocalisations to attract terns to the site (Kress, 1997). In Britain and Ireland, such restoration projects have been attempted at a number of sites, including Keeragh Islands (Co. Wexford), Samson (Isles of Scilly), Mew Island in the Copelands (Co. Down), Skerries in Anglesey (Gwynedd) and at Dalkey Island (Co. Dublin). The results of these projects have been disappointing, but the recent colonisation of Dalkey Island, following several years of management effort, is encouraging. Creation of artificial islands may also provide a means of increasing the availability and quality of colony sites, as evidenced by the construction and subsequent colonisation of an islet in Larne Lough. Expanding the range and population size of Roseate Terns will probably depend on the future success of such projects, and development of others throughout the species' historic range.

INTERNATIONAL CONTEXT

Roseate Terns have a very widespread global distribution, breeding around all continents and oceans, with the exception of Antarctica, reaching 56°N in the North Sea and 34°S in southern Africa. Gochfeld (1983) estimated the world population to be of the order of 55,500 pairs, but recent data suggest the figure is more than double this at 120,000–130,000 pairs (Table 2). The populations in Britain and Ireland are at the northern edge of the range of this species and represent less than 1% of the world total.

Roseate Terns are polytypic, with five recognised subspecies distinguished by wing length and bill length or colour, although the validity of these is questionable (Cramp, 1985; Gochfeld *et al.*, 1998).

Table 2 International context.

Country or region	Subspecies	Number of pairs		Year	Source
		Min	Max		
Great Britain, Isle of Man and Channel Isles	*dougallii*	52	52	2000	Seabird 2000
All Ireland	*dougallii*	738	738	2000	Seabird 2000
France	*dougallii*	72	83	2002	Le Nevé (2002)
Belgium, Netherlands and Germany	*dougallii*	1	3	1995–2000	miscellaneous
Portugal (Azores)	*dougallii*	1,000	1,500	2002	V. Neves & J. Ramos*,
Portugal (Madeira)	*dougallii*	5	15	1991	BirdLife International/EBCC (2000)
Spain (incl. Canary Islands)	*dougallii*	2	3	1987	BirdLife International/EBCC (2000)
Canada	*dougallii*	100	150	2002	A. Boyne*
NE USA	*dougallii*	4,000	4,000	2002	J. Spendelow*
Caribbean	*dougallii*	4,000	6,200	1998	Van Halewyn & Norton (1984), Saliva (2000)
S Africa	*dougallii*	250	260	2000	Randall *et al.* (1991), Tree & Klages (2003)
Mozambique	*arriidensis*	60	60	2003	A. J. Tree (pers. comm.)
E Africa (Kenya and Somalia)	*arriidensis*	10,000	10,000	1970s	Ash & Karani (1981), Britton & Brown (1974), Nisbet (1980)
Seychelles	*arriidensis*	1,000	1,300	2002	J. Ramos*
Middle East-Oman	*bangsi*	200	500	2000	Eriksen & Sargeant (2000)
Elsewhere Indian Ocean	*bangsi/korustes*	1,000	3,000	1970s	Nisbet (1980)
Japan and Taiwan	*gracilis*	15,000	15,000	2002	O'Neill (pers. comm.)*
Australia	*bangsi/gracilis*	83,000	83,000	2002	O'Neill (pers. comm.)*
Elsewhere Pacific Ocean	*bangsi/gracilis*	500	4,000	1980s	Gochfeld (1983)

Country or Region		Min	Max	Min % GB	Max % GB	Min % Ireland	Max % Ireland
Europe**	*dougallii*	1,900	2,400	2.2%	2.7%	30.8%	38.8%
World	all	120,000	130,000	0.0%	0.0%	0.6%	0.6%

* Proc. 9th Intern. Roseate Tern Workshop, 2003, Wexford, Ireland
** Stroud *et al.* (2001)

Nominate *dougallii* occurs in Europe, North America, the Caribbean and South Africa, with a total population of around 10,000–13,000 pairs, of which the British and Irish population comprises 6–8%. The *ariidensis* subspecies has an all-red bill and is found along the east coast of Africa and the Seychelles. The *bangsi* subspecies is similar to *ariidensis* (and considered by some authorities to be the same taxon), and occurs from the Arabian Sea and Gulf of Oman east through the Indian Ocean to New Guinea and Western Australia. The *korustes* subspecies has shorter wings and darker upperparts than the nominate subspecies and occurs from India and Sri Lanka to Burma. The *gracilis* subspecies has a short wing and longer, redder bill compared to *dougallii*, and occurs from north and east Australia to New Caledonia. Producing population estimates for each of the subspecies occurring through the Indian and Pacific Oceans is hampered by poor definition of the boundaries of their distribution, and the variable quality and spatial resolution of counts through much of the species range.

The European population of Roseate Terns is 1,900–2,400 pairs, of which 2–3% are in Britain and 31–39% in Ireland. Ringing data demonstrate that the colony in Brittany, France, is a component of the northwest European meta-population (Ratcliffe & Merne, 2002), and the occasional breeding records in Germany, Belgium and The Netherlands are probably also relate to birds fledged from established colonies further west (e.g. de Ruwe & de Smet, 1997; Ludwigs & Stöber, 2001). The Azores, Portugal, hosts the vast majority of the remaining European population, with colonies numbering up to several hundred pairs occurring on islets throughout the archipelago (del Nevo *et al.*, 1993; Monteiro *et al.*; 1996). There is no evidence of interchange of individuals between colonies in the Azores and those in mainland Europe and the British Isles; however, they do use the same wintering grounds in Ghana (Ratcliffe & Merne, 2002).

Population trends in Europe and North America are well documented. The population in France declined from 500–600 pairs in the 1950s–1970s to just 70–100 pairs during the 1980s and 1990s (Cadiou, 1996). The decline during the 1970s may have been due to trapping in the wintering grounds, with competition from gulls, human disturbance and predation by mustelids also contributing (Avery *et al.*, 1995; Cadiou, 1996). The population in the Azores has fluctuated between 500 and 1,200 pairs, with an occasional drop in numbers when colonies have been deserted because of human disturbance or habitat loss (Monteiro *et al.*, 1996).

The population in North America declined from 8,500 pairs in 1930 to 4,000 pairs in the 1950s and to 2,500 in 1979, and fluctuated between 2,500 and 3,300 during the 1970s and 1980s (Gochfeld *et al.*, 1998). Habitat loss due to competition with gulls, predation, pollution and winter trapping mortality may have played a role in the decline (Gochfeld *et al.*, 1998). The population has since staged a recovery to 4,000 pairs (J. Spendelow, pers comm.), although the long-term increase was punctuated by a decline in 1991–92 that was probably due to elevated mortality during a hurricane (Gochfeld *et al.*, 1998; Lebreton *et al.*, 2003).

The breeding population on Aride, in the Seychelles, declined from over 4,000 during the 1970s to 1,000 pairs in 1988, and has since fluctuated between zero and 1,300 pairs (Ramos, 2002). The decline is probably due to poor productivity associated with low food availability, exacerbated by predation by Barn Owls, conspecific aggression, parasitism by ticks and entanglement with the sticky seeds of *Pisonia* trees (Ramos, 2002). The population in South Africa, presently 250–260 pairs (Tree & Klages, 2003), has nearly doubled since 1977–1986 when estimates lay in the range 130–140 (Randall *et al.*, 1991). Population trends elsewhere in the Roseate Tern range are undocumented, although much more research activity is now underway in northeast Australia and this should greatly improve our understanding of subspecies, demography and migration patterns of the birds using this key area.

Common Tern *Sterna hirundo*

Norman Ratcliffe

INTRODUCTION

Common Terns are not the most abundant tern species in Britain and Ireland, but are probably the most familiar owing to their breeding range being among the widest of the seabird species breeding in Britain and Ireland. Colonies occur around most of the UK and Irish coasts, and inland on lakes, reservoirs and gravel pits. Common Terns are absent from most of mainland Wales and southwest England, and are comparatively scarce in the Northern and Western Isles, where they are replaced by Arctic Terns. Small colonies occur inland along the large river valleys of southeast and central England, notably the Thames, Ouse, Humber and Trent and their tributaries. Inland colonies are also scattered along rivers in southeast Scotland and on islets in the freshwater loughs of Ireland.

Tern populations in northwest Europe were bought to the brink of extirpation at the end of the 19th century by hunting of adults for the millinery trade, but recovered in response to protective legislation in the early-20th century (Parslow, 1967; Bijlsma *et al.*, 2001). Over the last three decades the population has remained broadly stable, although there have been marked variations in trends between regions. Declines have occurred between the SCR and Seabird 2000 surveys in northwest and southeast England, East Anglia, western Scotland, the Northern Isles and western Ireland, whilst increases have occurred in northeast England, southeast Scotland, Wales and northeast Ireland. The range of inland breeding Common Terns in Britain expanded between the 1970s and 1990s (Sears, 1993), but this trend may have reversed during the last decade.

Declines in western Scotland and England are probably due to increased predation by American Mink and Red Fox respectively, and conservation management to ameliorate these problems is being exercised. Competition with Arctic Terns is the putative cause of Common Tern population declines along the west coast of Ireland, although the form this competition takes is at present unknown. Common Terns have benefited from habitat creation by man in the form of gravel pits, tern rafts in reservoirs, islets in industrial lagoons and structures in ports, and from maintenance of habitat on reserves by control of vegetation succession and gull competition. Maintaining the Common Tern population at current levels is likely to depend on the continuation of such management in perpetuity.

CENSUS METHODS

Coverage of coastal Common Tern colonies in Britain and Ireland was probably broadly comprehensive during Seabird 2000, with the exception of western Ireland. This was rectified by inclusion of data from the 1995 All Ireland Tern Survey (Hannon *et al.*, 1997). During the SCR, coverage of the Northern Isles and west coast of Ireland was poor. This was overcome by inclusion of data from the 1989 survey of terns in Orkney and Shetland (Avery *et al.*, 1993) and the 1983–84 All Ireland Tern Survey (Whilde, 1985). The variation in time period over which trends are calculated between regions will produce some bias in the overall national population trend.

An inventory of inland colonies was made using county bird reports, and coordinators were asked to arrange for each of these, and any other colonies that they knew of in their county, to be surveyed. Some small colonies that were previously unoccupied or unreported may therefore have been missed. Coverage of inland sites was probably less extensive during the SCR than in Seabird 2000, so assessment of changes in range and status inland must be made with caution. Coverage of inland sites was most comprehensive during the New Breeding Atlas survey in 1989–91 (Gibbons *et al.*, 1993). The number of 10-km squares occupied during 1989–91 and Seabird 2000 is used as an index of changes in range and abundance over the last decade. In Ireland, changes in distribution and status were assessed using comparisons of the 1983–84 and 1995 All Ireland Tern Surveys.

Common Terns may move between colonies in different years in response to predation or habitat change, and so it is desirable to census all colonies within a single year to minimise double counting or omission of pairs that move between colonies. Most counts in Britain, Northern Ireland and the Irish Sea coasts of the Republic of Ireland were made during 2000, but those for the west of Ireland were from 1995 and those from Co. Wexford in 1999. Movements between these regions are unlikely to have caused severe bias in trend estimation. During the SCR, counts were made in different years within regions, and inter-colony movements may have produced greater inaccuracies.

Identification can present problems with surveys of Common Terns as adults are similar to Arctic Terns, and their nests and contents cannot be reliably separated. This is particularly a problem where the two species nest together in mixed colonies. In such situations, observers will sometimes combine counts of the two species and report them as Commic Terns rather than attempting to determine the numbers of each. This makes estimation of changes in numbers of each species difficult. Commic Terns only represent 1.6% of total Common Tern pairs counted during Seabird 2000, thus identification problems will not produce a large bias in estimation of status. However, during the SCR the percentage of Commic Terns was higher, at 12%, and so trends will be upwardly biased owing to a larger proportion of birds being identified during Seabird 2000. The majority of Commic Terns records were from western Scotland, the Northern Isles and western Ireland (Fig. 1).

Common Terns are most often counted in units of Apparently Occupied Nests (AONs), and during Seabird 2000 in Britain 81% of colonies and 91% of pairs were counted in this unit. During the SCR these percentages were similar such that changes in count methods are unlikely to cause bias in estimates of trends. AON surveys comprised counts of either nests along transects through the colony or of apparently incubating adults from a vantage point. Direct counts of nests along transects are generally the most accurate method of censusing Common Tern AONs especially where long vegetation or uneven ground obscures incubating adults from view.

Identification problems arise with AON counts where Common and Arctic Terns occur in the same colony. Common Terns often nest in more vegetated areas than Arctic, such that their distribution within a colony is discrete and counts of the two species can be separated spatially. At sites where nests of the two species are intermixed counts of incubating adults are preferable, but at some colonies vegetation cover or lack of suitable vantage points make this method impractical. In such cases, a count of the total number of nests needs to be made, followed by an estimate of the proportion of adults of each species circling over the colony. The number of breeding pairs of Common Terns is calculated as the product of the proportion of adult Common Terns and the number of nests of both species. Species-specific differences in adult colony attendance rates may lead to biases in such estimates.

Flush counts of adult birds were used to count 19% of colonies and 9% of pairs during the Seabird 2000 census. These were mainly in the Northern Isles and Western Isles where Common Terns nest within larger colonies of Arctic Terns. During the SCR, the proportion of colonies censused using flush counts and the distribution of these was broadly similar, and so there will be little bias in estimation of regional trends owing to changes in the methods used. Flush counts are less accurate than counts of AONs owing to variations in adult attendance (see Arctic Tern chapter). The number of birds counted were divided by 1.5 in order to convert them into AONs. This correction factor was estimated for Arctic Terns in the Northern Isles during 1980 and so will only be approximate for Common Terns during the Seabird 2000 survey.

Surveys must be timed to coincide with the peak of incubation activity when the maximum number of nests and incubating adults are present for AON counts, and when adult attendance for flush counts is most stable. Surveys prior to this date will omit pairs that have not yet laid, while those afterwards will omit nests that have failed or whose chicks have hatched and dispersed. Common Tern laying phenology is relatively synchronous and 80–90% of pairs will be incubating during mid-June, provided that flooding or predation do not cause large-scale nest losses (Nisbet, 2002). During Seabird 2000, 73% of colonies and 79% of pairs were counted within the recommended time period, thus the majority of counts should be accurate. Counts were conducted outside the recommended period for 11% of colonies and 8% of pairs, and for the remainder no accurate dates were reported.

Tern breeding populations can fluctuate between years owing to variations in the proportion of mature birds that attempt to nest. As such, counts that compare status in two years must be viewed with caution since one could coincide with a period during which the proportion of birds attempting to breed was depressed. This problem is likely to be less for Common than for Sandwich or Arctic Terns as their generalist diet and broad habitat selection mean they are less prone to environmental perturbation than those species. Annual counts of Common Terns are also available from sites throughout England, Wales, eastern Ireland and some sites in southwest and southeast Scotland, and these indicate that the counts during the SCR and Seabird 2000 were not atypically low. As such, the long-term trends estimated for Common Terns between the two surveys will be reasonably robust.

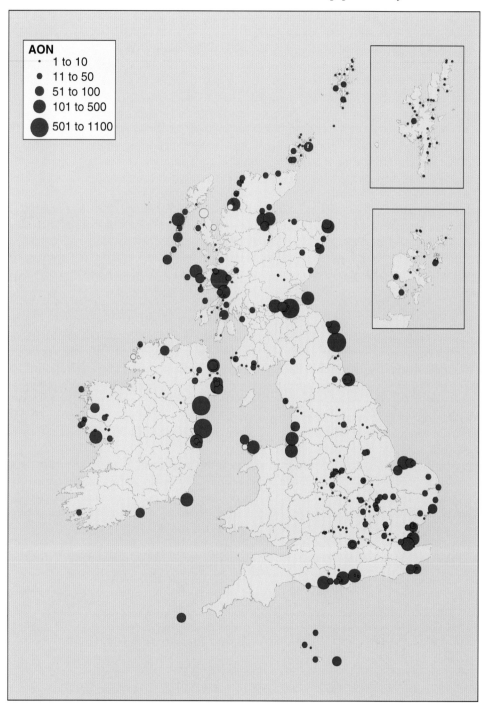

Figure 1   Abundance and distribution of breeding Common Terns in Britain and Ireland 1998–2002. Colonies of 'commic terns' (i.e. undistinguished Arctic and Common terns) are shown in yellow (the scale is same for Commic Terns and Common Tern colonies).

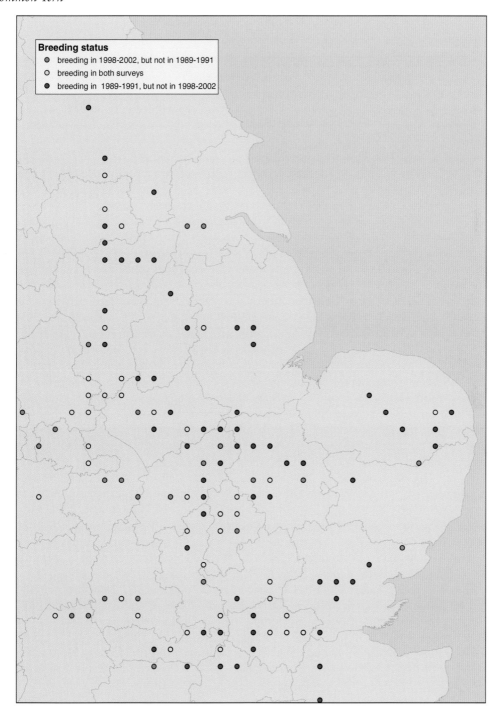

Figure 2   Comparison of Common Tern breeding occurrence in OS 10-km squares in inland central England during Seabird 2000 (1998–2002) and the New Atlas of Breeding Birds in Britain and Ireland 1989–1991 (Gibbons et al., 1993).

CURRENT STATUS AND TRENDS

The Seabird 2000 census estimated the population of Common Terns in Britain and Ireland at 14,497 pairs, making it the second-most abundant tern species in the region. Of these, 33% occurred in England and the Channel Isles (there were none on the Isle of Man), 33% in Scotland, 29% in Ireland and 5% in Wales. The majority of the population breed coastally, with inland breeders comprising only 8% and 19% of the British and Irish totals respectively. The five most important administrative areas for breeding Common Terns were Northumberland (8.6%), Co. Down (7.6%), Lochaber (6.4%), Co. Dublin (6.0%) and the City of Edinburgh (4.9%).

Common Terns are widely scattered around the coasts of Britain and Ireland, with notable concentrations occurring in western Scotland, northeast England and southeast Scotland, East Anglia and northeast Ireland (Fig. 1). Common Terns are relatively scarce in the Northern and Western Isles where they tend to be replaced by Arctic Terns. Colonies are absent from mainland Wales and southwest England, from the Tees to the north shore of the Wash, and are sparsely distributed along the English and Scottish coasts of the Irish Sea, southeast Ireland and the Channel coast of England. The coastal distribution of Common Terns has remained largely unchanged since the SCR survey.

Unlike other species of tern nesting in Britain and Ireland, Common Terns have an extensive inland component to their breeding range. Seabird 2000 found that 27% of colonies were inland in Britain, whilst the 1995 All Ireland Tern Survey reported a figure of 16% in Ireland. The majority of inland Common Tern colonies in Britain are associated with gravel pits and reservoirs along the major river valleys in southeast and central England, including the Thames, Ouse, Trent and Humber and their tributaries. Scattered inland colonies are also found on gravel bars in the main rivers of southeast Scotland. In Ireland, inland colonies are situated on islets in the larger freshwater loughs.

The distribution of inland colonies in Britain appears to have contracted 1989–91. The number of inland OS 10-km squares occupied by breeding Common Terns during the New Breeding Atlas Survey was 145, but this had declined by 51% to 71 during Seabird 2000. This decline occurred at a similar rate in both England (−50%) and Scotland (−56%), with the sole inland colony in Wales also being lost. Loss of occupation of 10-km squares in England appears to have been greatest in the eastern counties, with 10-km squares further west tending to have retained or gained breeding Common Terns since the New Breeding Atlas Survey (Fig. 2). The changes in distribution inland may be due to changes in survey effort, as coverage during the New Breeding Atlas Survey was likely to have been more comprehensive than that during Seabird 2000. In Ireland, the number of colonies inland declined only slightly from 23 in 1983–84 to 21 in 1995, and the geographic distribution of these remained similar (Hannon *et al.*, 1997).

The Common Tern population is generally scattered in a large number of small to medium-sized colonies, but some large colonies that hold a notable proportion of the national population were found during the Seabird 2000 survey. In Britain, the five largest colonies were on Coquet Island (Northumberland: 1,033 AON), Glas Eileanan, Sound of Mull (Argyll & Bute: 772), Leith Dock (City of Edinburgh: 690 AON), Shotton Steel Works (Clwyd: 490 AON) and the Isle of May (Fife: 303 AON), with these hosting 33% of the British population. In Ireland, the five largest colonies were Rockabill (Co. Dublin: 610 AON), Green Island (Co. Down: 509 AON), Lady's Island Lake (Co. Wexford: 480 AON), Blue Circle Island (Co. Antrim: 423 AON) and Dublin Port (Co. Dublin: 194), and these held 53% of the national population. Inland colonies are small, with the largest being 62 AON and 74% of colonies holding fewer than 10 AON.

The Common Tern breeding population in Britain and Ireland has declined very slightly over the last 15 years by −2.4%, and over 30 years has declined by −2.6%. The decline is likely to be slightly

Table 1   Numbers of breeding Common Terns (AON) in Britain and Ireland 1969–2002.

Administrative area or country	Operation Seafarer (1969–70)	SCR Census (1985–88)/ All Ireland Tern Survey (1984)[2]	Seabird 2000 (1998–2002)/ All Ireland Tern Survey (1995)	Percentage change since Seafarer	Percentage change since SCR/AITS (1984)	Annual percentage change since SCR/AITS (1984)
Shetland	404	1,020[1]	104	−74%	−90%	−10.8
Orkney	213	244[1]	125	−41%	−49%	−3.3
North coast Caithness		36	42		17%	1.1%
Inland Caithness		2	2		0%	0.0%
East coast Caithness		11			−100%	
Caithness total	*47*	*49*	*44*	*−6%*	*−10%*	*−0.8%*
Northwest coast Sutherland		138	95		−31%	−2.7%
East coast Sutherland		108	25		−77%	−9.9%
Sutherland total	*91*	*246*	*120*	*32%*	*−51%*	*−5.1%*
West coast Ross & Cromarty		18	109		506%	13.8%
East coast Ross & Cromarty		104	497		378%	11.9%
Ross & Cromarty total	*152*	*122*	*606*	*299%*	*397%*	*12.2%*
Inverness	106	315	10	−91%	−97%	−22.6%
Nairn	12			−100%		
Moray	43	166	24	−44%	−86%	−13.8%
Banff & Buchan	33	118	202	512%	71%	4.0%
Gordon	475	163	31	−93%	−81%	−12.0%
City of Aberdeen			68			
Kincardine & Deeside			13			
Angus	9	139	50	456%	−64%	−7.6%
Perth and Kinross		6	7		17%	1.3%
Northeast Fife	55	22	303	451%	1277%	20.7%
Dunfermline	55	97	135	145%	39%	2.7%
Falkirk		30	114		280%	9.4%
City of Edinburgh		592	700		18%	1.3%
East Lothian	865	128	0	−100%	−100%	
Tweedale		1			−100%	
Nithsdale	138			−100%		
Stewartry	99	50	6	−94%	−88%	−15.7%
Wigtown	48	52	55	15%	6%	0.4%
Kyle & Carrick	184		1	−99%		
Cunninghame	98	113	12	−88%	−89%	−14.8%
Inverclyde	1			−100%		
Dumbarton			16			
Stirling		2	1		−50%	−6.1%
Argyll & Bute	788	2,137	1,362	73%	−36%	−3.4%
Lochaber	69	375	130	88%	−65%	−7.8%
Skye & Lochalsh	244	44	43	−82%	−2%	−0.2%
Western Isles–Comhairle nan eilean	56	553	502	796%	−9%	−0.6%
Scotland Total	**4,285**	**6,784**	**4,784**	**12%**	**−29%**	**−2.3**
Northumberland	1,765	997	1,207	−32%	21%	1.5%
Tyne & Wear		3	5		67%	4.2%
Durham	30		32	7%		
Cleveland		30	369		1130%	18.9%
North Yorkshire		1	5		400%	11.3%
Humberside			2			
West Yorkshire		6	21		250%	10.6%
South Yorkshire		2			−100%	
Lincolnshire	122	40	46	−62%	15%	1.0%
Leicestershire		2	72		3500%	31.7%
Cambridgeshire		82	64		−22%	−1.7%
Northamptonshire			30			
Bedfordshire		9	44		389%	14.2%
Buckinghamshire		12	64		433%	12.6%
Hertfordshire		52	61		17%	1.2%

Table 1 continued

Administrative area or country	Operation Seafarer (1969–70)	SCR Census (1985–88)/ All Ireland Tern Survey (1984)[2]	Seabird 2000 (1998–2002)/ All Ireland Tern Survey (1995)	Percentage change since Seafarer	Percentage change since SCR/AITS (1984)	Annual percentage change since SCR/AITS (1984)
Berkshire		1	84		8300%	44.8%
Surrey		15			−100%	
Norfolk	1,904	810	502	−74%	−38%	−3.5%
Suffolk	313	85	184	−41%	116%	6.0%
Essex	53	404	289	445%	−28%	−2.4%
Greater London		14	40		186%	8.8%
Kent	419	516	333	−21%	−35%	−3.2%
East Sussex	118	70	57	−52%	−19%	−1.6%
West Sussex	33	57	1	−97%	−98%	−25.5%
Hampshire	254	456	311	22%	−32%	−2.8%
Isle of Wight	1	1	9	800%	800%	17.1%
Dorset	74	172	262	254%	52%	2.9%
Channel Islands	107	227	174	63%	−23%	−2.1%
Isles of Scilly	150	193	96	−36%	−50%	−5.7%
Gloucestershire			12			
Wiltshire			4			
Oxfordshire			18			
Warwickshire		20	28		40%	2.6%
Hereford & Worcester			4			
West Midlands		1	3		200%	9.6%
Staffordshire		1	30		2900%	28.7%
Derbyshire		10	56		460%	14.9%
Merseyside		1	157		15600%	40.4%
Lancashire	572	519	103	−82%	−80%	−11.3%
Cumbria	291	77	71	−76%	−8%	−0.6%
Isle of Man	1	7		−100%	−100%	
England, Isle of Man and Channel Isles Total	**6,207**	**4,893**	**4,850**	**−22%**	**−1%**	**−0.1%**
Gwynedd	222	327	184	−17%	−44%	−4.1%
Clwyd	70	187	490	600%	162%	7.7%
Wales Total	**292**	**514**	**674**	**131%**	**31%**	**2.1%**
Great Britain, Isle of Man and Channel Islands Total	**10,784**	**12,191**	**10,308**	**−4%**	**−15%**	**−1.1**
Co. Derry		8	2		−75%	−8.3
Co. Antrim	385	248	608	58%	145%	5.8
Co. Down	917	783	1,068	16%	36%	2.0
Co. Armagh		44	14		−68%	−6.9
Co. Fermanagh		13	12		−8%	−0.5
Co. Cavan		37	10[3]		−73%	−11.2
Co. Westmeath		5	0[3]		−100%	
Co. Dublin	68	132	847	1146%	542%	12.3
Co. Wicklow	15		0	−100%		
Co. Wexford	1,038	86	480	−54%	458%	11.3
Co. Cork	579	57	252[3]	−56%	342%	14.5
Co. Kerry	533	51	62[3]	−88%	22%	1.8
Co. Limerick		35	2[3]		−94%	−22.9
Co. Tipperary		28	55[3]		96%	6.3
Co. Clare			111[3]			
Co. Galway	189	654	177[3]	−6%	−73%	−11.2
Co. Roscommon		4	4[3]		0%	0.0
Co. Longford		14	120[3]		757%	21.6
Co. Mayo	119	211	118[3]	−1%	−44%	−3.6
Co. Sligo	133		47[3]	−65%		

Administrative area or country	Operation Seafarer (1969–70)	SCR Census (1985–88)/ All Ireland Tern Survey (1984)[2]	Seabird 2000 (1998–2002)/ All Ireland Tern Survey (1995)	Percentage change since Seafarer	Percentage change since SCR/AITS (1984)	Annual percentage change since SCR/AITS (1984)
Co. Tyrone		32	0[3]		−100%	−100.0
Co. Donegal	130	228	200[3]	54%	−12%	−1.2
All-Ireland Total	4,106	2,670	4,189	2.0%	56.9%	
Britain and Ireland Total	14,890	14,861	14,497	22.6%	22.4%	

Notes
[1] Northern Isles surveyed in 1980 (Bullock & Gomersall, 1982)
[2] All SCR counts in Ireland were conducted during the All Ireland Tern Survey in 1984 (Whilde, 1995)
[3] All counts in this administrative area were conducted during the All Ireland Tern Survey in 1995 (Hannon et al., 1997)

greater than this owing to improved coverage of inland colonies during Seabird 2000 compared to previous surveys and improved identification. Population trends have varied between countries over the last 15 years, with numbers in Ireland increasing by 57% and in Wales by 31%, whilst those in England declined by −0.9% and in Scotland by −30%. Trends have also been highly variable between regions within these countries. In Ireland, the increases occurred in the east (+124%) whilst declines were observed in the south and west (−12.6%). Overall, numbers nesting inland in Ireland increased by 24%. In Wales, the increase was due to growth of the Shotton Steelworks colony (Clwyd: +162%), whilst colonies on Anglesey declined (Gwynedd: −43.7%). In England, the declines were mainly in the northwest (-45%) and in the southeast and East Anglia (−28%), with increases occurring in the northeast (+57%). In Scotland, the trend was driven by overall declines along the west coast and Western Isles (−34%) and in the Northern Isles (−84%), whilst numbers on the east coast increased (+16%). No reliable estimates of trends inland in Britain can be made owing to poor coverage during the SCR, and analyses using the New Breeding Atlas data being constrained to comparisons of presence or absence.

CAUSES OF CHANGE

Common Tern distribution and status has remained broadly stable at a national level over the last 15 years. However, trends have varied considerably at finer spatial scales, and these are likely to reflect varying pressures facing Common Terns in different habitats across their wide geographic range.

Mammalian predation has probably been an important determinant of changes in Common Tern distribution and population trends over the last 15 years. Common Terns generally breed on islets, spits or remote beaches where visits by predators are infrequent, but few sites are completely inaccessible. Changes in the range, abundance or behaviour of predators can therefore result in breeding failures, declines in numbers, colony abandonment and long-term loss of breeding habitat. Mammalian predators on Common Terns in Britain and Ireland are Red Fox, American Mink, Badger, Stoat, Otter, Brown Rat and feral cats. Of these, American Mink and Red Fox have had the greatest influence on Common Tern distribution and population trends.

American Mink escaped from fur farms in the 1950s (Dunstone, 1993) and are now present as far north as Skye and Lochalsh, and throughout the Outer Hebrides (Green & Green, 1997; Clode & MacDonald, 2000). Mink predation of eggs and chicks over the last 15 years has caused breeding failures and colony abandonment (Craik, 1995; Rae, 1999), resulting in a decline in regional numbers and redistribution of the remainder to offshore islands or larger colonies (Craik, 1997; Craik & Campbell, 2000; Clode & MacDonald, 2000). Red Fox abundance and distribution increased over the past decades owing to relaxation of control by gamekeepers, especially in East Anglia, southeast England and southeast Scotland (Tapper, 1992). Fox predation on tern colonies has caused complete breeding failure of Common Terns in these regions, including at Sands of Forvie, Scolt Head, Hodbarrow, Foulness, Foulney and Dungeness, leading to population declines and redistribution. The only region where numbers have increased in England is the northeast, where birds mostly breed on offshore islands inaccessible to foxes. Active management work is being undertaken at some sites to conserve accessible colonies that are suffering from predation, including control of mink by trapping in Argyll (Craik, 1997), eradication of mink from the Western Isles, and exclusion of foxes using electric fences and nocturnal patrols. Future population trends of Common Terns in these areas are likely to depend on the efficacy of this management.

Common Terns require an open, well-drained substrate with scattered vegetation cover for nesting (Cramp, 1985; Neubauer, 1998; Nisbet, 2002), and changes in availability of this habitat have contributed to changes in their numbers and distribution in the UK and Ireland. Such habitats are naturally found only where succession by rank herbage and scrub is prevented by inundation, erosion or accretion during winter storms or floods (Nisbet, 2002). However, anthropogenic activities often create open, sparsely vegetated habitats that the opportunistic Common Terns are quick to exploit. Examples include structures in docklands (e.g. Dublin, Sunderland, Teesport and Leith), flat-topped roofs (e.g. in Angus), industrial compounds (e.g. Nigg Oil Terminal, Ross & Cromarty, and St Fergus Gas Terminal, Banff & Buchan), factory lagoons (e.g. Shotton Steel Works, Clwyd, and ICI Wilton, Cleveland), and islets in gravel pits or rafts in lakes and reservoirs (e.g. Breydon Water, Norfolk, and Abberton Reservoir, Essex). Breeding success at these artificial sites is often higher than at natural ones owing to lower predation rates (Walsh *et al.*, 1993; Becker, 1998).

Anthropogenic activity can also result in loss of natural habitats. Common Terns once bred on sandbars in rivers in England, as they still do in eastern Scotland, but such habitats were destroyed by canalisation (Sears, 1993). Human recreational disturbance has also rendered a number of previously occupied sites on beaches unsuitable for breeding (Cramp *et al.*, 1974; Lloyd *et al.*, 1975), but protection of colonies has now reduced this threat (Lloyd *et al.*, 1991). Natural processes can also result in loss of nesting habitat. Vegetation succession can result in nesting habitat in sites sheltered from winter storms or floods becoming overgrown with rank herbage or scrub, leading to abandonment of the colony. This can be prevented on tern reserves by killing, removing or burying encroaching vegetation (Neubauer, 1998; Nisbet, 2002). Elsewhere, erosion from wave action results in loss of nesting habitat. For example, Tern Island (Co. Wexford) was washed away completely in the 1970s and Green Island in Co. Down eroded to a fraction of its former size and lost all of its vegetation cover through the 1980s (Thomas, 1982). Tidal flooding at low-lying sites during incubation can also cause breeding failures in some years. Whilst erosion and tidal flooding has not been an important determinant of population change in the last 30 years, sea-level rise may result in these becoming a greater problem in the future, especially if maintenance of sea defences prevents establishment of natural coastal profiles inshore (Norris & Buisson, 1994; Südbeck, *et al.*, 1998).

Nesting habitat can also be lost when occupied by large gulls that gain advantage over terns in competition for space by being larger and more aggressive, and by establishing their territories prior to the terns returning from migration (Thomas, 1972; Kress, 1997). Gull predation of chicks is also sufficient to cause depressed productivity at some sites (Thomas, 1972; Becker, 1995, 1998; Kress, 1997). Common Tern colonies such as Inchmickery in southeast Scotland and Mew Island in northeast Ireland were abandoned after gull populations expanded and displaced nesting terns. Gull distribution is controlled annually to prevent similar extirpation of tern colonies on offshore islands such as the Isle of May, Coquet Island and the Farne Islands. Abandoned Common Tern colonies have been restored by removal of breeding gulls (Kress *et al.*, 1983; Kress, 1997); for example, the colony at Rockabill in Co. Dublin grew rapidly after Herring Gulls were controlled in the mid-1980s

(Casey *et al.*, 1995). There are probably many more sites around the UK from which Common Terns are excluded by presence of large gulls, such that their distribution and possibly population size is limited by gull competition.

Competition between Common Terns and large gulls is well documented, but competition among tern species may also occur. The decline in Common Terns along the coast of western Ireland has been matched by an increase in the numbers of Arctic Terns and Hannon *et al.* (1997) suggested this was due to inter-specific competition. Further research is required to elucidate the form of competition and how this is affected by latitude.

Common Terns have an extremely broad diet compared to many other tern species, thus their survival and productivity are less prone to changes in food availability. Failures due to food supply have been reported from Jura (1991), Rockliffe Marsh (Cumbria, 1992), Lady's Island Lake (1992) and St Fergus (1996 and 1997) but these were short-term and localised events that will not have caused significant population change. However, a reduction in food availability is likely to be the indirect cause of the decline in Common Terns on the Northern Isles. The availability of sandeel around Shetland was extremely low in 1984–1990, and Arctic Terns experienced complete breeding failure owing to nest abandonment and chick starvation (Monaghan *et al.*, 1992). The generalist Common Terns avoided this fate by switching from sandeel to gadoid prey, but still failed due to predation by gulls and Great Skuas that preyed more heavily on Common Tern chicks in the absence of those of Arctic Terns (Uttley *et al.*, 1989).

European Common Terns migrate along the eastern Atlantic seaboard to winter along the coasts of West Africa (Norman, 2002) and factors that affect survival there will influence subsequent population trends. Common Terns mainly feed on dense shoals of anchovy and sardine along the coastal shelf during winter (Cramp, 1985), and variation in availability of such prey may affect survival rates. Variations in sea temperatures, salinity and currents cause large fluctuations in sardine and anchovy stocks (Kwei, 1964; Cury & Roy, 1987; Mendelssohn & Cury, 1987; Cury & Fontana, 1988), and this may determine food availability to terns and hence their survival rates. This could be exacerbated by competition for food with EU industrial fisheries that have begun to exploit West African fish stocks over the last decade (MacKenzie, 2002).

Children in West Africa capture Common Terns for sport or food, and to collect the rings fitted on their legs by European ornithologists (Dunn & Mead 1982; Ntiamoa-Baidu *et al.*, 1992; Stienen *et al.*, 1998; Wendeln & Becker, 1999). This mostly affects birds in their first year of life (Dunn & Mead 1982; Ntiamoa-Baidu *et al.*, 1992), and elevated mortality from this source has the potential to reduce future recruitment into the British and Irish breeding population. Efforts to prevent trapping through education programmes have been successfully implemented in Ghana (Ntiamoa-Baidu, 1991, 1995), although recent research there has detected a resurgence of activity since the project ended in 1994 (Ghana Wildlife Society, unpubl.).

INTERNATIONAL CONTEXT

Common Terns have a breeding distribution that spans temperate and subtropical latitudes throughout the northern hemisphere. The estimated total world population of Common Terns is around 460,000–620,000 pairs (Table 2), but this figure is an underestimate as no counts are available for large parts of their Asian range.

The Common Tern is polytypic, with three recognised subspecies (Cramp, 1985). Nominate *hirundo* breeds in North America and through Eurasia as far east as Kazakhstan and western Siberia (Nisbet, 2002), wintering in South America, West Africa and the northern Indian Ocean (Norman,

2002). The population is between 370,000 and 501,000 (Table 1), but the true total is likely to be more than this as no counts from central and west Siberia or Iran are available. The *longipennis* subspecies has a shorter all-black bill, dark red legs and darker grey plumage than *hirundo* (Malling Olsen & Larsson, 1995). It breeds in central Siberia east to the Gulf of Anadyr and south into northeast China (Nisbet, 2002), and winters in New Guinea, Indonesia and Australia (Norman, 2002). Around 89,000 pairs of *longipennis* breed in northeast Siberia (Kondratyev *et al.*, 2000), but population status elsewhere in its range is unknown. The *tibetana* subspecies is similar to *hirundo* but with more extensive black on its shorter bill (Malling Olsen & Larsson, 1995). It is distributed through the Asiatic highlands from north India to west Mongolia and east China (Nisbet, 2002), and winters from east India to Malaysia (Norman, 2002). The size of the *tibetana* population is unknown.

The European population is around 220,000–340,000 pairs, of which Britain and Ireland hold 3–5% and 1–2% respectively (Table 2). Britain ranks eighth-most important country in Europe for breeding Common Terns and Ireland 17th. Common Terns are widespread throughout Europe, but tend to be most abundant in Scandinavia and eastern Europe where they have a large inland component to their range, becoming less common and increasingly coastal in the west.

Trends in range and population size in Europe are largely stable, but there is huge spatial variation. Populations along the southern coasts of the North Sea were reduced by human exploitation in the late 1920s and during the Second World War, but recovered in response to protective measures up until the 1960s when a pollution incident caused a population collapse (Stienen & Brenninkmeijer, 1998b; Südbeck *et al.* 1998; Stienen, 2002b). Since then, coastal populations have generally increased in response to protective measures and reduced pollution, and increased availability of habitat such as rafts has facilitated growth of populations inland (Becker & Sudmann, 1998; Südbeck *et al.*, 1998; Stienen, 2002b). However, declines have occurred along the coasts of Germany since 1990 (Hälterlein *et al.*, 2000) and growth of the Dutch population has slowed, probably owing to limitations imposed by food availability (Stienen & Brenninkmeijer, 1998b; Südbeck *et al.*, 1998).

Populations in Scandinavia or those countries along the Baltic Sea have declined overall owing to downward trends in Finland, Sweden and Estonia (BirdLife International, 2000). Predation by introduced American Mink (Nordström *et al.*, 2003) and competition with Arctic Terns (von Haartman, 1982; Klaassen & Lemmetyinen, 1998) are possible explanations for this. Populations along the southern Baltic coasts and in Norway have remained stable. In France, populations along the Atlantic coasts have remained stable over the last decade, whilst those inland have increased and those along the Mediterranean coasts have declined (Siblet, in press). Populations in other Mediterranean countries have remained mostly stable, although declines have occurred in mainland Spain (BirdLife International/EBCC, 2000). In Macaronesia, declines were evident in the Azores and Canaries whilst numbers on Madeira remained stable (BirdLife International/EBCC, 2000). In the countries bordering the Black Sea the population is broadly stable overall, although declines occurred in the large populations in the Ukraine and Romania that were offset by increases in Bulgaria (BirdLife International/EBCC, 2000). The declines in Ukraine were probably driven by vegetation succession, as reported for Sandwich Terns breeding there (Tucker & Heath, 1994). The population in European Russia is thought to be increasing (BirdLife International/EBCC, 2000)

In North America, populations were reduced to very low levels by persecution for the millinery trade by 1890 (Nisbet, 1973). Populations increased owing to protection and peaked in 1930, before declining again to a low point in the mid-1970s owing to competition with gulls, predation and pollution (Nisbet, 2002). Since then, the population has recovered owing to habitat management, removal of gulls, predator control and regulation of pollution (Nisbet, 2002). The small population in the West Indies is thought to have declined, with perceived threats including egging, predation, pollution and disturbance (Buckley & Buckley, 2000). In Asia, there is no information on the population trends of any of the subspecies.

Table 2   *International context.*

Country or region	Subspecies	Number of pairs Min	Number of pairs Max	Year	Source
Great Britain, Isle of Man and Channel Isles	*hirundo*	10,000	10,000	2000	BirdLife International / EBCC (2000)
All Ireland	*hirundo*	4,200	4,200	1995, 2000	BirdLife International / EBCC (2000)
Albania	*hirundo*	500	1,000	1991	BirdLife International / EBCC (2000)
Austria	*hirundo*	100	130		BirdLife International / EBCC (2000)
Belarus	*hirundo*	14,000	40,000	1988–98	BirdLife International / EBCC (2000)
Belgium	*hirundo*	2,246	2,246	2002	Stienen (pers. comm.)
Bulgaria	*hirundo*	200	500	1990–97	BirdLife International / EBCC (2000)
Croatia	*hirundo*	3,000	4,000		BirdLife International / EBCC (2000)
Czech Republic	*hirundo*	250	300	1985–95	BirdLife International / EBCC (2000)
Denmark	*hirundo*	1,000	1,000	1993–96	BirdLife International / EBCC (2000)
Estonia	*hirundo*	5,000	5,000		BirdLife International / EBCC (2000)
Finland	*hirundo*	40,000	60,000	1990–95	BirdLife International / EBCC (2000)
France	*hirundo*	4,680	5,000	1997–98	Siblet (in press)
Germany	*hirundo*	8,769	8,799	1996	BirdLife International / EBCC (2000)
Greece	*hirundo*	1,000	1,500		BirdLife International / EBCC (2000)
Hungary	*hirundo*	800	900	1998	BirdLife International / EBCC (2000)
Italy	*hirundo*	4,000	5,000	1988–97	BirdLife International / EBCC (2000)
Latvia	*hirundo*	1,500	2,000	1986	BirdLife International / EBCC (2000)
Lithuania	*hirundo*	5,000	7,000	1996–98	BirdLife International / EBCC (2000)
Moldova	*hirundo*	350	450	1988	BirdLife International / EBCC (2000)
Netherlands	*hirundo*	18,000	19,500	1998–2000	Stienen (2002)
Norway	*hirundo*	10,000	20,000	1990	BirdLife International / EBCC (2000)
Poland	*hirundo*	5,500	7,000		BirdLife International / EBCC (2000)
Portugal (Azores)	*hirundo*	4,000	4,500	1989	BirdLife International / EBCC (2000)
Portugal (Madeira)	*hirundo*	100	200	1991	BirdLife International / EBCC (2000)
Romania	*hirundo*	5,000	8,000		BirdLife International / EBCC (2000)
Russia	*hirundo*	30,000	60,000	1984–88	BirdLife International / EBCC (2000)
Slovakia	*hirundo*	20	40		BirdLife International / EBCC (2000)
Slovenia	*hirundo*	150	150		BirdLife International / EBCC (2000)
Spain (Canary Islands)	*hirundo*	38	51	1987	BirdLife International / EBCC (2000)
Spain (Mainland)	*hirundo*	5,800	11,000		BirdLife International / EBCC (2000)
Sweden	*hirundo*	20,000	25,000	1990	BirdLife International / EBCC (2000)
Switzerland	*hirundo*	340	380	1993–96	BirdLife International / EBCC (2000)
Turkey	*hirundo*	3,500	10,000	1998	BirdLife International / EBCC (2000)
Ukraine	*hirundo*	11,000	18,000	1986	BirdLife International / EBCC (2000)
Mauritania	*hirundo*	200	300		Urban *et al.* (1986)
North America, East Coast	*hirundo*	90,000	90,000		Nisbet (1999)
North America, Great Lakes	*hirundo*	9,000	10,000		Nisbet (1999)
North America, Interior	*hirundo*	36,000	36,000		Nisbet (1999)
Carribean	*hirundo*	290	490		Buckley & Buckley (2000)
Asian highlands	*tibetana*	3,000	30,000		Wetlands International (2002)
China (northeast)	*longipennis*	P	P		Nisbet (2002)
Iran breeder in wetlands	*hirundo*	P	P		Gallagher *et al.* (1984) Common
Russia (northeast Siberia)	*longipennis*	88400	89400		Kondratyev *et al.* (2000)
Russia (western & central Siberia)	*hirundo*	P	P		Nisbet (2002)
Turmekistan	*hirundo*	14,700	21800	1972–79	Golovkin (1984)

Biogeographic region	Sub species	Min	Max	Min % GB	Max % GB	Min % Ireland	Max % Ireland
Europe*	*hirundo*	220,000	340,000	2.9%	4.5%	1.2%	1.9%
World	All	460,000	620,000	1.6%	2.2%	0.7%	0.9%

* Stroud *et al.* (2001)

Arctic Tern *Sterna paradisaea*

Norman Ratcliffe

INTRODUCTION

Arctic Terns are the commonest tern breeding in Britain and Ireland, but their northerly distribution means they are less familiar to most observers than their congeners. The population in Britain and Ireland is concentrated in the Northern Isles, with 73% occurring there. Arctic Terns are also widespread in the Hebrides and islets along the west coast of Scotland. Along the Atlantic and Irish Sea coasts, the distribution extends south to Co. Kerry, Co. Wexford and Anglesey. In the North Sea, the distribution ends at a far higher latitude, in Northumberland, with the exception of three tiny colonies in East Anglia.

In common with other tern species, Arctic Terns were probably reduced to low levels by hunting for the millinery trade and egging, but have increased since the 1930s owing to legal protection. Sandeel stocks in waters around Shetland increased through the 1970s and early 1980s (Monaghan, 1992), and this improvement in food availability may have also contributed to Arctic Tern population growth. However, a collapse of the sandeel stock around Shetland between 1984 and 1990 (Wright & Bailey, 1993) resulted in a reversal in the fortunes of the Northern Isles Arctic Tern population. This caused repeated abandonment of eggs and starvation of chicks throughout the archipelago (Monaghan *et al.*, 1992), and the population of Arctic Terns on the Northern Isles declined between 1980 and 1989 in response to reduced recruitment and increased mortality or non-breeding (Avery *et al.*, 1993). Sandeel stocks have recovered since 1991 and productivity improved, with evidence of a population recovery between 1994 and 2000.

In western Scotland and the Western Isles, declines and redistribution of the population has resulted from predation by introduced American Mink (Clode & MacDonald, 2002; Craik, 1995, 1997; Rae, 1999). Future population trends will depend on the success of mink eradication and control projects being implemented in these areas. Many Arctic Tern colonies in the south of the British and Irish range are increasing, probably in response to site management for breeding terns. The population along the west coast of Ireland is increasing at the expense of Common Terns, possibly due to changes in climatic or oceanographic conditions shifting the balance of inter-specific competition in favour of Arctic Terns (Hannon *et al.*, 1997).

CENSUS METHODS

The Seabird 2000 census probably included counts from the vast majority of Arctic Tern colonies, with coverage being comprehensive within their British and Irish range. A small number of colonies formed for the first time since previous surveys may have been missed on Shetland, but these are likely to represent only a small percentage of the total. Most colonies were counted in 2000, but counts of the west coast of Ireland were taken from the 1995 All Ireland Tern survey (Hannon *et al.*, 1997). During the SCR, coverage was far from complete in the Northern Isles and the west coast of Ireland, but this was rectified by inclusion of data from the 1980 survey of Shetland and Orkney Bullock & Gomersall (1981), and the 1984 All Ireland Tern survey Whilde (1985) respectively. As such, trends between the two surveys are unlikely to be biased by spatial variations in coverage, but the differences in time periods over which trends are calculated among regions could produce some bias in the estimation of trends. There is debate concerning the degree to which coverage, changes in methods and timing of surveys have contributed to the changes in status since Operation Seafarer (Bullock & Gomersall, 1981; Avery, 1991; Bourne & Saunders, 1992), and so changes over the last 30 years should be treated with caution.

Arctic Tern nests are indistinguishable from those of Common Tern, and adults can appear similar to inexperienced observers. Many counts pool the numbers of both species and report them as Commic Terns. This makes estimation of the totals for each species during Seabird 2000 problematic, but since Commic Terns represent only 3% and 1% of the Arctic Tern population the SCR and Seabird 2000 surveys respectively this is likely produce only minor bias in the estimation of status and trends.

The proportion of surveys conducted using flush counts of adult birds was far higher for Arctic Terns than for other tern species. Arctic Terns breed mainly in the Northern and Western Isles, where there are a huge number of widely spaced colonies. These have to be counted within a single breeding season to avoid biases due to birds moving colonies between years. Counts of Arctic Tern AONs in the Northern and Western Isles are very time consuming owing to the low densities at which birds nest, crypsis of their nests against coastal heath and the lack of vantage points at many colonies for counts of incubating birds. Therefore, comprehensive AON counts within the incubation period of a single year are impractical, and counts of individuals, which allow rapid coverage of a large number of colonies within a season, are used instead (Bullock & Gomersall, 1981).

Using counts of adult birds to census Arctic Terns is complicated by the large variations in attendance between sites and years. Attendance is strongly related to breeding success, with adults tending to abandon the colony following breeding failure (Bullock & Gomersall, 1981). Biased estimates of status, trends and distribution could therefore result from variations in breeding success between sites and years. Abandonment of colonies in late incubation or chick-rearing was recorded in all years of census due to poor food availability, inclement weather or tidal flooding, and this will have caused underestimates of status. The degree to which breeding failure reduced counts varied between years. In 1989 complete failure of colonies occurred throughout Shetland, and consequently the percentage declines since the 1980 survey were far greater for those counts conducted late in the breeding season (Avery *et al.*, 1993). During the 1994 survey, breeding success was better than in 1989 but was still low owing to poor food availability, and during the 2000 survey a storm washed away colonies on the west coast of Shetland in mid-June. This will lead to biases in estimation of trends that examine raw counts of adults.

The biases associated with variations in attendance can be overcome by calibration of flush counts against the number of nests at a sample of colonies. Bullock & Gomersall (1981) estimated that during 1980 1.5 adults were present for every nesting pair during the incubation period, and 1.1 during chick-rearing. Counts of birds were divided by 1.5 to calculate the number of pairs in the Northern Isles for the SCR census. During 2000, calibration studies on Shetland and Orkney produced season and year-specific correction factors of 1.35 (25 May–10 June), 0.88 (11 June–28 June) and 0.61 (29 June–15 July). Adult counts were divided by the appropriate season-specific correction factor in order to estimate the number of pairs on the Northern Isles during the Seabird 2000 census. However, attendance was variable among colonies within years, such that estimates are subject to a large degree of error. Owing to the large proportion of Arctic Terns censused as adults and variations in attendance rates, trends for this species need to be viewed with greater caution than for other tern species.

Further south in their range, Arctic Terns tend to nest in discrete colonies on islets or sandy spits that are amenable to being surveyed in units of AONs by counting nests or incubating adults. Here, Arctic Terns usually nest sympatrically with Common Terns and this complicates counting, although differences in nest site selection often result in the two species nesting in discrete sub-colonies that can be delimited prior to counting. Where Common and Arctic Terns are intermixed, counts of incubating adults are the preferred method of estimating population status of each species. In situations where this method is impractical, total nest counts need to be conducted and the proportion of Common and Arctic Terns estimated from flush counts of adult birds. Such counts may be biased by species-dependent differences in colony attendance.

CURRENT STATUS AND TRENDS

Arctic Terns are almost exclusively coastal breeders in the UK and Ireland, with the only inland colonies being on Lough Corrib (Co. Galway) and Lough Conn (Co. Mayo: Fig. 1). Their distribution is far more northerly than other species of tern breeding in Britain and Ireland, with the majority of colonies occurring in Shetland, Orkney and the Outer Hebrides (Fig. 1). The limits of their range tend to extend further south in the west, reaching Co. Cork in western Ireland, Co. Wexford on the east cost of Ireland, Anglesey on the British coast of the Irish Sea, and Northumberland (with the exception of tiny colonies in East Anglia) on the British North Sea coast (Fig. 1). Breeding Arctic Terns are very rare or absent along the southern coasts of Britain despite other species of tern being common and widespread here, and it is likely that latitude-dependent inter-specific competition plays some role in the distribution of tern species in Britain and Ireland. The distribution of Arctic Terns around the British and Irish coasts has remained broadly similar over the last 30 years.

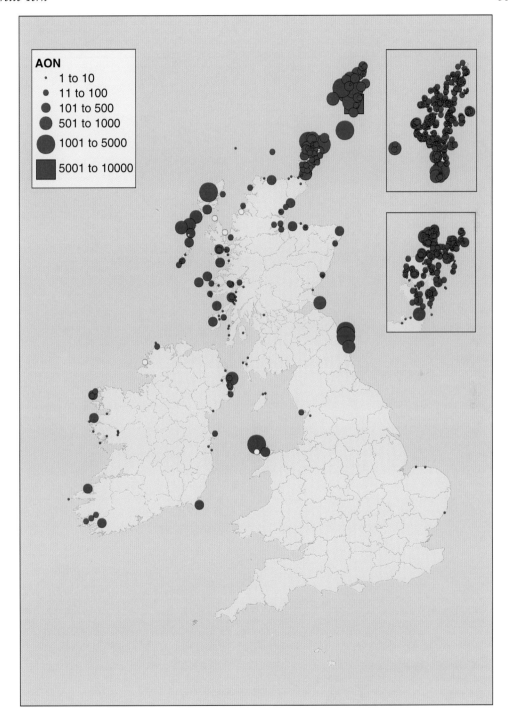

*Figure 1   Abundance and distribution of breeding Arctic Terns in Britain and Ireland 1998–2002. Colonies of 'commic'
terns (i.e. undistinguished Arctic and Common Terns) are shown in yellow (the scale is the same for Commic Tern and
Arctic Tern Colonies).*

Table 1   Numbers of breeding Arctic Terns (AON) in Britain and Ireland 1969–2002.

Administrative area or country	Operation Seafarer (1969–70)	SCR Census (1985–88)/All Ireland Tern Survey (1984)[2]	Seabird 2000 (1998–2002)/All Ireland Tern Survey (1995)	Percentage change since Seafarer	Percentage change since SCR/AITS (1984)	Annual percentage change since SCR/AITS (1984)
Shetland	7,295	30,332[1]	24,716	239%	−19%	−1.7
Orkney	32,535	33,455[1]	13,476	−60%	−60%	−5.6
North coast Caithness		697	585		−16%	−1.3%
Inland Caithness		4	9		125%	6.0%
East coast Caithness		13	0		−100%	
Caithness total	*2,073*	*714*	*594*	*−71%*	*−17%*	*−1.3%*
Northwest coast Sutherland		311	265		−15%	−1.2%
East coast Sutherland		13	236		1715%	23.0%
Sutherland total	*587*	*324*	*501*	*−15%*	*55%*	*3.2%*
West coast Ross & Cromarty		72	26		−64%	−7.2%
East coast Ross & Cromarty		7	129		1743%	23.3%
Ross & Cromarty total	*257*	*79*	*155*	*−40%*	*96%*	*5.0%*
Inverness	6	180	25	317%	−86%	−13.1%
Nairn	2	1		−100%	−100%	
Moray	89	30	244	174%	713%	16.2%
Banff & Buchan	45	58	184	309%	217%	8.6%
Gordon	125	49	76	−39%	55%	3.4%
Kincardine & Deeside	2	28	0	−100%	−100%	
Angus	70	103	82	17%	−20%	−1.8%
Northeast Fife		128	910		611%	15.1%
Dunfermline		20			−100%	
City of Edinburgh		24	0		−100%	
East Lothian	38	43	0	−100%	−100%	
Nithsdale	2			−100%		
Stewartry	23	10		−100%	−100%	
Wigtown	13	63	5	−62%	−92%	−18.3%
Kyle & Carrick	66	16	2	−97%	−88%	−13.8%
Cunninghame	12	6	7	−42%	17%	1.2%
Dumbarton						
Argyll & Bute	1,548	2,614	1,823	18%	−30%	−2.8%
Lochaber	139	542	149	7%	−73%	−9.9%
Skye & Lochalsh	281	1,258	209	−26%	−83%	−11.5%
Western Isles–Comhairle nan eilean	1,177	1,101	4,146	252%	277%	9.6%
Scotland Total	**46,385**	**71,178**	**47,306**	**2%**	**−34%**	**−3.6**
Northumberland	4,256	4,474	3,559	−16%	−20%	−1.8%
Norfolk	14	4	5	−64%	25%	1.6%
Suffolk						
Lancashire	1	20	2	100%	−90%	−14.7%
Cumbria	198	46	33	−83%	−28%	−2.5%
Isle of Man	29	22	8	−72%	−64%	−7.0%
England, Isle of Man and Channel Islands Total	**4,498**	**4,566**	**3,610**	**−20%**	**−21%**	**−1.7%**
Gwynedd	436	732	1705	291%	133%	6.5%
Wales Total	**436**	**732**	**1,705**	**291%**	**133%**	**6.4%**
Great Britain, Isle of Man and Channel Islands Total	**51,319**	**76476**	**52,621**	**3%**	**−31%**	**−3.2**
Co. Antrim	38		4	−89%		
Co. Fermanagh		7			−100%	
Co. Down	83	425	763	819%	80%	
Co. Longford		1			−100%	
Co. Dublin	129	30	99	−23%	230%	7.7

Administrative area or country	Operation Seafarer (1969–70)	SCR Census (1985–88)/All Ireland Tern Survey (1984)[2]	Seabird 2000 (1998–2002)/All Ireland Tern Survey (1995)	Percentage change since Seafarer	Percentage change since SCR/AITS (1984)	Annual percentage change since SCR/AITS (1984)
Co. Wexford	75	24	235	213%	879%	15.3
Co. Cork	115	119	29[3]	−75%	−76%	−12.0
Co. Kerry	51	168	288[3]	465%	71%	5.0
Co. Clare		6			2100%	2100.0
Co. Galway	188	691	1,061[3]	464%	54%	4.0
Co. Mayo	129	397	585	353%	47%	2.5
Co. Sligo		9	113[3]		1156%	25.9
Co. Donegal	161	411	325[3]	102%	−21%	−2.1
All-Ireland Total	969	2288	3502	261%	53%	
Britain and Ireland Total	52288	78764	56123	7%	−29%	

Notes

[1] Northern Isles surveyed in 1980 (Bullock & Gomersall, 1982)

[2] All SCR counts in Ireland were conducted during the All Ireland Tern Survey in 1984 (Whilde, 1985)

[3] All counts in this administrative area were conducted during the All Ireland Tern Survey in 1995 (Hannon *et al.*, 1997)

Seabird 2000 estimated the population of Arctic Terns breeding in Britain and Ireland at 56,123 pairs, making it by far the most abundant tern in the region. Of these, 85% occurred in Scotland, 6% in England, 6% in Ireland and 3% in Wales (Table 1). None occurred in the Channel Islands and only eight pairs bred on the Isle of Man. The most important regions for Arctic Terns were Shetland and Orkney which hosted 44% and 24% of the British population respectively, with most of the remainder occurring in the Western Isles (7%), Northumberland (6%) and Argyll & Bute (3%). In Ireland, the regional strongholds for Arctic Terns were in Co. Galway (30%), Co. Down (22%), Co. Mayo (17%) and Co. Donegal (9%). These regional patterns of abundance confirm the northerly and westerly distribution of Arctic Terns in Britain and Ireland.

Arctic Terns tend to be widespread in a large number of small to medium-sized colonies ranging between 1 and 100 pairs. However, large colonies do occur and these hold a significant proportion of the national population. The five largest colonies in Britain were Dalsetter (Shetland: 4,444 pairs), Farne Isles (Northumberland: 3,965), Papa Stour (Shetland: 2,007), Fair Isle (Shetland: 1,254) and Papa Westray (Orkney: 881), with these hosting 24% of the British population. In Ireland, the five largest colonies were Rock Island (Co. Galway: 388), Illaunamid (Co. Galway: 329), Cockle Island (Co. Down: 308), Strangford Lough (Co. Down: 281) and Lady's Island Lake (Co. Wexford: 235), with these hosting 42% of the Irish population.

The Arctic Tern population has declined by 29% since the SCR (Table 1). This trend needs to be treated with caution, as the years in which estimates were made differ widely among regions. Trends on Orkney and Shetland are best examined using the complete surveys in 1980, 1989, 1994 and 2000 (Table 2). During 1980, Bullock & Gomersall (1981) counted 83,200 birds in the whole of the Northern Isles, with 51% of these in Orkney. By 1989, this had fallen by 47% to 44,400 birds, with the proportion breeding in Orkney rising to 67% (Avery *et al.*, 1993). By 1994, counts had declined further by 27% to 32,400 birds, and the percentage breeding in Orkney had declined markedly to 48% (Brindley *et al.*, 1999). In 2000, the number counted had increased by 27% to 41,200 with the percentage occurring in Orkney declining further to 36%. Since these counts are of adult birds, it should be noted that lower attendance in 1989 and to a lesser extent in 1994 partially explains these changes. The number of pairs can only be estimated with any degree of confidence in 1980 and 2000, and these show a 41% decline from 64,900 to 38,200 pairs. Therefore, a large decline has occurred in the Northern Isles since 1980 that is not wholly explicable by changes in attendance patterns, but there is evidence that the population has started to recover since 1994.

Outside the Northern Isles, patterns of change have been spatially variable. In Scotland, numbers along the east coast increased by 170% and in the Outer Hebrides increased by 252%. In contrast, a widespread decline of 45% occurred along northern and western coasts of mainland Scotland and the Inner Hebrides. Colonies in England declined by 20% mainly owing to changes in the northeast stronghold, where declines at the Farne Isles have not been fully compensated by increases at Long Nanny (Northumberland). The Welsh population breeding on two islands in Anglesey increased by 133% from 732 to 1,705 pairs. In Ireland the population has increased overall by 53%, although declines occurred in Co. Cork (75%) and Co. Donegal (21%), and Co. Fermanagh, Co. Longford and Co. Clare lost all of their small colonies.

Annual population indices derived from the SMP are generally unreliable for Arctic Terns as sampling is biased towards the southern part of their range where colonies occur on nature reserves. The high rate of inter-colony movements in the Northern Isles result in the small number of colonies monitored there being inadequate to interpret trends between surveys with any degree of confidence.

Table 2   Population status of Arctic Terns in the Northern Isles in 1980, 1989, 1994 and 2000.

Year	Unit	Shetland	Orkney	Total
1980	Birds[1]	40,800	42,400	83,200
1989	Birds[1]	14,700	29,700	44,400
1994	Birds[1]	16,800	15,600	32,400
2000	Birds[1]	26,400	14,800	41,200
1980	Pairs	31,794	33,069	64,863
2000	Pairs	24,716	13,476	38,192

Note

[1] Figures presented in units of birds are the number of birds counted, not an estimate of the total breeding

CAUSES OF CHANGE

The trends of Arctic Terns in the Northern Isles are linked to variations in food availability. Arctic Terns in Orkney and Shetland are almost entirely dependent on sandeel as prey during the breeding season, and their productivity is strongly affected by the size of the sandeel stock (Monaghan *et al.*, 1989b; Suddaby & Ratcliffe, 1997). Sandeel stocks increased through the 1970s and early 1980s (Monaghan, 1992), and this was associated with an increase in the population of Arctic Terns between Operation Seafarer and the 1980 survey (Cramp *et al.*, 1974; Bullock & Gomersall, 1981). Debate exists over the extent to which survey coverage, timing of counts and methods contributed to this change (Bullock & Gomersall, 1981; Avery, 1991; Bourne & Saunders, 1992), but it is probable that at least some of the increase was due to population growth (Bullock & Gomersall, 1981). Sandeel stocks declined rapidly in 1983–90, probably owing to changes in oceanography affecting larval transport and causing recruitment failures (Wright & Bailey, 1993). Arctic Terns experienced complete breeding failures throughout the archipelago between 1984 and 1990 (Monaghan *et al.*, 1989a; Monaghan *et al.*; 1992; Suddaby & Ratcliffe, 1997). During this period, clutch sizes were atypically small, eggs were abandoned during incubation and chicks starved within days of hatching, all of which are symptomatic of severe food shortage (Monaghan *et al.*, 1989a; Monaghan *et al.*, 1992).

The population declines between 1980 and 1989 are unlikely to have been caused by reproductive failures since Arctic Terns breed at four years old (Coulson & Horobin, 1976). The population would have experienced only two years of recruitment failure by 1989, and so given an adult survival rate

Arctic Tern aerobatically feeding a chick (Mike Brown)

of 87% (Coulson & Horobin, 1976) the population would have been expected to decline by 24% rather than 47% (Avery *et al.*, 1993). Adult weights were depressed during the period of poor food supply (Avery *et al.*, 1992; Sim *et al.*, 1993; Suddaby & Ratcliffe, 1997), and this may have resulted in increased rates of mortality or intermittent breeding that in turn caused the population to decline more rapidly than expected (Avery *et al.*, 1993). Further declines up to 1994 can be explained by recruitment failures from the 1986–90 cohorts (Brindley *et al.*, 1999). Since these counts are based on numbers of adult birds counted, reduced colony attendance rates in response to poor food supply and breeding failures could also explain a proportion of the declines.

In 1991, the sandeel stock recovered owing to larval advection from Orkney (Wright & Bailey, 1993), and productivity of Arctic Terns in Shetland improved subsequently (Suddaby & Ratcliffe, 1997). The population in Shetland remained broadly stable between 1989 and 1994 whilst that on Orkney declined by 47% (Brindley *et al.*, 1999). Population models based on intra-archipelago productivity patterns suggested that the Shetland population should have declined by 47% and the Orkney population by only 14% (Brindley *et al.*, 1999). The most plausible explanation for this was that *c.*10,000 Arctic Terns emigrated from Orkney to Shetland to take advantage of improved food availability there (Brindley *et al.*, 1999). The populations on Shetland and Orkney can therefore be regarded as components of a meta-population, with breeding birds moving among archipelagos in response to changing environmental conditions.

Improvements in productivity on Shetland in response to increased sandeel availability through the 1990s have probably allowed the population in the Northern Isles as a whole to recover slightly between 1994 and 2000. However, several years of poor productivity have been recorded on both Shetland and Orkney during the 1990s (Table 3), owing to poor sandeel availability and inclement weather during hatching, which caused chilling and death of young chicks. Arctic Tern populations in the Northern Isles are therefore likely to decline further in future years owing to poor recruitment.

Table 3 Productivity of Arctic Terns at a sample of colonies throughout Shetland and Orkney in 1990–99

Year	No. chicks fledged per pair	
	Shetland	Orkney
1990	0.00	0.02
1991	0.70	0.12
1992	0.72	0.46
1993	0.38	0.29
1994	0.21	0.18
1995	0.52	0.79
1996	0.25	0.17
1997	0.12	0.51
1998	0.01	0.12
1999	0.29	0.10

Further monitoring of population status and productivity in the Northern Isles is clearly essential to understand the effects of varying sandeel stocks on tern population dynamics.

The decline of Arctic Terns along the west coast of Scotland and the Outer Hebrides is almost certainly due to predation by American Mink. Mink escaped from fur farms during the 1950s and 1960s (Dunstone, 1993) and by 1994 were widespread along the west coast of Scotland as far north as Fort William and throughout Lewis and Harris (Green & Green, 1997). Further expansions of their range south into the Uists (Clode & MacDonald, 2002) and northward along the mainland coast and into Skye have occurred since. Mink predation at tern colonies causes complete breeding failure, occasional adult mortality and eventual abandonment of the site (Craik, 1995, 1997; Rae 1999). Colonies have moved to offshore islets free from American Mink (Craik, 1997; Craik & Campbell, 2000) in west Scotland and may have aggregated into larger colonies to improve defence in the Western Isles (Clode *et al.*, 2000; Clode & MacDonald 2002). Despite this, their numbers have still declined, probably owing to predation causing recruitment failures prior to redistribution. It is possible that numbers will remain depressed owing to increased density-dependent competition for nest sites or food where birds are concentrated at fewer, larger colonies.

Measures are being taken to prevent predation by American Mink on seabirds, including annual control at several islets in Argyll (Craik, 1995, 1997) and an eradication programme in the Outer Hebrides. The fate of Arctic Terns nesting along west Scottish coasts is likely to depend on the success of these projects. Monitoring of productivity and population trends in response to this management should be regarded as a high priority.

Some colonies of Arctic Terns are increasing in the south of their range in response to sympathetic reserve management. Management of predation, nest site competition and disturbance by large gulls is likely to have permitted increases in Arctic Tern numbers on Skerries (Gwynedd) and the Isle of May (North East Fife). Exclusion of foxes from colonies is likely to have led to population increases at Rhosneiger (Gwynedd) and Long Nanny (Northumberland). Control of Brown Rats on Inish Island in Lady's Island Lake (Co. Wexford) probably facilitated an increase of Arctic Tern breeding numbers there. However, reserve management does not always meet its objectives of increasing Arctic Tern populations. On the Farne Islands (Northumberland), the numbers declined despite management, probably due to reductions in food availability (J. Walton, pers. comm.).

In western Ireland, Arctic Terns are increasing at the expense of Common Terns, and Hannon *et al.* (1997) suggest that this is due to ecological competition between the two species. It appears conditions have changed over the last 15 years in a manner permitting Arctic Terns to out-compete Common Terns further south in their sympatric range. Further research into comparative foraging efficiency, chick growth and productivity at mixed colonies of Arctic and Common Terns at locations around the coast of Ireland, and their interactions with weather and sea conditions, might elucidate the mechanisms through which inter-specific competition operates.

Arctic Terns undertake the longest migration of any bird species, and spend the winter in the pack-ice region of Antarctica (Monaghan, 2002). Since this region is largely uninhabited, man's activities are likely to have only minor effects on overwinter survival, and natural variation in food supply or inclement weather are probably the main factors causing mortality. Arctic Terns migrate along the West African coast and some are deliberately trapped here, but the rate at which this occurs is lower than for other species owing to Arctic Terns only being transient visitors (Monaghan, 2002).

INTERNATIONAL CONTEXT

Arctic Terns have a circumpolar breeding distribution, extending south into the boreal zone as far south as Brittany, in France, Massachusetts, in the USA, British Columbia, in Canada, and Kamchatka in Russia (Hatch, 2002). The majority of Arctic Terns breed in coastal areas on sparsely vegetated islands, remote beaches and coastal heath, but their distribution also extends far inland along oligotrophic rivers and lakes in the tundra zone, where birds breed on marshes and shingle (Klaassen & Lemmetyinen, 1998). Owing to the vastness of the species' breeding range and the remoteness of its habitat, quantitative estimates are unavailable from the core range, and figures are based on incomplete counts or guesswork. Estimates from countries such as Greenland, Russia, Alaska and Canada should therefore be treated with caution. Accurate counts are available only for countries at the southern limits of the range, where only a small percentage of the global population breeds.

Arctic Terns are monotypic, with no recognised subspecies or races, suggesting a large degree of population mixing throughout the range (Monaghan, 2002). There are probably between 800,000 and three million pairs breeding globally, with the largest populations occurring in Russia, Canada, Alaska, Greenland and Iceland (Table 4). Arctic Tern populations in Britain and Ireland are relatively small when placed in a global context, hosting 2–7% and less than 1% of the world population respectively.

The European and North Atlantic population (defined as the relevant biogeographic population by Stroud *et al.*, 1991) is estimated at between 490,000 and 1,800,000 breeding pairs. The populations in Britain and Ireland represent 3–11% and 0.2–0.7% of European and North Atlantic numbers, with Britain ranking second in importance for Arctic Tern numbers in Europe behind Iceland (Klaassen & Lemmetyinen, 1998). Other important countries in Europe for Arctic Terns are Finland, Norway and Sweden, all of which hold 5–10% of the total (Klaassen & Lemmetyinen, 1998; BirdLife International, 2000). Small populations occur in Germany, Estonia, Denmark, Svalbard and The Netherlands.

Information on trends of Arctic Terns in their core northern range is patchy. In Canada and Alaska, declines have been observed at a small number of colonies, but these may not be representative of trends in the population as a whole (Hatch, 2002). An aerial waterfowl survey of a region of Alaska found increases of Arctic Terns in 1990, but the confidence limits are wide and it is uncertain whether censuses designed for wildfowl produce reliable trends for terns (Hatch, 2002). In Greenland, Arctic Terns have experienced large population declines due to over-exploitation of eggs for commercial sale as food (Boertmann, 1994; Hansen, 2001). The population in Iceland fluctuated by less than 20% between 1970 and 1990 with no long-term trend (Klaassen & Lemmetyinen, 1998). Trends in European Russia indicate a decline of 25–49% between the 1970s and 1990s (BirdLife International/EBCC, 2000) but trends further east in Russia are unknown.

Detailed information on trends of Arctic Tern populations is available from countries at the southern limits of their range in Europe and North America. The Arctic Terns range has extended in the inner zone of the Baltic archipelagos, possibly owing to eutrophication improving availability of chironomid prey (von Haartman, 1982; Klaassen & Lemmetyinen, 1998). The population in Finland increased in 1940–70, but recent declines have resulted from American Mink predation (Klaassen & Lemmetyinen, 1998). Experimental control of mink in southern Finland produced increases in densities of breeding Arctic Terns and other seabirds (Nordström *et al.*, 2003), and future trends there are likely to depend on the extent to which such management is implemented. Populations in The Netherlands declined by *c.*25% in 1978–90, but increased to *c.*108% of the 1990 total by 2000 (Kasemir & Lutterop, 2002). In Germany, the population has remained broadly stable over the last 20 years, although declines have been evident since 1990 in the small populations that breed along the Baltic Sea coast (Hälterlein *et al.* 2000). In Denmark, numbers increased by 25–50% between 1978–81 and 1993–96 (Grell, 1998). Populations along the eastern seaboard of the USA have declined since 1950 (Hatch, 2002). In the Russian Far East, threats include predation by dogs, trampling and grazing by cattle and reindeer and egging (Kondratyev *et al.*, 2000).

Table 4   International context.

Country or region	Number of pairs		Year	Source
	Min	Max		
Great Britain, Isle of Man and Channel Isles	52,600	52,600	2000	Seabird 2000
All Ireland	3,500	3,500	1995, 1999, 2000	Seabird 2000
Belgium	1	1	1996	BirdLife International / EBCC (2000)
Denmark	8,000	9,000	1993–1996	BirdLife International / EBCC (2000)
Estonia	7,000	8,000		BirdLife International / EBCC (2000)
Faeroe Islands	2,000	2,000	1995	BirdLife International / EBCC (2000)
Finland	50,000	60,000	1990–95	BirdLife International / EBCC (2000)
France	1	5		Klassen & Lemmetyinen (1998)
Germany	6,000	6,000	1999	Hälterlein *et al.* (2000)
Greenland	30,000	60,000	1996	BirdLife International / EBCC (2000)
Iceland	250,000	500,000	1990	BirdLife International / EBCC (2000)
Latvia	80	100		BirdLife International / EBCC (2000)
Lithuania	0	5	1996–98	BirdLife International / EBCC (2000)
Netherlands	1,900	2,300	1998–2000	Kasemir & Lutterop (2002)
Norway	20,000	60,000	1990	BirdLife International / EBCC (2000)
Norway (Jan Mayen)	500	1,000		Klassen & Lemmetyinen (1998)
Norway (Svalbard)	1,000	10,000		BirdLife International / EBCC (2000)
Russia (Europe)	25,000	30,000		BirdLife International / EBCC (2000)
Sweden	20,000	25,000	1990	BirdLife International / EBCC (2000)
Canada (East)	10,000	1,000,000		Lloyd *et al.* (1991)
USA (East coast)	5,740	5,740	1999–2002	Hatch 2002
Russian (Far East)	6,500	6,500		Kondratyev *et al.* 2000
Russia (Central)	P	P		Hatch 2002
USA (Alaska)	300,000	900,000		Lensink (1984)

Biogeographic region*	Min	Max	Min % GB	Max % GB	Min % Ireland	Max % Ireland
Europe & N. Atlantic*	493,000	1,800,000	2.9%	10.7%	0.2%	0.7%
World	800,000	2,700,000	1.9%	6.6%	0.1%	0.4%

* Stroud *et al.* (2001)

Little Tern *Sterna albifrons*

Georgina Pickerell

INTRODUCTION

The Little Tern is the smallest of the five species of tern that breed in Britain and Ireland, and nests exclusively on the coast. They nest in well-camouflaged shallow scrapes on sand and shingle beaches, spits or inshore islets. Birds do not forage far from their breeding site, which dictates that they nest close to shallow, sheltered feeding areas where they can easily locate the small fish and invertebrates that comprise their diet (Fasola *et al.*, 2002). Although colonies may be found around much of the coastline, breeding is concentrated in south and east England (Fig. 1), where the species' preference for breeding on beaches also favoured by people makes it vulnerable to disturbance.

Following a decline during the 19th century, the Little Tern population in Britain increased during the early-20th century, peaking in the 1930s. Thereafter, numbers once again fell (Parslow, 1967). An incomplete survey in 1967 found just 1,600 pairs (Norman & Saunders, 1969) and the first full census, during Operation Seafarer (1969–70) estimated the British and Irish population to be 1,900 pairs (Cramp *et al.*, 1974). Increased protection of colonies during the 1970s and early 1980s may have enabled numbers to increase to 2,800 pairs by the SCR Census (1985–88: Lloyd *et al.*, 1991). A subsequent analysis of the population trend between 1969 and 1998 showed that numbers peaked in the mid-1970s and then went into a long-term decline, reaching an all-time low in 1998. The decline was most severe at colonies along the English Channel coast, but it was not restricted to this region, indicating that the problem was widespread (Ratcliffe *et al.*, 2000).

CENSUS METHODS

The count unit for Little Terns during Seabird 2000 was the Apparently Occupied Nest (AON). Little Terns usually breed at low densities and have inconspicuous nests (i.e. scrapes in the ground), and well-camouflaged eggs and chicks. Thus, counts of nests along transects usually underestimate the number of AONs present. AONs are much more conspicuous when an adult is in attendance, either incubating or brooding chicks. Thus, counts of AONs are best made from a good vantage point far enough away from the colony to not disturb the attending adults. In Britain during Seabird 2000, 81% of AONs were counted from a vantage point, 9% were counted from within the colony and the remaining 10% were estimated from counts of individuals attending the colony (no information on methods was available from the All Ireland Tern survey in 1995—Hannon *et al.* 1997). During the SCR Census (1985–88) count methods were not recorded, but 97% of AONs were counted directly, with only 3% estimated from counts of individuals. Counts of individuals were performed when there was no suitable vantage point and the colony could either not be accessed or the level of disturbance caused by doing so was deemed unjustifiable by the surveyor. During both censuses, counts of individuals were divided by 1.5 to give an estimate of AONs (Bullock & Gomersall, 1981). The conversion of counts of individuals to counts of AONs is prone to error resulting from the inclusion of attending non-breeders and variations in nest attendance by the adults depending on time of day and season. Furthermore, the correction factor was estimated for Arctic Terns in the Northern Isles rather than for Little Terns.

The recommended count period for Seabird 2000 was mid-May to late June, coinciding with the peak nesting period. Pairs that failed or deserted early in the season may have been missed during surveys, and those that moved to other colonies may have been counted twice. In Britain during Seabird 2000, 40% of the population was counted within the recommended dates, 28% were outside and no date was recorded for 31% of counts, compared to 31%, 14% and 55% respectively during the SCR Census (1985–88). In Ireland, 70% of the population was counted within the recommended dates during Seabird 2000, but count dates were not available for the those made during the All Ireland Tern Survey in 1984 (Whilde, 1985) and incorporated into the SCR Census (see below).

Complete coverage of Little Tern colonies was achieved in Britain and Ireland during Seabird 2000, as in Operation Seafarer (1969–70) and the SCR Census (1985–88). Little Terns, like other terns, exhibit low site-fidelity in some areas, readily switching breeding sites both within and between years. During Seabird 2000 93% of the population in Britain was counted in 2000. This was a marked improvement on the SCR Census when counts were spread over four years, with 13% of the British population counted in 1985, 21% in 1986, 63% in 1987 and the remainder in 1988. In the Republic of Ireland (there are no Little Terns breeding in Northern Ireland), Seabird 2000 surveys were conducted in 1999 in Co. Louth and Co. Dublin, in 2000 in Co. Mayo and Co. Wexford, and in 2001 in Co. Wicklow. Counts from all other administrative areas in the Republic were taken from the 1995 All Ireland Tern Survey (Hannon *et al.*, 1997), and these constituted 65% of colonies and 48% of AONs in Ireland (1995–2001). Movements between administrative areas in successive years could have led to an over- or underestimate of the size of the population in Ireland. For the SCR Census in Ireland, Lloyd *et al.* (1991) used counts of Little Terns conducted during the 1984 All Ireland Tern Survey (Whilde, 1985) together with more recent counts (i.e. 1985–88) where available.

This probably led to an overestimate of the population for the mid-1980s and so for the SCR Census results in Table 1 we have used only counts from the All Ireland Tern Survey in 1984, which were less likely to be affected by movement of birds between colonies. However, any errors/biases in the estimate for Ireland would have only a small effect on the accuracy of the total population estimate for Britain and Ireland, since only 10% of the population bred in Ireland during Seabird 2000 (see below).

Whilst the similarity in methods employed in both the SCR Census and Seabird 2000 ensures a valid comparison of the population estimates from both censuses, the apparent population trend from a comparison of two such widely spaced surveys may be misleading. This is because the proportion of adult Little Terns choosing to nest in any given year fluctuates. However, annual monitoring of Little Tern colonies has been conducted in Britain since 1969, such that population flunctuations can be discriminated from long-term trends.

CURRENT STATUS AND TRENDS

During Seabird 2000 there were 2,153 AON in Britain and Ireland, of which 72% were in England and the Isle of Man, 15% in Scotland, 10% in Ireland and 4% in Wales (Table 1). The overall distribution of breeding Little Terns (Fig. 1) was similar to that during the SCR Census (1985–88). Little Terns require a mix of bare or sparsely vegetated sand and shingle, and suitable shallow feeding areas close to the colony. Around 70% of the British and Irish population breed on the east and south coasts of England (from Northumberland to Dorset), where low-lying sandy coastlines predominate. Breeding colonies ranged in size from 1 to over 200 AON (Fig. 1).

The population in Britain and Ireland has declined by 25% since the SCR Census (1984–88), but was 12% larger than during Operation Seafarer (1969–70: Table 1). The declines since the SCR Census were widespread, but most substantial in eastern Scotland, northeast England, southeast England and parts of Ireland. Numbers increased in a few areas, notably western Scotland and Wales. The number of occupied colonies fell to 130 in 2000, from 168 in 1984–88 and 154 in 1969–70. However, there was no evidence to suggest that a higher proportion of the population was breeding in large colonies during Seabird 2000 compared to the SCR Census (1984–88), as the frequency distribution of colony size in each census was similar (Fig. 3). Three colonies, the same number as in the SCR Census, held more than 100 AON in 2000: 220 AON at Great Yarmouth, 115 AON at Blakeney Point (both in Norfolk) and 102 at Hamford Water (Essex). This represents a slight increase in the proportion of the British and Irish population in colonies of more than 100 AON: 21% of AONs in 2000, compared to 12% and 17% in 1984–88 and 1969–70 respectively.

Using counts from a sample of colonies in Britain and Ireland, Ratcliffe *et al.* (2000) estimated the total population size in each year between 1969 and 1998 (Fig. 2). The mean of their annual population estimates in 1984–88 was 2,350 pairs, which was somewhat lower than the SCR Census estimate of 2,857 AON (Table 1). The estimated annual population size declined steadily by 38% to *c.*1,700 AON in 1998. Subsequent monitoring of a sample of colonies that contained around two-thirds of the British population showed that in 1999–2002 the population remained around 17% higher than it had been in 1998 (Upton *et al.*, 2000; Mavor *et al.*, 2002, 2003). Hence, the decline of 25% between the SCR Census (1984–88) and Seabird 2000 appears representative of the annual changes that have occurred during the intervening period.

The population in England has declined by 29% since the SCR Census to 1,541 AON. Numbers in eight of the 15 occupied administrative areas declined by more than half in the last 15 years, with the only increases being in Norfolk, Dorset and Humberside. Two-thirds of the English population,

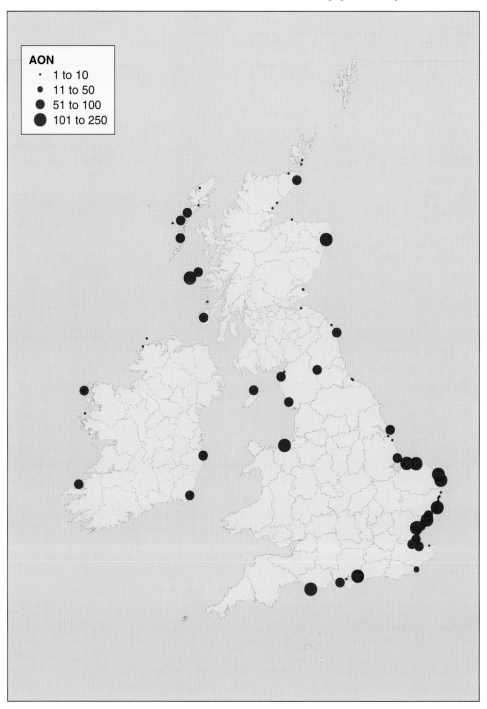

Figure 1   Abundance and distribution of breeding Little Terns in Britain and Ireland 1998–2002.

Table 1 Numbers of breeding Little Terns (AON) in Britain and Ireland 1969–2002.

Administrative area or country	Operation Seafarer (1969–70)	SCR Census (1985–88)/ All Ireland Tern Survey (1984)[1]	Seabird 2000 (1998–2002)/ All Ireland Tern Survey (1995)	Percentage change since Seafarer	Percentage change since SCR/AITS (1984)	Annual percentage change since SCR/AITS (1984)
Orkney			4			
North coast Caithness			1			
East coast Caithness		10	14		40%	2.4%
Caithness total	*3*	*10*	*15*	*400%*	*50%*	*3.0%*
East coast Sutherland		14	8		−43%	−4.2%
Sutherland total	*6*	*14*	*8*	*33%*	*−43%*	*−4.2%*
Inverness		2			−100%	
Moray	11		2	−82%		
Banff & Buchan	3		0	−100%		
Gordon	21	27	58	176%	115%	6.1%
Kincardine & Deeside	32	22	0	−100%	−100%	
Angus	55	64	0	−100%	−100%	
Northeast Fife	8	2	5	−38%	150%	8.3%
Dunfermline		5			−100%	
East Lothian	22	35	2	−91%	−94%	−20.5%
Nithsdale	2			−100%		
Wigtown	1	3		−100%	−100%	
Kyle & Carrick	6	4		−100%	−100%	
Argyll & Bute	75	119	126	68%	6%	0.4%
Skye & Lochalsh	6			−100%		
Western Isles–Comhairle nan eilean	57	66	111	95%	68%	3.6%
Scotland total	**308**	**373**	**331**	**7%**	**−11%**	**−0.9%**
Northumberland	20	71	73	265%	3%	0.2%
Durham	2			−100%		
Cleveland		44	19		−57%	−6.3%
Humberside	4	4	49	1125%	1125%	22.2%
Lincolnshire	63	156	46	−27%	−71%	−8.6%
Norfolk	416	508	600	44%	18%	1.3%
Suffolk	80	378	148	85%	−61%	−6.7%
Essex	163	370	262	61%	−29%	−2.5%
Kent	55	135	38	−31%	−72%	−8.8%
East Sussex	70	60	11	−84%	−82%	−12.3%
West Sussex	62	25	1	−98%	−96%	−20.6%
Hampshire	82	245	151	84%	−38%	−3.6%
Isle of Wight	5	1		−100%	−100%	
Dorset	120	30	81	−33%	170%	7.9%
Cumbria	105	60	42	−60%	−30%	−2.7%
Isle of Man	19	60	20	5%	−67%	−7.1%
England total	**1,266**	**2,147**	**1,541**	**22%**	**−28%**	**−2.4%**
Gwynedd	24	8		−100%	−100%	
Clwyd	4	47	75	1775%	60%	3.7%
Wales total	**28**	**55**	**75**	**168%**	**36%**	**2.3%**
Great Britain, Isle of Man and Channel Islands total	**1,602**	**2,575**	**1,947**	**22%**	**−24%**	**−2.1%**
Co. Londonderry	6	2	0	−100%	−100%	
Co. Louth	0	36	0		−100%	
Co. Dublin	8	14	0	−100%	−100%	
Co. Wicklow	49	30	40	−18%	33%	1.7
Co. Wexford	99	45	40	−60%	−11%	−0.7
Co. Cork	2	2	0	−100%	−100%	
Co. Kerry	11	10	38	245%	280%	12.9
Co. Galway	65	45	45	−31%	0%	0.0
Co. Mayo	26	80	28	8%	−65%	−6.4
Co. Donegal	49	18	15	−69%	−17%	−1.6
All−Ireland total	**315**	**282**	**206**	**−35%**	**−27%**	
Britain and Ireland total	**1,917**	**2,857**	**2,153**	**12%**	**−25%**	

Note

[1] All SCR counts in Ireland were conducted during the All Ireland Tern Survey in 1984 (Whilde, 1985)

compared with about half in both Operation Seafarer and the SCR Census, were breeding along the East Anglian coast, especially in Norfolk. The population increase in Norfolk was largely due to the expansion of the colony at Great Yarmouth from a just few pairs in the 1980s to over 200 AON, making it the largest colony in Britain. Two large colonies remained on the south coast of England: at Langstone Harbour (Hampshire), where four sub-colonies totalled 108 AON, and 81 AON were at Chesil Bank (Dorset). But along the same stretch of coast, from Kent to Dorset, total breeding numbers decreased by 43% since the SCR Census, to 282 AON.

Seabird 2000 recorded 325 AON of Little Tern in Scotland. Although the 10% decline since the SCR Census (1985–88) was not as severe as in England, breeding only occurred in eight administrative areas, compared to 13 in 1985–88 and 15 in 1969–70. In the Western Isles the population doubled in size since the SCR Census and, together with Argyll & Bute, held most of the breeding Little Terns in Scotland. In contrast, the east coast population has halved in size during the same period, with Little Terns no longer breeding in Kincardine & Deeside and Angus. However, the colony of 58 AON at Forvie (Gordon) remained the largest colony in Scotland and two new colonies, of just 2 AON each, were found in Orkney.

The only colony in Wales was at the long-established site at Gronant (Clwyd), which increased from 47 AON in 1987 to 75 AON in 2000. Two other small colonies of 3 AON and 4 AON in Gwynedd during the SCR Census (1985–88) have since disappeared.

In Ireland, the Little Tern population has declined by 27% since 1984 and 35% since 1969, to just 206 AON. Little Terns no longer breed in Northern Ireland; the small colony in Co. Londonderry disappeared at some time since 1984. In southeast Ireland breeding Little Terns have disappeared from Co. Louth and Co. Dublin, and are now concentrated at just two sites (compared to nine in 1984): Wexford Harbour (Co. Wexford) and Kilcoole (Co. Wicklow), where there were 40 AON at each in Seabird 2000. In western Ireland, the single colony in Co. Kerry at Illauntannig

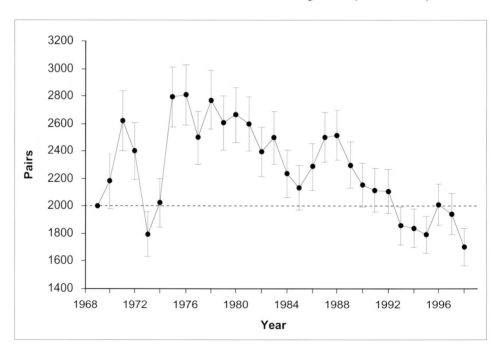

Figure 2   Numbers of breeding Little Terns in Britain and Ireland 1969–1998. Error bars denote 2*S.E. Dashed line denotes population size in 1969. Source: Ratcliffe et al. (2000).

increased from 10 AON in 1984 to 36 AON in 1995, whilst populations elsewhere declined. In Co. Mayo only 28 AON were found at three colonies in 1995, compared to 80 AON at 11 colonies in 1984.

CAUSES OF CHANGE

The decline in numbers of Little Terns breeding in Britain and Ireland throughout the 1980s and 1990s has been coincident with a reduction in breeding success (Ratcliffe *et al.*, 2000). Estimates of breeding success from colonies throughout Britain between 1990 and 1998 as part of the Seabird Monitoring Programme (Ratcliffe *et al.* 2000) have shown overall annual breeding success to fluctuate between 0.19 and 0.70 (median 0.45) chicks fledged per pair. This level of productivity is insufficient to maintain the population by recruitment alone and is likely to have contributed to the population decline. Ratcliffe (2003) found that a simple population model incorporating annual estimates of breeding success of British Little Terns with constant values for adult survival and age at first breeding predicted the observed decline in population size of Little Terns in Britain with reasonable accuracy.

There is little evidence to suggest that there have been any major changes in other parameters such as adult survival or emigration that would have contributed to the declines in the British and Irish breeding populations of Little Terns. Unlike some other terns, there is no evidence to suggest that trapping on their wintering grounds in West Africa has been a major contributor to adult mortality (Dunn & Mead, 1984). A recent study has also revealed that Little Terns do not suffer from a lack of food in winter (Brenninkmeijer *et al.*, 2002). Both adults and young ringed at colonies in Britain have subsequently been found at breeding colonies in mainland northern Europe (Wernham *et al.*, 2002). However, there is no evidence for a widespread emigration of Little Terns from Britain or Ireland, since, with the exception of France and Belgium, numbers elsewhere in northern Europe are thought to be stable or have increased only slightly (Fasola *et al.*, 2002). Thus, reduced breeding success and subsequent recruitment appear to be the main causes of decline in the numbers of Little Terns breeding in Britain and Ireland.

A major and longstanding cause of low breeding success in Little Terns has been human disturbance (Lloyd *et al.*, 1975; Fasola *et al.*, 2002). The largest numbers of Little Terns, along the east and south coasts of England, are adjacent to some of the most densely populated areas in Britain. Since the mid-1970s many colonies have been supervised by wardens, and the use of signs and fences has substantially reduced the extent of human disturbance. Hence, at most colonies, human disturbance is an unlikely cause of more recent declines in breeding success.

Predation of eggs and/or chicks is the most commonly cited cause of breeding failure at colonies monitored as part of the Seabird Monitoring Programme (Mavor *et al.*, 2002, 2003). Predation may have increased owing to recreational disturbance reducing availability of nesting habitat, such that birds are concentrated into a smaller number of larger and less mobile colonies. However, there is no evidence to suggest that larger colonies suffer higher levels of predation (Sears & Avery, 1993) and, furthermore, data from Seabird 2000 indicate that there has been no real change in the proportion of birds breeding in larger colonies.

The predators most often reported at Little Tern colonies were foxes, Carrion Crows, Magpies and Kestrels, although these may simply be the easiest to detect. Other predators include hedgehogs, other birds of prey, gulls and dogs. Foxes have quadrupled in number over the last 40 years, following the cessation of game-keeping in many parts of Britain (Tapper, 1992). Their range has also spread into many areas where Little Tern numbers are declining. Thus, there is certainly reason to suspect that predation by foxes has been a major and widespread contributor to Little Tern breeding failures since 1969. Numbers of crows have risen steadily since the 1960s, but Kestrel numbers are thought to have remained stable or declined slightly over the last 15 years (Baillie *et al.*, 2002). Information supplied from 27 colonies (*c.*940 AON) in 2001 (Pickerell, 2002) recorded the causes of breeding failure as follows (note that not all pairs in a colony necessarily failed and some colonies recorded more than one reason for failure): Kestrel (seven colonies totalling 552 AON), high tides and bad weather (seven colonies totalling 118), foxes (three colonies totalling 118), other predators (three colonies totalling 64), human disturbance (three colonies totalling 44) and other causes (four colonies totalling 135). At Britain's largest colony, at Great Yarmouth, Kestrels were observed taking 526 Little Tern chicks in 2001 alone.

Within the last five years, the use of certain types of mesh electric fencing and 24-hour wardening has proved effective at deterring ground predators (Pickerell, 1998; Thompson *et al.*, 1998). However, reducing the impact of aerial predators remains fraught with difficulties. Supplementary feeding of Kestrels at Great Yarmouth had no demonstrable effect on predation levels and indeed may have acted to artificially inflate the local population (Smart & Ratcliffe, 2000). Furthermore, the provision of chick shelters cannot be relied on to protect the young as they are not always used and kestrels and able to capture chicks in these. Thus, unless effective counter-measures can be found, aerial predators will continue to have a significant impact on Little Tern breeding success in the future.

Little Terns have a propensity for nesting close to the high-water mark and so nests are vulnerable to flooding by high tides. In some cases, such as at South Binness, Langstone Harbour (Hampshire) the expanding colonies of other species of terns and gulls have forced the Little Terns to nest closer to the high water mark (Pickerell, 2001). Elsewhere, natural erosion (Brindley, 1995; 1996) and the encroachment of vegetation nearer to the tideline have reduced the area of suitable nesting habitat above the high-water mark (Brindley, 1998). Attempts by site managers to move the nests to safer

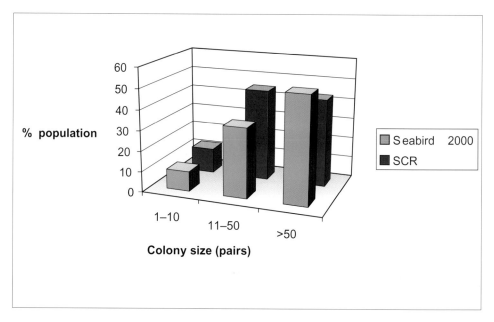

Figure 3   The proportion of the population of Little Terns in Britain and Ireland nesting in colonies of varying sizes during the SCR Census (1985–88) and Seabird 2000 (1998–2002).

At some Little Tern colonies managers use drain pipes to provide shelter for chicks (Mark Thomas)

locations have had limited success. Substantial sea-level rise predicted for the end of the 21st century, especially along the south and east coasts of England, will exacerbate the problem of nest flooding. As existing nesting sites are covered by the rising sea levels, the availability of alternative sites may by limited by the maintenance of sea defences (Norris & Buisson, 1994). Conversely, such structures, may provide new opportunities for breeding; for example if seawall remnants or beach recharge create new nesting habitat.

Little Terns readily nest on artificial islets, newly-deposited soil and on excavated areas of gravel or shell (Higgins & Davies, 1996) as demonstrated at Hayling Oysterbeds, Langstone Harbour (Hampshire) and at Hamford Water (Essex). The former site was restored in 1996 and further recharged with shingle during 2000. In 2001, 115 pairs bred on the site and fledged 179 young (Pickerell, 2002). Three sites at Hamford Water were recharged between 1998 and 1999, to protect coastal habitat. In 2000, at one site which was recharged with silt, numbers of breeding Little Terns increased 750% to 102 pairs (Woodrow, 2003). The creation and restoration of breeding habitats such as small islands is an important management tool for combating the threats from predation, disturbance and climate change, and may provide the opportunity for future conservationists to halt or even reverse the decline of the Little Tern population in Britain and Ireland.

INTERNATIONAL CONTEXT

Little Terns are widely distributed, breeding throughout the Western Palearctic, and in Asia and Australasia, mainly in coastal areas but also adjacent to inland lagoons and rivers (Cramp, 1985).

Poor monitoring in much of the species' range makes it is impossible to accurately estimate the total world breeding population. The estimate of 44,000–130,000 pairs (Table 2) is the best guess using the available data. Therefore, Britain holds 1.5–4.3% and Ireland 0.2–0.5% of the world breeding population of Little Terns.

Of the three subspecies, nominate *S. a. albifrons* breeds in Europe, North Africa, and the Middle East as far as India. The population is thought to be in the region of 34,000–59,000 pairs, although information is lacking from some parts of the range (i.e. Kazakhstan, Libya, Morocco). The subspecies *guineae* (650–1,000 pairs) occurs in West and central Africa. Least is known concerning numbers of the subspecies *sinensis*, of which 8,600–68,600 pairs breed in south and east Asia, from India to Japan, through the Phillipines and Indonesia to New Guinea and northern and eastern Australia (Wetlands International, 2002).

In Europe, the Little Tern's breeding range has contracted in the last two centuries and the population has undergone a long-term decline (Fasola *et al.*, 2002). There are 17,000–22,000 pairs of *S. a. albifrons* breeding in Europe (excluding Turkey and Russia, Table 2), of which 8.6–11.2% breed in Britain and 1.0–1.2% in Ireland. Trends since the mid-1980s in other European countries vary. Recent counts show numbers have increased in Belgium (E. M. W. Stienen, *in litt.*) and in Poland, and following long-term declines due to disturbance and habitat change, numbers have recently increased in the Netherlands (Meininger, 2002), France (Cramm & Muselet, in press) and Germany (Hälterlein *et al.*, 2000). Elsewhere in northern Europe, numbers have generally remained stable. In Italy, numbers have fallen by two-thirds to 2,000 pairs since the early 1980s, declines being especially evident in the Po Delta (Fasola *et al.*, 2002). In other Mediterranean countries the population has remained stable. In eastern Europe numbers are generally stable or decreasing. The population trend for the North African and Middle Eastern countries comprising the remainder of *albifrons* range is unknown.

Information on the population status of the *guineae* subspecies in southern Africa is unavailable. The trend for *sinensis* in south and east Asia and Australia is also poorly understood, but it is thought to be in decline. The only detailed information available is that for Australia, where the breeding population has recently been estimated at *c.*2,000 pairs (3,000 birds: Garnett & Crowley, 2000). This is an underestimate as new breeding colonies are being found in the north of the country, where the population is considered stable. The eastern population has declined in the past, although colony management has led to recent increases.

Country or region	Subspecies	Min	Max	Year	Source
Great Britain, Isle of Man and Channel Isles	albifrons	1,900	1,900	2000	Seabird 2000
All Ireland	albifrons	210	210	1995–2001	Seabird 2000
Albania	albifrons	500	1,000	1991	BirdLife International / EBCC (2000)
Belarus	albifrons	900	1,100	1990	BirdLife International / EBCC (2000)
Belgium	albifrons	224	224	2000	E. M. W. Stienen (in litt.)
Bulgaria	albifrons	200	500		BirdLife International / EBCC (2000)
Croatia	albifrons	100	150		BirdLife International / EBCC (2000)
Denmark	albifrons	464	464	2001	Grell (2002)
Estonia	albifrons	200	400	1991	BirdLife International / EBCC (2000)
Finland	albifrons	50	60	late 1980s	BirdLife International / EBCC (2000)
France	albifrons	1,717	1,831	1997	Catry *et al.* (in prep)
Germany	albifrons	870	870	1999	Halterlein *et al.* (2000)
Greece	albifrons	1,500	2,000	1988–1990	BirdLife International / EBCC (2000)
Hungary	albifrons	10	10	late 1970s–early 1980s	Thomas (1982)
Italy	albifrons	2,000	2,000	late 1990s	Fasola *et al.* (2002)
Lithuania	albifrons	100	400	1985–89	BirdLife International / EBCC (2000)
Moldova	albifrons	50	70	1988	BirdLife International / EBCC (2000)
Netherlands	albifrons	500	500	1998–2000	Meininger (2002)
Poland	albifrons	1,000	1,300		BirdLife International / EBCC (2000)
Portugal	albifrons	332	332	2000–2002	Catry *et al.* (in prep)
Romania	albifrons	300	400	1986–1992	BirdLife International / EBCC (2000)
Russia	albifrons	5,000	9,000	1984–88	BirdLife International / EBCC (2000)
Slovenia	albifrons	2	3		BirdLife International / EBCC (2000)
Spain	albifrons	2,500	3,000		BirdLife International / EBCC (2000)
Sweden	albifrons	400	600	late 1980s	BirdLife International / EBCC (2000)
Turkey	albifrons	5,000	15,000		BirdLife International / EBCC (2000)
Ukraine	albifrons	1,200	2,500		BirdLife International / EBCC (2000)
Kazakhstan[1]	albifrons	?	?		Wetlands International (2002)
Israel[1]	albifrons	250	250	1991	Wetlands International (2002)
Egypt[1]	albifrons	2,900	3,800	1990	Wetlands International (2002)
Libya[1]	albifrons	?			Wetlands International (2002)
Tunisia[1]	albifrons	800	1,000	?	Wetlands International (2002)
Algeria	albifrons	8	8	1978	Jacob & Jacob (1980)
Morocco[1]	albifrons	?			Wetlands International (2002)
Mauritania[1]	albifrons	2	2	1995	Wetlands International (2002)
Africa (west & central)[1]	guineae	650	1,000		Wetlands International (2002)
Asia (southwest)[1]	albifrons	3,300	8,300		Wetlands International (2002)
Asia (India, Sri Lanka, Myanmar, Sumatra, Java)[1]	sinensis	3,300	33,300		Wetlands International (2002)
Asia (east & southeast)[1]	sinensis	3,300	33,300		Wetlands International (2002)
Australia[2]	sinensis	2,000	2,000	2000	Garnett & Crowley (2000)

Biogeographic Region	Subspecies	Min	Max	Min % GB	Max % GB	Min % Ireland	Max % Ireland
Europe*	albifrons	17,000	22,000	8.6%	11.2%	1.0%	1.2%
World	all	44,000	130,000	1.5%	4.3%	0.2%	0.5%

* Stroud *et al.* (2001)

Notes

[1] Wetlands International (2002) provided population estimates as the number of birds. These were divided by three to estimate the number of pairs, according to WI guidelines.

[2] Garnett & Crowley (2000) estimated the Australian population as the number of birds. This was divided by 1.5 to estimate the number of pairs, according to Bullock & Gomersall (1982)

Common Guillemot *Uria aalge*

Mike P. Harris and Sarah Wanless

INTRODUCTION

The Common Guillemot is one of the most abundant seabirds in temperate and colder parts of the northern hemisphere, with very large populations in the Atlantic and the Pacific Oceans, and adjacent areas of the Arctic Ocean. In the northeast Atlantic its range extends from Portugal in the south to Spitsbergen in the north and includes the Baltic. Two subspecies, not easily separable in the field, breed in our area: the dark-mantled nominate race *aalge* occurs in most of Europe including Scotland and possibly northern England, and the smaller, much browner mantled *albionis* occurs in England, Wales, Ireland, Helgoland, France and Iberia. A bridled morph, with a striking white eye-ring and spectacle occurs in the Atlantic but not in the Pacific. The frequency of this morph increases with latitude from less than 1% in southern Britain and southern Ireland to 20–25% in Shetland and is a classic example of a stable ratio-cline polymorphism (Birkhead, 1984).

Common Guillemots feed on a variety of small pelagic shoaling fish, especially lesser sandeels, sprat and members of the family Gadidae, which they catch by underwater pursuit after diving from the surface. Guillemots feed mainly just offshore and are numerous around Britain and Ireland throughout the year. It is a dispersive rather than a migratory species with many adults remaining within a few hundred kilometres of the colonies throughout the year, and at some colonies adults continue to visit their nest sites in late autumn/winter once they have completed the main (post-breeding) moult of the year, during which they are flightless (Harris & Wanless, 1990a; Harris & Swann, 2002b). Most Common Guillemots do not breed until they are 5–6 years old and during immaturity individuals move substantially further from their natal colonies than adults and may visit several colonies during a single summer (Halley & Harris, 1993; Harris *et al.*, 1994). Numbers in Britain and Ireland have increased substantially during the last 30 years, and the increase continued up to Seabird 2000, albeit at a reduced rate.

Common Guillemots breed at most places around the coasts of Britain and Ireland where there is suitable cliff habitat. However, as with many other seabirds, the main concentrations are in the north and west (Fig. 1). Guillemots are extremely gregarious, colonial breeding is the norm and colonies can contain many tens of thousands of individuals. Breeding areas are situated in areas safe from mammalian predators such as foxes, feral cats, and mink. In mainland areas this means that they are confined to sheer cliffs or among boulders at the bases of cliffs where access is difficult even from the sea. On islands, cliffs and the tops of large stacks are preferred, but where such habitat is absent guillemots breed among rocks or even on flat open ground. No nest is built, the single relatively large egg being incubated on the bare rock, guano or soil. A wide variety of breeding sites is utilised, including large flat, broad ledges, where birds are crowded together at average densities of about 20 pairs/m^2, narrow ledges, isolated sites that are little more than toeholds, grassy banks, on top of, or under, boulders and elsewhere, even under bushes (Harris & Birkhead, 1985). Breeding success is highest where birds breed at high density or where sites are well protected from Common Ravens, gulls and other avian predators (Birkhead, 1977; Harris *et al.*, 1997).

CENSUS METHODS

Colonies are usually very conspicuous and are therefore easily found. The locations of most are well known so coverage for this species is likely to have been extremely high. With the exception of Aughris Head (Co. Sligo), which held 1,012 birds in 1985–88, only the very smallest and most isolated, for instance Rockall 300 km west of St Kilda where a single pair bred in 1992 (Belaoussoff, 1993), and those that have just been established will have not been visited during Seabird 2000.

A large colony of cliff-nesting seabirds is an awe-inspiring and noisy place. In Britain and Ireland, Common Guillemots often breed in association with Black-legged Kittiwakes, Razorbills and Northern Fulmars. The size and scale of some colonies can be intimidating to the counter, but most nesting areas can be viewed from comfortable and safe cliff-top vantage points. Few colonies can be counted from below the cliff as birds breeding towards the rear of ledges are often hidden from view. The normal counting method is to divide a cliff-face into manageable sections using prominent cracks and other physical features, make a diagram of the area and then count each section systematically. Birds on tidal rocks and those on the sea are excluded. Counting from the sea is difficult and often very uncomfortable for those not used to small boats; as a result, counts of large colonies from the sea can be subject to significant error and should only be made in good conditions and when there is no reasonable alternative counting method. Colonies where birds breed out of sight in caves or under boulders pose particular problems and estimates usually have to be based on brief visits to the colony to count eggs and chicks.

The census unit for the Common Guillemot is the individual bird. Some previous estimates were solely based on counts of birds thought to be incubating eggs or brooding chicks (Gibson, 1950), but this technique is unreliable for large-scale censuses. It is impossible to know for some counts made prior to Operation Seafarer whether apparently incubating/brooding birds or all individuals were counted, which reduces their usefulness (Lloyd *et al.*, 1991). When reporting the result of any count, the units involved must be unambiguously stated.

Counts of individuals comprise birds with eggs or chicks, their mates, failed breeders and immatures. Although an egg or chick is rarely left unattended, since there is serious risk of either being predated, there is considerable daily, annual and seasonal variation in attendance by other birds. Conveniently, it is well established that numbers are relatively stable in the middle part of the day during late incubation and the main chick-rearing periods, even in the Arctic in continuous daylight (Lloyd, 1975; Richardson *et al.*, 1981; Harris *et al.*, 1983; Barrett, 2001). In some colonies, but not all, the numbers of birds present are depressed during or immediately after heavy rain or strong winds, so counts are normally not made in bad weather. The timing of breeding is fairly consistent among colonies in Britain and Ireland, thus during Seabird 2000 observers were requested to make counts between 08.00 and 16.00 BST between 1 and 21 June, on days when the wind was not stronger than Beaufort force 4 and not during heavy or continuous rain. About 43% of the Seabird 2000 counts were conducted during the prescribed conditions, a further 25% were counted within the recommended dates but either outwith the recommended times or gave no time. Most of the remainder came from counts made, often for understandable logistical reasons, in late June or early July. Such late counts will have substantially underestimated colony size since by then many of the successful males will have taken their chicks to sea, leaving the females to attend the nest site. In addition, the numbers of non-breeders visiting the ledges will also have declined considerably (Harris *et al.*, 1986; Halley *et al.*, 1995). This problem was particularly acute in Caithness where 75% of the total Seabird 2000 count came from parts of the coast counted late in the season. Numbers there will have been substantially higher than the count of over 225,000 individuals suggested. During the SCR Census (1985–88) the proportion of counts within the optimum dates was 42%, and date was not recorded in 11%. The time of counts was not routinely recorded during the SCR Census. Therefore, there was a considerable imprecision in the calculation of rates of change between the two censuses. However, the general findings are supported by systematic standardised counts made annually at 15–20 colonies dispersed throughout Britain (Mavor *et al.*, 2002).

All counts relating to Seabird 2000 refer to individuals counted at colonies. Counts of birds can, if required, be converted into an approximate estimate of the number of pairs by multiplying by a correction factor 0.67 to allow for the presence of mates and non-breeders. This factor has been shown to be generally applicable in Britain (Harris, 1989), but there will inevitably be differences between years and between colonies depending on local feeding conditions and whether the population is increasing or declining. British and Irish totals have been converted to pairs for comparison with counts from other countries that are almost always expressed as pairs or breeding adults.

CURRENT STATUS AND TRENDS

During Seabird 2000 a total of 1,559,484 individual Common Guillemots was counted (Table 1). This is equivalent to about one million pairs, making it the most numerous seabird in both Britain and Ireland. The majority (75%) was in Scotland with 15% in Ireland, 6% in England, the Isle of Man and the Channel Islands, and 4% in Wales.

Within Scotland the largest concentrations were in Caithness, Orkney, Shetland, Sutherland and the Western Isles. By far the largest colony, of 112,676 individuals, was on the vast red cliffs of Handa (northwest Sutherland). The next three largest colonies were of 95,117 individuals on Rathlin Island (Co. Antrim), 79,071 on the mainland cliffs at Berriedale (east Caithness) and 60,754 on Lambay

Table 1 Numbers of Common Guillemots in Britain and Ireland 1969–2002.

Administrative area or country	Operation Seafarer (1969–70)	SCR Census (1985–88)[1]	Seabird 2000 (1998–2002)	Percentage change since Seafarer	Percentage change since SCR	Annual percentage change since SCR
Shetland	76,155	151,110	172,681	127%	14%	1.0%
Orkney	127,015	198,776	181,026	43%	−9%	−0.7%
North coast Caithness		22,348	30,959		39%	2.5%
East coast Caithness		124,405	195,295		57%	3.5%
Caithness total	*63,096*	*146,753*	*226,254*		*54%*	*3.4%*
Northwest coast Sutherland		115,703	161,858		40%	2.7%
Sutherland total	*50,212*	*115,703*	*161,858*	*222%*	*40%*	*2.7%*
East coast Ross & Cromarty		933	1,944		108%	5.0%
Ross & Cromarty total	*750*	*933*	*1,944*	*159%*	*108%*	*5.0%*
Banff & Buchan	17,192	23,992	73,970	330%	208%	7.8%
Gordon	2,488	3,829	3,345	34%	−13%	−0.9%
City of Aberdeen		12	395		3192%	30.9%
Kincardine & Deeside	49,412	57,723	72,179	46%	25%	1.7%
Angus	178	1,808	1,002	463%	−45%	−4.3%
Northeast Fife	9,008	18,387	28,103	212%	53%	2.7%
Kirkcaldy		49	48		−2%	−0.2%
East Lothian	1,217	5,601	8,266	579%	48%	3.2%
Berwickshire	7,221	25,585	44,636	518%	74%	4.5%
Stewartry	399	650	335	−16%	−48%	−5.0%
Wigtown	2,503	4,646	3,931	57%	−15%	−1.2%
Kyle & Carrick	6,234	4,988	9,415	51%	89%	4.7%
Argyll & Bute	4,056	23,289	42,697	953%	83%	4.6%
Lochaber	2,159	11,117	8,692	303%	−22%	−1.7%
Skye & Lochalsh	543	3,800	6,470	1092%	70%	4.3%
Western Isles–Comhairle nan eilean	99,623	144,347	120,594	21%	−16%	−1.5%
Scotland Total	**519,461**	**943,098**	**1,167,841**	**125%**	**24%**	**1.6%**
Northumberland	4,381	17,776	31,542	620%	77%	3.9%
North Yorkshire	23	914	530	2204%	−42%	−3.6%
Humberside	17,963	32,288	46,625	160%	44%	2.9%
Isle of Wight	97	95	337	247%	255%	8.3%
Dorset	550	831	954	73%	15%	1.0%
Channel Islands	201	345	476	137%	38%	2.6%
Cornwall	449	1,019	1426	218%	40%	2.5%
Isles of Scilly	90	148	196	118%	32%	2.4%
Devon	2,473	3,091	3,926	59%	27%	1.8%
Cumbria	3,884	4,908	6,450	66%	31%	2.1%
Isle of Man	1,050	2,195	4,566	335%	108%	5.7%
England Total	**31,161**	**63,610**	**97,028**	**211%**	**53%**	**3.1%**
West Glamorgan	140	85	190	36%	124%	5.5%
Dyfed	9,370	16,772	35,912	283%	114%	5.7%
Gwynedd	7,728	15,269	21,859	183%	43%	2.6%
Wales Total	**17,238**	**32,126**	**57,961**	**236%**	**80%**	**4.4%**
Great Britain, Isle of Man and Channel Islands Total	**567,860**	**1,038,834**	**1,322,830**	**133%**	**27%**	**1.8%**
Co. Antrim	33,234	45,047	98,546	197%	119%	6.0%
Co. Dublin	11,438	46,384	63,837	458%	38%	2.5%
Co. Wicklow		83	706		751%	18.0%
Co. Wexford	9,729	16,544	21,436	120%	30%	1.9%
Co. Waterford	1,104	1,246	1,055	−4%	−15%	−1.2%
Co. Cork	6,075	4,745	3,763	−38%	−21%	−1.6%
Co. Kerry	5,951	4,341	7,406	24%	71%	4.3%
Co. Clare	8,526	16,967	24,962	193%	47%	3.0%
Co. Galway[2]	1,644		3,444	109%		
Co. Mayo	2,211	978	3,830	73%	292%	11.3%
Co. Sligo[3]	2,985	1,012				
Co. Donegal	1,418	6,610	7,669	441%	16%	1.2%
All-Ireland Total	**84,315**	**143,957**	**236,654**	**181%**	**64%**	**4.7%**
Britain and Ireland Total	**652,175**	**1,182,791**	**1,559,484**	**139%**	**32%**	**2.2%**

Notes

[1] Figures for the SCR are actual counts and do not include adjustments made in order to account for unsurveyed colonies (see Lloyd *et al.*, 1991)

[2] Inishmore, Aran Isles not counted in 1985–88 (1,238 individuals in 1990)

[3] Aughris Head not counted during Seabird 2000

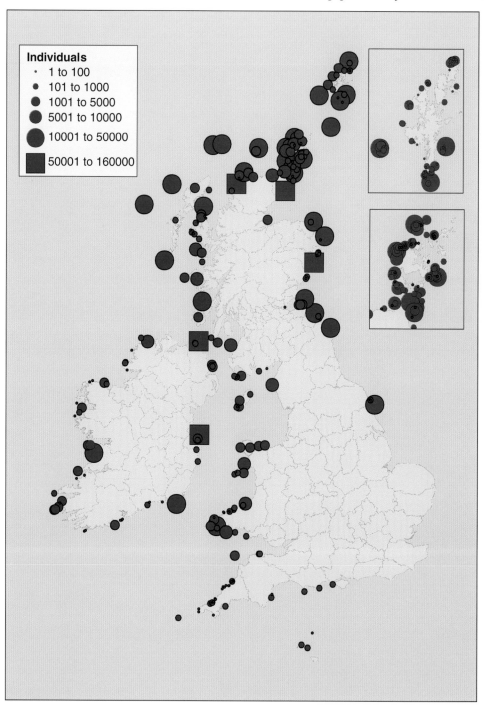

Figure 1   Abundance and distribution of Common Guillemots in Britain and Ireland 1998–2002.

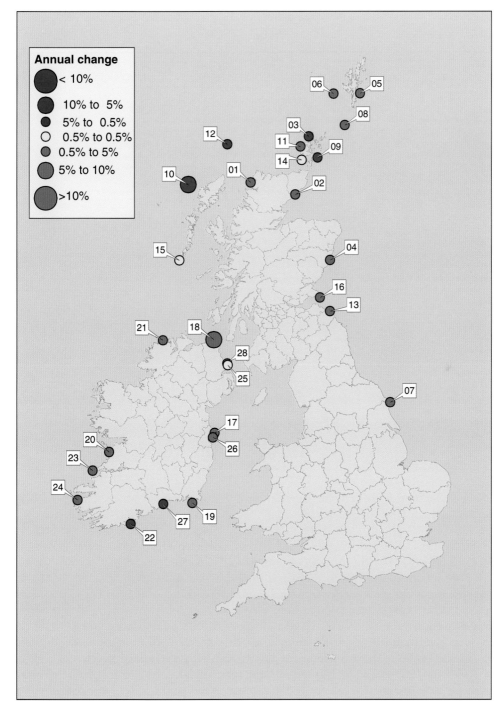

Figure 2   Changes in the number of Common Guillemots at major sites in Britain and Ireland between the SCR census (1985–88) and Seabird 2000 (1998–2002). Major sites are those that contained the top 50% of the British population or the top 95% of the Irish population during the SCR census. Numbers correspond to colonies listed in Table 2.

Table 2   *Changes in the number of Common Guillemots at major sites in Britain and Ireland between SCR Census (1985–88) and Seabird 2000 (1998–2002). Major sites are those that contained the top 50% of the British population or the top 95% of the Irish population during the SCR census. ID corresponds to the colony symbols in Fig. 2.*

ID	Colony	SCR Census (1985–88)	Seabird 2000 (1998–2002)	Percentage change since SCR	Annual percentage change since SCR	Percentage of population in Britain or Ireland 1998–2002
1	Handa	98,686	112,676	14%	1.2%	8.5%
2	Berriedale Cliffs SSSI	69,176	79,071	14%	1.0%	6.0%
3	West Westray (SSSI)	60,742	54,718	−10%	−0.9%	4.1%
4	Fowlsheugh (SSSI)	52,355	61,420	17%	1.2%	4.7%
5	Noss	37,680	45,777	21%	1.4%	3.5%
6	Foula	37,500	41,435	10%	0.8%	3.1%
7	Bempton Cliffs (incl. N. Flamborough Head)	32,578	46,685	43%	2.8%	3.5%
8	Fair Isle	32,437	39,257	21%	1.6%	3.0%
9	Copinsay	29,448	20,045	−32%	−2.9%	1.5%
10	Flannan Isles	26,733	14,638	−45%	−5.9%	1.1%
11	Marwick Head (SSSI)	26,350	34,679	32%	2.1%	2.6%
12	Sula Sgeir	25,382	20,877	−18%	−1.6%	1.6%
13	St Abb's Head to Fast Castle Head (SSSI)	25,187	43,744	74%	4.5%	3.3%
14	Hoy and South Walls	20,819	21,777	5%	0.3%	1.7%
15	Berneray	19,881	19,083	−4%	−0.3%	1.4%
16	Isle of May	18,387	28,103	53%	2.7%	2.1%
17	Lambay Island	44,495	60,754	37%	2.6%	25.7%
18	Rathlin Island	41,887	95,117	127%	6.1%	40.2%
19	Great Saltee	16,329	21,436	31%	2.1%	9.1%
20	Cliffs of Moher	12,957	19,962	54%	4.0%	8.4%
21	Horn Head	4,806	6,548	36%	2.6%	2.8%
22	Old Head of Kinsale	4,179	3,610	−14%	−1.0%	1.5%
23	Loop Head	4,010	5,000	25%	1.5%	2.1%
24	Doulus Head	3,497	4,253	22%	1.6%	1.8%
25	Gobbins	1,540	1,484	−4%	−0.3%	0.6%
26	Ireland's Eye	1,458	2,191	50%	3.2%	0.9%
27	Helvick Head	1,132	990	−13%	−1.0%	0.4%
28	Muck Island	1,039	1,321	27%	1.6%	0.6%

Island (Co. Dublin). The largest English and Welsh colonies were 46,685 at Bempton Cliffs/Flamborough Head (Humberside) and 13,852 on Skomer Island (Dyfed), respectively.

Overall, the total population of Britain and Ireland increased by 32% since the SCR Census (1985–88), a markedly smaller increase than recorded between Operation Seafarer (1969–70) and the SCR Census (81%). The increase in numbers of Guillemots between the SCR Census and Seabird 2000 was greatest in Wales (80%) and Ireland (64%) and least in Scotland (24%), with an intermediate rise in England, the Isle of Man and the Channel Islands (53%). The rate of increase in Britain and Ireland has gradually slowed from 4–5% per annum between 1969–70 and 1985–88 to 2.0% subsequently (Stowe & Harris, 1984; Rothery *et al.*, 1988; Lloyd *et al.*, 1991).

Increases were recorded at most Common Guillemot colonies during Seabird 2000 and the ranking in size of the 27 largest colonies in Britain and Ireland remained largely unchanged since the SCR Census (1985–88; Table 2, Spearman rank correlation $r_{s,27} = 0.94$, $P < 0.001$). Three of the largest major colonies appeared to have declined in size by more than 10% (Table 2, Fig. 2), with the most marked decrease of 45% on the Flannan Isles (Western Isles). To the northwest, on Sula Sgeir, numbers were down 18%. Both sites were counted from the sea during Seabird 2000. However, numbers were also down at several other substantial colonies in the Western Isles, e.g. North Rona (decrease of 40%) and the Shiant Isles (10%), suggesting that in marked contrast to almost everywhere else in Britain and Ireland, numbers of Common Guillemots in the Western Isles were declining (Table 1). In Orkney numbers were down by 32% on Copinsay. This appears to have been a real decline, probably occurring between 1986 and 1994 (E. R. Meek, pers. comm.). The largest recorded increase was on Rathlin Island (Co. Antrim), where numbers had more than doubled. However, differences in counting methods used by Seabird 2000 and the SCR Census made it difficult to be certain about the magnitude of this change. Thus, the former took only two days, was completely land-based and may have been an underestimate (L. McFaul, pers. comm.) whilst the latter took 19 days and included counts made from the sea.

The highest per capita increases were recorded at the smallest colonies, and colony size (log-transformed) explained 14% of the variation in the mean annual rates of increase for 52 colonies where the SCR Census and Seabird 2000 counts covered exactly the same areas (Fig. 3). Similar negative relationships between rates of increase and colony size, suggesting density-dependent population growth, have previously been noted for Black-legged Kittiwake, Herring Gull and Northern Gannet (Coulson, 1983; Raven & Coulson, 1997; Moss *et al.*, 2002). The average rate of increase at these guillemot colonies was also significantly related to latitude, with the southern colonies increasing at a significantly faster rate than northern ones ($r^2 = 17\%$). However, larger colonies tended to be in the north, and smaller ones in the south, so that colony size and latitude were highly correlated ($r = 0.59$, $P < 0.001$), making it difficult to decouple the effects of latitude and colony size on the rate of increase.

Although the general pattern of increase was clear, the rate of population growth was not always linear. For instance, numbers on the Isle of May declined during the mid and late 1980s before increasing again from 1990 (Fig. 4). Similarly, annual counts at sample plots in Shetland declined each year between 1986 and 90, since when there has been a gradual recovery (Heubeck, 2000). Repeated counts of a series of colonies (plotted on a log scale in Fig. 4 so that a constant rate of increase would be represented by a straight line) confirm that the rate of increase is slowing down.

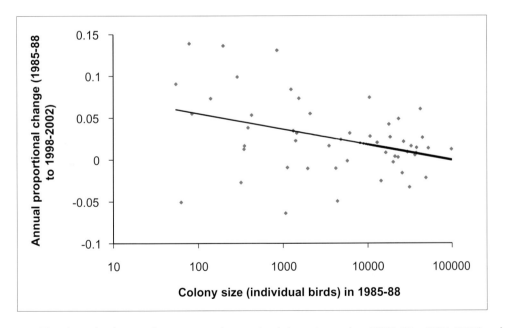

Figure 3   The relationship between the mean annual proportional change in numbers (1985–88 to 1999–2002) and colony size in 1985–88 (individual birds, log-scale) at 51 Common Guillemot colonies. The decline in rate with increasing size was highly significant ($y = -0.0081Ln(x) + 0.092$, $r^2 = 0.14$, $P < 0.001$)

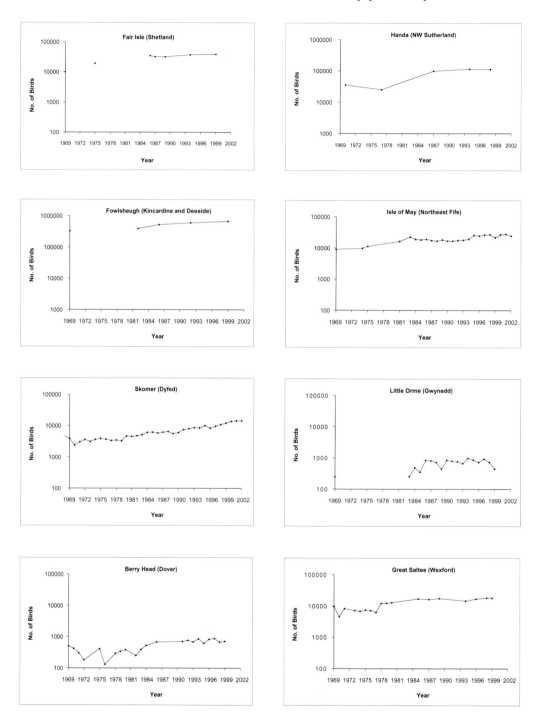

Figure 4   Numbers of Common Guillemots at colonies in Britain and Ireland where repeated counts were conducted 1968–2002 (data from Seabird Colony Register Database, JNCC/Seabird Group, Aberdeen). Note: counts are plotted on a log-scale.

Common Guillemots on a crowded breeding ledge on the Isle of May (NE Fife) illustrate the difficulties in counting individuals and of separating breeders from non-breeders (Ian Mitchell)

CAUSES OF CHANGE

Few reliable counts of Common Guillemots in Britain and Ireland were available prior to Operation Seafarer in 1969–70, but Cramp *et al.* (1974) considered that numbers at the southern, mostly small, colonies had probably declined considerably during the previous 30 years. In contrast, some northern Scottish colonies were markedly larger than had been previously thought. Since Operation Seafarer, numbers have increased substantially but the rate of increase now appears to be slowing. We have no strong evidence as to what factor allowed the population to increase in the first place; perhaps there had been some oceanographic change or the intensity of man's fishing had resulted in an increase in the numbers of small fish that guillemots eat (Furness, 1984; Evans & Nettleship, 1985). The slowing down in the rate of increase apparent in the results of Seabird 2000 is consistent with density dependent population growth but the mechanisms involved are unclear.

In general, breeding success of Common Guillemots at colonies in Britain and Ireland has remained consistently high over the last 15 years (Mavor *et al.* 2002) and major breeding failures have been associated with stochastic events such as heavy seas washing eggs or chicks off ledges (Heubeck, 1999).

A wide range of factors are known to affect the survival of adult and immature Common Guillemots (Evans & Nettleship, 1985). The shooting of adults and drowning of birds in fishing nets set close to colonies have had serious adverse effects on numbers in California and Norway (Barrett & Golovkin, 2000; Carter *et al.*, 2001). Drift-nets, often illegally set inshore for salmon off west and north Ireland in the 1970s and 1980s, drowned many auks and may have been responsible for the decrease in auks at some local colonies (Whilde, 1979; Lloyd *et al.*, 1991). Bag nets set for salmon near colonies in northeast Scotland also caught Common Guillemots, although the extent of mortality amongst adults was thought not to be sufficient to affect local breeding numbers (Murray *et al.*, 1994). Survival of adult Common Guillemots in Scotland and Wales appears to have remained high for the last 15–20 years (Harris *et al.*, 2000; T. R. Birkhead, pers. comm; pers. obs.). However, there are as yet few useful data on the survival of young birds from the time that they leave the colony to the age of first breeding.

Away from the colonies, Common Guillemots are unusually susceptible to a wide range of disasters, both man-induced and natural. The large numbers that die during oiling incidents, and the images of dying auks on beaches, mean that the names of the ships involved in these events are etched on the memories of both birdwatchers and the general public: *Torrey Canyon* (1967), *Amoco Cadiz* (1978), *Christos Bitas* (1978), *Braer* (1993), *Sea Empress* (1996), *Erika* (1999) and *Prestige* (2002). Many, perhaps even more, guillemots die each year due to chronic oiling resulting from minor, often unreported, spillages and the illegal discharges of fuel oil residues by shipping. Large numbers of British auks have also been drowned in fishing nets, for instance in the Kattegat during the 1980s, but, in contrast, the number of auks shot in Scandinavia is now much lower than during the 1960s and 1970s (Heubeck *et al.*, 1991).

Natural 'wrecks' of Common Guillemots, when large numbers of birds die in a restricted area over a short time period, occur sporadically throughout the range, typically following unusually windy weather or periods when food appears to have been difficult to find (Bailey & Davenport, 1972; Bourne, 1976; Mudge *et al.*, 1992; Harris & Wanless, 1996). The most thoroughly investigated wreck was that in September–October 1969, when *c.*15,000 dead Common Guillemots were washed ashore around the Irish Sea and Firth of Clyde. These birds were *c.*40% underweight, and anecdotal accounts suggested that they had been unable to find food. However, chemical analyses indicated very high levels of toxic chemicals such as PCBs, DDE and dieldrin in their livers. These chemicals normally concentrate in fat reserves and it is possible that they had entered the blood when the birds had been forced to metabolise virtually all their fat, resulting in death (Holdgate, 1971; Parslow & Jefferies, 1973). These findings led to concern about the discharge of PCBs into the sea and the initiation of long-term population studies of auks in Britain.

Serious and prolonged exposure to oiling can result in the decimation or even extinction of auk populations, such as occurred in southern Britain following the Second World War and around San Francisco in the early-20th century (Fisher & Lockley, 1954; Carter *et al.*, 2001). The very large numbers of Common Guillemots killed in some of these disasters have sometimes been followed by short-term declines in nearby colonies, e.g. at Berry Head (Devon), Skomer (Dyfed) and Great Saltee (Co. Wexford), following the 1969 Irish Sea wreck (Fig. 4), and at Pembrokeshire colonies in 1996 after the *Sea Empress* incident. However, major oiling incidents, even of the size of the *Erika* oil spill off Brittany in 1999/2000, when possibly more than 120,000 guillemots died, and wrecks have had remarkably few detectable long-term effects on the numbers of Common Guillemots in Britain and Ireland (Heubeck, in press). Of course, numbers may have increased even faster during the last 30 years without such events.

Several aspects of the Common Guillemot's biology buffer the population from the worst effects of a disaster. First, breeding success is generally high. Second, birds do not breed until on average six years old, and during the period between leaving the colony as flightless chicks and first breeding, they disperse widely so that only a very widespread event will remove the majority of immatures. Third, at least some birds are sexually mature from their third year (Harris *et al.*, 1994), and (presumably) these would breed at a younger age than normal if many experienced breeders were killed. Many but not all wrecks have recorded a high proportion of immatures among birds found dead (Anker-Nilssen *et al.*, 1988; Heubeck *et al.*, 1992; Mudge *et al.*, 1992), presumably because young birds are less experienced than adults in dealing with adverse conditions. Young birds also outnumber adults caught in fishing gear (Anker-Nilssen & Lorentsen, 1995). The situation with oiling is less clear, although some incidents have also recorded rather few adults, e.g. 16% in the large oiling in the Skagerrak in 1981 (Anker-Nilssen *et al.*, 1988).

Currently, the Common Guillemot population in Britain and Ireland is about one million pairs and each year these produce about 800,000 young (an average of 0.80 young per pair). The mortality of breeding adults is *c.*5% per annum (Harris *et al.*, 2000), so 102,000 recruits are needed to replace expected normal losses from two million breeding adults and to sustain the current 2% annual increase in numbers. Therefore, each year, 698,000 immature guillemots will die, so it is no surprise that so many dead guillemots are found on beaches. It is unclear whether the deaths resulting from wrecks and other disasters are additive to the normal mortality. Unless there is a very major loss of adults, for example due to an oiling incident near a colony during the breeding season, or a truly catastrophic mortality of immatures, we are unlikely to detect an effect on breeding numbers by censuses every 10–15 years. In order to detect an annual decline in excess of 20% at a colony with *c.*95% certainty, five repeat counts of birds in five plots (each containing at least 200 birds) must be made each year between 1 and 20 June; to detect a change of 15%, ten counts per year are needed (Rothery *et al.*, 1988). This level of monitoring occurs at few colonies (Mavor *et al.*, 2002).

There are currently two other potential threats to Common Guillemots and other seabirds. The first of these is the industrial fishery for sandeels on which many top marine predators depend. Catches of these fish around Britain and Ireland increased during the 1970s and 1980s, and the fishery in the North Sea is currently the largest single-species fishery in the area with annual catches approaching one million tonnes (ICES, 1997). Sandeels are an important source of food for Common Guillemots during the breeding season. In general, Common Guillemots do not appear to be as sensitive to changes in sandeel availability as some of the surface-feeders such as Black-legged Kittiwakes and terns, and at least in some areas, can exploit alternative prey such as sprat and small herring (Furness & Tasker, 2000). However, an increasing number of studies are demonstrating that reductions in prey availability do have a negative impact on Common Guillemot breeding performance. For example, intensive work in Shetland during the sandeel crisis in the early 1990s, showed that Common Guillemots substantially increased their feeding effort when sandeel abundance was low (Monaghan *et al.*, 1994). On the Isle of May, breeding success was positively correlated with the catch per unit effort of boats fishing commercially for sandeels on the nearby Wee Bankie fishing grounds (Rindorf *et al.*, 2000). Common Guillemot numbers on Bear Island and in northern Norway crashed when stocks of capelin, another small oily fish targeted by both seabirds and a large industrial fishery, declined (Barrett & Golovkin, 2000).

The second potential threat to Common Guillemots is climate change, which is predicted to increase summer storms at mid to high latitudes in the northern hemisphere (Overpeck *et al.*, 1987; Mitchell & Ericksen, 1992). Stormy weather can increase the probability of eggs and chicks being washed off the breeding ledges (Heubeck, 1999). However, it can also have more subtle effects, resulting in poorer quality prey being brought for the chicks and increased diving effort by the parents (Finney *et al.*, 1999). Clearly, such changes have the potential to reduce breeding success and more work needs to be carried out on this topic.

After Operation Seafarer, Cramp *et al.* (1974) considered that the recent decline in numbers of the Common Guillemot gave cause for concern. Since then the population has increased by a factor of 2.5 and, although the rate of increase is now slowing down, there is at present no obvious threat to the well-being of this species in Britain and Ireland. One interpretation of the slowing of the rate of increase is that density-dependence, perhaps reducing the survival of immatures, is beginning to be seen, i.e. there may just not be room or food resources to support many more. Nevertheless, we must continue to monitor the numbers, survival and breeding of these important populations so as to be able to detect changes in the marine environment be they due to climate change, over-fishing or pollution.

INTERNATIONAL CONTEXT

The problems of censusing seabirds in Britain and Ireland pale into insignificance when compared to those encountered elsewhere in the range of the Common Guillemot. Assessments have now been made of the status of Common Guillemots in most areas but, as in Britain, the actual figures must be treated with caution.

The other main concentration of Common Guillemots in the northeast Atlantic is in Iceland where 990,000 pairs were estimated in 1983–85 and numbers at two colonies have subsequently increased (Gardarsson, 1995). The Faeroes had 175,000 pairs in 1987 (B. Olsen in Skov *et al.*, 2002); monitoring at one colony indicated a decline during the 1980s but a subsequent increase since 1990 (Gaard *et al.*, 2002).

In 1995 there were 100,000 pairs on Bear Island. This was a partial recovery following a dramatic decline, from 245,000 pairs in 1986 to 36,000 pairs in 1987, associated with a collapse of capelin stocks in the Barents Sea. This collapse resulted from oceanographic change and probable over-fishing (Krasnov & Barrett, 1995; Barrett & Golovkin, 2000). At the extreme north of the range, about 200 individuals were counted among Brünnich's Guillemots at three colonies in Spitsbergen in 1986, but none was seen at two of these during subsequent surveys (Barrett & Golovkin, 2000). The entire Greenland population probably did not exceed 3,000 individuals in the early 1990s (Lyngs, 2003). Norway is currently thought to hold 20,000–25,000 individuals following a dramatic decline during the last 50 years as a result of drowning in fishing gear, hunting and food shortages. There are signs of recovery in Norwegian colonies east of the North Cape, but those further west are approaching extinction, with perhaps too few pairs remaining for them to be viable (Krasnov & Barrett, 1995; van Franeker *et al.*, 1998; Barrett & Golovkin, 2000; Lorentsen, 2001). Around 20,000–30,000 pairs breed in northwest Russia, and fewer than 1,000 pairs were estimated on Jan Mayen in 1983 (van Franeker *et al.*, 1998; Barrett & Golovkin, 2000). The Baltic population has increased steadily over the last 100 years and is currently estimated at 15,000 pairs (Olsson *et al.*, 2000).

As well as England, Wales, Ireland and the Channel Islands, the race *albionis* breeds in Europe from Germany south. The single German colony, on Helgoland, has increased for several decades to 2,500 pairs in 2001 (Dierschke *et al.*, 2002). In contrast, numbers in France declined from several thousand pairs in the 1940s to about 250 pairs in 1977–78 and have subsequently remained at this level (Monnat & Cadiou, in press). The Iberian population similarly declined from 20,000 birds in the 1950s to fewer than 100 individuals in three colonies in the late 1990s, due to oiling, direct persecution, disturbance and drowning in fishing nets (Nettleship & Evans, 1985; Mouriño *et al.*, in press). Oil spilled from the wreck of the *Prestige* off northwest Spain in November 2002 killed most of the few remaining individuals and in 2003 only 2–4 pairs were present at the last remaining colony (Garcia *et al.*, 2003). Combining all available counts suggests a total population of about 200,000 pairs of *albionis*, with 99% being in Britain and Ireland.

The total population of Common Guillemots in Europe and Russia appears to be about 2.3 million pairs and there are a further 500,000 pairs in the northwest Atlantic, including 340,000 pairs on Funk Island (G. J. Robertson, Canadian Wildlife Service, unpubl.). Britain and Ireland therefore respectively hold around 31% and 5% of the biogeographic population of the North Atlantic (as defined by Stroud *et al.*, 2001).

Estimates for the Pacific vary from 3,000,000–5,000,000 pairs (Gaston & Jones, 1998; Carter *et al.*, 2001). Combining all these somewhat speculative totals suggests a world population of *c.*7,300,000 pairs, with 12% of these in Britain and 2% in Ireland.

Table 3 International context.

Country or region	Subspecies	Number of pairs		Year	Source
		Min	Max		
Great Britain, Isle of Man and Channel Isles[1]	*aalge & albionis*	890,000	890,000	1998–2002	Seabird 2000
All Ireland[1]	*aalge & albionis*	160,000	160,000	1999–2002	Seabird 2000
Sweden	*aalge*	12,500	15,000	2000	Olsson (2000). P. Lyngs (pers. comm)
Denmark	*aalge*	2,500		2000	Olsson (2000). P. Lyngs (pers. comm)
Finland	*aalge*	50		2000	Olsson (2000). P. Lyngs (pers. comm)
Faeroes	*aalge*	175,000	175,000	1987	B. Olssen in Skov *et al.* (2002)
France	*albionis*	250	250	2000	Monnat & Cadiou (in press)
Germany	*albionis*	2,500	2,500	2001	Dierschke *et al.* (2002)
Spain	*albionis*	10	10	2001	Mouriño *et al.* (in press)
Portugal	*albionis*	25	25	1995	L. Morais in Mourino *et al.* (in press)
Iceland	*aalge*	990,000	990,000	1983–85	Gardarsson (1995)
Norway	*aalge*	10,000	12,500	2002	Barrett & Golovkin (2000); Lorentsen (2001)
Norway (Bear Island)	*aalge*	100,000	100,000	1995	Barrett & Golovkin (2000)
Norway (Jan Mayen)	*aalge*	500	1,000	1983	van Franeker *et al.* (1998)
Norway (Spitzbergen)	*aalge*	100	100	1986	Barrett & Golovkin (2000)
Russia	*aalge*	20,000	30,000	1960–76	Barrett & Golovkin (2000)
Greenland	*aalge*	2,000	2,000	early 1990s	Lyngs (2003)
Canada	*aalge*	500,000	500,000	1998	G.J. Robertson/Canadian Wildlife Servive
Pacific (incl. eastern Russia, USA (Alaska), Canada (west), Japan)	*aalge*	4,500,000	4,500,000		Carter *et al.* (2000); Gaston & Jones (1998)

Biogeographic region		Min	Max	Min % GB	Max % GB	Min % Ireland	Max % Ireland
N Atlantic*	all	2,800,000	2,900,000	30.7%	31.8%	5.5%	5.7%
World	all	7,300,000	7,400,000	12.0%	12.2%	2.1%	2.2%

* Stroud *et al.* (2001)

Note

[1] Counts of birds at British and Irish colonies have been multiplied by 0.67 to estimate pairs. (For elsewhere, published counts of breeding adults have been divided by two to estimate pairs.)

Razorbill *Alca torda*

Oscar J. Merne & P. Ian Mitchell

INTRODUCTION

The Razorbill is a bird of the temperate North Atlantic and adjacent parts of the Arctic Ocean. They breed on both sides of the Atlantic and in the east they breed as far south as Brittany (France), north to Svalbard and east to the White Sea in northwest Russia. Razorbills breeding in Britain and Ireland winter along the Atlantic coast of Europe, from southwest Norway to Iberia, and North Africa and into the western Mediterranean. Immature Razorbills move significantly further from their natal colonies than do adults and generally further south, though occasionally they stray west as far as Greenland and the Azores (Merne, 2002).

Razorbills are difficult to census (see below) and prior to Operation Seafarer (1969–70), very little was known concerning their numbers and population trends in Britain and Ireland (Cramp *et al.*, 1974). Between 1900 and 1969, 32 Razorbill colonies were repeatedly surveyed and at most of these numbers declined or remained stable (Cramp *et al.*, 1974). Interpreting differences between counts of Razorbills conducted during Operation Seafarer (1969–70) and the SCR Census (1985–88) was difficult, since most counts in Operation Seafarer were expressed as pairs, whilst the SCR Census counted the number of birds attending the colonies (on land). Despite methodological differences between the two censuses, in 1969–1988, there appeared to be an increase in the total number of

Razorbills breeding in Britain and Ireland (Lloyd *et al.*, 1991). In Shetland, where individual birds were counted in both censuses, numbers of Razorbills doubled between 1969 and 1988. During the same period, there was a three-fold increase in numbers at Bempton Cliffs (Humberside), the largest colony in eastern England. Numbers appeared more stable in southern England, but declined substantially on the Isles of Scilly. In Wales, numbers at most colonies in 1985–88 had remained stable or declined slightly since 1969–70. The increase in numbers throughout most of Britain between Operation Seafarer and the SCR Census may have been enhanced by a coincident reduction in the numbers of Razorbills (and other auks) that were shot for food and sport (Lloyd *et al.*, 1991). Shooting in Norway and Denmark was an important cause of overwinter mortality for British and Irish breeding Razorbills, and accounted for 20% of all ringing recoveries (Merne, 2000). But in Norway, where 30,000–40,000 auks were shot each winter in the 1970s (Barrett & Vader, 1984), shooting auks was banned in 1979.

Ireland held 20% of the British and Irish Razorbill population in 1985–88 and though total numbers had remained stable since 1969–70, substantial increases on the east coast were offset by declines in the south and west (Lloyd *et al.*, 1991). These declines were coincident with large numbers of Razorbills recorded drowned in fishing nets, especially in mono-filament salmon drift-nets that were set close to colonies on the south and west coasts of Ireland in the 1970s (Bibby, 1971, 1972; Melville, 1973; Whilde, 1979).

CENSUS METHODS

Razorbills mainly breed on small ledges or in cracks of rocky cliffs and in associated screes, and on boulder-fields. Rarely, colonies have been found up to 300 m inland (Harris & Wanless, 1997b). Razorbills are usually associated with colonies of other seabirds, and small numbers scattered among large concentrations of Common Guillemots and Black-legged Kittiwakes can easily be overlooked. Razorbill 'nest' sites are usually hidden from view, but the presence of a colony is clearly indicated by the attendance of off-duty birds close by. Since it is not usually possible to count occupied sites, the count unit specified for Razorbills during Seabird 2000 was 'individuals on suitable breeding ledges', which excluded birds on rocks below the high-water mark and on the sea adjacent to the colony. Counts of individual birds included off-duty adults, non-breeders and immatures as well as—where nest-sites were visible—brooding and incubating birds.

At a few sites it was possible to actually find and count apparently occupied sites or nests (AOS or AON) of Razorbills. However, in order to compare counts between sites and between years, all counts of AOSs and AONs were divided by 0.67 to estimate the equivalent count of individuals (after Lloyd *et al.*, 1991). This conversion factor was based on studies on the Isle of May and Skokholm, where the ratio of AONs or AOSs to birds present ranged from 0.59–0.77 (Harris, 1989) and 0.30–0.55, respectively (Lloyd, 1975). In Seabird 2000, only 3% of the population estimate (in terms of birds) of Britain and Ireland was converted from counts of AOSs and AONs.

To permit comparison between Seabird 2000 and the two previous censuses, counts of AOSs and AONs from Operation Seafarer and the SCR Census were converted to counts of birds using the same adjustment used for Seabird 2000 counts (see above). In the SCR Census, converted counts comprised only 5% of the total estimate of Razorbills in Britain and Ireland. In contrast to both the SCR Census and Seabird 2000, most counts of Razorbills in Operation Seafarer were expressed as pairs (i.e. AOSs or AONs) and comprised 78% of the total population estimate for Britain and Ireland in 1969–70. Whilst the organisers of Operation Seafarer recognised the difficulties involved in surveying breeding Razorbills, it is unclear how surveyors determined the number of pairs present

All Razorbills attending a colony are counted, excluding birds on the sea or on rocks below the mean high water mark (Tim Dunn)

in each colony (Cramp *et al.*, 1974). Therefore, comparisons of Operation Seafarer counts of pairs of Razorbill with subsequent counts of individuals should be treated with caution.

In Britain and Ireland, egg laying usually begins in late April or early May, with a peak in mid-May. The single chick hatches from the last week in May and leaves, with its male parent, *c.*3 weeks later. Most chicks have left the colonies by late July, with stragglers sometimes remaining to mid-August. Seabird 2000 prescribed counting Razorbills between 1–21 June, to coincide with the late incubation and main nestling period, and during 08:00 to 16:00 hrs (BST) to coincide with the period of most consistent attendance by birds at the colony from day-to-day (Lloyd, 1975; Harris, 1989; Walsh *et al.*, 1995). This period does not necessarily coincide with the maximum numbers of birds attending the cliffs during a season, but instead provides the most comparable measure of attendance when using one-off counts during censuses such as Seabird 2000.

In Seabird 2000, 43% of counts were conducted at the prescribed date and time, and a further 21% were on the prescribed date, but either not at the correct time or at a time that was not noted by the surveyors. Some 36% of counts were conducted outside prescribed date and time, but the majority of these were within one week either side of the prescribed count period. During the SCR Census, surveyors were instructed to count Razorbills within the same dates and times as prescribed during Seabird 2000, but the actual time was not recorded by surveyors. However, 37% of counts were conducted on the correct dates, but 51% were conducted outside this period and no date was recorded by surveyors for the remaining 12%. The same times and dates were not prescribed during Operation Seafarer and some counts were carried out late in the season (in July or even early August), when many successful adults would have left with their chicks and when failed breeders would have deserted.

During Seabird 2000 and the SCR Census, surveyors were instructed to avoid counting Razorbills during heavy rain or fog, and in winds higher than Beaufort scale force 4, which all affect the level of attendance by Razorbills at a colony, as well as the ability of the observer to count them (no guidance in this respect was given for Operation Seafarer). Any one of these conditions constituted 'poor' weather, whereas all other weather conditions were described as 'good'. At least 73% of Seabird 2000 counts were conducted during 'good' weather and only 5% in 'poor' weather (weather conditions were not recorded for 22% of counts). Weather conditions were not recorded by surveyors during the SCR Census.

Coverage in Britain and Ireland during Seabird 2000 was almost complete, although some Irish colonies were not surveyed, at Inishark (Co. Galway), Aughris Head (Co. Sligo) and Bray Head (Co. Wicklow); these colonies, however, were relatively small during the SCR Census (22, 133 and 19 birds, respectively).

CURRENT STATUS AND TRENDS

The total number of individual Razorbills counted in Britain and Ireland during the Seabird 2000 census was 216,087, of which 64% were in Scotland, 24% in Ireland, 6% in England (including the Isle of Man and the Channel Islands) and 6% in Wales.

The distribution of Razorbill colonies in Britain and Ireland has changed little over the last 30 years (Fig. 1). The distribution coincides with stretches of rocky coastline of cliffs, headlands and offshore islands. They are thus absent from the east and south coast of England between Flamborough Head (Humberside) and Purbeck (Dorset), and no longer breed on the Isle of Wight. However, they have colonised Inchcolm, Firth of Forth (Dunfermline; 6 individuals), Marsden Bay (Tyne & Wear; 36) and Boulby Cliffs (Cleveland; 7).

In Britain and Ireland, the trends recorded between Operation Seafarer (1969–70) and the SCR Census (1985–88: Lloyd *et al.*, 1991) appear to have continued in most areas except in the Northern Isles. In Orkney, numbers of Razorbills changed little since the SCR Census (1985–88) and numbers in Shetland declined by a third (Table 1). This was in contrast to the increases that occurred in the Northern Isles between Operation Seafarer (1969–70) and the SCR Census (1985–88). The decline of Razorbills in Shetland was mainly due to decreases of over 4,000 on Foula and 350 on Fair Isle (Table 2). Numbers on Fair Isle decreased sharply from 3,950 in 1986 to 3,053 in 1988 and have increased gradually since then (Fig. 3). Annual monitoring of colony size throughout the rest of Shetland demonstrated a significant decline in the late 1980s, followed by a subsequent recovery in the early 1990s (Mavor *et al.*, 2002). Along the British mainland North Sea coast, numbers of Razorbills have continued to rise since the SCR Census (Table 1), including increases of 13%, 44% and 11% at the largest colonies, at Berriedale Cliffs (east Caithness), Fowlsheugh (Kincardine & Deeside) and Bempton Cliffs (Humberside), respectively (Table 2). In 1986–2001, annual monitoring of Razorbill numbers in study plots at colonies in northeast and southeast Scotland has shown significant ($P<0.01$) rises of 2.6% and 4.5% per annum respectively (Mavor *et al.*, 2002). Annual counts of Razorbills on the Isle of May have increased linearly since 1969, although none were conducted in 1970–80 (Fig. 3).

Changes in breeding numbers of Razorbills in colonies along the north and west coasts of Scotland since 1985–88 were much less consistent than on the east. Numbers along the north Caithness coast declined by 40% and possibly by more, since most of the counts from the SCR Census were conducted late in the season (23 June–9 July) and were probably lower than counts conducted during the prescribed period i.e. 1–21 June (see above). However, in northwest Sutherland, Razorbill

Table 1   Numbers of Razorbills in Britain and Ireland 1969–2002.

Administrative area or country	Operation Seafarer (1969–70)	SCR Census (1985–88)[1]	Seabird 2000 (1998–2002)	Percentage change since Seafarer	Percentage change since SCR	Annual percentage change since SCR
Shetland	9,357	14,247	9,492	1%	−33%	−2.9%
Orkney	10,468	10,821	10,194	−3%	−6%	−0.4%
North coast Caithness		1,938	1,172		−40%	−3.8%
East coast Caithness		15,438	19,161		24%	1.7%
Caithness total	*26,138*	*17,376*	*20,333*	*−22%*	*17%*	*1.2%*
Northwest coast Sutherland		19,155	21,657		13%	0.9%
Sutherland total	*14,592*	*19,155*	*21,657*	*48%*	*13%*	*0.9%*
West coast Ross & Cromarty		66	37		−44%	−3.9%
East coast Ross & Cromarty		41	214		422%	11.6%
Ross & Cromarty total	*64*	*107*	*251*	*292%*	*135%*	*5.9%*
Banff & Buchan	1,465	1,969	7,606	419%	286%	9.4%
Gordon	30	146	547	1723%	275%	9.2%
City of Aberdeen		73	157		115%	6.1%
Kincardine & Deeside	8,549	6,493	9,760	14%	50%	3.1%
Angus	149	938	562	277%	−40%	−3.8%
Northeast Fife	351	1,825	4,114	1072%	125%	5.2%
Kirkcaldy		50	85		70%	4.5%
Dunfermline			6			
East Lothian	91	260	566	522%	118%	6.7%
Berwickshire	384	2,017	3,534	820%	75%	4.5%
Stewartry	134	64	111	−17%	73%	4.3%
Wigtown	370	395	421	14%	7%	0.5%
Kyle & Carrick	3,397	1,001	1,477	−57%	48%	3.1%
Argyll & Bute	2,737	4,454	9,056	231%	103%	5.5%
Lochaber	1,743	1,960	1,200	−31%	−39%	−3.6%
Skye & Lochalsh	457	1,429	623	36%	−56%	−6.3%
Western Isles–Comhairle nan eilean	30,562	38,806	37,434	22%	−4%	−0.3%
Scotland Total	**111,038**	**123,586**	**139,186**	**25%**	**13%**	**0.9%**
Northumberland	10	93	271	2610%	191%	7.4%
Tyne & Wear			36			
Cleveland			7			
North Yorkshire	11	182	176	1500%	−3%	−0.2%
Humberside	2,573	7,662	8,438	228%	10%	0.7%
Isle of Wight	9	4		−100%	−100%	
Dorset	22	27	41	86%	52%	3.0%
Channel Islands	63	81	65	3%	−20%	−1.8%
Cornwall	605	632	465	−23%	−26%	−2.2%
Isles of Scilly	597	238	261	−56%	10%	0.8%
Devon	1,496	1,053	1,137	−24%	8%	0.6%
Cumbria	82	210	312	280%	49%	3.1%
Isle of Man	897	848	1,524	70%	80%	4.5%
England Total	**6,365**	**11,030**	**12,733**	**100%**	**15%**	**1.1%**
West Glamorgan	70	39	60	−14%	54%	2.9%
Dyfed	7,185	7,173	9,619	34%	34%	2.1%
Gwynedd	2061	2,289	2,959	44%	29%	1.8%
Wales Total	**9,316**	**9,501**	**12,638**	**36%**	**33%**	**2.1%**
Great Britain, Isle of Man and Channel Islands Total	**126,719**	**144,117**	**164,557**	**30%**	**14%**	**1.0%**
Co. Antrim	5,213	11,027	24,084	362%	118%	5.9%
Co. Down		4			−100%	
Co. Dublin	1,762	4,169	5,175	194%	24%	1.7%
Co. Wicklow	18	99	186	933%	88%	5.0%
Co. Wexford	6,844	5,193	3,739	−45%	−28%	−2.3%
Co. Waterford	1,700	184	56	−97%	−70%	−8.7%

Administrative area or country	Operation Seafarer (1969–70)	SCR Census (1985–88)[1]	Seabird 2000 (1998–2002)	Percentage change since Seafarer	Percentage change since SCR	Annual percentage change since SCR
Co. Cork	2,938	717	149	−95%	−79%	−10.4%
Co. Kerry	4,449	1,183	1,149	−74%	−3%	−0.2%
Co. Clare	2,475	2,503	7,721	212%	208%	10.0%
Co. Galway	317	22[2]	345	9%	1468%	26.0%
Co. Mayo	2,261	89	705	−69%	692%	17.9%
Co. Sligo[3]	82	133				
Co. Donegal	12,905	6,695	8,221	−36%	23%	1.7%
All-Ireland Total	**40,964**	**32,018**	**51,530**	**26%**	**61%**	**4.4%**
Britain and Ireland Total	**167,683**	**176,135**	**216,087**	**29%**	**23%**	**1.7%**

Notes

[1] The figures for the SCR are actual counts and do not include adjustments to totals made in order to account for unsurveyed colonies (see Lloyd et al., 1991)

[2] Inishmore, Aran Isles not counted in 1985–88 (53 individuals in 1990)

[3] Aughris Head not counted during Seabird 2000 (90 individuals in 1997)

Table 2   Changes in the number of Razorbills at major colonies in Britain and Ireland between the SCR Census (1985–88) and Seabird 2000 (1998–2002). Major colonies are those that contained the top 50% of the British population and the top 95% of the Irish population during the SCR. ID corresponds to the colony symbols in Fig. 2.

ID	Colony	SCR Census (1985–88)	Seabird 2000 (1998–2002)	Percentage change since SCR	Annual percentage change since SCR	Percentage of population in Britain or Ireland 1998–2002
1	Handa	16,394	16,991	4%	0.3%	10.3%
2	Berneray	11,893	16,513	39%	2.6%	10.0%
3	Shiant Islands	10947	8,046	−27%	−2.3%	4.9%
4	Bempton Cliffs (incl. N. Flamborough Head)	7,688	8,539	11%	0.8%	5.2%
5	Foula	6,200	2,121	−66%	−7.9%	1.3%
6	Berriedale Cliffs (SSSI)	5,873	6,630	13%	0.9%	4.0%
7	Mingulay	5,000	6,387	28%	1.9%	3.9%
8	Fowlsheugh (SSSI)	4,467	6,425	44%	2.8%	3.9%
9	Fair Isle	3,950	3,599	−9%	−0.7%	2.2%
10	Flannan Isles	3,889	1,569	−60%	−8.7%	1.0%
11	Skomer	3,578	3,898	9%	0.6%	2.4%
12	Rathlin Island	8,922	20,860	134%	6.3%	40.5%
13	Horn Head	5,628	6,739	20%	1.5%	13.1%
14	Great Saltee	4,673	3,239	−31%	−2.4%	6.3%
15	Lambay Island	3,648	4,337	19%	1.5%	8.4%
16	Cliffs of Moher	2,398	7,700	221%	10.0%	14.9%
17	Sheep Island	940	963	2%	0.2%	1.9%
18	Tory Island	614	1,002	63%	4.2%	1.9%
19	Puffin Island	600	35	−94%	−17.4%	0.1%
20	Gobbins	475	552	16%	1.2%	1.1%
21	Little Saltee	450	500	11%	0.9%	1.0%
22	Old Head of Kinsale	383	104	−73%	−8.9%	0.2%
23	Tormore	362	480	33%	2.4%	0.9%
24	Muck Island	315	746	137%	5.9%	1.4%
25	Carrick-a-Rede	314	281	−11%	−0.7%	0.5%
26	Ireland's Eye	272	522	92%	5.1%	1.0%
27	Howth Head	249	316	27%	1.7%	0.6%
28	Inishnabro	193	319	65%	3.9%	0.6%

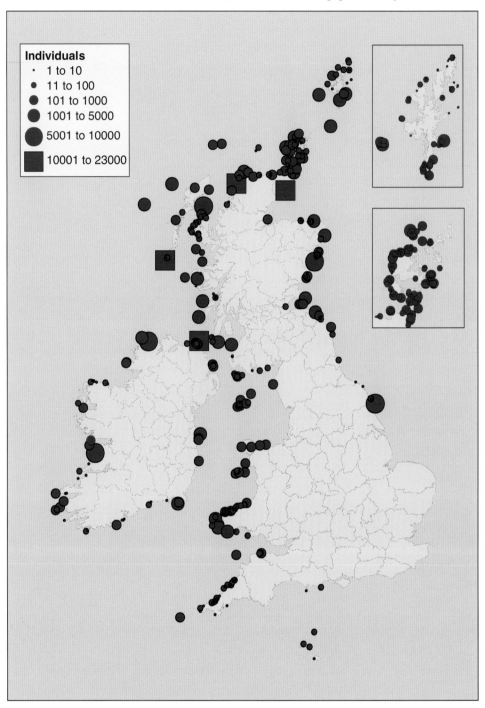

Figure 1   Abundance and distribution of Razorbills in Britain and Ireland 1998–2002.

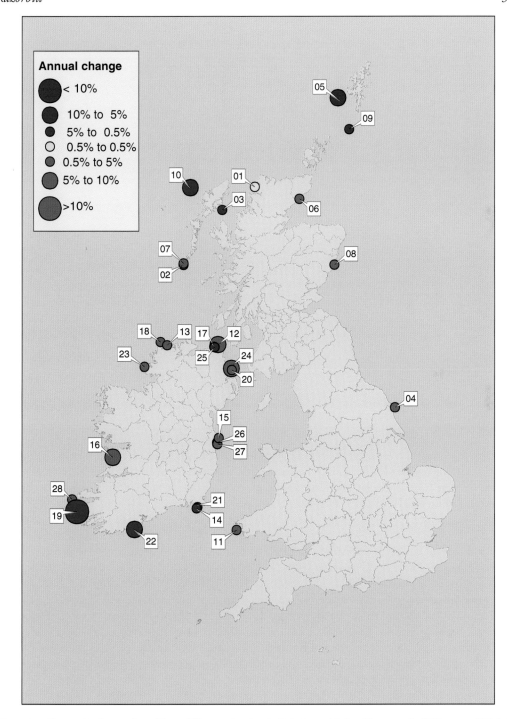

Figure 2   Changes in the number of Razorbills at major sites in Britain and Ireland between the SCR census (1985–88) and Seabird 2000 (1998–2002). Major sites are those that contained the top 50% of the British population and the top 95% of the Irish population during the SCR. Numbers correspond to colonies listed in Table 2.

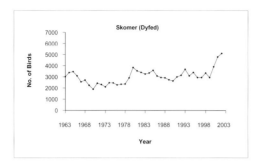
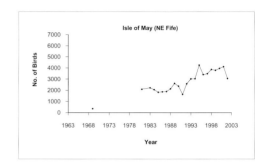
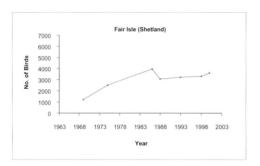
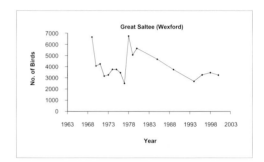

Figure 3   Numbers of Razorbills at colonies in Britain and Ireland where repeated counts were conducted 1963–2002 (data from Seabird Colony Register Database, JNCC/Seabird Group, Aberdeen.

numbers remained stable, largely due to little change on Handa (Table 2) which held most of the Razorbills in the region (17,000 birds). Further south, the total number of Razorbills in west Ross & Cromarty, Skye and Lochalsh and Lochaber had declined by 46%; but from Argyll & Bute to Stewartry, numbers had increased by 87% since 1985–88 (Table 1).

The Western Isles held the largest concentration of Razorbills in Britain and Ireland, but total numbers there had changed little (4% decrease) since 1985–88. Mingulay and Berneray held a combined total of almost 23,000 birds in 1998, an increase of 35% since 1985. However, numbers on the Shiants declined by 27% since 1986, to 8,000 in 1999, and on the Flannan Isles numbers decreased by 60% between 1988 and 1998 to 1,569 (Table 2), continuing the decline since Operation Seafarer (1969–70: Lloyd *et al.*, 1991). Razorbill numbers on Sula Sgeir and Hirta (St Kilda), which had apparently declined between 1969–70 and 1985–88 (Lloyd *et al.*, 1991), appear to have changed little since 1985–88.

In southwest England, the number of Razorbills on Lundy and the Isles of Scilly increased by 25% and 10% respectively since the SCR Census (1985–88), representing a slight recovery from the declines that followed Operation Seafarer (1969–70).

Total numbers of Razorbills breeding in Wales increased by 33% since 1985–88. Annual monitoring of Razorbill numbers in study plots at various colonies in Wales has shown a significant ($P<0.001$) rise of 3.8% per annum since 1986 (Mavor *et al.*, 2002). The colony on Skomer, the largest in Wales, has fluctuated in size since annual surveys commenced in 1963, peaking at similar levels in the mid-1970s, mid-1980s and the latter half of the 1990s (Fig. 3). Since the Seabird 2000 count of 3,894 in 2000, numbers rose to 5,095 in 2002, the highest recorded on the island.

The largest colony of Razorbills in Britain and Ireland was on Rathlin Island (Co. Antrim), where numbers have more than doubled from around 9,000 birds in 1985 to almost 21,000 in 1999. However, this increase may be due in part to a greater survey effort during the 1999 survey, which was conducted over 19 days from both land and sea, in contrast to just two days of land-based counts in 1985 (L. McFaul, pers. comm.). Numbers of Razorbills in eastern Ireland (Co. Dublin and Co. Wicklow) continued to rise following the SCR Census (Table 1), including increases of 19% on Lambay Island, 27% at Howth Head and 92% on Ireland's Eye (all in Co. Dublin; Table 2). In contrast, total numbers in southern Ireland in Co. Wexford, Co. Waterford, Co. Cork and Co. Kerry continued to decline, from 15,931 birds in 1969–70 and 7,277 in 1985–88 to 5,093 during Seabird 2000. On Great Saltee (Co. Wexford), the colony had apparently declined in size throughout the 1980s but has been fairly stable since 1990 (Fig. 3). However, the sudden rise from 2,500 in 1977 to 6,736 in the following year (Fig. 3) may be a reflection of the difficulties of counting Razorbills and a change in observer, rather than a real change in breeding numbers. On Puffin Island (Co. Kerry) only 35 Razorbills were present in 2000 compared with 600 in 1985. However, further north in Clare, where most Razorbills were found at the Cliffs of Moher, numbers more than trebled since 1985–88, but had remained stable before then (Table 2). Increases in the number of Razorbills in Co. Mayo and Co. Donegal since the SCR Census (1985–88) represented partial recoveries from the substantial declines (70% and 36%, respectively) between 1969–70 and 1985–88. Numbers at all the large colonies in Co. Donegal (Horn Head, Tory Island and Tormore) showed substantial rises since 1985–88 (Table 2).

CAUSES OF CHANGE

The problems associated with counting Razorbills make it extremely difficult to interpret apparent trends in numbers. However, in some areas, the change in numbers of Razorbills that has occurred since the last two censuses appears to be consistent with those of other species. For example, the increase in numbers that occurred in colonies of Razorbills throughout most of Britain and Ireland since Operation Seafarer (1969–70) appears to be waning in Orkney, Shetland and the Western Isles (see above), which is also true for populations of Northern Fulmars and Common Guillemots in the same areas (see respective chapters). Furthermore, throughout Britain and Ireland, the percentage changes since the SCR Census in the number of Razorbills within each administrative area were significantly positively correlated with those of Common Guillemots in the same areas (Spearman Rank Correlation $r_{s, 47}$ = 0.496, P<0.001). Both Razorbills and Common Guillemots breed along rocky coasts and cliffs, lay a single egg and the young fledge at three weeks old to be fed at sea by the male parent; thus, both species may be affected by similar factors. Density-dependent effects have been suggested as a likely cause of the downturn in numbers of Common Guillemots in the most densely populated parts of their range (i.e. the Northern and Western Isles; see Common Guillemot chapter), and may also affect Razorbill numbers. Limits to resources such as food and suitable nest sites in some areas may be preventing further increases in the size of the resident Razorbill population.

Food availability close to the colony is an important determinant of breeding success of seabirds. Razorbills feed their young on lesser sandeels, sprats and herring, which they pursue and capture underwater to depths of up to 120 m or more (Piatt & Nettleship, 1985). Productivity of diving species (Common Guillemots and European Shags) and surface-feeders (Black-legged Kittiwakes) on the Isle of May is correlated with the magnitude and timing of sandeel availability to the commercial fishery in the North Sea (Rindorf *et al.*, 2000). But Razorbills, like other diving species, have the advantage over surface-feeders that they can capture prey at a greater variety of depths, including demersal species such as whiting and saithe. During the late 1980s, changes in currents are believed to have created a scarcity of sandeels in the waters around Shetland, which resulted in almost total breeding failure of surface-feeders such as Arctic Terns and Black-legged Kittiwakes (Bailey, 1991). During the same period, Razorbill productivity was relatively unaffected throughout most of Shetland (Heubeck, 1989), except on Foula where breeding success was described as poor and where sandeels constituted only 43% of the diets of chicks compared with 100% in 1971–80 (Furness, 1999a). Since 2000, there has been a ban on commercial sandeel fishing in the North Sea, and during this time productivity of European Shags on the Isle of May has been the highest since records began in 1986, and the productivity of Black-legged Kittiwakes and Atlantic Puffins has also been higher than the long-term (1986–2002) average (Wilson *et al.*, 2003). However, since the late 1990s, productivity of Razorbills (and Common Guillemots) on the Isle of May has been consistently lower than the long-term average. Razorbills on the Isle of May feed their chicks predominantly on sandeels, whereas the recent fall in the productivity of Common Guillemots was coincident with a switch in prey from sandeels to herring and sprats (Wilson *et al.*, 2003). It thus appears that the productivity of Razorbills and Guillemots on the Isle of May is limited by sandeel availability despite the recent fishing ban.

Since 1986, annual monitoring of breeding success (number of chicks fledged per pair) of Razorbills has been undertaken at up to six colonies in Britain and adult survival has also been measured at two of these—the Isle of May (Harris *et al.*, 2000; Wilson *et al.*, 2003) and Skomer (Perrins, 2002). The mean annual breeding success at each of the six colonies was between 0.58 (Skomer) and 0.84 (Skokholm) chicks fledged per pair and similar to that of Guillemots at a much larger number of colonies (Mavor *et al.*, 2003). On Skomer breeding success has declined in recent years (Perrins, 2002), but on Fair Isle, the only colony in Shetland where breeding success has been measured regularly, there has been no discernable trend in annual breeding success since monitoring began in 1991, fluctuating around a mean of 0.62 chicks per pair (Shaw *et al.*, 2002). Razorbills first breed at around five years old and tend to return to breed at or close to their natal colonies (Merne, 2002). Thus, the level of breeding success in a given year would be expected to impact upon breeding numbers five years hence. However, the survival rates of immature Razorbills is unknown and the imprecision involved in censusing Razorbills (in that counts of birds attending the colony include non-breeders and immatures as well as breeders) makes it difficult to directly link breeding success to future changes in numbers of Razorbills attending a colony. However, this is no reason to abandon measurement of breeding success of Razorbills, since it provides a useful indicator of the 'health' of a colony and can help to determine likely impacts on colony size (e.g. food availability; see Rindorf *et al.*, 2000).

Razorbills have a high life expectancy (sometimes over 20 years: O Merne, pers. obs.) and in such long-lived birds, changes in adult survival have the greatest impact on population size (Croxall & Rothery, 1991). But on Skomer and the Isle of May annual survival has remained high at a mean of 90.5% and 90.7%, respectively, in 1986–2000 and has varied little from year to year, except in 1995 on the Isle of May, when survival rate fell to 73% following a large 'wreck' in the North Sea (Harris *et al.*, 2000). Surprisingly, counts of Razorbills in 1995 were higher than any other year during the period 1963–2002 (Fig. 3), highlighting again the difficulty in directly linking demographic parameters with counts of individual Razorbills.

The large wrecks of non-oiled Razorbills (and Common Guillemots) that have occurred during stormy winter weather (Camphuysen *et al.*, 1999) tend to be composed mainly of immatures that had empty stomachs and depleted fat reserves (Mudge *et al.*, 1992); it is likely that adults are much more able to sustain themselves during winter food shortages. Large numbers of Razorbills from colonies in Britain and Ireland were killed during the two recent oil spill disasters in the Bay of Biscay, the *Erika* in winter 1999/2000 and the *Prestige* in November 2002, but of the birds recovered during both spills, over two-thirds were immature (Camphuysen *et al.* 2003; B. Cadiou, pers comm.).

However, acute losses of immatures during bad weather and oil spills and the resultant isolated years of low recruitment are unlikely to have measurable long-term effects on the size of the breeding population.

The population on the south and west coasts of Ireland decreased following Operation Seafarer and has continued to do so since the SCR Census on the south coast, whereas populations on the west have started to recover. Entrapment of Razorbills in salmon-fishing nets may have contributed to declines in Ireland during the 1970s and 1980s (see above), but this may no longer pose a significant threat; since 1990 annual catches of salmon in Ireland have fallen by 57% compared with 1962–1989 (North Atlantic Salmon Conservation Organisation, 2003). No systematic monitoring of bycatches of salmon nets has been conducted, but this should be instigated to assess the current impact on populations of Razorbills and other auks along the south coast of Ireland.

Predation of Razorbills, their eggs and chicks, has had a measurable impact on some colonies: for example, on Skomer predation of nests by Herring Gulls and Ravens has reduced Razorbill productivity on some parts of the island (Birkhead & Hatchwell, 2000). Nest predation by introduced mammalian predators such as Brown Rats and American Mink has significantly reduced productivity at colonies of ground-nesting seabirds and in some cases has resulted in the desertion of entire colonies (Craik, 1995). Razorbills nesting in boulder beaches or on low cliffs may be susceptible to predation from mammals. Egg predation of Razorbills by Brown Rats has been noted on Canna (Swann, 2003) and has resulted in the abandonment of some traditional nest sites under boulders. Likewise in Shetland and Orkney, Black Guillemots avoid nesting in boulder beaches on islands inhabited by Brown Rats and Stoats and prefer to nest on steep cliffs, out of reach of the predators (Ewins & Tasker, 1985). Recent declines in Black Guillemot numbers in parts of Scotland may have resulted from predation by mink (see Black Guillemot Chapter). It may be more than coincidence that along the northwest mainland coast of Scotland, from Lochaber to north Caithness, there have been considerable declines since the SCR Census in the numbers of both Razorbills and Black Guillemots, whereas during the same period numbers of Common Guillemots, which nest in less accessible sites, have increased. The extent of the impact of mink and other mammalian predators on Razorbills in Scotland needs to be addressed.

INTERNATIONAL CONTEXT

Despite the fact that identifying and counting AONs and AOSs of Razorbills is impossible to do accurately at most colonies, the size of international populations are almost always cited as pairs (Table 3). Therefore, in order to put the British and Irish Razorbill populations into an international context, the Seabird 2000 population estimates of birds were converted to breeding pairs by multiplying by 0.67 (see above, after Harris, 1989). The estimated populations of 110,000 pairs in Britain and 35,000 pairs in Ireland represent around 18% and 5.5% of the world population of Razorbills, respectively (Table 3).

There are two subspecies of Razorbill, *A. t. islandica* and *A. t. torda*. *A. t. islandica* breeds in Britain, Ireland, Iceland, the Faeroes, France and Germany. Stroud *et al.* (2001) considered the relevant comparable biogeographic population for Razorbills in Britain and Ireland to be the world population of *islandica*, of which they hold 21% and 6.6%, respectively (Table 3). Iceland is by far the most important breeding area in the world for Razorbills (*islandica*) and held 380,000 breeding pairs in 1983–85 (Gardarsson, 1995a). In the Faeroes the population of 4,500 breeding pairs is thought to be stable or perhaps increasing as a result of recent protection (Skov *et al.*, 1999). Elsewhere, there is a tiny colony of *islandica* on Helgoland, Germany (16 pairs in 2002: Dierschke *et al.*, 2002) and just 25 pairs in France, now confined to a few sites on the north coast of Brittany and are no longer breeding on the west coast (Cadiou *et al.*, in press).

The main concentration of *A. t. torda* is in the east Atlantic on the Norwegian coast, where the population is estimated to be 20,000–40,000 pairs (BirdLife International/EBCC, 2000) and decreasing, particularly in the south. The isolated, and apparently largely sedentary population in the Baltic Sea (including the Gulfs of Bothnia and Finland) has increased during the latter half of the 20th century, following protection, though severe winters have been known to cause declines in breeding numbers in subsequent years (Merikallio, 1958; Hilden, 1978). The Arctic Ocean islands of Jan Mayen, Bear Island and Svalbard have very small colonies totalling less than 350 pairs. In northwest Russia, there may be about 3,500 pairs, with several hundred pairs along the Murman coast of the Kola Peninsula and nearly 3,000 pairs in the White Sea (Anker-Nilssen *et al.*, 2000). Breeding has yet to be proved on Novaya Zemlya, where several Razorbills were seen in a seabird colony in 1995 (Anker-Nilssen *et al.*, 2000).

On the west side of the North Atlantic, the breeding Razorbill population (*A. t. torda*) is relatively small, accounting for *c.*6% of the total world population (Table 3). In Canada, Razorbills breed along the Labrador coast, on the island of Newfoundland, on the north side and islands of the Gulf of St Lawrence, and on Nova Scotia. The largest colonies, situated on Gannet Island (Labrador) and on the migratory bird sanctuaries on the north shore of the Gulf of St Lawrence, have increased substantially in size in the last 20 years (Chapdelaine *et al.*, 2001; Hipfner & Chapdelaine, 2002). In the USA, Razorbills are confined to two colonies on the northeast coast of Maine, which hold a total of 277 pairs (Chapdelaine *et al.*, 2001). Razorbills breeding in Greenland are concentrated in about six main colonies along the southwest coast, from Cape Farewell to *c.*74°N. The population in Greenland may be lower than the published estimate of 2,000–5,000 pairs (BirdLife International/EBCC 2000), due to recent high levels of harvesting (Hansen, 2002).

Table 3   International context.

Country or region	Subspecies	Number of pairs		Year	Source
		Min	Max		
Great Britain, Isle of Man and Channel Isles[1]	*islandica*	110,000	110,000	1998–2002	Seabird 2000
All Ireland[1]	*islandica*	35,000	35,000	1999–2002	Seabird 2000
Denmark	*torda*	610	610	1996	BirdLife International / EBCC (2000)
Faeroes	*islandica*	4,500	4,500	1995	Skov *et al.* (1999)
Finland	*torda*	6,000	6,500	1990–95	BirdLife International / EBCC (2000)
France	*islandica*	25	25	1997–2001	Cadiou *et al.* (in press)
Germany	*islandica*	16	16	2002	Dierschke (2002)
Greenland	*torda*	2,000	5,000	1996	BirdLife International / EBCC (2000)
Iceland	*islandica*	380,000	380,000	1983–85	Gardarsson (1995)
Norway	*torda*	20,000	40,000	1970–90	BirdLife International / EBCC (2000)
Norway (Bear Island)	*torda*	15	50	1980	Barrett & Golovkin (2000)
Norway (Jan Mayen)	*torda*	100	100	1983	van Francker *et al.* (1998)
Norway (Svalbard)	*torda*	100	200		BirdLife International / EBCC (2000)
Russia	*torda*	3,500	3,500	1990s	Anker-Nilssen *et al.* (2000)
Sweden	*torda*	9,000	11,000	1990	BirdLife International / EBCC (2000)
Canada (East)	*torda*	37,800	37,800	mostly 1995–2000	Chapdelaine *et al.* (2001)
USA (Maine)	*torda*	277	277	2000	Chapdelaine *et al.* (2001)

Biogeographic region		Min	Max	Min % GB	Max % GB	Min % Ireland	Max % Ireland
NW Europe*	*islandica*	530,000	530,000	20.8%	20.8%	6.6%	6.6%
World	all	610,000	630,000	17.5%	18.0%	5.4%	5.6%

* Stroud *et al.* (2001)

Note

[1] Counts of birds at British and Irish colonies have been multiplied by 0.67 to estimate pairs.

Black Guillemot *Cepphus grylle*

P. Ian Mitchell

INTRODUCTION

The Black Guillemot or 'Tystie' is one of the more problematic seabird species to survey. It tends to breed away from the large seabird cliff colonies and prefers small rocky islands and low-lying, indented stretches of rocky coast. Black Guillemot nests are hidden in rock crevices and under boulders, which makes them extremely difficult to census during the breeding season. During Operation Seafarer (1969–70; Cramp *et al.*, 1974), counts were conducted along with other cliff-nesting seabirds during June. At this time of year, Black Guillemots are either hidden away in nest chambers brooding young or are away feeding. Most Black Guillemots feed close inshore, so may be visible to surveyors, but may be easily missed, especially if they are feeding or breeding away from colonies of other nesting seabirds. Operation Seafarer therefore underestimated the British and Irish population by an unknown amount. Between 1982 and 1991, as part of the SCR Census (Lloyd *et al.*, 1991), a survey of the number of adult Black Guillemots was conducted prior to the breeding season (late March–early/mid-May), during the first three hours of daylight (06.00–09.00 BST) when they congregate close inshore for courtship and mating. Ewins (1985a) found such counts to be the most repeatable and accurate method of assessing the size of Black Guillemot populations in Shetland, the species' stronghold in Britain. Unfortunately, during the SCR census, counts of Black Guillemots in The Republic of Ireland were conducted in June and not during the pre-breeding period.

The total of 38,000 pre-breeding Black Guillemots in Britain and Northern Ireland counted during the SCR Census (1982–91) was more than double the total of counts conducted in June during Operation Seafarer (1969–70). However, the difference in survey techniques invalidate any comparison between the two censuses. Despite this, Lloyd *et al.* (1991) suggested that the British and Northern Irish population had increased between 1969 and the 1980s, but by an unquantifiable extent.

During the SCR Census (1982–91) the British Black Guillemot population was concentrated in the Northern Isles and northwest Scotland. In 1982–84 Shetland held 31% and Orkney 19% of the British population. The distribution of Black Guillemots in Orkney and Shetland was determined by the availability of suitable nesting habitat, which varied depending on the presence or absence of mammalian predators (Ewins & Tasker, 1985). On predator-free islands, a larger proportion of Black Guillemots nested on the ground under boulders than on islands with rats and/or Stoats where most nested in crevices on cliffs inaccessible to ground predators. In December 1978 the oil spill from the *Esso Bernica* almost wiped out the Black Guillemot colonies in Yell Sound (Heubeck & Richardson, 1980).

Lloyd *et al.* (1991) noted an expansion in the range of Black Guillemots since Operation Seafarer, in particular the colonisation of new sites around the Irish Sea. These mainly included man-made sites (e.g. harbour walls, jetties, piers) in Northern Ireland and the Clyde Estuary, southwest Scotland. On the east coast of Scotland Black Guillemots had been expanding since the 1950s, when only one pair nested south of Caithness; by the mid-1980s there was a total of 36 adults in four counties from east Ross & Cromarty to Kincardine and Deeside (Table 1).

In the Republic of Ireland Black Guillemots were much less numerous but were widely distributed in small colonies (<30 adults) found in all coastal counties apart from Co. Meath, Co. Limerick and Co. Leitrim. The total of 580 Black Guillemots counted in the Republic of Ireland during the SCR Census in June 1985–87 was almost half the total of 969 during June 1969/70 (Lloyd *et al.*, 1991).

During Seabird 2000 a pre-breeding survey of Black Guillemots was conducted throughout Britain and Ireland. This was the first opportunity in many areas to examine changes in the population of Black Guillemots since 1982–91. In The Republic of Ireland, this was the first national pre-breeding survey.

CENSUS METHODS

Methods followed those developed by Ewins (1985a) and detailed in Walsh *et al.* (1995). The methods were identical to those used during the SCR Census, when pre-breeding surveys of Black Guillemots were conducted in Britain and Northern Ireland in 1982–1991 (see Lloyd *et al.*, 1991). Note that the results of pre-breeding surveys conducted in 1991 in parts of Argyll & Bute and in Kyle & Carrick, Stewartry and Wigtown were not included in Lloyd *et al.* (1991) but are included in the results of the SCR Census summarised in Table 1). The count unit was the number of adult Black Guillemots visible on land or on the sea within 300 m of the shore. Adults seen more than 300 m offshore were assumed to be feeding rather than associated with a pre-breeding courtship group. At some colonies it is actually possible to find nest chambers and these were counted as Apparently Occupied Sites (AOS). Counts of AOS were converted to individuals by multiplying by two (Lloyd *et al.*, 1991).

Black Guillemots are surveyed by counting pre-breeding adults which gather to display in the first few hours of daylight from late March to early May (Steve Newton)

Surveyors were instructed to count Black Guillemots between 26 March and 15 May at 05.00–09.00 (BST), in winds no stronger than Beaufort force 4 and in calm sea conditions. Overall, 86% of counts were conducted on the prescribed date and at the prescribed time, 9% on prescribed date but the time was not recorded, 3% on the prescribed dates but later than 09.00 (BST) and just 2% were conducted outside the prescribed dates.

In Britain most counts (72%) were conducted from boats, whereas in Ireland 67% of counts were conducted from land. The use of fast inflatable boats allowed long stretches of coast of 20–30 km to be covered in a single morning, in contrast to only 5 km on foot. Small inflatable boats are advantageous in that they can move very close to the shore, entering geos and coves where Black Guillemots are often difficult to see, especially when they are perched on rocks. Later on during the survey period, Black Guillemots are more likely to be on land and may be difficult to see from cliffs above, and often require active flushing to be visible to observers. In Scotland, boats enabled small teams of surveyors to cover large stretches of coastline in single years. In 2000, the entire northwest mainland coast of Scotland was surveyed from Cape Wrath (Sutherland) south to Oban (Argyll & Bute), including the Isles of Skye and Mull, in addition to eastern Caithness and half of the sites on the Isle of Lewis (Western Isles). The following year, just three survey teams covered the remainder of the Argyll & Bute coastline (Oban to Campbelltown, Kintyre, including Islay and Jura), the north coast of mainland Scotland, the southern Western Isles and Wigtown. Table 1 lists the year in which surveys in each county were conducted during both Seabird 2000 and the SCR census.

Site-by-site comparisons of counts from the SCR Census and Seabird 2000 where only possible in Britain and Northern Ireland. In the Republic of Ireland most counts of Black Guillemots

Table 1   Numbers of individual pre-breeding Black Guillemots in Britain and Ireland 1982–2003

Administrative area or country	SCR Census		Seabird 2000		Percentage change since SCR
	Year	Individual adults	Individual adults	Year	
Shetland	1982–85	12040	15739	1998–2000	31%
Orkney	1983–84	6878	5820	1999–2001	−15%
East Caithness	1985	1701	1104	1999–2001	−35%
East Sutherland	1985	?	0	1999	
East Ross & Cromarty	1985	17	nc		
Moray	1986	2	9	2001	350%
Banff & Buchan	1986	14	14	2001	0%
Kincardine & Deeside	1986	3	3	2002	0%
Stewartry	1985–91	10	nc		
Wigtown	1991	223	174	2001	−22%
Kyle & Carrick	1988–91	38	302	2001–02	695%
Cunninghame	1991	57	98	1999–2001	72%
Inverclyde	1987	24	84	2001	250%
Dumbarton	1987	3	nc		
Argyll & Bute	1987–91	4288	3046	1999–2002	−29%
Lochaber	1989–90	1657	1335	2000–01	−19%
Skye & Lochalsh	1987–89	2961	2672	2000–03	−10%
West Ross & Cromarty	1987–89	1613	1490	2000	−8%
North & West Sutherland	1986–89	1214	895	2000–01	−26%
North Caithness	1985–86	329	143	2001	−57%
Western Isles–Comhairle nan eilean	1986–89	4100	4577	2000–02	12%
Scotland Total	**1982–91**	**37172**	**37505**	**1999–2003**	**1%**
Cumbria	1989	14	7	1999	−50%
Isle of Man	1987	303	602	1999	99%
England and Isle of Man Total	**1987–89**	**317**	**609**	**1999**	**92%**
Gwynedd	1987	26	28	2000–02	8%
Wales	**1987**	**26**	**28**	**2000–02**	**8%**
Great Britain and Isle of Man Total	**1982–91**	**37515**	**38142**	**1999–2003**	**2%**
Co. Londonderry	1987	40	60	2000	50%
Co. Antrim	1985–88	338	865	1999–2002	156%
Co. Down	1985–88	155	249	2000	61%
Northern Ireland Total	**1985–88**	**533**	**1174**	**1999–2002**	**120%**
Co. Louth[1]			23	1998	
Co. Dublin[1]			190	1998–99	
Co. Wicklow[1]			201	1998–99	
Co. Wexford[1]			15	1998	
Co. Waterford	1986	61	34	1998–99	
Co. Cork[1]			679	1998–2001	
Co. Kerry[1]			315	1999	
Co. Clare[1]			155	1998–2000	
Co. Galway[1]			326	1999–2000	

Administrative area or country	SCR Census		Seabird 2000		Percentage change since
	Year	Individual adults	Individual adults	Year	SCR
Co. Mayo[1]			376	1999–2000	
Co. Sligo[1]			101	2000	
Co. Donegal[1]			952	1999–2002	
Republic of Ireland Total[1]			**3367**	**1998–2002**	
All-Ireland Total[1]			**4541**	**1998–2002**	
Great Britain, Ireland and Isle of Man Total[1]			**42683**	**1998–2003**	

Note

[1] Pre-breeding counts were not conducted in the Republic of Ireland (except Co. Waterford) during the SCR Census (1985–88)

during the SCR Census were conducted in June and were not comparable with Seabird 2000 pre-breeding counts. The Black Guillemot is the only species in this book for which comprehensive site-by-site comparisons with the SCR Census have been possible (see Data Processing and Analysis). The main reason for this is that the spatial scales at which counts were conducted during the SCR Census and Seabird 2000 were much more comparable in the case of Black Guillemots than any other species. During most of the SCR Census, the position of each distinct group of pre-breeding birds was recorded with a single OS grid reference. During Seabird 2000, surveys of all coastal-nesting species, including Black Guillemots, were conducted along discrete sections of coastline called 'sub-sites', 1 km or more in length (see chapter on Census Methods). It was therefore straightforward to compare counts from Seabird 2000 sub-sites with those of the contiguous SCR count points.

The intervening period between the SCR Census and Seabird 2000 counts varied considerably between different areas, e.g. 15–19 years on Shetland and 10–11 years in Argyll. Therefore, the change in numbers at each individual site was expressed as percentage change per annum (see Fig. 2).

CURRENT STATUS AND TRENDS

Seabird 2000 pre-breeding surveys (1998–2003) recorded 42,638 Black Guillemots in Britain and Ireland of which 87% were in Scotland, 11% in Ireland, 1% in the Isle of Man and the remainder in England (seven birds in Cumbria) and Wales (28 birds in Gwynedd). The population in Britain appears to have been stable since the last pre-breeding surveys conducted in 1982–91 (Table 1). In Northern Ireland the total of 1,174 Black Guillemots in 1999–2002 represented an increase of 120% on pre-breeding surveys conducted in 1985–88.

Fig. 2 shows the percentage change per annum at individual sites since the SCR Census (1982–91). Sites were excluded from Fig. 2 where no birds were recorded during the SCR and only a single bird was recorded in Seabird 2000 and vice versa.

The breeding range of Black Guillemots in Britain during Seabird 2000 was similar to the SCR Census (1982–91). The southeastern limit of their range remained at Muchalls (Kincardine & Deeside), 15 km south of Aberdeen. On the west coast of Britain, the only colonies south of Scotland were at St Bees Head (Cumbria) and at two sites on Anglesey (Gwynedd), as in 1982–91. However,

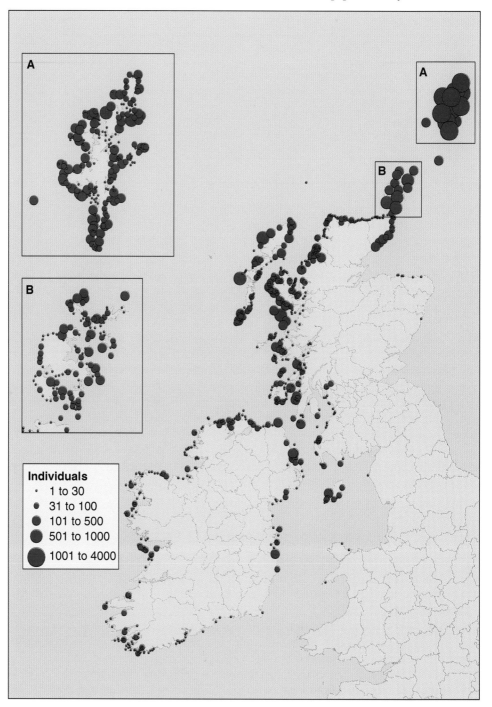

Figure 1   Abundance and distribution of pre-breeding Black Guillemots in Britain and Ireland 1998–2003.

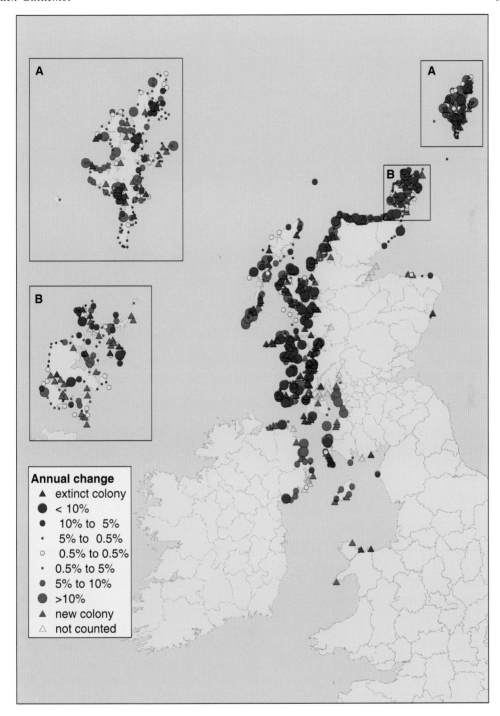

Figure 2   Changes in the number of adult Black Guillemots during pre-breeding counts in Britain and Northern Ireland between the SCR Census (1982–91) and Seabird 2000 (1998–2003).

Table 2   Numbers of individual pre-breeding Black Guillemots in Orkney and Shetland 1982–2002. Regions are defined in Ewins & Tasker (1985).

Region	SCR Census 1982–85	Seabird 2000 1998–2001	Percentage change	Annual percentage change
North Ronaldsay	374	476	27%	1.5%
Papa Westray	667	485	−27%	−2.0%
Westray	930	468	−50%	−4.0%
Faray, Eday, Sanday	1042	899	−14%	−0.9%
Rousay	420	348	−17%	−1.1%
Shapinsay	260	273	5%	0.3%
Stronsay	662	414	−37%	−2.8%
West Mainland	372	319	−14%	−0.9%
South and East Mainland	989	803	−19%	−1.3%
Hoy	802	745	−7%	−0.5%
South Ronaldsay	360	582	62%	3.1%
Orkney total	**6878**	**5812**	**−15%**	
Unst	1071	1062	−1%	−0.1%
Fetlar	1174	1347	15%	0.9%
North and east Yell	955	1267	33%	1.7%
Yell Sound	559	1285	130%	5.3%
Whalsay and Out Skerries	805	1175	46%	2.3%
East Mainland (Delting)	898	975	9%	0.5%
Bressay and Noss	389	617	59%	2.8%
South Mainland	2138	2029	−5%	−0.3%
Scalloway Islands	1004	1051	5%	0.3%
West Mainland	1538	2791	81%	3.7%
Northwest Mainland (Northmavine)	1038	1778	71%	3.3%
Fair Isle	338	191	−43%	−3.3%
Foula	133	171	29%	1.4%
Shetland total	**12040**	**15739**	**31%**	

in 2000 the southwestern limit of their range was extended 70 km south when a pair nested on Ynys Gwylan Fawr off the Llyn Peninsula (Gwynedd).

Some 41% of the British population was in Shetland where numbers have increased by 31% since 1982–85. Table 2 compares Seabird 2000 and SCR Census counts conducted in the Northern Isles summarised by region (as defined by Ewins & Tasker, 1985). Populations of Black Guillemot in Shetland have increased in all regions except Fair Isle, South Mainland and Unst. On Fair Isle monitoring has shown that numbers peaked in 1989 but have declined steadily since (Shaw *et al.*, 2002). The overall stability on Unst (Table 2) is somewhat misleading as the majority of colonies on the main island of Unst have been increasing or remained stable, but this has been offset by substantial declines in numbers on islands in Bluemull Sound, south of Unst (Fig. 2). These islands are included in the regions Unst and Fetlar in Table 2, but collectively the population on these islands has decreased from 245 to 85. The largest proportional increase on Shetland occurred in Yell Sound where numbers increased by 5.3% per annum, from 559 in 1983 to 1,285 in 2000. Intervening counts in Yell Sound showed that in 1983–88 the rate of increase was in fact much higher, at 12.1% per annum, than in 1991–98 when it slowed to 3.9% (Heubeck, 2000).

Table 3   *Numbers of individual Black Guillemots nesting in man-made structures 1983–2001.*

Administrative area or country	SCR Census			Seabird 2000		
	Year	Individual adults	Sites	Year	Individual adults	Sites
Orkney	1983	169	3	2000	85	1
Skye & Lochalsh				2000	19	1
Argyll & Bute	1989–91	51	5	2000	41	5
Inverclyde	1987	24	not specified	2001	84	11
Cunninghame	1991	8	3	2001	44	5
Kyle & Carrick	1988–89	11	2	2001	88	6
Scotland Total		**263**	**13**		**361**	**29**
Co. Antrim	1987	13	1	2000	84	3
Co. Down	1985–88	89	9	2000	177	9
Northern Ireland Total		**102**	**10**		**261**	**12**
Scotland and Northern Ireland Total		**365**	**23**		**622**	**41**

In Orkney, numbers have declined by 15% since 1982–84. Numbers have decreased in all regions of the archipelago (Table 2) except Shapinsay, where the population has remained stable, and on South Ronaldsay and North Ronaldsay, where the populations have increased by 62% and 27% respectively. The greatest decline in proportional and absolute terms was on Westray (Table 2).

In the Western Isles, numbers have increased by 12% but have declined on Lewis from 1,866 in 1987–88 to 1,756. Most of this decline occurred in the northeast of the island (Fig. 2), but the considerable population around Loch Roag on the northwest side remained stable at 957 adults. Numbers had increased at most sites south of the Sound of Harris, except on the Monach Isles west of North Uist, where the population (819 adults in 2002) has changed little since 1988, but remains the densest aggregation of Black Guillemots in Britain and Ireland.

Numbers of Black Guillemots have declined in all administrative areas throughout the rest of their core range in northern Scotland, between east Caithness and Argyll & Bute (Table 1). Fig. 2 shows that the declines are more widespread in some administrative areas than in others, where the decline has been more localised. In northwest Scotland notable exceptions to this widespread decline occurred on the Summer Isles in west Ross & Cromarty, where numbers increased from 373 to 609 adults, and on the Small Isles, Lochaber, where numbers remained stable at 1,302 adults, compared to 1,252 adults in 1989. The largest and most widespread declines occurred in Argyll & Bute. Here, most Black Guillemots bred on small inshore islands and around large inhabited islands such as Mull, Islay and Jura. On Mull, Black Guillemots are concentrated around the lochs and islands off the west coast, but numbers were down by 40% from 733 adults in 1989–90 to 443 adults in 2000. In contrast, numbers had either changed little or increased on the nearby islands of Staffa (30 in 1991, 83 in 2000), Treshnish Isles (223 in 1989, 197 in 2000), and Coll and Tiree (40 in 1991, 83 in 2001). However, on Islay numbers declined by 36% from 943 in 1990. To the east of Islay, the island of Gigha held 473 adults in 1991 but only 275 in 2001. The only part of the mainland coast of Argyll occupied by Black Guillemots was the southern Kintyre Peninsula where the population had also decreased, from 139 in 1991 to 91 in 2001. However, just 2.5 km offshore, the population on the Sanda Islands of 442 adults in 2001 was almost double that of 281 in 1991.

In southwest Scotland, between the Clyde Estuary (Cunninghame and Inverclyde) and Loch Ryan (Kyle & Carrick), numbers have trebled since the SCR Census (Table 1). A large proportion (45%) of Black Guillemots in this area were nesting on piers and other man-made structures (Table 3).

On the Isle of Man, the population of Black Guillemots has doubled since 1985–86 (Table 1) and the increase has occurred throughout the island (Fig. 2, Sharpe & Sapsford 1999).

The Black Guillemot population in Northern Ireland has more than doubled since 1985–87 (Table 1). Previously, numbers had also doubled in 1969–87, but whilst differences in methods between the two surveys accounted for much of the change, new colonies were formed in Co. Down and Co. Londonderry (Greenwood, 1988). This expansion in 1969–87 was attributed in part to an increased use of man-made structures for nest sites. Indeed, harbour walls and piers are still an important nesting habitat in Northern Ireland and numbers of Black Guillemots using them have continued to increase, by 156% since 1985–87, and now support 22% of the population (Table 3). The largest colony in the province, on Rathlin Island, has experienced a much more modest increase, from 144 adults in 1987 to 203 in 2001.

In The Republic of Ireland it is impossible to assess whether the Seabird 2000 pre-breeding total of 3,367 Black Guillemots represents a change compared to the counts conducted in June during the SCR Census in 1985–87. From a total count of 580 in June 1985–87, Lloyd *et al.* (1991) proposed a breeding population of around 2,500 adults. However, counts during the SCR Census in Co. Waterford were conducted in April 1986 and had decreased from 61 adults to 34 in 1998–99. The current distribution of pre-breeding Black Guillemots in The Republic of Ireland is broadly similar to that of the June counts in 1985–87 (see Fig. 1 and Lloyd *et al.*, 1991). In the southwest of the Republic, Black Guillemots showed a preference for offshore islands rather than the mainland coast (Galvin *et al.*, 1999). Notable aggregations occurred at the following sites: 350 at Elengad Head/Lough Swilly area (Co. Donegal), 253 on the Aran Islands (Co. Galway), 116 at Bray Head, 85 at Wicklow Head (both in Co. Wicklow), 111 on Cape Clear Island (Co. Cork) and 83 on Rockabill (Co. Dublin).

CAUSES OF CHANGE

The lifecycle of Black Guillemots is different from the three other species of auk breeding in Britain and Ireland, and this means that their populations are controlled by a quite different suite of factors. Firstly, Black Guillemots lay two eggs as opposed to one. Cairns (1987a) suggested that this life-history strategy evolved in Black Guillemots but not in other auks, because by feeding much closer inshore, Black Guillemots were more able to ensure sufficient food provisioning to raise two chicks. Black Guillemots feed mainly on inter-tidal species (Ewins, 1990), which tend not to be of commercial interest and so are potentially less affected by direct competition with commercial fishing activities. However, commercial species, particularly sandeels, are taken if locally available and Black Guillemots in Shetland have been known to scavenge behind sandeel trawlers (Ewins, 1987) and scallop dredgers (Ewins, 1986a). Some localised mortalities do occur from entanglement with shallow-water nets and fish farm cages (Okill, 2002). They have a very eclectic diet consisting of zooplankton, crustaceans, fish and molluscs, and appear capable of switching preferences according to local abundance (Ewins, 1990). It therefore seems unlikely that food supply contributed significantly to the changes in population size of Black Guillemots in Britain and Ireland.

Another unique feature of British and Irish Black Guillemots compared to other seabirds and, indeed, more northern populations of the species, is that they do not disperse away from their breeding sites in winter (Ewins 1986b; Ewins & Kirk, 1988; Greenwood 1987, 1991; Okill, 2002). In Shetland, during the non-breeding season, Black Guillemots feed in shallow water less than 40 m

Black Guillemots tend to feed inshore on non-commercial species such as this very large butterfish (Liam Ryan)

deep, usually no more than 2 km offshore (Ewins & Kirk, 1988). This has made Black Guillemots particularly at risk from oil spills, which tend to occur close inshore and during severe winter storms.

The Shetland population has been most affected by serious oil spills in recent years. In December 1978 the *Esso Bernica* spilled 1,174 tonnes of bunker fuel oil at the Sullom Voe terminal and wiped out most of the Black Guillemots present in Yell Sound at that time, with 729 found oiled (Heubeck & Richardson, 1980). Despite the high localised mortality, the breeding population in Yell Sound recovered rapidly; in 1983 the first complete pre-breeding census of the area found 555 adults (Ewins & Tasker, 1995). The recovery continued throughout the 1980s and the population has continued to rise during the 1990s (Heubeck 2000, see above). More recently, on 5 January 1993, the oil tanker *Braer* ran aground at Garths Ness on the southwestern tip of Mainland Shetland, spilling 85,000 tonnes of crude oil. Following the spill, 219 oiled Black Guillemots were found but the total number killed was thought to be around 1,300 of which 84% were adults (Heubeck *et al.*, 1993). Populations on southwest Mainland and on Fair Isle appeared to be most affected by the *Braer* disaster and subsequent monitoring showed that recovery to pre-spill levels took 1–5 years (Heubeck, 2000). Other minor oiling incidents occurred in Shetland in 1985 and 1991, killing sufficient Black Guillemots to cause measurable declines in the population on southeast Mainland (Heubeck, 2000). However, despite the mortality caused by oil spills, the Shetland population appears to be thriving (Table 1).

The ability of the Shetland population to recover so quickly from large-scale mortality caused by oil spills suggests that the main factor controlling breeding population size is highly density-dependant. Since this is unlikely to be food supply (see above), a more likely candidate is nest site availability. Certainly the distribution of Black Guillemots in Britain and Ireland is controlled by the availability of suitable nesting habitat. They are dependant on rocky mainland coasts and islands indented by geos and headlands. The success of Black Guillemots in southwest Scotland and Northern Ireland is in part due to their utilisation of man-made nest sites such as piers, jetties, harbour walls and nest-boxes in areas where there is no available natural habitat (Carnduff, 1981; Greenwood, 1988). One particularly resourceful pair nested for several years onboard an operational car ferry in Argyll (Dickson, 1998).

Within suitable habitat, nest cavity choice is dictated largely by predator accessibility (Ewins, 1989; Greenwood, 2002) and the least accessible and visible burrows are occupied by the better quality pairs (Asbirk, 1979). Otter predation of adult Black Guillemots as well as chicks and eggs is widespread throughout Shetland (Ewins, 1985b) and probably more locally throughout the rest of Scotland. Nest cavity choice is an important factor in evading otter predation, and pairs nesting in cavities with lower ceilings and more than one entrance are more successful in otter-predated colonies on Shetland (Ewins, 1989). Good choice of nest cavities can also evade potential aerial predators, such as crows, gulls and skuas; but adult Black Guillemots away from the nest do suffer from kleptoparasitism and even direct predation by gulls and skuas. However, any cavity that is accessible to an adult Black Guillemot is in theory also accessible to mammalian predators such as rats, Stoats and possibly American Mink, provided the mammals can reach them. In Orkney and Shetland, Black Guillemots nesting on islands with rats and Stoats appeared to avoid predation by nesting in crevices high off the ground on cliffs, rather than in boulder beaches that were accessible to rats and Stoats (Ewins & Tasker, 1985). For example, on Fair Isle, Black Guillemots no longer nest in boulder beaches in response to predation by cats, which has substantially reduced numbers breeding on the island since 1989. On the Kintyre Peninsula (Argyll & Bute), where numbers are also declining, adults have been seen entering and leaving crevices around 300 m high on sheer cliffs (B. Zonfrillo, pers. comm.).

It appears that by reducing the number of safe nest sites available to Black Guillemots, the presence of mammalian predators can potentially reduce the maximum limit on population size at a colony. Thus, the introduction of predators to a previously predator-free colony may result in a decline in breeding numbers. At some sites, particularly on small low-lying islands, all potential nest cavities may be accessible to smaller mammalian predators such as rats, Stoats and mink. If predators are introduced to the site or colonise naturally, the whole site would become unsuitable for breeding Black Guillemots. Existing colonies of Black Guillemots at such sites could become extinct following the introduction (or colonisation) of predatory mammals. Conversely, Black Guillemots would be expected to return to breed at these sites following the eradication of the predators (assuming there is a surplus of non-breeders elsewhere due to a shortage of nest sites). An example of the latter scenario is available from Ailsa Craig (Kyle & Carrick) where rats were successfully eradicated in 1991 and the same year Black Guillemots raised the first-ever chick on the island (Zonfrillo & Nogales, 1992), and by 2001 there were 12 pairs breeding. Likewise, the first pair of Black Guillemots bred on Puffin Island (Gwynedd) in 2002, four years after rats were eradicated.

Eradication of predatory mammals will only lead to successful recolonisation by susceptible species like Black Guillemots if there is no chance of the predators returning. This is usually the case for rats removed from offshore islands, where they have usually been introduced by man rather than colonised naturally. Otters and American Mink are both proficient swimmers and are much more able to naturally colonise or simply visit offshore islands than rats. However, the small size of mink would suggest that they are able to access many more Black Guillemot nest cavities than otters and potentially limit the number of available safe nest sites to a much greater extent. There is some circumstantial evidence to suggest that the spread of American Mink into several areas is affecting distribution and numbers of Black Guillemots.

North American Mink were brought to fur farms in Britain around 50 years ago and have since escaped and colonised much of the country. The last survey, in 1991–97 (Green & Green, 1997), found mink to be present throughout mainland Scotland, mainly south of the Great Glen, but also in Lochaber, on the Isles of Mull, Islay and Jura (all in Argyll & Bute), in east Ross & Cromarty, Sutherland and throughout the islands of Lewis and Harris (Western Isles). Anecdotal evidence suggests that since then they have spread to other parts of mainland Scotland, the Isle of Skye and the southern Western Isles, where an eradication project is currently underway. The negative effect of mink predation on seabird numbers and breeding success has been well documented in Argyll & Bute and Lochaber (Craik, 1995, 1997, 1998). Mink are proficient swimmers and capable of covering stretches of water of 2 km or more, so that most of the network of lochs and islands in Argyll is accessible. The most devastating effects of mink have occurred since 1989 (Craik, 1997). Whilst most of the published observations are of impacts on gulls and terns, there is little doubt that the disappearance of Black Guillemots from numerous islands in Argyll & Bute is a result of mink. Fig. 2 shows that all along the mainland coast of Argyll & Bute and Lochaber, Black Guillemot colonies, with few exceptions, have reduced in size or disappeared. Most notable exceptions are islands more than 2 km offshore which are probably less accessible to mink, e.g. Staffa Island and Torran Rocks, off western Mull. Since 1995, mink have been killed at the sites of former seabird colonies in Argyll & Bute and Lochaber, and at these sites gulls and terns have recolonised and breeding success has returned to previous levels. Two such sites are the small adjacent islands of Carraig an Daimh and Dubh Sgeir in the Sound of Jura from which mink were removed in 1998 (Craik, 1998), which are virtually the only islands in the area where Black Guillemots have increased or even remain since they were last surveyed in 1990. A mink was even caught shortly after it arrived on the Sanda Islands in 1999, which is over 2 km offshore and separated from Kintyre by strong currents, which may normally prevent most mink from reaching the island, as the Black Guillemot population here is burgeoning. On Islay the core of the Black Guillemot population, on two peninsulas on the southwest side, has declined substantially but birds are now breeding in new areas around the island.

Whilst the disappearance of Black Guillemots from many small islands in Argyll & Bute appears to be consistent with the impact of mink on other breeding seabirds in the area, more detailed up-to-date information on the distribution of mink is required in order to assess the true extent of their effect on Black Guillemot populations throughout Scotland. In northern Scotland, in west Ross and Cromarty, north and west Sutherland, and north Caithness the pattern of increase and decline of Black Guillemots is very patchy (Fig. 2), representing very localised effects. The declines of most of the Scottish population outside Shetland is worrying in terms of the ability of Black Guillemots to recover. Movements of ringed birds suggest that British and Irish Black Guillemots move on average only 10.5 km and rarely more than 50 km from their natal colony (Okill, 2002). Hence, the danger is that populations become fragmented in some areas, with colonies so widely dispersed that they are unable to be sustained by immigration from other colonies.

INTERNATIONAL CONTEXT

The Black Guillemot is a circumpolar species, concentrated around the North Atlantic, Barents Sea and the Baltic, with smaller numbers around the Chukchi Sea in northern Alaska and northeast Siberia. The global population is 260,000–410,000 pairs (Table 4), although this is mainly based on rough estimates throughout most of the range due to the difficulties in estimating breeding numbers and the remoteness of breeding locations. In order to compare international totals, measured in pairs, the British and Irish counts of individuals have been used to give a maximum estimate of pairs and divided by two to reach a minimum estimate of pairs (Table 4). Thus, Britain holds 4.6–14.6% of the world population and Ireland 0.6–1.7%.

There are five subspecies (Cramp, 1985). Nominate *C. g. grylle* is confined to the Baltic coasts of Finland and Sweden (unfortunately, BirdLife International/EBCC, 2000 do not provide a separate count for the Swedish Baltic population), with fewer than ten pairs in Estonia and an unknown number on the Russian Baltic coast. Since 1970, populations in Sweden and Finland have declined by at least 20% (BirdLife International/EBCC, 2000), with the decline in the Swedish Baltic being attributed to the invasion of islands by mink (Olsson, 1974). There is little contact between *C. g. grylle* and the Black Guillemot population in the Kattegat (Denmark and southwest Sweden) of the subspecies *C. g. arcticus*. The Danish Kattegat population is one of the few outside Britain and Ireland that has been accurately and regularly surveyed: numbers have more than doubled, between 1987 and 1996, apparently as a result of immigration from the larger Swedish population (Asbirk, 1988; BirdLife International/EBCC, 2000).

C. g. arcticus is distributed throughout the Atlantic, from Britain and Ireland in the southeast, north along the Norwegian coast into the White Sea and the coast of Murmansk and the Kola Peninsula, Russia. In the western Atlantic, *C. g. arcticus* breeds off eastern Greenland (to 69°N) and southwest Greenland (to 72°N) (Cramp, 1985), off southeast Canada (Labrador, Newfoundland and Nova Scotia) and as far south as Maine, USA. The Norwegian population appears to be declining (BirdLife International, 2000) as a result of mink predation in at least the southwest of the country (Evans, 1984a), whereas the populations in Russia and Greenland appear to stable (BirdLife International, 2000), although those in Greenland have been caught as by-catch of the salmon gill-net fishery in the past (Evans, 1984b). The British population of *C. g. arcticus* is similar in size to populations in Norway and in southwest and eastern Greenland (Table 4).

The arctic subspecies *C. g. mandtii,* is concentrated in the Barents Sea on Svalbard, Jan Mayen and Bear Island, extending east off northern Russia to the Chuckchi Sea. On the opposite side of the Chuckchi Sea there are 'a few hundred pairs' (Lensink, 1984) in northern Alaska, but the majority of North American birds are confined to the edge of the ice in northeast Canada and as far south as Hudson Bay. *C. g. mandtii* also occurs in northern Greenland. Very little is known about the population status and trends of *C. g. mandtii*, since systematic surveys, usually from aircraft, are few and restricted to relatively small parts of its range (e.g. Bradstreet, 1979; Prach & Smith, 1992), but its appears to be the most numerous of the five subspecies (Table 4).

Table 4   International context.

Country or region	Subspecies	Pairs Min	Pairs Max	Year	Source
Britain	*arcticus*	19,000[1]	38,000[2]	1999–03	Seabird 2000
Ireland	*arcticus*	2,300[1]	4,500[2]	1998–02	Seabird 2000
Denmark	*arcticus*	1,067	1,111	1996	BirdLife International/EBCC (2000)
Estonia	*grylle*	6	10	1993–2000	BirdLife International/EBCC (2000)
Faeroe Islands	*faeroensis*	3,500	3,500	1995	BirdLife International/EBCC (2000)
Finland	*grylle*	12,000	15,000	1993	BirdLife International/EBCC (2000)
Iceland	*islandicus*	30,000	50,000	1990	BirdLife International/EBCC (2000)
Norway	*arcticus*	20,000	40,000	1990	BirdLife International/EBCC (2000)
Norway (Bear Island)	*mandtii*	300	300		Evans (1984a)
Norway (Jan Mayen)	*mandtii*	100	1,000		Evans (1984a)
Norway (Svalbard)	*mandtii*	5,000	50,000	1993–2000	BirdLife International/EBCC (2000)
Russia (Murman coast of Barents Sea and White Sea)	*arcticus*	2,710	2,710[3]		Golvokin (1984)
Russia Baltic)	*grylle*	?	?		Golvokin (1984)
Sweden (Kattegat)	*arcticus*	7,000	10,000	1990	BirdLife International/EBCC (2000)
Sweden (Baltic)	*grylle*				BirdLife International/EBCC (2000)
Canada	*ultimus/arcticus*	71,500	71,500		Nettleship & Evans (1985)
Greenland (southwest and east)	*arcticus*	15,300	41,000		Evans (1984b)
Greenland (northwest)	*ultimus*	7,650	23,750		Evans (1984b)
Russia	*mandtii*	55,150	55,150		Golvokin (1984)
USA (Maine)	*arcticus*	5,000	5,000	1977	See Lloyd *et al.* (1991)
USA (Alaska)	*mandtii*	200	300		Lensink (1984)

Biogeographic Region*	Subspecies	Min	Max	Min % GB	Max % GB	Min % All Ireland	Max % All Ireland
World	All	260,000	410,000	4.6%	14.6%	0.6%	1.7%

* Not an SPA qualifying species.
Notes
[1] Total count of individuals has been divided by two to estimate minimum number of pairs
[2] Total count of individuals was used to estimate maximum number of pairs
[3] Minimum total, no maximum given

Atlantic Puffin *Fratercula arctica*

Mike P. Harris and Sarah Wanless

INTRODUCTION

The Atlantic Puffin is the most instantly recognisable and popular of all North Atlantic seabirds. Colonies are frequently major tourist attractions and puffins are used on tourist brochures from the Isles of Scilly to the Shetlands. Each year many thousands of people take boat trips to see these birds. Most visitors have a memorable experience though, even in midsummer, a colony can appear deserted during the middle of the day as most birds are either in their burrows or at sea feeding. At other times awe-inspiring numbers can be seen standing on the slopes, bobbing around on the sea or flying in vast wheels over the colony.

There are four species of puffin, all restricted to colder parts of the northern oceans. Three occur in the North Pacific whilst the fourth, the Atlantic Puffin, is found in the North Atlantic and adjacent Arctic Ocean. The breeding range of the Atlantic Puffin extends from Spitsbergen and northwest Greenland, in the high arctic, south to Brittany and the Bay of Fundy, but the species' stronghold is the low arctic coasts of the northeast Atlantic in Iceland and north Norway. The species is highly colonial with pairs typically nesting underground burrows dug in the soil of offshore islands. Where such habitat is in short supply birds nest among boulder screes or at low densities in cracks in sheer cliffs rather like Black Guillemots or Razorbills. Most colonies occur where nesting birds are safe from mammalian predators.

In most parts of Britain and Ireland, Atlantic Puffins normally attend their colonies between April and early August, although in some years a few may still be feeding chicks in early September. In general, the season starts several weeks earlier in east Britain than in the west or Ireland, with numbers of birds increasing from late February. Young puffins are independent at fledging and, as adults continue to visit east-coast colonies for up to a month after their chicks have fledged, the season tends to end synchronously on both sides of Britain (Harris, 1985).

Puffins are pelagic and we are still largely ignorant of how they spend their time away from the colony. Unlike other Atlantic auks which moult after the end of the breeding season, Atlantic Puffins postpone the main moult until the late winter, when they shed all the primaries and become flightless (Harris & Yule, 1977). Individuals from northwest Britain and Ireland disperse widely outside the breeding season with reports of ringed birds from Newfoundland and Greenland south to the Canary Islands and into the Mediterranean as far east as Italy (Harris, 2002a). In contrast, most birds from east Britain remain within the North Sea, although in recent decades some ringed puffins have been reported in the Bay of Biscay. It is possible that the rapid increase in numbers at these colonies in recent decades has resulted in an expansion of the winter range. Chicks are fed on small fish that the adult carries cross-wise in its beak. In Britain and Ireland the commonest prey is the lesser sandeel, followed by sprat, herring and a wide range of small juvenile gadoid fish (Harris, 1984), whilst in arctic waters capelin can be a staple. Fish are caught by underwater pursuit and a bird can catch several during a dive. In winter puffins eat a variety of fish, squid and pelagic crustaceans and polychaete worms.

The old ornithological and even general travel literature has graphic accounts of countless thousands of Puffins carpeting islands, whirling in front of cliffs like bees at a honey pot and even darkening the sky. The extreme of many exaggerations must be the 'twelve raik a day and 156 million thousand to a raik' that came to Ailsa Craig (Kyle & Carrick) in 1888 (Gibson, 1951). Lesser estimates must also be treated with extreme caution but even so, by the late 1800s it was apparent that numbers of puffins were starting to decline. It is impossible to construct a meaningful timetable of changes, but the most dramatic declines almost certainly occurred in the first half of the 20th century: Grassholm (Dyfed) 1893–1928, Ailsa Craig 1910–34, St Tudwals (Gwynedd) 1922–51 and St Kilda (Western Isles) 1947–57. Declines generally occurred first and were most severe in the southernmost colonies. An important finding of Operation Seafarer (1969–70) was that Britain and Ireland had many fewer Atlantic Puffins than anticipated, but it is only since then that we have obtained reliable information on population status. The decline seemed to have halted during the second half of the 20th century and numbers at some colonies, notably those on North Sea coasts increased. Harris (1984) was optimistic about the future of the Atlantic Puffin and considered that the general state of was better than it had been for almost a century. Twenty years on, the situation still seems generally favourable.

CENSUS METHODS

Puffins are censused by counting Apparently Occupied Burrows (AOB) or individual birds attending the colony area. The former is the preferred method and during both Seabird 2000 and the SCR Census (1985–87) most of the larger colonies were estimated in this way. An AOB is one with signs of current use such as fresh digging, squirts of droppings radiating from the entrance, hatched eggshells, broken vegetation or dropped fish in the entrance. Puffin burrows can generally be distinguished from rabbit burrows since the latter are usually larger and have piles of soil and pellet-like droppings at the entrance. However, there is no easy way to separate a burrow of a Manx Shearwater from that of an Atlantic Puffin. Mixed colonies of these species are relatively uncommon, but where they co-exist, for example in southwest Britain and Ireland, tape playback of Manx Shearwater calls has recently been used to distinguish burrows of the two species (see general chapter on Census Methods). Counts of AOBs are best made before or during the laying period, when birds are digging or cleaning out their burrows and when the vegetation is short. However, acceptable counts can be made at any time from late April to early August provided the vegetation does not obscure burrow entrances.

At some colonies such as those on the Farne Islands and Coquet (both in Northumberland), the Isle of May (Fife), North Rona (Western Isles) and Ynys Gwylan-fawr (Gwynedd) all, or most, of the AOBs were counted and here the main source of error would be the misclassification or overlooking of burrows. An intensive investigation (on hands and knees) of 522 AOB in ten plots during a whole-colony count on the Isle of May (a colony with rabbits but no shearwaters) found that 45 burrows had been classified wrongly (30 were too short for a puffin to nest in and 15 joined another burrow underground). However, 54 burrows had been overlooked. Assuming that these plots were representative of the survey area, the overall count was 2% too low (Harris & Wanless, 1998).

For logistical reasons such complete coverage is impossible to achieve at many colonies. In such situations the density of burrows must be determined in sample plots, the area of the colony estimated and the measures combined to arrive at an estimated population size. This approach is associated with some major sources of error. The first is a statistical problem resulting from scaling-up to estimate population size as this assumes that the sampled areas were representative of the whole colony. An attempt was made to assess the precision of estimates for St Kilda and Sule Skerry (Orkney); in the former there was a 95% chance that the true population was within 12% of the estimate (P.I. Mitchell, unpubl.), and in the latter the figure was 20% (Mitchell *et al.* in prep.). The second error is associated with determining the area of the colony, either by direct measurement or by the use of aerial photographs. To date, no rigorous check of this error has been attempted at any colony in Britain or Ireland. However, both sources of error could be avoided in at least some colonies by having many small study plots distributed evenly over the true topographic surface of the whole colony (Anker-Nilssen & Røstad, 1993).

Where birds nest under boulders (e.g. The Shiants, Western Isles), in mixed colonies with Manx Shearwaters (Skomer and Skokholm, Dyfed), in completely inaccessible places (Foula, Shetland) or at low densities along stretches of cliffs (mainland colonies), counts of burrows are impractical. In these cases there is no alternative but to count birds attending the colony. Several different approaches were used during Seabird 2000. On the Shiant Islands and at Hermaness (Shetland) counts of birds were converted to AOBs by making simultaneous calibration counts of birds ashore in areas where the number of AOBs was known. On Fair Isle (Shetland) counts were converted to pairs (taken as equal to AOBs) by concurrent observations of known numbers of colour-ringed adults seen ashore. The ratio of birds to AOBs obtained on Fair Isle was also used to convert counts of birds to AOBs on Foula (Shetland). On Skomer and Skokholm, all adults present on land and on the sea below the colony were counted on several evenings of peak attendance early in the season, when only breeders would have been present, and the maximum count was taken. Where time constraints prevented such a detailed approach, observers were requested to make counts of birds on land, close inshore or in the air during April and May, before substantial numbers of immatures begin to attend the colony, preferably in the evenings or during foggy conditions when maximum numbers of breeding adults are usually present. The high variability of such counts both within and between days, and the lack of any obvious factor influencing attendance, means that such counts are of rather limited value in assessing breeding numbers (Calvert & Robertson, 2002), but they do at least give some idea of colony size.

In Seabird 2000 the majority of colonies were surveyed in 1999–2002. However, the large colonies on Sule Skerry (Orkney), Mingulay (Western Isles) and the Isle of May (Harris & Wanless, 1998) were surveyed in 1998, and that on the Farne Islands was surveyed in 2003. The Seabird 2000 population estimate for Atlantic Puffins on Eilean Mor, the largest of the Flannan Isles (Western Isles) consisted of a sample count of AOBs in the densest part of the colony, conducted in 1998, added to a complete count of AOBs on the rest of the island, conducted in 2001.

For the calculation of total populations, some arbitrary decisions had to be made to allow the combination of counts of individuals and AOBs. The previous practice of assuming that one individual corresponded to one AOB (Cramp *et al.*, 1974; Lloyd *et al.*, 1991) was continued and applied to counts from Seabird 2000, Operation Seafarer (1969–70) and the SCR Census (1985–88). However, this approximation may result in a serious underestimate of the number of AOBs. For example, in an area containing 350 AOB on the Shiant Islands, over 21 days on average only 34 birds were visible, no birds were present on 24% of checks and the maximum count was 200 (Brooke, 1972). On Skomer and Skokholm, counts were made during known peaks of attendance prior to egg laying during both Seabird 2000 and the SCR Census. Counts made at both colonies during both censuses were divided by 1.5 assuming that 75% of all breeding adults were present.

In both the SCR Census and Seabird 2000, 83% the of the total population estimates came from counts or estimates of AOBs. In the SCR Census 65% of the counts of individual birds came from the preferred counting months and in Seabird 2000 the figure was 73%. The overall estimates of the two surveys should be broadly comparable, but detailed comparisons of numbers in the largest colonies (Table 2) recorded in the SCR Census and Seabird 2000 were restricted to colonies where counting methodologies was similar in both censuses.

CURRENT STATUS AND TRENDS

As with most of other cliff- and island-nesting seabirds in Britain and Ireland, the strongholds of the Atlantic Puffin, both in terms of colonies and total numbers, are in the north and west, with a marked gap in distribution in southern England between Flamborough Head (Humberside) and Dorset (Fig. 1). None was reported from the Isle of Wight during Seabird 2000. The distribution of puffin colonies has changed little since Operation Seafarer in 1969–70. A few small colonies have been formed, e.g. in southeast Scotland where numbers have increased spectacularly. A few very small colonies may have been lost, e.g. that on Grassholm (Dyfed), but it is quite likely that with such low numbers and irregular attendance, small peripheral colonies may have been overlooked in Seabird 2000.

Seabird 2000 estimated a total Atlantic Puffin population (including estimates of pairs from counts of individuals) of 600,751 AOB, of which 82% were in Scotland, 13% in England, 4% in Ireland and 2% in Wales (Table 1). By far the largest concentration was on St Kilda, with 55,400 AOB recorded on Dun, 51,000 AOB on Boreray, 27,500 AOB on Soay and 1,800 AOB on Hirta (plus an additional 6,000 individuals elsewhere). The next largest concentrations (rounded to the nearest 100) were on the Shiant Islands (65,200 AOB), Sule Skerry (59,500 AOB), the Farne Islands (Northumberland, 55,700 AOB), Isle of May (42,000 AOB), Fair Isle (40,000 pairs), Foula (22,500 AOB) and Coquet Island (Northumberland, 17,200 AOB). The main Welsh colonies were on Skomer and Skokholm (peak counts before the breeding season of 10,614 and 3,083 individuals, respectively). Coverage in Ireland was less complete. At the main colony on Puffin Island (Co. Kerry) 600 individuals were counted ashore and a further 4,500 individuals were estimated flying over the island in late May.

Table 1   Numbers of breeding Atlantic Puffins (AOB) in Britain and Ireland 1969–2002.

Administrative area or country	Operation Seafarer (1969–70)	SCR Census (1985–88)	Seabird 2000 (1998–2002)	Percentage change since Seafarer	Percentage change since SCR	Annual percentage change since SCR
Shetland	65,054	104,381	107,676	66%	3%	0.0%
Orkney	63,330	54,883	61,758	−2%	13%	0.9%
North coast Caithness		2,076	781		−62%	−7.2%
East coast Caithness		599	497		−17%	−1.4%
Caithness total	*28,198*	*2,675*	*1,278*	−95%	−52%	−5.5%
Northwest coast Sutherland		7,341	9,046		23%	1.6%
Sutherland total	*3,476*	*7,341*	*9,046*	*160%*	*23%*	*1.6%*
Banff & Buchan	636	213	1,026	61%	382%	10.9%
Gordon		71	619		772%	15.5%
City of Aberdeen			75			
Kincardine & Deeside	139	599	768	453%	28%	1.9%
Angus	181	2,540	190	5%	−93%	−17.1%
Northeast Fife	2,580	12,000	42,000	1528%	250%	9.4%
Kirkcaldy		860	1,641		91%	5.5%
Dunfermline			40			
City of Edinburgh			22			
East Lothian	465	1,425	28,412	6010%	1894%	27.0%
Berwickshire	39	92	21	−46%	−77%	−10.6%
Stewartry			4			
Wigtown	2	5		−100%	−100%	
Kyle & Carrick	18		20	11%		
Argyll & Bute	1,239	2,636	2,597	110%	−1%	−0.1%
Lochaber	617	1,140	1,073	74%	−6%	−0.5%
Skye & Lochalsh	502	628	110	−78%	−82%	−12.7%
Western Isles–Comhairle nan eilean	243,535	246,612[1]	234,666	−4%	−5%	−0.4%
Scotland Total	**410,011**	**438,101**	**493,042**	**20%**	**13%**	**1.2%**
Northumberland	7,200	29,559	72,882	913%	147%	6.4%
North Yorkshire		139	38		−73%	−8.3%
Humberside	997	6,946	2,612	162%	−62%	−7.3%
Isle of Wight	4			−100%		
Dorset	35		26	−26%		
Channel Islands	1,116	335	311	−72%	−7%	−0.6%
Cornwall	233	66	33	−86%	−50%	−5.1%
Isles of Scilly	100	106	121	21%	14%	1.1%
Devon	41	39	13	−68%	−67%	−7.6%
Cumbria	6	13	9	50%	−31%	−3.1%
Isle of Man	82	93	85	4%	−9%	−0.7%
England, Isle of Man and Channel Islands Total	**9,814**	**37,296**	**76,130**	**676%**	**104%**	**6.9%**
West Glamorgan		3	2		−33%	−2.7%
Dyfed	3,650	10,301	9,170	151%	−11%	−0.9%
Gwynedd	605	812	1,156	91%	42%	2.5%
Wales Total	**4,255**	**11,116**	**10,328**	**143%**	**−7%**	**−0.5%**
Great Britain, Isle of Man and Channel Islands Total	**424,080**	**486,513**	**579,500**	**37%**	**19%**	**1.7%**
Co. Antrim	1,328	2,412	1,610	21%	−33%	−2.8%
Co. Dublin	108	266	295	173%	11%	0.9%
Co. Wicklow		1	1		0%	0.0%
Co. Wexford	775	1,240	1,822	135%	47%	3.3%
Co. Cork	412	4		−100%	−100%	
Co. Kerry	18,428	12,424	9,514	−48%	−23%	−2.1%
Co. Clare	646	944	1,365	111%	45%	3.4%
Co. Mayo	3,756	2,066	5,053	35%	145%	7.4%
Co. Donegal	2,536	756	1,591	−37%	110%	6.4%
All-Ireland Total	**27,989**	**20,113**	**21,251**	**−24%**	**6%**	**0.5%**
Britain and Ireland Total	**452,069**	**506,626**	**600,751**	**33%**	**19%**	**1.6%**

Note

[1]   Includes a count for the Shiant Islands of 76,900 AOB from 1970, as these were not surveyed as part of the SCR Census; a count of 6,250 AOB for Flannan Isles East from 1992

Table 2   Changes in the number of breeding Atlantic Puffins (AOB) in Britain and Ireland at colonies where the same count units were used in the SCR Census (1985–88) and Seabird 2000 (1998–2002). ID corresponds to the colony symbols in Fig. 2.

ID	Colony	SCR Census (1985–88)	Seabird 2000 (1998–2002)	Percentage change since SCR	Annual percentage change since SCR	Percentage of population in Britain or Ireland 1998–2002
1	St Kilda[1]	154,001	142,264	−8%	−0.6%	24.5%
2	Foula[1]	48,000	22,500	−53%	−5.7%	3.9%
3	Sule Skerry[1]	46,900	59,471	27%	2.0%	10.3%
4	Farne Islands[1]	26,329	55,674	112%	5.5%	9.6%
5	Hermaness (SSSI)[1]	25,413	25,094	−1%	−0.1%	4.3%
6	Fair Isle	20,244[2]	40,000[3]	98%	5.0%	6.9%
7	Isle of May[1]	12,000	42,000	250%	9.4%	7.2%
8	Bempton Cliffs (incl. N. Flamborough Head)[2]	7,000	2,615	−63%	−7.3%	0.5%
9	Skomer	6,700[2]	7,076[4]	6%	0.5%	1.2%
10	Flannan Isles[1]	6,279	15,761	151%	8.8%	2.7%
11	Clo Mor[2]	5,870	1,502	−74%	−10.7%	0.3%
12	North Rona[1]	4,750	5,265	11%	0.7%	0.9%
13	Shetland, SW Mainland: The Nev to Kame[2]	4,682	4,853	4%	0.3%	0.8%
14	Skokholm	3,582[2]	2,055[4]	−43%	−4.5%	0.4%
15	Coquet Island[1]	3,230	17,208	433%	11.8%	3.0%
16	Berneray[2]	3,062	1,979	−35%	−3.3%	0.3%
17	Whiting Ness to Ethie Haven (SSSI)[2]	1,910	138	−93%	−17.5%	0.0%
18	Noss[2]	1,891	1,892	0%	0.0%	0.3%
19	Canna[2]	1,000	945	−6%	−0.4%	0.2%
20	Inchkeith[2]	860	1,641	91%	5.5%	0.3%
21	Handa[2]	803	735	−8%	−0.6%	0.1%
22	Great Saltee[2]	1,128	1,522	35%	2.5%	7.2%

Notes
[1] Counts of AOBs
[2] Counts of birds: 1 bird approximates to 1 AOB
[3] Counts of breeding adults: 2 adults approximate to 1 AOB
[4] Early season counts of birds: 1.5 birds approximate to 1 AOB

The general picture since the SCR Census (1985–88) has been of substantial increases in England (104%) and Scotland (13%). The increase was less pronounced in Ireland (6%) and a slight decline in the Dyfed colonies (e.g. Skomer, Skokholm) produced a decline of 7% in Wales. Numbers in the small southernmost colonies, in the Channel Islands, Devon and Cornwall, continued to decline.

Many of the counts made during Operation Seafarer (1969–70) were of low accuracy, so the percentage changes between estimates made then and during Seabird 2000 (Table 1) should be treated with caution. However, in general, numbers of Atlantic Puffins throughout most of Britain and Ireland have been increasing for the last 30 years. The most spectacular changes have undoubtedly been in east Britain. The Isle of May had 2,000 burrows in 1970, 12,000 in 1984 and 42,000 in 1998. A repeat count in 2003 found that the population had increased to 69,000 burrows, making this the largest single-island colony in Britain and Ireland (Wanless *et al.*, 2003). There was

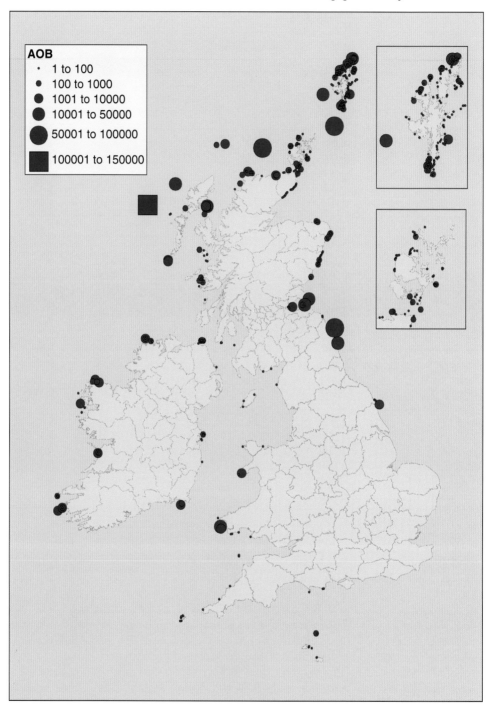

Figure 1   Abundance and distribution of breeding Atlantic Puffins in Britain and Ireland 1998–2002.

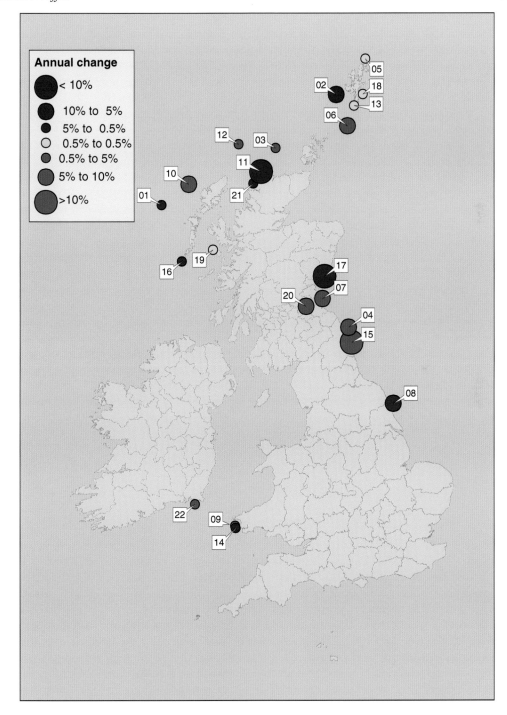

Figure 2   Changes in the number of Atlantic Puffins at colonies where the same count units were used in the SCR census (1985–88) and Seabird 2000 (1998–2002). Numbers correspond to the colonies in Table 2.

a similar dramatic increase on Coquet Island. Puffins were first seen ashore here in 1962, there were 3,000 pairs in 1986 and over 17,000 AOB in 2001. The count for the Farne Islands was delayed until 2003. Then there were 55,700 AOB. Although this was more than double the number in 1985 the rate of increase appeared to be declining, so perhaps suitable habitat is becoming limited. Between the Moray Firth (Banff & Buchan) and Flamborough Head (Humberside) numbers have increased 12–fold since Operation Seafarer (1969–70) at a mean annual rate of 8.4% (Fig. 3). There are now some 150,000 pairs of Atlantic Puffins breeding in east Britain at colonies easily visited by birdwatchers, more than at the remote and isolated St Kilda.

Access to some of the largest British colonies is far from easy and the terrain so difficult that, in general, few counts of burrows have been made in the past and/or during Seabird 2000. Where previous counts are available, interpretation of trends or even change can be difficult. For instance, between 1975 and 1999 nine estimates were made of the number of AOBs on Dun, St Kilda, through calculation of average densities (Fig. 4). Overall it appears that numbers increased, although the 1990 count was markedly lower. Counts at the other three main islands in the St Kilda archipelago are less reliable but, in contrast, suggest a decline over the same period. Undoubtedly one of the largest declines has been on Foula where annual estimates have yielded 70,000 burrows in 1976, 48,000 AOB in 1987, and 20,000–25,000 pairs in 2000. The last estimate was based on counts of birds ashore on one evening in June corrected using a conversion factor of one adult ashore per 1.6 breeding pairs derived from studies on Fair Isle (Harvey *et al.*, 2000). A second assessment in 2000, made by counting the AOBs in an accessible area and then scaling up across all suitable habitat, was only 13,000 AOB, so the decline could be even greater than stated. Estimates of breeding pairs on Fair Isle, within sight of Foula, obtained by counting all birds ashore prior to laying, whilst at the same time acquiring a correction factor for attendance from observations of colour-ringed breeders, indicated totals of 35,000, 20,000 and 40,000 pairs in 1989, 1995 and 2000, respectively (counts of adults were halved to estimate the number of pairs). The large colony on Fair Isle has undoubtedly increased, although it is far from clear by how much. Evidence from both St Kilda and Shetland suggests that nearby colonies may show contrasting trends.

CAUSES OF CHANGE

A range of factors have been suggested for the decline of the Atlantic Puffin in the early-20th century, such as oiling, contamination by toxic residues, drowning in fishing nets, harvesting by man, predation by rats, gulls and skuas, and even damage to colonies by rabbits and sheep (Harris, 1984). A good case can be made for many of these at different colonies, but earlier declines were so widespread and gradual as to suggest some common factor acting over a wide geographic area. Harris (1984) hypothesised, on rather limited and circumstantial information, that the most likely factor was a deterioration in the food supply during the breeding season, resulting from a gradual warming of the sea (Dickson & Lee, 1972). The importance of food influencing the numbers of puffins has subsequently been clearly demonstrated by the continuing decline in numbers on the Lofoten Islands, Norway, following repeated reproductive failures and periods of reduced adult survival caused by reduced prey availability after the Norwegian spring-spawning herring stock collapsed due to over-fishing in the late 1960s and climate change (Anker-Nilssen, 1992; Durant *et al.*, 2003).

Since 1984–85, Black-legged Kittiwakes and Arctic Terns, both sandeel specialists, have suffered periods of severe breeding failures in Shetland in years when changes of oceanic currents resulted in an almost complete absence of 0–group sandeels (young of the year: Wright, 1996). As another species heavily dependent on sandeels, Atlantic Puffin would also have been expected to have

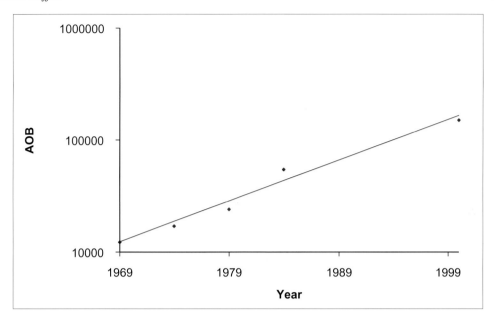

Figure 3   Numbers of Atlantic Puffins (AOB on a log-scale) in east Britain, 1969–2000. The regression indicates a mean rate of increase of 8.4% per annum (Ln(y) = 0.084x − 156, r² = 0.98, P<0.001).

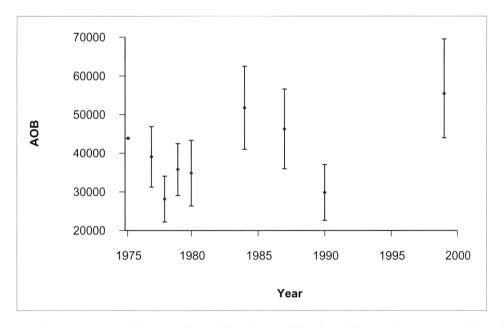

Figure 4   Estimated number of Atlantic Puffins (AOB) on Dun, St Kilda derived from complete censuses in 1975 and 1999, and from measurements of burrow density in fixed monitoring plots 1976–90. Error bars denote 95% Confidence Limits. Details from Harris & Murray (1977), Harris & Rothery (1988), Thomson & Walsh (1996) and Mitchell et al. (in prep.).

shown reductions in breeding success in this area. There was no evidence of problems until 1985 when puffins on Foula had a poor season (R. W. Furness, pers. comm.). Between 1986 and 2002 dead emaciated chicks and a low frequency of puffins seen carrying fish were recorded at the three Shetland colonies where puffins were observed in some detail. During this period, partial or complete breeding failure was recorded in ten out of 18 years of monitoring at Foula in the west (R. W. Furness, pers. comm.), in six out of 11 years at Hermaness in the north (Martin, 1989, 2002), and once in 15 years at Fair Isle in the south (Fair Isle Bird Observatory reports). In 1987–89 very low success was recorded at Hermaness and Foula, whereas on Fair Isle, 70–76% of burrows were successful. When provisioning chicks, Atlantic Puffins in Britain are thought to feed within 15–20 km of the colony (Harris, 1984). Fair Isle and Foula are 65 km apart so it is likely that the adults from the two colonies feed in different areas. On Fair Isle the breeding success of Atlantic Puffins (which have a single-egg clutch) and kittiwakes (2–3 eggs) tended to fluctuate in synchrony, suggesting that their common food source was the main determinant of breeding success in both species (Fig. 5). However, the amplitude of these fluctuations was less extreme in the Atlantic Puffin, for two probable reasons. First, with the chick safe down a burrow, both adults can be away foraging almost all of the time, whereas when both adult kittiwakes are away the chicks are at serious risk of predation by larger gulls and Great Skuas. Second, being a diving species the puffin can exploit prey unavailable to the kittiwake, which is limited to the near-surface of the sea. Numbers of kittiwakes in Shetland declined significantly during the 1980s and 1990s (Heubeck *et al.*, 1999), as apparently did puffins on Foula. However, that the total count of puffins in Shetland during Seabird 2000 was higher than previously shows how resilient Atlantic Puffins can be to periodic failures in breeding.

During the above studies in Shetland, no measurements were made of chick condition. However, on Dun, St Kilda, fledglings have been weighed in most years since 1973, and fledging weight has been shown to be a strong predictor of annual breeding success (Harris *et al.*, 1998). There has been

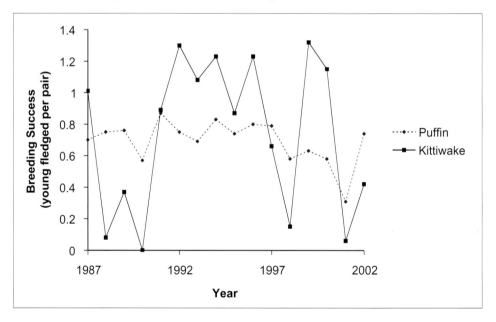

Figure 5   Breeding success of Atlantic Puffin and Black-legged Kittiwake on Fair Isle 1987–2002. Atlantic Puffin only ever has a single-egg clutch whereas the kittiwake lays up to three eggs. (Data from annual contract reports of Fair Isle Bird Observatory Trust to JNCC.)

a highly significant decline in fledging weights over the last 30 years with chicks being notably light in five of the last 13 years, suggesting that breeding success may also have declined. In contrast, success at most British colonies outside Shetland appears to have been high in the last 15–20 years (Mavor *et al.*, 2002). Years of poor productivity have tended to occur when large numbers of burrows excavated at flat colonies have been flooded by heavy rain (several east coast colonies in 1997–98) or where cats and ferrets killed chicks. Conditions must have been outstandingly favourable in the North Sea to allow the prolonged period of rapid increase.

Puffins cause severe damage to the ground where they burrow at high density in shallow soil in flat areas or overlaying steep sloping rock, and appear to have dug themselves out of house-and-home on Grassholm. Part of the colony on Dun, St Kilda, containing some 5,000 burrows, disappeared between 1974 and 2000, apparently due to severe soil erosion (Mitchell *et al.*, in prep.).

Brown Rats eating eggs and chicks have been cited as the cause for many declines in puffin numbers, for example on some of the Faeroe Islands, Lundy (Devon), St Tudwals Islands (Gwynedd) and Handa (Sutherland). Numbers of puffins on Ailsa Craig (Kyle & Carrick) declined dramatically in the late 1800s, following the arrival of rats, and by the 1930s the puffin was virtually extinct as a breeder. After rats were eliminated in 1990–91, puffins started to be seen ashore again within a few

Atlantic Puffin with sandeels (Chris Gomersall)

years and were seen carrying fish in 2002 (Zonfrillo, 2002). A similar rat eradication programme was undertaken on Handa (Sutherland) and this was followed by an increase in the area occupied by puffins on the main island in 2000, following an initial recolonisation the year before (Stoneman, 2000). Where Atlantic Puffins and Brown Rats occur on the same island, numbers of puffins are either small or the birds nest out of reach of the rats on offshore stacks or on the cliffs. Puffins can, however, co-exist with Black Rats, for instance on the Shiant Islands numbers have remained more-or-less constant for 30 years, despite Black Rats seeming to take some eggs and/or chicks (Harris, 1984; Brooke *et al.*, 2002).

Adult puffins have an annual survival in excess of 90% per annum, so that any increase in mortality can potentially have a serious effect on breeding numbers (Harris *et al.*, 2000). Hunting for meat and feathers caused large declines and extirpations in the southern part of the range in North America in the 18th and 19th centuries (Lowther *et al.*, 2002). Such practices are now unknown in Britain and Ireland but there is a continuing annual harvest of 90,000 in the Faeroes and 180,000 in Iceland (for local consumption and export to the Faeroes) that may be adversely affecting local populations (A. Petersen, pers. comm.; J.-K. Jensen, pers. comm.). At some colonies Great Black-backed Gulls kill large numbers of puffins (7,800 corpses were collected on Dun in three years), although perhaps half of these are naïve immatures that spend much time flying over the colonies (Harris, 1980). Predation by Great Black-backed and Herring Gulls was found to be responsible for some declines at Russian colonies (Anker-Nilssen & Tatarinkova, 2000). These gulls appear not to be a threat to adult Atlantic Puffins in Britain and Ireland, but at some colonies Herring and Lesser Black-backed Gulls steal substantial numbers of fish being brought to puffin chicks. Numbers of these large gulls have been controlled at some seabird colonies, mainly as a precautionary measure since there are few quantitative data on their effects on other species. However, on the Isle of May the presence of gulls has been shown to significantly reduce the local recruitment of young puffins breeding for the first time, and the removal of gulls increased the attractiveness of areas of the colony to puffins (Finney *et al.*, 2003).

Given that puffins spend so much of their time away from land it is difficult to assess the main sources of mortality during the winter. Despite the fact that perhaps two million puffins attend British and Irish colonies, individuals are only infrequently seen during at-sea surveys outside the breeding season and large concentrations of birds are rarely reported. This suggests that when away from the colonies, puffins occur at low density over vast areas of sea and hence are generally less vulnerable to local disasters than species such as Common Guillemot that often occur in flocks.

Wrecks, where large numbers of birds are washed ashore dead or dying, often after severe weather, are rarely recorded for the Atlantic Puffin. However, one occurred in east Britain in February 1983 (when many of the birds were flightless) and another in Shetland in December 1990–January 1991 (Jones *et al.*, 1985; Harris *et al.*, 1991). These wrecks can be severe enough for their effects to be detected by studies monitoring the survival rates of adult puffins (Harris *et al.*, 2000). The dispersed pelagic lifestyle of the puffin means that in general the species is less affected by oil spills than, for instance, Common Guillemot and Razorbill, but again there are exceptions. Oil from the *Torrey Canyon* (1967), *Amoco Cadiz* (1978) and *Tanio* (1980) disasters was probably the major cause of the decline in auks at the Breton colonies (Siorat, in press a). The sinking of the oil tanker *Prestige* off northwest Spain in November 2002 killed at least 2,000 Atlantic Puffins, mainly from colonies in north and west Britain and Ireland (Camphuysen *et al.*, 2002). Although this is the largest man-induced mortality of Atlantic Puffins yet recorded it is unlikely that the effect will be noticeable at the colonies. The levels of toxic chemicals and heavy metals in Atlantic Puffins appear too low to depress survival or breeding success, and although Atlantic Puffins accumulate plastic and similar artefacts in their stomach, these again appear not to cause mortality (Harris & Osborn, 1981; Harris & Wanless, 1994).

The greatest threat to British and Irish Atlantic Puffins would appear to be changes in the summer food supply, either resulting from man's over-exploitation of sandeel stocks or by some natural event such as climate change. However, one should perhaps not be too complacent and care must be exercised in keeping island colonies free of rats, mink, foxes and other predatory mammals.

INTERNATIONAL CONTEXT

In recent times, the Atlantic Puffin has usually been considered to comprise three subspecies, separated solely on size, although probably only two deserve recognition. Nominate *F .a. arctica* breeds in Iceland, most of Norway and Russia, and the west Atlantic. Atlantic Puffins breeding in Britain, Ireland, France, the Faeroes and southwest Norway tend to be smaller, and were assigned the name *grabae*. However, within Europe there is a continuous latitudinal cline in wing length, with large birds in the north and small birds in the south, and no obvious discontinuity that makes it easy to assign geographical limits to *grabae* and *arctica*. Protein evidence also suggests that there is no justification for separating *grabae* in the southeast Atlantic colonies from *arctica* in the north, and thus the name *grabae* is best discarded (Moen, 1991; Lowther *et al.*, 2002). The distinctive large and massive-beaked *F. a. naumanni* is confined to the Arctic, with colonies in Spitsbergen, Jan Mayen and northernmost Greenland.

Britain holds 9–11% and Ireland around 0.3% of the total population of *F. a. arctica*, and to all intents and purposes a similar proportion of the world population of Atlantic Puffins, as there are relatively few of the other subspecies *naumanni* (Table 3).

The puffin is one of the most numerous birds in Iceland with an estimated 2–3 million pairs distributed in several hundred colonies, the largest being on the Westmann Islands (Petersen, 1998). Numbers at some colonies have declined following over-hunting or due to predation by introduced mink, but little is known of overall changes (A. Petersen, pers. comm.). The population in the Faeroes is put at roughly 550,000 pairs, but it is unclear whether numbers are stable or declining (Skov *et al.*, 2002).

The Norwegian population is currently 1.5–2 million pairs (T. Anker-Nilssen, pers. comm.). Numbers at Røst, in the Lofoten Islands, declined from almost 1.5 million pairs in 1979 to fewer than 400,000 pairs in 2002 as a result of a failure in the food supply (Anker-Nilssen, 1992; Anker-Nilssen & Aarvak, 2003). In contrast, further north in Finnmark, where puffins depend on capelin and sandeels, numbers have been either stable or slightly increasing, whilst the largest colony in southern Norway, Runde (50,000–100,000 pairs), has increased slightly since 1980 (Lorentsen, 2001).

The Russian population of 5,000 pairs decreased sharply during the 1960s and 1970s but has since remained fairly stable (Anker-Nilssen & Tatarinkova, 2000). Numbers in France have declined dramatically over the last 50 years, from around 8,000 pairs in 1950 to fewer than 1,000 in 1969–70 and about 250 pairs in 1987–88 and subsequently (Siorat, in press a).

The North American population of *arctica* is around 350,000–400,000 pairs and is probably increasing (Lowther *et al.*, 2002). In addition there are some 5,000–8,000 pairs in the low-arctic part of Greenland (Boertmann 1994).

The population of high-arctic *naumanni* is very small, perhaps 10,000 pairs in Svalbard, 1,000 pairs on Jan Mayen, a few hundred pairs in northwest Greenland, fewer than 100 pairs in Novaya Zemlya, and 10–20 pairs on Coburg Island, in northeast Canada (Nettleship & Evans, 1985; van Franeker *et al.*, 1998; Bakken, 2000; Robards *et al.*, 2000).

Table 3   International context.

Country or region	Subspecies	Number of pairs		Year	Source
		Min	Max		
Great Britain, Isle of Man					
and Channel Isles	*arctica*[1]	600,000	600,000	1998–2003	Seabird 2000
All Ireland	*arctica*[1]	21,000	21,000	1998–2001	Seabird 2000
Fareoes	*arctica*[1]	550,000	550,000	1987	Skov *et al.* (2002)
France	*arctica*[1]	257	257	2000	Siorat (in press)
Greenland	*arctica*	5,000	8,000	1994	Boertmann (1994)
Greenland	*naumanni*	300	300		Nettleship & Evans (1985)
Iceland	*arctica*	2,500,000	3,000,000	1998	Petersen (1998)
Norway	*arctica*[2]	1,500,000	2,000,000	2000	T. Anker-Nilssen (pers. comm.)
Norway (Jan Mayen)	*naumanni*	1,000	1,000	1983	van Francker *et al.* (1998))
Norway (Spitsbergen)	*naumanni*	10,000	10,000	1989	Bakken (2000
Russia	*arctica*	5,000	5,000	2000	Anker-Nilssen & Tatarinkova (2000)
Russia (Novaya Zemlya)	*naumanni*	50	50	1996	Bakken (2000)
Canada	*arctica*	350,000	400,000	2000	Lowther *et al.* (2002)
Canada[3]	*naumanni*	14	14	1998	Robards *et al.* (2000)
USA	*arctica*	550	550	2002	S. Kress (pers. comm.)

Biogeographic region		Min	Max	Min % GB	Max % GB	Min % Ireland	Max % Ireland
Atlantic*	*arctica*	5,500,000	6,600,000	9.1%	10.9%	0.3%	0.4%
World	all	5,500,000	6,600,000	9.1%	10.9%	0.3%	0.4%

* Stroud *et al.* (2001) used the total population of *grabae* as the relevant biogeographic population, but this is now considered to be indistinct from *artica*, so the total population for *arctica* has been used here.

Notes

[1] Formerly considered as *P. a. grabae*

[2] Southern birds formerly considered as *P. a. grabae*

[3] Coburg Island, Nunayut (min only, max not given).

(Chris Gomersall)

Causes of Seabird Population Change

Norman Ratcliffe

INTRODUCTION

The populations of the 25 seabird species that breed in Britain and Ireland show contrasting trends since the mid-1980s, and within species there are often varying trends among regions (see species chapters). Understanding the reasons for changes in seabird populations is important for several reasons. From an academic point of view, it provides insight into the population biology of seabirds (Croxall & Rothery, 1991), how their populations might be regulated (Birkhead & Furness, 1985) and pressures operating on fitness and life-history tactics (Newton, 1989; Stearns, 1992). From an applied point of view, accurate diagnosis of the causes of seabird population change is essential for implementation of appropriate management, be it remedial conservation action for declining species (Green & Hirons, 1991; Green, 2002) or control of expanding populations of pest species (Feare, 1991; Wanless *et al.*, 1996).

DEMOGRAPHIC CAUSES OF POPULATION CHANGE

Diagnosing or predicting the effects of threats on seabird populations requires some understanding of seabird population dynamics and the manner in which these influence population size (Croxall & Rothery, 1991). The trends of seabird breeding populations are determined by the balance between losses to adult mortality and gains from recruitment. Where the mortality is equal to recruitment the population will remain stable, but declines will occur where mortality exceeds recruitment and growth in the reverse case (Newton, 1998).

CHARACTERISTICS OF SEABIRD DEMOGRAPHY

The characteristics of seabird population dynamics are quite different from those of most landbirds (Weimerskirch, 2002). Annual adult survival rates are high and usually fall between 80 and 95%, with those of cormorants, gulls and terns generally lower than those of auks, gannets and petrels (Buckland, 1982; Wanless *et al.*, 1996; Catchpole *et al.*, 1997; Prévot-Julliard *et al.*, 1998; Fredriksen & Bregnballe, 2000b; Harris *et al.*, 2000b; Ratcliffe *et al.*, 2002). Adult survival rates also exhibit a relatively low variability among years, although mass-mortality events can reduce survival to atypically low levels (Potts *et al.*, 1980; Coulson & Strowger, 1999; Harris *et al.*, 2000b).

Productivity is comparatively low in seabirds owing to small clutch sizes. Petrels, gannets, guillemots, puffins and Razorbills lay a single egg, skuas, Black Guillemots, Roseate and Sandwich Terns lay two eggs, and gulls and other terns a maximum of three eggs whilst cormorants and shags lay up to five eggs but with a modal average of three (Cramp & Simmons, 1977, 1983 Cramp 1985). Clutch or chick mortality rates may be high at some sites in some years (Monaghan *et al.*, 1989; Hamer *et al.*, 1991; Craik, 1997; Nur & Sydeman, 1999; Ratcliffe *et al.*, 2000), with the severity and frequency of loss tending to be higher in terns, cormorants, gulls and skuas than in auks, gannets and petrels. Losses can be compensated to some extent by replacement clutches (Brown & Morris, 1996; Mínguez, 1997; Heubeck, 1999; Wendeln & Becker, 2000), but double-brooding (raising more than one brood in a year) is rare in seabirds (Hays, 1984; Wanless & Harris, 1997). Most British and Irish seabirds are capable of breeding annually, but intermittent breeding (birds with previous breeding experience refraining from breeding for one or more years) occurs in some species. The occurrence of intermittent breeding is low in auks and skuas (Harris & Wanless, 1995; Catry *et al.*, 1998) but can be high in European Shags and gulls (Aebischer & Wanless, 1992; Calladine & Harris, 1997; O'Connell *et al.*, 1997).

Juvenile survival is lower than adult survival, generally falling between 30 and 70% and tends to be more variable between years than adult survival (Catchpole *et al.*, 1997; Wernham *et al.*, 1997; Fredriksen & Bregnballe, 2000b; Lebreton *et al.*, 2003). Maturity is delayed, with several years elapsing between fledging and recruitment into the breeding population. The modal age of first breeding is 2–3 years old for cormorants and Black Guillemots (Potts *et al.*, 1980; Hudson, 1985; Fredriksen *et al.*; 2001), three for terns (Lebreton *et al.*, 2003), 4–5 for gulls, gannets and the other British breeding auk species (Chabrzyk & Coulson, 1976; Nelson, 1978; Hudson, 1985; Porter & Coulson, 1987), seven for Great Skuas (Ratcliffe *et al.*, 1998a) and nine for fulmars (Ollason & Dunnet, 1978). The delay in maturity results in the total seabird population being divided into non-breeding and breeding components. The census results presented in this book and hence the discussion within this chapter are concerned with the breeding component of the population. However, non-breeding populations are still an important component of population dynamics, as these birds provide future recruitment and can buffer changes in breeding population sizes (Klomp & Furness, 1992).

Recruitment is the rate at which immatures join the breeding population for the first time, and is determined by productivity, the age at which birds breed for the first time and the likelihood of a bird surviving to this age. Variation in any one of these parameters can cause changes in recruitment rate. Due to low productivity and immature survival, and delayed age of first breeding, the rate of recruitment is low in seabirds. This means that the rate at which seabird breeding populations can increase is relatively slow compared to most landbirds. As such, seabird populations can only increase slowly in response to improvements in habitat quality, and may take several years to recover from a discrete mass adult mortality event (Potts *et al.*, 1980; Ford *et al.*, 1982).

There is a clear pattern to demographic parameters across taxonomic groups, with families such as cormorants, terns and gulls having relatively low survival and high recruitment rates, and the converse being true of the petrels, auks, gannets and Great Skuas (Weimerskirch, 2002). These contrasting life-history strategies have important implications for the rate at which populations change in response to given percentage changes in survival and recruitment.

SENSITIVITY OF BREEDING POPULATIONS TO CHANGES IN DEMOGRAPHIC PARAMETERS

Seabird population trends can be affected by changes in any one of the above parameters, but the sensitivity of the population to given changes in the rates of each parameter varies (Croxall & Rothery, 1991). High breeding adult survival rates and low recruitment rates mean that 85–95% of a seabird breeding population comprises experienced adults as opposed to first-timers. Seabird population trends are therefore extremely sensitive to a given change in a parameter that affects the number of experienced breeding adults (Croxall & Rothery, 1991). Small long-term reductions in adult mortality can cause rapid declines in population size (Croxall *et al.*, 1990), and mass-mortality incidents affecting adults can cause catastrophic declines in breeding populations (Potts *et al.*, 1980). Those seabird species with high survival rates and low recruitment are especially sensitive to changes in adult mortality. The breeding population size is also very sensitive to changes in the proportion of mature birds that attempt to breed, and non-breeding events may cause notable short-term declines in population size (Aebischer, 1986; Nur & Sydeman, 1999).

In contrast, the small proportion of the population comprising first-time breeders results in population trends being relatively insensitive to a given change in those parameters that affect recruitment (Croxall & Rothery, 1991). Those seabird species with relatively low survival rate and high recruitment will have relatively high sensitivity to changes in those parameters that determine recruitment rates. Even if no recruitment whatsoever occurred in a given year the breeding population would only decline at the rate of adult mortality (5–15% in most species). Hence even complete breeding failures or juvenile mass-mortality events occurring in a single year have relatively small effects on the breeding population size. Furthermore, deferred breeding means that several years will elapse before the cohort affected by such an event reaches the age at which they recruit into the breeding population (Croxall & Rothery, 1991).

IMMIGRATION AND EMIGRATION

Movements of seabirds can also be important in determining population trends at spatial scales smaller than the species' biogeographic range. Immigration and emigration of birds may occur among a group of colonies, collectively termed as a metapopulation (Spendelow *et al.*, 1996). The limits of the metapopulation can straddle administrative and political boundaries, such that emigration and immigration has the potential to affect regional and national trends (see Roseate Tern chapter). Dispersal is most common between fledging and recruitment (Lebreton *et al.*, 2003), and immigration can be an important determinant of population trends at small colonies receiving recruitment from larger ones (Murray & Wanless, 1997; Ratcliffe *et al.*, 1998b). Seabirds are generally site-faithful once they have bred at a colony for the first time, although some species may exhibit significant movements of adults among colonies (Spendelow *et al.*, 1996; Danchin *et al.*, 1998; Crawford, 2003).

POPULATION REGULATION AND DENSITY-DEPENDENCE

In stable and undisturbed habitats, bird populations do not normally grow or decline without bounds. Populations tend to stabilise or fluctuate around an average level, with the fluctuations in size being lower than would be expected if the demographic parameters for a population varied independently (Newton, 1998). Breeding numbers are therefore regulated in some manner by factors that curb the rate of increase as numbers rise, and slow the rate of decrease as numbers decline. This is due to demographic parameters being affected by the density of birds in a population, usually owing to intra-specific competition for resources such as food or nesting sites (Birkhead & Furness, 1985; Newton, 1998). For example, a decline in density owing to reduced adult survival rate may free nest sites, such that rates of recruitment or immigration increase and the population returns to the equilibrium level. There is evidence for density-dependent variation in productivity (Potts *et al.*, 1980; Coulson *et al.*, 1982; Spaans *et al.*, 1987), recruitment age (Croxall *et al.*, 1990; Klomp & Furness, 1992), intermittent breeding (Migot, 1992), inter-site movements (Duncan, 1978; Potts *et al.*, 1980) and adult survival (Coulson & Wooller, 1976; Fredriksen & Bregnballe, 2000a). Changes in each of these with density have the potential to buffer the rates at which populations change.

Density-dependence obviously does not maintain all seabird populations at a stable level as many of the species breeding in Britain and Ireland exhibited marked population changes between the SCR and Seabird 2000 censuses. The most obvious cause of this is that the resources seabirds require for reproduction or survival change, and so the population grows or declines until a different equilibrium level is reached. However, seabird populations can also decline owing to losses that are unrelated to resource availability (e.g. due to predation, disease, exploitation, pollution or storms) where these exceed the mechanisms of density-dependent compensation in the population. These can reduce the population to levels well below those expected from resource availability, and may result in extinction (Newton, 1998). Once these factors cease to operate, density-dependence will allow the population to recover back to the carrying capacity. Given the slow recruitment rates in seabirds recovery may take several years or even decades, and during this period the population size is limited by phenotypic constraints on population growth rates (e.g. maximum clutch size and minimum age of sexual maturity) rather than the availability of resources.

METHODS OF DIAGNOSIS OF POPULATION CHANGE

Accurate diagnosis of population trends is problematic for all bird groups, but is especially so for seabirds. Seabirds spend a large proportion of their time at sea and many species are migratory, wintering in areas far removed from the breeding colonies where population trends are detected. The distribution and ecology of many seabird species in the marine environment throughout the year is poorly understood, and there is usually a paucity of quantitative information on interactions of seabirds with perceived threats. Population level experiments to determine causes of change robustly are generally unfeasible owing to the large scale at which treatments must be implemented and an inability to manipulate key variables. Despite these difficulties, attempts to diagnose the causes of population change of all seabird species breeding in Britain and Ireland have been made throughout this book. The reliability of these diagnoses varies from speculative to robust according to the analytical methods employed and the quality of information available.

DIAGNOSIS USING CENSUS DATA

The diagnosis of factors driving population change can be achieved purely from two discrete censuses such as the SCR and Seabird 2000. A list of variables that could plausibly be driving the decline is produced based on knowledge of the species' biology. Correlations between trends in population size and these external variables are then examined across regions, with association being assumed to indicate causation (Green & Hirons, 1991). This approach has been applied successfully to many declining species (Green, 1995) and is used in many of the species chapters in this book. The problem with this approach is that factors identified as being spatially associated with population change may be merely coincidental rather than causal, and factors operating away from the colonies may not be identified at all. Many populations of seabirds that breed in different regions of Britain and Ireland also have different wintering areas (Wernham *et al.*, 2003) and, in such cases, the risk of misdiagnosis using the correlative approach is especially high.

DIAGNOSIS USING ANNUAL MONITORING DATA

Inclusion of more information reduces the risk of misdiagnosis using the correlative approach. Annual population trends at sample colonies surveyed as part of the Seabird Monitoring Programme can provide information on patterns of change between the two surveys that narrow the list of candidate variables explaining the change further. Correlations with explanatory variables can be examined in relation to time as well as space, which improves the reliability of the diagnosis. Annual trends within sites may also indicate the changes in demographic parameters responsible for population change and facilitate a more accurate diagnosis. For example, sudden large declines in population size among successive years followed by a period of slow recovery is likely to be indicative of a mass-mortality incident (Potts *et al.*, 1980), whereas a sudden decline followed by an immediate recovery probably indicates a year in which birds deferred breeding (Nur & Sydeman, 1999). However, this approach is only applicable to such extreme events, and is of little help in determining causes of slow, long-term declines that could be due to chronic reductions in either survival or recruitment.

DIAGNOSIS USING DEMOGRAPHIC DATA

Direct information on the demographic parameters driving the population decline are often of enormous assistance in identifying or narrowing the list of candidate external variables driving it (Green & Hirons, 1991). The minimum demographic parameters required to effectively diagnose declines in seabird populations are age-specific survival rates, productivity, the proportion of mature birds that breed and age of first breeding (Croxall & Rothery, 1991). Simulation models can be used to assess which demographic parameters have changed sufficiently to cause the observed population declines. Attention is then focused on those external variables most likely to affect the implicated parameter (Green & Hirons, 1991). For example, if productivity were driving the decline, investigation would focus on factors operating around the colony, whereas if overwinter survival were affected attention would shift to those operating along migration routes and in wintering areas.

The availability of demographic parameters to enable robust diagnosis of trends varies enormously according to the species and the parameter in question, as well as spatially and temporally. The Seabird Monitoring Programme collects productivity data for most species at a wide geographical range of sites, and this can be useful for diagnosis of trends driven by this parameter. Data from burrow-nesting species are seldom available however, and few data for any species are available from the west coasts of Scotland and Ireland. Survival estimates are scarce for most species, and there are considerable problems in estimating age-dependent survival rates accurately. The most reliable estimates of survival rates, breeding likelihood and age of first breeding are derived from resighting colour-marked birds at colonies (Clobert & Lebreton, 1991), but the intensive nature of such studies and necessity for easy access to the colony result in the number of sites and range of species studied being relatively small. Permanent emigration, especially between fledging and recruitment will also result in survival being underestimated (Clobert & Lebreton, 1991; Lebreton *et al.*, 2003). Survival rate estimates from recoveries of dead ringed birds do not suffer from problems with emigration since recoveries are collected globally. However, the low recovery rates in seabirds combined with the non-random spatial, temporal and age-specific patterns of ringing often result in survival estimates derived from ring recoveries being imprecise and biased (Anderson *et al.*, 1985; Clobert & Lebreton, 1991).

EXTERNAL FACTORS

Even in cases where the trends of a species and the demographic causes of this are well known, the ultimate causes of the decline can still be extremely difficult to identify with confidence (Harris *et al.*, 2000b). Data on factors affecting seabird demography at sea, where they spend the majority of their lives, are often anecdotal or altogether absent. Information on distribution of birds outside the breeding season and factors causing mortality comes mainly from ring recoveries, but these are generally highly biased towards those locations and causes of death that make recovery more likely (Wernham *et al.*, 2003). Trends in many anthropogenic threats causing mortality such as fishery bycatch or shooting are poorly known, and may be under-reported for fear of intervention by conservationists or the fact that such practices are illegal. Trends in marine food supply are likely to be important in driving seabird population trends, but fisheries data are seldom available for the fish species or age-classes that seabirds feed on. Even in cases where data for appropriate fish species and ages are available, these are often not sampled at the scales and locations that would provide information on prey availability to seabirds. Research can be focused on likely factors causing decline once the population trends has been recognised and the demographic causes of this have been diagnosed. However, such initiatives often occur well after the population decline has occurred and the factor causing it has ceased to be important. Furthermore, the complexities of the interactions of seabird populations with the marine environment, and difficulty in quantifying explanatory variables often make the questions posed by such research intractable.

FUTURE MONITORING & RESEARCH

Further monitoring and research into seabird population trends and demographics, and the factors determining these are clearly required in the future. Another complete census similar to that in Seabird 2000 will be carried out around 2015, and improved monitoring of annual population trends at sample colonies between these surveys is now being planned and implemented. The monitoring of demographic rates of seabirds is also likely to expand to study a wider range of parameters at more sites and for more species. Increasingly, links are being forged between seabird biologists and other research areas in the marine environment in order to improve understanding of factors affecting seabird demography and trends in these. These data will be pivotal to describing and diagnosing population trends of seabirds over the next 15 years.

CAUSES OF CHANGE

Any factor that affects a demographic parameter of seabirds can cause a change in population status. Whether it does so is dependent on the magnitude of its effect on the demographic parameter, and the sensitivity of the seabird population to changes in this parameter. The level and magnitude of the effects of most factors upon demography will vary through space and time, and so may be important in determining population trends in some time periods or areas but not in others. Factors also affect different species to different degrees depending on their ecology, demography and distribution throughout the year. Studies of seabirds throughout the world have identified a large number of factors that are likely to affect their demography and population trends, and these are outlined in the following sections.

EXPLOITATION AND PERSECUTION

Historic exploitation and persecution in Britain and Ireland

Exploitation of seabirds by man has occurred throughout human history and remains a threat to seabird populations in many regions of the world (Croxall *et al.*, 1984; Boersma *et al.*, 2002). Seabird exploitation has occurred in Scotland since prehistoric times, with the bones of seabirds being discovered in middens dating back to the Neolithic period on Papa Westray (Serjeantson, 1988). Exploitation of seabirds for food in the form of meat and eggs, fuel in the form of oil or bait for fishing was an important aspect of subsistence in remote communities along the coasts of Scotland and Ireland until the late 1800s (Lloyd *et al.*, 1991).

Exploitation of seabirds probably reached a peak during the 19th century owing to increased human populations and their demand for seabird products. Wealthy Victorian gentlemen accumulated large private collections of eggs and stuffed birds, whilst fashionable ladies of the time wore hats elaborately decorated with feathers (Lloyd *et al.*, 1991). Improvements in design of boats and guns at this time permitted the demands of this market to be met (Furness, 1993). Seabirds are vulnerable to such high levels of persecution owing to their colonial and often confiding nature making it simple to kill large numbers of birds, and the sensitivity of their populations to small increases in adult mortality. The Great Auk that nested in the North Atlantic, including some islands off Scotland, was driven to extinction by exploitation for food and collecting by the mid-1800s (Nettleship & Evans, 1985). Other species were fortunate not to follow the same fate. The millinery trade and egging drove tern populations in northern Europe and North America to critically low levels in the late 1800s (Parslow, 1967; Gochfeld *et al.*, 1998; Bijlsma *et al.*, 2001; Nisbet, 2002), and collecting threatened the persistence of the Great Skua population on Shetland during the early 1800s (Furness, 1987).

During the mid-1800s, public opinion turned against exploitation of seabirds. The Protection of Birds at Sea Bill was passed in 1869, and development of legislation to protect seabirds and their habitats has occurred throughout Britain and Europe since then. It is likely to be at least partially responsible for the increases in most seabirds species observed between the 1930s and the mid-1980s in Britain (Coulson, 1963; Potts *et al.*, 1980; Lloyd *et al.*, 1991).

CURRENT EXPLOITATION AND PERSECUTION IN BRITAIN AND IRELAND

Whilst the persecution of seabirds has been enormously reduced, some killing of adults or removal of eggs is still undertaken. Herring, Great Black-backed and Lesser Black-backed Gull numbers are controlled by a combination of poisoning, disturbance and nest raking at islands and moors around Britain and Ireland with the aim of limiting their adverse impacts on other nesting seabirds, gamebirds or upon human health or property (Duncan, 1978; Wanless & Langslow, 1983; Casey *et al.*, 1995; Wanless *et al.*, 1996). The rapid growth of urban-nesting gulls has given rise to concerns over health and property damage (Hatch, 1996; Rock, 2003). This has lead to demands for culls, although practical problems of control in urban areas (Rock, 2003) have prevented widespread culling to date.

Great Cormorants continue to be shot under license to protect angling and commercial fishery interests, and illegal persecution occurs in some areas at rates that may affect population trends (see Great Cormorant chapter). Great and Arctic Skuas are also shot under license or illegally in some parts of Scotland, and this may affect local population trends and distribution (see Great and Arctic Skua chapters). Harvesting of Black-headed Gull eggs for food under license still occurs in some parts of Britain. Illegal egg collecting still results in the loss of clutches of rarer species such as Roseate Tern, Little Tern and Mediterranean Gull. A traditional harvesting of gannet chicks on Sula Sgeir in the Western Isles persists under license to the present day, and this appears to have slowed population growth there (see Northern Gannet chapter).

EXPLOITATION AND PERSECUTION OF BRITISH AND IRISH SEABIRDS ABROAD

Whilst persecution of seabirds within Britain and Ireland has largely abated, many seabird species winter outside our waters and may suffer exploitation there. Boys in West Africa trap large numbers of immature terns for sport, food and sale (Dunn & Mead, 1982; Ntiamoa-Baidu *et al.*, 1992; Stienen *et al.*, 1998). Reduced recruitment owing to this may have played a role in the decline of Roseate Terns in Britain and Ireland (see Roseate Tern chapter). Protective legislation and education in Ghana caused a cessation of tern trapping along the coast by 1994 (Ntiamoa-Badiu, 1991), but subsequent research has demonstrated a resurgence of this activity in recent years (Ghana Wildlife Society, unpubl.). Large numbers of auks were shot around the coasts of Norway in the 1960s and 1970s (Barrett & Vader, 1984) and these included auks ringed in Britain and Ireland wintering there (Merne, 2002; Harris, 2002a,b). Shooting auks in Norway was made illegal in 1979 and the number of auks reported as shot has since declined (Heubeck *et al.*, 1991).

INCIDENTAL MORTALITY

BYCATCH IN NETS

Monofilament gill nets are set to catch pelagic or demersal fish or squid by entanglement, but these may also catch and kill seabirds. These nets may drift on a line of buoys in deeper offshore waters, or be fixed using weights or stakes in inshore waters or near wrecks and reefs (Potter & Pawson, 1991). Pelagic drift nets were several kilometres long, and killed millions of seabirds, turtles and cetaceans before they were banned in 1993 (Montevecchi, 2002). However, their use in the northeast Atlantic was confined to a small tuna fishing fleet and no seabird bycatch was recorded in this during observations (Woodley & Earle, 1991), such that effects on British and Irish Seabirds were likely to have been minor.

Inshore fixed gill nets may be a source of considerable mortality for pursuit-diving seabirds, especially if set close to large breeding colonies (Piatt & Nettleship, 1987). Net entanglement is thought to have caused reduced alcid populations in Norway (Straan *et al.*, 1991), Greenland (Evans & Nettleship, 1985), Japan (Piatt & Gould, 1994) and Canada (Carter & Sealy, 1984), and shag populations in Spain (Velando & Freire, 2002).

In Britain and Ireland the use of fixed gill nets targeting salmonids, gadoids and bass increased through the 1970s and 1980s and their use was widespread by the late 1980s (Northridge, 1988; Northridge *et al.*, 1991; Potter & Pawson, 1991). Studies of bycatch mortality in Britain showed that large numbers of auks may be caught and drowned in these nets but the rates were insufficient to cause local population declines (Robins, 1991; Harrison & Robins, 1992; Thomas, 1992; Murray, 1993; Dunn, 1994; Murray *et al.*, 1994). Bycatch of seabirds in salmon nets also occurs in Ireland (Bibby, 1971; Melville, 1973; Whilde, 1979; Watson & Radford, 1982; Smiddy, 1987; Murray, 1993) and this has been associated with population declines at some auk colonies along these coasts during the 1970s and 1980s (Brazier & Merne, 1989; Lester & Kavanagh, 1982; Lloyd *et al.*, 1991). Over the past decade, the gill net fishery in British and Irish waters has declined owing to dwindling fish stocks, and so the bycatch threat posed to auks is now reduced.

The use of fixed nets was also widespread along the coasts of Europe (Northridge *et al.*, 1991), and ringing studies show that British and Irish auks wintering in these areas were often trapped and drowned (Mead, 1989; Harris, 2002a,b; Merne, 2002). Mortality is especially heavy in gill nets along the coasts of Norway, Sweden and Denmark (Barrett & Vader, 1984, Oldén *et al.*, 1985; Peterz & Oldén, 1987). Mortality of British and Irish ringed Razorbills was also high in Iberia (Castro, 1984; Teixeira, 1986; Lester & Kavanagh, 1992), although numbers caught at some localities have declined (Granadeiro & Silva, 1993). Thousands of auks were also killed annually in the Baie de Seine in France (Vincent, 1990). Mortality in nets outside British waters during winter was insufficient to cause population declines of auks in Britain and Ireland to date and, unless there are large increases in fishing effort using these methods, it is unlikely to do so in the future.

BYCATCH ON LONGLINES

Longlining is a fishing method that involves setting several kilometre-long fishing lines with thousands of baited hooks (Bjordal & Løkkeborg, 1992). Scavenging seabirds attempt to snatch bait from the hooks as the line is set, and some become hooked and drowned (Brothers *et al.*, 1999). Bycatch mortality of petrels and albatrosses in the southern hemisphere can be extremely high (Brothers *et al.*, 1999) and can elevate mortality to the degree that chronic populations declines occur (Croxall *et al.*, 1990; Weimerskirch & Jouventin, 1987; Weimerskirch *et al.* 1997).

In the northeast Atlantic, longlining targets ling, tusk, hake, grenadiers (Family Macrouridae), and greater forkbeard (ICES, 2002a), and occurs along the shelf edges off Norway, Scotland and Ireland and around Iceland and the Faeroes (Brothers *et al.*, 1999). Northern Fulmar is the seabird species most often accidentally caught on longlines in the northeast Atlantic, but large gulls, Northern Gannets and Great Skuas have also been reported as bycatch (see Dunn & Steel, 2001 for review). The levels of longline mortality suffered by Northern Fulmars are poorly quantified. The population growth rate of fulmar has slowed between SCR and Seabird 2000 compared to previous decades, and declines have occurred on Shetland (see Northern Fulmar chapter). However, changes in food availability may also be involved in these changes in population trends and so the role of longline mortality is unclear (see Northern Fulmar chapter).

The deep-water longline fishery has grown since the late 1980s as traditional shelf-trawling fisheries have declined (ICES, 2002a). The potential for increased bycatch mortality may be cause for concern, but the adoption of mitigation measures may compensate for increased fishing effort. Mitigation measures include use of streamer lines to scare birds away from the bait, underwater tubes to set lines below the depth birds can reach bait, or setting lines at night when fewer birds are feeding (Løkkeborg, 1998; Brothers *et al.*, 1999). Since reduction in bycatch mortality also results in reduced loss of bait, and hence improved target fish catches, there is incentive for fishermen to adopt these practices (Løkkeborg, 2000). Furthermore, many of the fish species exploited by longline fleets are declining and so fishing effort at current levels appears to be unsustainable (ICES, 2002a). Fisheries scientists have recommended an immediate reduction in fishing pressure on overexploited deep-sea stocks (ICES, 2002a), and this may lead to concomitant declines in fulmar bycatch mortality.

During fishing activities, gear is occasionally lost or discarded. Nylon nets and lines are very durable in the marine environment, and so entanglement can continue to cause mortality long after regulations to prevent this have been implemented (Montevecchi, 2002). Seabirds collected dead on beaches are often entangled in fishing gear (Tasker *et al.*, 2000), and nets or lines are incorporated into nests of gannets and cormorants that may subsequently entangle adults or chicks (Montevecchi, 1991). However, the level of mortality caused by lost nets and lines is likely to be relatively minor at the population scale.

COLLISION WITH WIND TURBINES

Offshore wind farms are at present a rarity, but increases in construction are forecast over the next decade in order to meet the UK governments target to obtain 10% of electrical energy from renewable resources by the year 2010. Substantial landbird mortality owing to collision with rotor blades or guy lines of wind turbines has been documented at terrestrial sites (Winkleman, 1985; Orloff & Flannery, 1996; Johnson *et al.*, 2001), and in some cases may be sufficient to affect population growth (Hunt *et al.*, 1999).

The levels of mortality caused by offshore wind farms is poorly understood owing to the lack of a reliable method to estimate collision mortality at sea where corpses float away or sink (ICES, 2002b). Behavioural studies have found that a large proportion of seabirds fly at heights within the span of turbine rotors, and so there is potential for collision mortality (Kürger & Garthe, 2001; ICES, 2002b). Radar studies have proved that birds display avoidance behaviour when approaching turbines, but this is impaired where visibility is poor or in tail winds (ICES, 2002b).

Prior to a wind farm licensing round the UK government will undertake a Strategic Environmental Assessment (SEA) that will assess the potential environmental impacts, including impacts on seabirds, of installing wind farms. This will allow wind farms to be placed where the environmental impacts of development will be minimised.

PREDATION

Seabirds nest colonially in dense aggregations that represent abundant food sources for predators. Their predator defence behaviour is generally poorly developed and their demography makes them sensitive to small increases in mortality, especially if this is focused on adults. The strategy that most seabirds adopt to cope with predation pressure is avoidance, with most species nesting in sites such as cliffs, offshore islands, spits or remote beaches where predators are scarce or absent. The distribution and availability of such predator-free nesting sites is an important determinant of seabird range, and is likely to regulate population size to some extent by preventing colonisation of areas that would otherwise be suitable for breeding (Birkhead & Furness, 1985).

Changes in the distribution, behaviour or diet of predators can result in seabirds suffering extremely high predation rates, with consequent declines in productivity, increased emigration, extirpation of colonies and long-term loss of breeding sites, and these may lead to overall population declines. The best examples of this come from introductions of mammalian predators to islands, which have resulted in many seabird species being reduced to perilously low global levels (Moors & Atkinson, 1984).

Mammalian predation

In Britain, Brown Rats are the species of mammalian predator that has been most commonly introduced to offshore islands. Rats can cause severe predation of seabird eggs and chicks, with cavity- or burrow-nesting species being particularly susceptible (Atkinson, 1985). Rat predation has been associated with population declines and extirpation of Manx Shearwaters on Canna, Western Isles, and the Calf of Man, and of puffins on Ailsa Craig, Argyll & Bute, and Puffin Island, Gwynedd (see Atlantic Puffin and Manx Shearwater chapters). The distribution of European and Leach's Storm-petrels is confined to islands without rats (see relevant species chapters). Advancements in rodenticides and methods of deploying these have resulted in it being possible to eradicate rats from large islands (Buckle, 1994), and this form of seabird colony restoration is becoming increasingly common in Britain. Rat eradication projects have been implemented on Ailsa Craig (Zonfrillo, 2000), Puffin Island (Ratcliffe & Sandison, 2001), Handa (Willcox, 2001), Ramsey (Bell *et al.*, 2000), Lundy (Appleton *et al.*, 2002) and uninhabited islands in the Scillies (Heaney *et al.*, 2002). The results of some of these projects are encouraging, with species recolonising islands following rat removal (Zonfrillo & Nogales, 1992; Zonfrillo, 2002; Willcox, 2002). However, assessing their success in terms of influencing regional and national population trends will demand long-term monitoring work.

American Mink were introduced to Britain and Ireland when they escaped from fur farms (Dunstone, 1993) and now occupy Lewis, Harris and mainland Scotland as far north as the Great Glen (Green & Green, 1997). Mink are adept swimmers and can easily gain access to inshore colonies of terns, gulls and Black Guillemots. Their predation causes complete breeding failures, adult mortality and ultimately site abandonment (Craik, 1995, 1997; Rae, 1999; Clode & MacDonald, 2000). This has resulted in a redistribution of birds to offshore islands free of mink along the west coast of Scotland (Craik, 1997) and an overall decline in numbers (see Common and Arctic Tern, Common and Black-headed Gull and Black Guillemot chapters). Mink control has been implemented at key colonies along the west coast of Scotland and these are effective in increasing productivity and preventing extirpation (Craik, 1997, 1998). A five-year project to eradicate mink from the Uists and reduce numbers in Harris is currently being implemented in the Western Isles (Scottish National Heritage, 2001). The trends of seabirds in these areas are likely to depend on the success of these projects.

American Mink (Mustela vison) *(NHPA/Stephen Krasemann)*

Mink predation—these Common Tern chicks and adults were recovered from the cache of a single American Mink on an island in Loch Linnhe (Argyll and Bute) in 1989. The colony was subsequently deserted (J.C.A. Craik)

Feral cats have been responsible for catastrophic declines of seabird populations on oceanic islands around the world (e.g. Bloomer & Bester, 1992; Ashmole *et al.*, 1994). In Britain, cats are believed to have caused population declines of nocturnal petrels on Foula, Noss and Fetlar in Shetland, and on Canna in the Hebrides. Cats also prey on tern chicks at some colonies along the coasts of mainland Scotland. The effects of cat predation on seabird population distribution and populations has to date been localised, and is unlikely to influence seabird numbers in the future unless feral populations establish on other offshore islands.

Indigenous predators can also cause declines of seabirds when their abundance, distribution or behaviour alters in a manner that brings them into increasing contact with colonies. Red Foxes have increased in Britain and Ireland in the last decades owing to a relaxation in game-keeping, and their range has expanded into East Anglia, southeast England and southeast Scotland (Tapper, 1992). In these regions, low-lying offshore islands are rare and competition for space on these can be intense (see below). Consequently, a large proportion of the populations of some tern species in Britain and Ireland nest on remote beaches, sand spits and inshore islets that are accessible to foxes (see tern and gull species chapters). Once a colony has been discovered it will often be repeatedly attacked until successive years of breeding failures lead to abandonment of the site (Ratcliffe *et al.*, 2000). Repeated breeding failures, elevated intermittent breeding and a loss of available nesting sites may ultimately lead to population declines owing to reduced productivity and recruitment (see tern species chapters). Wardens attempt to protect terns from fox predation at key sites using electric fencing, nocturnal patrols or shooting (Patterson, 1977; Haddon & Knight, 1981). These doubtless reduce incursion rates of foxes into a colony but are not completely reliable, and even a single visit by a fox can cause large-scale losses of eggs and chicks (Ratcliffe *et al.*, 2000).

AVIAN PREDATORS

Seabirds nesting on offshore islands and cliffs free from mammalian predators are not altogether safe from predation. Important avian predators of seabirds in Britain and Ireland are raptors, skuas and gulls, with owls and corvids being occasional predators. The distribution of some seabird predators has expanded during last few decades and predation at some colonies has increased in consequence. Furthermore, avian predation on seabirds is generally conducted by a small number of specialist birds (Spear, 1993; Votier, 2001) and so changes in predator behaviour rather than abundance can be the most important determinant of the level of mortality (Furness, 1997b).

Great Skuas are formidable predators and are capable of killing all seabird species breeding in Britain and Ireland including adult gannets and Great Black-backed Gulls, but smaller species such as petrels, kittiwakes and puffins are generally favoured (Furness, 1997b). Great Skua population and range have increased enormously in Britain and Ireland over the last 30 years (see Great Skua chapter) and the proportion of these feeding on seabirds has increased owing to reductions in availability of alternative prey in the Northern Isles and a preference for seabird prey in smaller peripheral colonies (Furness, 1997b). The numbers of seabirds killed by Great Skuas annually can be substantial. Great Skuas on St Kilda and Hermaness have been estimated to kill 40,800 and 11,000 seabirds per annum respectively (Phillips *et al.*, 1999a; Votier, 2001). Predation rates on some seabird species seem likely to cause population declines. The decline of kittiwakes on St Kilda and some colonies in Shetland is likely to be at least in part due to Great Skua predation (Heubeck *et al.*, 1999; Phillips *et al.*, 1999b). The large number of Leach's Storm-petrels taken on St Kilda (Phillips *et al.*, 1999a) is also unlikely to be sustainable in the long term, and monitoring on the island of Dun in 2003 has detected declines since 1999 (P. I. Mitchell, pers. comm.). Declines of Arctic Skuas in Shetland and Orkney are possibly in part due to Great Skua predation of fledglings (see Arctic Skua chapter). Given the conservation value and protected status of Great Skuas, these conflicts of conservation interest are difficult to reconcile (Phillips *et al.*, 1999b).

Gulls are also predators of seabirds, with Great Black-backed Gulls being predators of adult Atlantic Puffins and Herring, Lesser Black-backed and Black-headed Gulls predating tern chicks (Thomas, 1972; Harris, 1984). The impacts of this predation on populations are poorly quantified but probably minor in most cases, although predation on tern chicks at some sites in some years is certainly sufficient to reduce future natal recruitment. Large gulls are controlled at some offshore islands to protect nesting terns, but this is generally targeted more at preventing nest site competition than predation (see below).

Conspecific predation of eggs and chicks can also be high in gull and Great Skua colonies. During periods of food shortage conspecific predation increases as parents must spend more time foraging for chicks rather than guarding them (Hamer *et al.*, 1991; Bukacinski *et al.*, 1996, 1998; Perrins & Smith, 2000) and hungry chicks tend to wander into neighbouring territories (Hunt & McLoon, 1975; Bukacinski *et al.*, 1998). Conspecific predation also increases with colony density and is likely to be an important mechanism for density-dependent population regulation in gulls and Great Skuas (Spaans *et al.*, 1987).

Raptors can also prey on seabirds, and their populations have generally increased in Britain and Ireland following relaxation of persecution and cessation of DDT pollution. Raptor predation is unlikely to be a factor driving seabird population trends at the national level, but can be locally significant at some sites in some years. Kestrel predation on Little Tern chicks has caused almost complete breeding failure in some years at site like Great Yarmouth, Chesil Beach and Langstone Harbour (see Little Tern chapter). Peregrines prey on adult seabirds (Paine *et al.*, 1990; Nisbet, 1992), and it is possible that their predation at colonies in Anglesey led to regional declines of Roseate Terns by increasing mortality and causing emigration to Ireland (Avery & del Nevo, 1991). Short-eared Owls have caused significant predation on adult terns and their chicks at some sites, such as Holy Island and Kilcoole, although their effects on population trends are localised. The decline of European Storm-petrels on Skomer is probably due to predation by introduced Little Owls (see European Storm-Petrel chapter). Introduced White-tailed Sea Eagles in western Scotland prey on seabirds during summer, especially Northern Fulmars (A. Dowse, pers. comm.), but the effects of this on the local colony trends are as yet unknown. Some raptors are species of conservation concern and all are protected by law, such that conflicts of interest with seabird conservation are difficult to mange.

DISEASE AND NATURAL TOXINS

Seabirds nest in dense colonies and many species feed their chicks and partners by regurgitation. Transmission rates of parasites and disease would therefore be expected to be high compared to other avian groups. Birds are hosts to a wide range of viruses, diseases and internal and external invertebrate parasites (Friend & Franson, 1999). There is some evidence for adverse effects of some parasites and diseases on seabird demography, but their effects on population trends is generally poorly understood.

AVIAN BOTULISM

Avian botulism is caused by *Clostridium botulinum*, a widespread bacterium that occurs in dead animal tissue and within the digestive tracts of saprophytic invertebrates (Friend & Franson, 1999).

The bacterium produces a neuroparalytic toxin that induces paralysis and death in birds which ingest sufficient quantities of carrion or infected invertebrates (Friend & Franson, 1999). In Britain and Ireland *C. botulinum* occurs at rubbish tips where there is abundant decaying food and in stagnant freshwater and brackish pools (Lloyd *et al.*, 1976). Gulls commonly scavenge on rubbish tips (Kihlman & Larsson, 1974; Greig *et al.*, 1986; Horton *et al.*, 1993) and bathe and roost in pools (Lloyd *et al.*, 1976), and so are exposed to botulism toxins more than other seabirds. Mass-mortality incidents involving gulls displaying symptoms of botulism poisoning were first recognised in 1975 (Lloyd *et al.*, 1976) and have frequently recurred since then (see gull species chapters). Reductions in numbers at affected colonies explain a large proportion of the decline in the British and Irish Herring Gull population (see Herring Gull chapter). Improved waste management at tips such as burying refuse shortly after it is deposited and waste incineration may lead to reductions in the frequency of botulism epizootics in the future.

PUFFINOSIS

Puffinosis is a condition that affects Manx Shearwater chicks approaching fledging age on Skomer and Skokholm in Pembrokeshire. Symptoms include blistering on the feet, conjunctivitis and paralysis, and results in the death of 75% of affected birds (Brooke, 1990). The cause of Puffinosis is still unknown, but it is likely to be some form of corona virus (Nuttall *et al.*, 1982). The condition occurs annually, but the number of chicks affected varies among years. In severe years, Puffinosis can result in the death of *c*.4% of the fledglings on Skomer and Skokholm. This may produce small reductions in subsequent recruitment rate, but is unlikely to have large effects on breeding population trends (Brooke, 1990).

TICKS

Of the many ectoparasites found on seabirds, ticks are those most often associated with effects on demography. Ticks are arachnid haematophagous ectoparasites that spend most of the year in the hosts' nesting substrate and attach themselves to hosts for a few days once a year to ingest a blood meal (Danchin, 1992). In addition to causing blood loss, ticks can transmit disease to seabirds (Chastel, 1988). Infestation can be sufficiently high at some colonies to cause chick mortality and reduced productivity (Feare, 1976; Duffy, 1983; Danchin *et al.*, 1998; Ramos *et al.*, 2001), and may exacerbate the effects of poor food availability when chicks are already weak (Ramos *et al.*, 2001). Tick abundance increases with the age of a colony (Danchin, 1992) and high infection rates may result in reduced recruitment, adult emigration or colony abandonment (Duffy, 1983; Danchin *et al.*, 1998). Ticks may therefore have some influence over seabird distribution and local population trends.

RED TIDES

Dinoflagellate algae produce a potent neuroparalytic toxin, and can form dense blooms known as red tides. During red tides large numbers of dinoflagellates are ingested by fish eaten by seabirds, causing paralysis and death. Mass mortalities of seabirds attributed to red tides occurred in northeast England in 1968, 1978 and 1997/98 (Coulson *et al.*, 1968; Armstrong *et al.*, 1978; Coulson & Strowger 1999). A wide range of seabird species were killed, but population effects were manifested mainly in shags on the Farnes during 1968 (Potts *et al.*, 1980) and kittiwakes at Tyneside in 1997/98. (Coulson & Strowger, 1999). These incidents are infrequent and have only been reported from northeast England, and so are only likely to have short-term and localised effects on population trends.

FOOD AVAILABILITY

Seabird demography is strongly affected by the availability of food. Availability of prey is related to its abundance in the wider environment, but other factors such as prey behaviour, weather, oceanography and interactions with other marine organisms may also affect it. Relationships between food availability and demographic parameters are generally non-linear. When food availability is very low all seabirds will fail to breed or starve, but as availability improves these parameters will increase to a threshold level beyond which factors other than food are limiting (Cairns, 1987). Several studies of seabirds have found such sigmoidal relationships between demography and food availability (Cairns, 1987; Phillips *et al.*, 1996a; Suddaby & Ratcliffe, 1997; Anker-Nilssen & Aarvak, 2001).

Reproductive performance is adversely affected by relatively small reductions in food availability and many studies have described associations between food availability and seabird breeding likelihood (Boekelheide & Ainley, 1989; Crawford & Dyer, 1997; Crawford, 2003) or success (Monaghan *et al.*, 1992; Pons & Migot, 1995; Oro *et al.*, 1996; Phillips *et al.* 1996a; Ratcliffe *et al.*, 1998b; Nur & Sydeman, 1999; Anker-Nilssen & Aarvak, 2001). Adult survival rates tend to be less sensitive to reductions in food availability (Pons & Migot, 1995). These differences in sensitivity of

Common Tern with a fish (Eddie Dunne)

Sandeel fishing by Danish trawlers has been banned along the east Scottish coast since 2000, with the reopening of this area to fishing being dependent on the future breeding success of Black-legged Kittiwakes there (Chris Gomersall)

productivity and survival to changes in food availability are designed to maximise lifetime reproductive success. Reproduction is costly in terms of energy, and expending high effort in reproduction may reduce seabird survival rates (Reid, 1988; Pugesek & Diem, 1990). Seabirds are long-lived and so refrain from exerting high breeding effort in years of poor food supply in order to improve their chances of surviving to future breeding seasons (Cairns, 1987; Martin, 1987). However, reductions in adult survival have also been associated with periods of exceptionally poor food availability (Vader *et al.*, 1990; Massey *et al.*, 1992; Nur & Sydeman, 1999; Anker-Nilssen & Aarvak, 2001; Oro & Furness, 2002; Ratcliffe *et al.*, 2002), probably owing to there being insufficient food for self-maintenance. Emigration and immigration may also be related to local availability of food, especially in mobile species such as terns (Crawford, 2003).

The levels of food abundance that affect reproduction and survival of seabirds are strongly dependent on the species concerned. Effects will be manifested over higher levels of food abundance in those species that feed on the surface since these are only able to access a small proportion of the prey present (Furness & Tasker, 2000). Those that have short foraging ranges, inflexible time budgets and restricted diets are also adversely affected at higher levels of food abundance as these are unable to buffer reductions in food availability by altering their behaviour, foraging areas or diet (Furness & Tasker, 2000).

Intra-specific competition for food will also have a strong effect on availability *per capita*, and therefore competition for food will play an important role in density-dependent regulation of seabird population size (Birkhead & Furness, 1985; Newton, 1998). Competition for food could take the form of widespread depletion of food resources during winter (Lack, 1966) or local depletion within the foraging range of a colony in summer (Ashmole, 1963). Even in the absence of depletion, interference competition can cause density-dependent reductions in the availability of food owing to avoidance behaviour of prey (Lewis *et al.*, 2001) or birds accidentally or deliberately blocking one another's access to food (Caldow & Furness, 2001). Inter-specific competition for food can also be important in determining food availability. Some species are dominant in such contests (Duffy, 1986; Hudson & Furness, 1988; Shealer & Burger, 1993) and some species actively rob prey from others (Phillips *et al.*, 1996b; Ratcliffe *et al.*, 1997; Stienen *et al.*, 2002). As such, population trends of different species may be interdependent.

Food distribution is also an important determinant of seabird breeding range, since seabirds are obliged to breed on suitable predator-free nesting habitat that is within foraging range of sufficient prey resources (Birkhead & Furness, 1985). The availability of such sites may be limited for many species, especially those with short foraging ranges such as terns.

Anthropogenic activity has caused enormous changes in the types of food available to seabirds and their abundance. These have mostly produced increases in food availability that may have allowed many species to increase between the 1930s and mid-1980s. However, there has been a reduction in many of these sources over the last 15 years and this has often been associated with slower rates of increase or even declines of seabird populations.

EFFECTS OF FISHERIES ON FOOD AVAILABILITY

Harvesting by man has led to changes in the fish community composition in the northeast Atlantic and North Sea. Introduction of steam trawling and power winches between 1870 and 1900 led to a huge increase in fishing power, and this led to rapid over-exploitation and stock declines of whitefish, herring and mackerel (Furness, 1982), which are important predators of, or competitors with, smaller fish such as sandeel and sprat that form the bulk of the diet of many seabirds in Britain and Ireland (Furness, 1982). Consequent increases in abundance of small prey fish is likely to have facilitated growth of many seabird populations (Furness, 2002). Predatory fish remain important predators of sandeel, and even at depleted levels take up to ten times more sandeel than seabirds (Furness, 1990). Increasingly strict regulations on the fishing industry to protect remaining commercial fish stocks have been enforced over the last 15 years, and this may lead to a recovery of predatory fish populations. Seabirds may therefore face a reduction in availability of small prey fish in the future owing to increased competition from predatory fish, with resultant declines in population size.

Whilst the availability of small fish is likely to have increased in the long term, their population trends can be very erratic due to fluctuations in natural predation rates (Bogstadt & Mehl, 1997) and large variations in recruitment owing to spawning stock fecundity, juvenile survival and spatial patterns of larval advection (Cury & Roy, 1989; Wright & Bailey, 1993). Such fluctuations can affect the demography of seabirds and hence population size. In Shetland, failed sandeel recruitment between 1985 and 1990 (Wright & Bailey, 1993) led to successive years of breeding failure of Arctic Terns (Monaghan *et al.*, 1992), Arctic Skuas (Phillips *et al.*, 1996a), Great Skuas (Hamer *et al.*, 1991), kittiwakes (Danchin, 1992; Hamer *et al.*, 1993) and puffins (Martin, 1987). This event may have also led to reduced adult survival in some species (Oro & Furness, 2002; Ratcliffe *et al.*, 2002). Sandeel stocks have fluctuated since 1991 and produced variable breeding success in seabirds. Breeding success in Shetland during 2002 and 2003 was among the worst on record for many species, and was attributed to exceptionally poor sandeel availability (Mavor *et al.*, 2003; M. Heubeck, pers comm.). Poor availability of sandeel is probably played a role in the low productivity, reduced adult survival and population declines of kittiwakes in southeast Scotland in 1986–2000 (Harris & Wanless, 1997; Harris *et al.*, 2000; Rindorf *et al.* 2000).

The role of industrial fishing in determining sandeel population trends independently of oceanography and natural predation is poorly understood (Monaghan, 1992; Furness, 1999a,b). The amount of sandeel landed from the North Sea increased rapidly from the 1960s, and during the 1980s and 1990s 600,000–1,000,000 tonnes were taken annually (Furness, 1999b). It seems intuitive that this fishery would compete with seabirds for food. However, the reduced predation by whitefish and mackerel on sandeels appears to have compensated for increased fishing effort at broad spatial scales. Furthermore, most of the harvesting occurs in the central North Sea, beyond the foraging range of most seabird colonies and so the spatial overlap between the two is low (Wright & Begg, 1997). In situations where the ranges of foraging seabirds and sandeel fisheries overlap, such as the waters around Shetland and the Isle of May, there may be scope for localised depletion to affect seabird demography (Furness, 1999a). There is no conclusive evidence to support or refute this suggestion but, despite this, a precautionary approach to management of these fisheries has been adopted. The sandeel fishery around Shetland was closed in 1990–95 and now catches are limited to a very low level, and an industrial fishery exclusion zone has been imposed along the east Scottish coast since 2000, with the reopening of this area to fishing being dependent of future breeding success of kittiwakes there.

Whilst the extent to which fisheries have affected availability of small prey fish to seabirds is poorly understood, it is certain that waste products from fishing have provided an abundant novel food source for scavenging seabirds. Demersal and benthic fisheries produce enormous volumes of unwanted moribund fish and offal that are discarded overboard, providing food for scavenging seabirds such as fulmars, gannets, Great Skuas and gulls (Reeves & Furness, 2002). At some colonies, discards or offal comprise the majority of the diet of these species (Evans, 1973; Hamer *et al.*, 1997; Votier, 2001) and it is plausible that this food source facilitated increases in scavenging seabird populations until the late 1990s.

Over the last decade, reductions in fishing effort, increasing mesh sizes and retention of offal for conversion to fish meal has reduced the availability of this food source to seabirds, and this trend is likely to continue (Furness, 1992; Reeves & Furness, 2002). Reductions in availability of trawler discards have led to lower productivity of Audouin's (Oro *et al.*, 1996) and Yellow-legged Gulls (Oro *et al.*, 1995) in Spain, and of Lesser Black-backed Gulls on Skomer, Pembrokeshire (Perrins & Smith, 2000). Variations in availability of discards also affect winter body condition of gulls at Helgoland in the southern North Sea (Hüppop & Wurm, 2000), and so reductions in discarding rates may affect overwinter survival. The effects of reductions in discard availability may not be distributed evenly among scavenging seabird species owing to unequal inter-specific competition for this resource. In northerly waters Fulmars tend to dominate the competition for offal, and gannets and Great Skuas that for discards (Hudson & Furness, 1988). Large gulls obtain a larger proportion of discards with decreasing latitude as their competitors become rarer (Furness *et al.*, 1992; Camphuysen *et al.*, 1995; Garthe *et al.*, 1996; Walter & Becker, 1997). However, the effects of reductions in discarding on scavenging seabird population are difficult to predict as the species concerned have broad diets and can compensate by switching to alternative food sources (Phillips *et al.*, 1999c; Reeves & Furness, 2002).

EFFECTS OF DEVELOPMENT ON FOOD AVAILABILITY

Development offshore has the potential to affect seabird foraging habitats by changing abundance or availability of prey species. The construction of offshore wind farms is likely to increase greatly over the next decade in order to meet the UK government's renewable energy targets (see Incidental mortality section). This has the potential to affect seabird foraging habitats by disturbance, barrier effects or a loss of feeding habitat (BMT Cordah, 2003). Shallow sandbanks are the habitats that are the current focus of wind farm developments, and this is the favoured habitat of sandeels. Sandeels have specific habitat requirement in terms of sediment particle size and water circulation (Wright & Bailey, 1993), and the potential effects of offshore turbine construction upon these characters are presently poorly understood. The presence of turbines may also cause disturbance such that birds avoid the area (ICES, 2002b), and this may result in reduced food availability where alternative feeding sites are scarce.

Marine aggregate extraction has increased since the 1970s owing to elevated demand and improvements in dredging technology. Over the last 15 years the weight of aggregates extracted has fluctuated at 18–23 million tonnes per annum (Crown Estate, 2003). Interest in marine aggregate extraction is also growing in Ireland (ICES, 2000). Marine aggregates meet 24% of the UK sand and gravel demands, and is used for construction and beach recharge (Crown Estate, 2003). Dredging is spatially restricted by aggregate quality, water depth and proximity to markets, and is licensed by government. The main areas of exploitation in the UK are shallow sandbanks off the Humber, Great Yarmouth, Outer Thames, Isle of Wight, Severn Estuary and Liverpool Bay (Crown Estate, 2003), and the Celtic and Irish Seas in Ireland (ICES, 2000). Removal of material, alteration of particle size and fouling from sediment plumes has the potential to detrimentally affect benthic fauna and flora, including fish with specific sediment habitat requirements (ICES, 2000). As such, local sandeel abundance could be adversely affected by aggregate extraction and, if this were to occur adjacent to a colony, could impact seabird demography. However, there is no evidence to suggest adverse impacts of aggregate extraction at present and, in view of its concentration in areas sparsely populated by breeding seabirds, these are unlikely to occur in the future.

EFFECTS OF REFUSE MANAGEMENT ON FOOD AVAILABILITY

Man's wasteful habits have created novel feeding opportunities for seabirds inland as well as at sea. Enormous volumes of waste food are discarded at rubbish dumps throughout Britain and Ireland, and this represents an abundant and easily collected food source for gulls. The widespread utilisation of food on tips by gulls (Kihlman & Larsson 1974; Mudge, 1978; Horton et al., 1983; Greig et al., 1986) has probably in part facilitated increases of large gull populations during the 1970s by improving overwinter survival and productivity. Changes in management of refuse, such as burying of rubbish and incineration, are likely to have reduced availability of waste food to gulls and may affect population sizes. For example, the productivity and population of a Herring Gull colony in northern France declined following the closure of a dump (Pons & Migot, 1995). However, studies have shown that refuse is a relatively poor quality food source for gulls (Annett & Pierotti, 1999) and that alternatives such as fish are preferred (Belant et al., 1993; Oro, 1996; Bertellotti et al., 2001). As such, the availability of refuse may have less effect on gull populations than is generally thought.

Waste food sometimes never makes it to dumps but is made directly available on streets in urban areas. The growth in popularity of fast-food outlets has resulted in more food being discarded into open-topped bins or directly onto roads and pavements where it is available to gulls. Street lighting permits gulls to forage at night and exploit food dropped by revellers prior to morning road-sweeping operations (Rock, 2003). Many gulls in seaside towns also obtain food by begging fast food from tourists or taking food intended for wildfowl or pigeons. These food sources may have, in part, fuelled the spectacular growth of urban gull populations (Rock, 2003). The nuisance and health threats caused by expanding urban gull populations is a cause for concern to local councils and measures are being taken to reduce food supplies through improved waste management and byelaws

Ploughing uncovers invertebrates that are an important food source for gulls (Chris Knight)

to prohibit feeding of gulls (Rock, 2003). However, much of the food of urban gulls is obtained at sea, from tips or agricultural land (Belant *et al.*, 1993; Rock, 2003) such that removal of food supplies from the streets may have minimal effects on urban gull numbers.

EFFECTS OF FARMING ON FOOD AVAILABILITY

Changes in farming practices can also lead to increased availability of food for gulls. The trend from battery farms to free-range pig rearing has lead to large quantities of spilled animal feed becoming available to gulls in East Anglia. This is likely to have partially fuelled the increase of the gull colony at Orford Ness in Suffolk (D. Cormack, pers. comm.). Waste fish feed at the growing number of salmon farms along the coasts of west Scotland and the Northern Isles have also provided an additional source of food for gulls (ICES, 2001) and may be responsible for local colony growth (Craik & Campbell, 2000). Increased tillage may have improved availability of earthworm prey for Black-headed Gulls, but increased use of pesticides may have reduced abundance of invertebrates and caused a shift in distribution to the coast (see Black-headed Gull chapter).

NESTING HABITAT AVAILABILITY

Availability of nesting habitat operates on seabird populations and distribution at a variety of spatial scales. The availability of colony sites with suitable nesting substrates that are also free from predators and within foraging range of adequate food resources are limited for some seabird species around Britain and Ireland, and this will play an important role in determining the distribution of seabirds around our coasts. For example, the lack of cliffs and rocky offshore islands in southeast England is likely to explain the absence of many seabird species from these coasts. This could also limit population size since, if nesting habitat existed in these areas and food availability were sufficient, additional colonies might exist there. Within colonies, the availability of space for territories or sites suitable for nest building may limit population size. This is especially true where predators force birds to nest on small islets, or for species with specialist and scarce nesting habitat types.

Intra-specific competition for nest sites within colonies is among the factors responsible for density-dependent population regulation of seabird populations (Birkhead & Furness, 1985). Studies of gannets and shags show that decreasing availability of nest sites with increasing colony size result in reduced colony growth rates (Potts *et al.*, 1980; Moss *et al.*, 2002). Inter-specific competition for nest sites can also be important in determining population trends at colonies, with some species having a competitive advantage owing to larger size, greater aggression or early time of arrival compared to subdominant species. The expanding range of Great Skuas in Shetland and Orkney has displaced Arctic Skua territories and colonies (Furness, 1987). Gulls out-compete terns for nesting space on offshore islands in Britain, Ireland and North America (Thomas, 1972; Kress *et al.*, 1983), displacing the terns onto inshore islands where they suffer higher predation and reduced population size (Kress, 1997). Disturbance by gulls also reduces local recruitment of Atlantic Puffins (Finney *et al.*, 2003). Control of gull distribution on islands plays an important role in maintaining tern colonies on offshore islands in Britain and Ireland (Thomas, 1972), and removal of gulls has restored abandoned tern colonies in the USA (Kress, 1997), Isle of May (Wanless, 1988) and Rockabill (Casey *et al.*, 1995).

FACTORS CAUSING LOSS OF NESTING HABITAT

Loss of colony sites in the UK and Ireland have resulted from introduction of predators onto islands or expansion of a predators' range into areas where they were formerly scarce (see Predation section).

Many seabirds have specific nesting substrate requirements and changes in the area of these may affect local or regional population trends. Most terns require open, well-drained substrates with scattered vegetation cover for nesting. Vegetation succession can result in habitat becoming gradually overgrown with rank herbage or scrub until the colony is abandoned (Neubauer, 1998; Nisbet, 2002). At many sites, winter storms and floods prevent succession occurring, but on some reserves active management is necessary to maintain suitable nesting substrates (Nisbet, 1999, 2002). At some sites, coastal erosion results in islets being eroded with resultant loss of nesting habitat. Tern Island in Co. Wexford hosted a colony of thousands of terns in the 1960s but was washed away by storms in the mid-1970s (Cabot, 1994). Green Island in Carlingford Lough was eroded during the 1980s and lost all its vegetation, and this probably led to the loss of the Roseate Tern colony there (Cabot, 1994). Currently, the shingle spit at Lough Ryan is being eroded and this may result in loss of the tern colony there. Relative sea level rise is likely to lead to further losses of coastal habitat for terns and gulls in future decades, particularly if maintenance of existing sea defences prevents natural coastal profiles from forming inland (Norris & Buisson, 1994).

Human activity may result in loss of nesting sites and could affect distribution and possibly population size. Development for housing, industry or agriculture has resulted in widespread loss of habitat for landbirds, but seems to be a relatively minor problem for seabirds owing to their remote and coastal nesting habitats. Land claim and canalisation of rivers may have had minor effects on distribution of terns (Sears, 1993). Disturbance by humans may result in habitat becoming unsuitable for breeding seabirds. Recreational disturbance of beaches in Europe increased massively during the last century and is believed to have resulted in breeding failure and permanent abandonment of some tern colonies (Lloyd *et al.*, 1975; Thomas, 1982). Climbing on sea cliffs may also disturb birds breeding there, but there is no evidence to demonstrate this results in long-term habitat loss. Human disturbance at seabird colonies is now generally controlled by fencing and patrols by wardens (Lloyd *et al.*, 1991; Sears & Avery, 1989) and, provided this management is maintained, disturbance is unlikely to cause sufficient habitat loss in the future to influence seabird numbers.

Factors causing increases in nesting habitat

Some human activities have accidentally produced nesting habitat for seabirds in novel sites or situations. Roofs of buildings provide excellent predator-free nesting substrates, and the adoption of such habitat has permitted the rapid growth of urban gull populations (see Herring Gull chapter). Terns have also started to nest on roofs in southeast Scotland and kittiwakes nest on dock walls and warehouse window-ledges in eastern Britain where cliff habitat is unavailable. Flooded gravel workings provide nesting habitat for Common Terns and this has facilitated an expansion of their range in southeast and central England (see Common Tern chapter). Recharge of beaches or estuarine islands with dredge spoil as part of sea defence programmes has also created habitat for Little Terns in Essex (see Little Tern chapter), and for Herring Gulls in the Wash (see Herring Gull chapter). Fenced industrial enclosures and docks also provide nesting habitat for terns and Common Gulls (see Common Gull & Tern chapters). Nesting habitat for seabirds can also be created deliberately in the form of rafts for terns in reservoirs (see Common Tern chapter) or construction of dredge-spoil islands offshore (Burgess & Hirons, 1992). The latter plays an important role in conservation of terns in the USA and Australia, and has provided a new colony site for terns and Black-headed Gulls at Larne Lough, Co. Antrim. Artificial habitat has been created for kittiwakes in some parts of Britain to reduce the numbers nesting on buildings. Nest boxes can also be provided to increase the number of nest sites at a colony and the number of birds able to nest there (e.g. Avery & del Nevo, 1991).

POLLUTION

Human activities have resulted in large volumes of anthropogenic substances being released into the marine environment, and some of these may adversely affect the demography and population trends of seabirds.

Oil pollution

Oil is the most widely recognised of all threats to seabirds owing to high-profile media coverage of dead and dying birds washed ashore during spills. Even slight exposure to oil can be fatal owing to fouling of feathers and pathological effects of oil ingestion (Leighton, 1991; Briggs *et al.*, 1997). Rehabilitation of most seabird species is ineffective owing to only a small proportion of affected birds being recovered alive and the low survival rates of birds post-release (Sharp, 1996; Wernham *et al.*,

On 6 January 1993 the oil tanker Braer was grounded in storms at Garths Ness, Shetland spilling 85,000 tonnes of Gulfaks crude oil (Chris Gomersall)

1997). Seabirds may die from exposure to oil released during natural seepage but the majority of deaths accrue from either the accidental spillage of large volumes of crude oil during extraction or transportation of oil, the chronic and widespread release of fuel oil from vessels washing their tanks at sea or as run off from land (Burger, 1997).

The chronic release of fuel oil by vessels washing out their tanks kills more birds through space and time than do large industry-related spills. Beached bird surveys show that the proportion of dead oiled auks in Britain is highest in the English Channel and southern North Sea coasts (Camphuysen, 1998). The proportions of oiled birds have declined from the 1970s to the present, indicating a reduction in this source of mortality in the North Sea (Camphuysen, 1998). This is probably due to tighter legislation and enforcement of laws against this practice, and to provision of facilities at ports where vessels can wash tanks.

Tanker spills can cause mass mortality of seabirds in the affected area, and several such incidents occurred between the SCR and Seabird 2000 surveys, including the *Braer* (Shetland, January 1993), the *Sea Empress* (Pembrokeshire, February 1996), the *Erica* (Brittany, France, December 1999) and the *Prestige* (Galicia, Spain, November 2002). These have been associated with the death of large numbers of seabirds, especially auks, but the effects of such mortality on subsequent population trends has been variable. Tanker spills close to seabird colonies where local adult breeders are killed tend to have greater effects on population trends than those distant from colonies where wintering immature birds from a wide geographic area tend to be affected. The spills from the *Braer* and *Sea Empress* caused mortality and population declines of some local breeding seabirds in the following year (Baines & Earl, 1996; Heubeck, 1997). These occurred in winter when birds are relatively dispersed; had they occurred during the breeding season mortality may have been far higher. The spill from the *Erica* in Brittany killed mostly wintering immatures from the entire Irish Sea and west Scotland and was not associated with subsequent declines of the affected populations. Where oil spills have affected adult survival population declines occur in the following year, but seabird populations generally recover subsequently (Roseneau *et al.*, 1998; Heubeck, 2000). However, the low recruitment rates and deferred breeding found in seabirds mean that it might take many years before the population reaches pre-spill levels (Ford *et al.*, 1982).

The effects of large oil spills are therefore relatively short-term and localised, with no evidence of wide-scale, long-term effects on auk population trends (Clark, 1984). However, spills near colonies

An oiled Common Guillemot, which despite rehabilitation would have a very low chance of survival (Michael W Richards)

of species with a restricted range during the breeding season are of conservation concern as a large proportion of breeders could be killed and compensatory immigration would be small (Cairns & Elliot, 1987). Reduction in the risk of spills is therefore desirable, and this is being accomplished through improvements in safety procedures such as rerouting of tankers away from risk areas and provision of tugs around the coastline to rescue stricken vessels. Improvements in design are also being implemented, with single-hulled tankers being replaced by double-hulled vessels and ballast-tanks being subdivided to reduce spill volumes. All vessels are required to meet these specifications by 2015, but the delay means that the risk of large oil spills will remain for over a decade.

ORGANOCHLORIDE POLLUTION

Organochlorides are a group of compounds that are toxic to birds (Burger & Gochfeld, 2002). DDT causes eggshell thinning, and was responsible for population declines of British raptors during the 1960s and 1970s (Newton, 1972). Monitoring programmes of seabird eggs in Britain and Ireland showed that organochlorides occurred in seabirds during the 1960s, but were at levels too low to cause adverse effects (Furness, 1993). Levels of such compounds in seabirds have declined following the banning of their usage in the UK in 1964 (Furness, 1993). Spills of the pesticide Dieldrin from the Rhine in 1967 caused mass mortality of gulls and terns in the southern North Sea (Becker, 1991). This reduced the tern populations there to perilously low levels from which they are still recovering (Stienen, 2002). Seabird populations in Britain were unaffected by this incident, nor have there been any recorded mass-poisoning incidents in this country. PCBs caused embryo mortality, deformity and population declines in cormorants, gulls and terns breeding in the Great Lakes during the 1970s (Burger & Gochfeld, 2002), but levels of these compounds in Europe are below the levels required to cause these symptoms (Becker, 1991).

OTHER POLLUTANTS

Seabirds are also exposed to other pollutants such as heavy metals or plastics that they may ingest or become entangled in (Burger & Gochfeld, 2002), but these appear not to reach levels sufficient to affect seabird population trends in British and Irish waters (Furness, 1993).

OCEANOGRAPHY, CLIMATE AND WEATHER

Changes in characteristics of oceanography and climate that occur over decades or centuries and perturbations of weather that last for a matter of hours or days can affect seabird populations and hence population trends or distribution. These may act upon seabird populations by altering the abundance or distribution of food, changing nesting habitat availability or quality, or by directly affecting demography and distribution.

GLOBAL CLIMATE CHANGE

Since the 1970s, emissions of greenhouse gasses have led to a global increase in temperature at an unprecedented rate, with associated changes in climatic conditions (Intergovernmental Panel on

Climate Change, 2001). These have the potential to affect the distribution of seabirds and alter their demography directly or by altering food availability and nesting habitat (Green *et al.*, 2001). Separating the confounding effects of climate change and other anthropogenic influences on long-term seabird population trends can be difficult. Despite this, some studies have associated changes in the range and population size of seabirds with altered climatic conditions (Montevecchi & Myers, 1997; Kitaysky & Golubova, 2000; Oedekoven, 2001; Wilson *et al.*, 2001; Bunce *et al.*, 2002; Croxall *et al.*, 2002; Durant *et al.*, 2003; Weimerskirch *et al.*, 2003), but at present evidence for this affecting British and Irish seabird populations is scant. Many species in Britain do exhibit clear latitudinal patterns of distribution and abundance that may be related to temperature (e.g. skuas), and global warming may lead to northward migration of ranges (Green *et al.*, 2001). Further studies of long-term trends in seabird population status and range in relation to climate change are desirable.

LARGE-SCALE ATMOSPHERIC AND OCEANOGRAPHIC EVENTS

Large-scale oceanographic or atmospheric events have strong effects on seabird demography. The best documented of these are El Niño Southern Oscillations (ENSO), which occur when Pacific trade winds fail and permit warm water from the western Pacific to reach the eastern seaboard of the Americas (Schreiber, 2003). These events have been associated with large declines in food availability, breeding failure and elevated mortality of seabirds breeding in the Pacific (Schreiber, 2003). There is evidence that these may also affect seabird demography in the South Atlantic (Schreiber, 2003), but there is little evidence to suggest that their influence extends as far as the North Atlantic.

Climate in the North Atlantic is dominated by fluctuations of the North Atlantic Oscillation (NAO), which are caused by variations in the relative pressures of tropical and polar air masses. Positive NAO indices are caused by the pressure differentials in tropical and polar air masses being higher than normal, whilst negative indices are due to these being lower (Hurrell, 2003). This influences winter weather patterns in northern Europe, with positive indices bringing warm, wet and stormy weather and negative indices producing colder, drier conditions (Hurrell, 2003). The NAO fluctuates annually, but has a tendency to remain in one phase for several successive years (Hurrell, 2003). In 1960–80, the NAO was mostly negative, whereas in 1980–2000 it was mostly positive (Hurrell, 2003). Positive values of NAO are associated with lower abundance of zooplankton (Planque & Taylor, 1998) and lower recruitment of sandeels (Arnott & Ruxton, 2002) in the northeast Atlantic and North Sea. Fluctuations of the NAO would therefore be expected to affect availability of prey to seabirds and their populations. The likelihood of breeding fulmars attending the colony at Eynhallow in Orkney and their hatching and fledging success were all negatively related to NAO index (Thompson & Ollason, 2001). Positive NAO may also result in reduced food availability for Little Auks in Svalbard owing to intrusion of Atlantic water into the Arctic region which causes displacement of favoured plankton prey species (Karnovsky *et al.*, 2003). However, the NAO has little effect on herring recruitment and puffin demography in Norway (Durant *et al.*, 2003). Further analysis of long-term seabird demography datasets are required to elucidate the influence NAO has on seabird population trends.

SHORT-TERM WEATHER EVENTS

Seabird demography can also be influenced by short-term weather events. Storms or high spring tides can result in the nests of seabirds breeding at low elevations being washed away (Heubeck,

Severe storms in June 2000 washed eggs and chicks from seabird colonies at Sumburgh Head, Shetland (Mick Mellor)

1999; see Little Tern chapter). Storms can also elevate mortality or reduce growth rate in tern chicks owing to chilling or reduced feeding frequency (Robinson & Hamer, 2002). Heavy rain can also flood nest chambers of burrow-nesting species and cause breeding failure (Harris, 1984; Thompson & Furness, 1991). In exceptional circumstances, weather can cause elevated mortality of adults or immatures. Shag populations at the Isle of May crashed after a prolonged period of onshore winds caused a wreck during 1994 (Harris & Wanless, 1996) and reduced adult survival rates (Harris *et al.*, 2000). Hurricane Hugo reduced adult and juvenile survival of Roseate Terns and caused subsequent population declines when it passed through the staging grounds in Maine during 1991 (Lebreton *et al.*, 2003). Guillemots are also prone to massive wrecks during winter storms (Bailey & Davenport, 1972; Mudge *et al.*, 1992; Harris & Wanless, 1996) but these appear to affect mainly juveniles and have little effect on breeding population sizes in the following year (Camphuysen *et al.*, 1999). The effects of severe weather events on demography are generally occasional and localised, and are not an important determinant of long-term, large-scale population change. However, storm events may become more common in the future owing to climate change (Mitchell & Ericksen, 1992; Christensen & Christensen, 2003), and relative sea-level rise may result in greater likelihood of low-lying nests suffering tidal flooding (Norris & Buisson, 1994). Hence, weather and flooding events may become frequent and severe enough to affect population trends.

SEABIRD CONSERVATION

The growing levels of human population and demand for resources mean that wildlife and their habitats are being placed under ever-increasing pressure. Conservation is increasingly necessary to

Important colonies of ground nesting seabirds must be kept rat-free and on St Kilda measures are taken to ensure that no rats are accidentally introduced to the island when supply vessels dock (Tim Dunn)

allow biodiversity to persist, and has gained increased popularity and credibility over the past century. Seabird populations have benefited from this trend over the last several decades.

LEGISLATION

Legislation is an important component of seabird conservation, and improved enforcement of laws to protect seabirds has probably aided population increases of many species over the last 100 years (Lloyd *et al.*, 1991). The first legislation to protect seabirds was the Protection of Birds at Sea Bill (1869) and the Wildlife and Countryside Act and the Birds and Habitats Directives have provided further protection to seabirds since then. Nesting habitats have also been protected by designation of the most important seabird colonies as SPAs (Stroud *et al.*, 2001). Legislation has also been implemented that protects seabirds in the wider marine environment, such as the Merchant Shipping Act (1995) which governs pollution from ships. These are generally applied at broad spatial scales and the regulations upon activities and enforcement of these tend to be limited. Methods are now being developed to identify the offshore limits of marine extensions to seabird colony SPAs in order to protect resting, bathing and foraging areas of breeding seabirds (BirdLife International, 2000; McSorley *et al.*, 2002). Methods are also being developed to identify discrete offshore aggregations of seabirds that may eventually qualify for site designation (Skov *et al.*, 1995, 2000; Webb *et al.*, 2002). The scope for regulations and enforcement within these areas is likely to be higher than would be possible for the wider marine environment, and will provide spatially targeted protection for seabirds and their marine habitats.

ACTIVE MANAGEMENT

Law is not always sufficient to protect seabirds or their habitats because some threats to populations do not respond directly to legal regulations. Active management of colonies may be required to maintain or enhance some populations. Many seabird colony reserves are actively managed to maintain or enhance their seabird populations by organisations such as the Statutory Agencies, Royal Society for the Protection of Birds, the Wildlife Trusts and local councils. Management includes prevention of illegal exploitation and human disturbance, management of vegetation succession and exclusion or control of predators and competitors. This action has almost certainly played an important role in conserving populations of terns in Britain and Ireland (Lloyd *et al.*, 1991). Increasingly attention is focusing on restoration of sites previously important for seabirds which became unsuitable due to arrival of mammalian predators. Examples of seabird restoration projects in the UK include rat eradication on the Scilly Isles, Ailsa Craig, Lundy, Ramsey and Puffin Island, and mink control on the Argyll coast and Outer Hebrides (see Predation section). Restoration of islands by removing competing gulls forms an important component of tern conservation on the east coast of the USA (Kress, 1997), and played a role in the increase of Roseate Terns on Rockabill, Co. Dublin (Casey *et al.*, 1995). Recolonisation of abandoned colonies following restoration can be facilitated by use of decoy seabirds and playing courtship calls to attract the focal species to the site (Kress, 1997). Entirely new sites can also be created for seabirds, e.g. tern nesting rafts and dredge-spoil islands (Burgess & Hirons 1992). Nest boxes can also be used to increase the number of suitable nest sites for some species, including Roseate Tern (Avery & del Nevo, 1991).

CONFLICTS OF INTEREST

Whilst conservation has benefited seabirds and will play an important role in maintaining their populations in the future, there is a possibility that conservation will also cause problems. The diversity of the taxa receiving conservation attention is expanding rapidly and conflicts among interest features are likely to arise in consequence. Seabirds form components of complex marine and coastal communities, and interactions between species owing to competition or predation may mean that conservation efforts to increase one species lead to declines in others. For example, increasing populations of Great Skuas and birds of prey may result in declines of other seabird populations owing to increasing predation, expanding gull populations may displace tern colonies, and conservation of fish stocks may result in loss of food to seabirds owing to increased competition for small fish from larger ones and reductions in discarding. Conservationists must accept that increases in all biodiversity interest features may not be achievable, and this will force them to make difficult choices concerning the levels of the various interest features they want to be represented in their vision of an ideal coastal and marine community.

THE ROLE OF RESEARCH AND MONITORING IN CONSERVATION

Conservation legislation and management needs to be underpinned by scientific knowledge to ensure it is appropriate, and monitoring is required to determine whether policy and action is having the desired effect (Green, 2002). Further monitoring and research is therefore required to determine threats to seabirds, design appropriate policies or management measures and determine the effect of these on population trends. Periodic census work is also required to revise the list of sites that qualify as SPAs or Ramsar sites. The repeat national seabird breeding population census during 2015, and monitoring and research planned for the intervening period (see Diagnosis of change section) is likely to play an important role in informing and testing conservation initiatives in the future.

(Mike Brown)

International Importance of the Seabird Population of Britain and Ireland

James B. Reid

The effective conservation of seabirds in Europe, or anywhere, depends on knowledge of a variety of population parameters. Seabird 2000 directly addressed two crucial features of breeding populations of seabirds in Britain and Ireland, their sizes and likely trends over three decades. Whilst of absolute and intrinsic importance, irrespective of their size, the relative importance of these populations requires to be identified in order to enable practical conservation and management, as well as to inform conservation policy. Placing British and Irish seabird populations in their proper international contexts ensures that their significance is appropriately acknowledged. In the species accounts, two international contexts were recognised, the biogeographical and the global. The biogeographical context is particularly important with regard to the conservation of seabirds in Europe. Under Article 4 of the EU Directive on the Conservation of Wild Birds (EC/79/409), the 'Birds Directive', member states of the European Union are required to classify Special Protection Areas (SPAs) for important populations of birds. In Britain and Ireland, the importance of many bird populations using particular sites is assessed in the biogeographical context. The results of Seabird 2000, the third complete survey of British and Irish seabird colonies, update and redefine the biogeographical context within which seabird populations must be assessed in order to comply with the Birds

Directive. However, the extent to which the current suite of SPAs in the UK (Stroud *et al.*, 2001) or the Republic of Ireland (Larner & Douglas, 2002) remains adequate for the protection of seabirds is outwith the scope of this account.

Tables 1–2 summarise the biogeographical and global importance of the breeding seabird populations of Britain and Ireland, and are derived from the international context tables presented in the individual species chapters in this book (see chapter on Data Processing and Analysis).

Clearly, Britain and Ireland host a breeding seabird assemblage that is of outstanding international importance. Of the 25 species of seabird that breed in Britain, more than 50% of the biogeographical population of four of them breed here. Another two species have more than 30% of their biogeographical population breeding in Britain, and more than 10% of the biogeographical population of at least another seven breeds in Britain. Ireland hosts more than 10% of the biogeographical populations of at least two species.

More than 50% of the world breeding population of three species, more than 30% of another two, and more than 10% of at least a further three breeds in Britain; at least one and possibly two species have more than 10% of their world populations breeding in Ireland. More than 1% (the threshold that indicates international importance) of the global breeding populations of at least 21 species

Table 1   Biogeographical importance of breeding seabird populations in Britain and Ireland. Figures indicate the minimum and maximum percentages of the relevant biogeographical population that the British and Irish populations represent. The relevant biogeographical populations for each species are defined in Stroud et al. (2001) and are specified in the species accounts. Black Guillemot does not feature in the Table as it falls outside the scope of the EU Birds Directive.

Species	Britain min	Britain max	Ireland min	Ireland max
Northern Fulmar	12.2%	18.5%	1.0%	1.4%
Manx Shearwater	68.3%	91.2%	6.6%	17.9%
European Storm-petrel	3.1%	11.3%	10.7%	42.7%
Leach's Storm-petrel	0.7%	1.3%	0.0%	0.0%
Northern Gannet	59.0%	59.0%	8.5%	8.5%
Great Cormorant[1]	13.4%	13.7%	9.8%	10.0%
European Shag	39.7%	43.9%	5.1%	5.6%
Arctic Skua	6.0%	14.0%	0.0%	0.0%
Great Skua	60.0%	60.0%	0.0%	0.0%
Mediterranean Gull	0.1%	0.1%	0.0%	0.0%
Black-headed Gull	4.6%	6.2%	0.5%	0.7%
Common Gull	7.4%	12.0%	0.2%	0.4%
Lesser Black-backed Gull	65.4%	65.4%	2.7%	2.7%
Herring Gull	17.9%	20.3%	0.8%	0.9%
Great Black-backed Gull	16.8%	17.0%	2.2%	2.2%
Black-legged Kittiwake	12.3%	14.8%	1.6%	2.0%
Sandwich Tern	13.9%	15.9%	4.7%	5.4%
Roseate Tern	2.2%	2.7%	30.8%	38.8%
Common Tern	2.9%	4.5%	1.2%	1.9%
Arctic Tern	2.9%	10.7%	0.2%	0.7%
Little Tern	8.6%	11.2%	1.0%	1.2%
Common Guillemot	30.7%	31.8%	5.5%	5.7%
Razorbill	20.8%	20.8%	6.6%	6.6%
Atlantic Puffin	9.1%	10.9%	0.3%	0.4%

Note

[1] refers only to *P. c. carbo*

Table 2   Global importance of breeding seabird populations in Britain and Ireland. Figures indicate the minimum and maximum percentages of the world population that the British and Irish populations represent.

Species	Britain min	Britain max	Ireland min	Ireland max
Northern Fulmar	7.0%	9.3%	0.5%	0.7
Manx Shearwater	68.3%	91.2%	6.6%	17.9%
European Storm-petrel	3.0%	11.0%	10.6%	41.3%
Leach's Storm-petrel	0.3%	0.7%	0.0%	0.0%
Northern Gannet	59.0%	59.0%	8.5%	8.5%
Great Cormorant[1]	1.4%	1.5%	0.9%	0.9%
European Shag	34.9%	39.7%	4.5%	5.1%
Arctic Skua	0.6%	2.5%	0.0%	0.0%
Great Skua	60.0%	60.0%	0.0%	0.0%
Mediterranean Gull	0.1%	0.1%	0.0%	0.0%
Black-headed Gull	4.6%	6.2%	0.5%	0.7%
Common Gull	7.3%	11.7%	0.2%	0.4%
Lesser Black-backed Gull	37.0%	43.8%	1.5%	1.8%
Herring Gull	11.9%	13.0%	0.5%	0.6%
Great Black-backed Gull	9.4%	10.0%	1.2%	1.3%
Black-legged Kittiwake	7.1%	8.6%	0.9%	1.1%
Sandwich Tern	6.5%	6.9%	2.2%	2.3%
Roseate Tern	0.0%	0.0%	0.6%	0.6%
Common Tern	1.6%	2.2%	0.7%	0.9%
Arctic Tern	1.9%	6.6%	0.1%	0.4%
Little Tern	1.5%	4.3%	0.2%	0.5%
Common Guillemot	12.0%	12.2%	2.1%	2.2%
Razorbill	17.5%	18.0%	5.4%	5.6%
Black Guillemot	4.6%	14.6%	0.6%	1.7%
Atlantic Puffin	9.1%	10.9%	0.3%	0.4%

Note

[1] refers only to *P. c. carbo*

breeds in Britain and more than 1% of the global populations of at least nine species breeds in Ireland.

It should be borne in mind that the importance of breeding seabird populations in Britain and Ireland is assessed in contexts whose accuracy is in many cases unknown. For example, it is only recently that robust techniques for censusing nocturnal petrels have been devised, and these have yet to be applied in most countries in the North Atlantic that host breeding populations of these birds. The estimates for British and Irish populations of storm-petrels presented herein reflect a real advance over this survey's predecessors, and provide a sound basis for future monitoring. However, whilst the international context of these species has been made easier to identify, it remains that their colonies are difficult to locate, their nesting sites are hard to find, and that they remain difficult to survey. As further advances are made in survey methodology, and logistical and resource problems are surmounted in poorly populated and remote areas, we might find that the importance of British and Irish populations will change. Previous estimates of population sizes in Britain and Ireland based on ringing (Lloyd *et al.*, 1991) proved to be very different to the numbers that were more robustly estimated from playback surveys in Seabird 2000. The estimated population of European Storm-petrels in Britain in the latter census was at the lower end of the range predicted in Lloyd *et al.* (1991). In Ireland, however, the estimated population proved to be at the upper end of the previous range estimate, probably because knowledge of the location of colonies was so much poorer at the time of the SCR Census (1985–88). The locations of colonies in Iceland are well known, so it might prove that existing estimates not based on playback surveys exaggerate the size of the population there, whereas in the Faeroes, where the distribution and number of breeding colonies is less well known, the population might actually be larger than existing estimates.

Of course, the true importance of British and Irish populations of seabirds lies in their absolute numbers. About 8 million seabirds of 25 species breed in Britain and Ireland. This compares favourably with seabird assemblages in other parts of the world. For example, more than 13 million seabirds of 25 species breed in the much larger Barents Sea region (Anker-Nilssen *et al.*, 2000), more than 4 million of 22 species breed in the Falkland Islands at about the same latitude south as the British Isles is north (White *et al.*, 2001), perhaps more than 20 million of 55 species breed in New Zealand (Robertson & Bell, 1984), an estimated 40 million of 24 species breed in Alaska (Lensink, 1984), and about 1.3 million of 22 species breed in the Caribbean (van Halewyn & Norton, 1984).

That Britain and Ireland host such important seabird populations is due to many reasons. Certainly, the very nature of the coastal scene, offering a wide spectrum of nesting habitats including low-lying rocky habitat with and without boulders, high cliffs and stacks with abundant ledges, dunes and shingle beaches, and grassy slopes, ensures a diversity of species and of form and function. The extent of such habitats for the most part is greater in Scotland, especially on the islands and it is here also that disturbance to nesting seabirds is minimised by the remoteness of many of the more important colonies. For the same reason, and notwithstanding the presence of American Mink and Brown Rats at many colonies, most seabird colonies are free from ground predators. In addition, human exploitation of seabirds and their eggs in Britain and Ireland is minimal, in marked contrast to, for example, some parts of the Arctic (CAFF, 2001).

The marine environment around Britain and Ireland is physically and hydrographically diverse. A rich array of deep water and surface currents, and an equally complex spatial and seasonal pattern of thermal and saline frontal systems results in high primary productivity over and beyond the continental shelf. The associated growth and concentration of zooplankton and fish offers rich feeding resources for seabirds as well as mammals (see Reid *et al.*, 2003).

Perhaps the single most important factor in sustaining an internationally important assemblage of seabirds over the course of the last century or so, certainly of those species that scavenge at sea, has been the fishing industry. Britain and Ireland are not unique in creating a ready food supply for seabirds at sea in the form of fisheries waste and discards (see chapter on Causes of Seabird Population Change). Most scavenging at sea occurs outside the breeding season, but breeding populations, certainly of scavenging species, are probably augmented through higher recruitment rates to the breeding colonies via increased winter survival of both adults and juveniles (Reeves & Furness, 2002). As discards become less available at sea in future we may see the absolute size of some British and Irish seabird populations diminish. Their international importance, however, will still be assessed in relation to populations in other countries and these might be expected to respond in a similar way to any widespread reduction in the availability of fisheries waste and discards.

References

AEBISCHER, N. J. 1986. Retrospective investigation of an ecological disaster in the shag, *Phalacrocorax aristotelis*: a general method based on long-term marking. *J. Anim. Ecol.* 55, 613–29.

AEBISCHER, N. J. 1993. Immediate and delayed effects of a gale in late spring on the breeding of the Shag *Phalacrocorax aristotelis*. *Ibis* 135, 225–32.

AEBISCHER, N. J. 1995. Philopatry and colony fidelity of Shags *Phalacrocorax aristotelis* on the east coast of Britain. *Ibis* 137, 11–18.

AEBISCHER, N. J., Coulson, J. C. & Colebrook, J. M. 1990. Parallel long-term trends across four marine trophic levels and weather. *Nature* 347, 753–5.

AEBISCHER, N. J. & Wanless, S. 1992. Relationship between colony size, adult non-breeding and environmental conditions for Shags *Phalacrocorax aristotelis* on the Isle of May. *Bird Study* 39, 43–52.

AGUILAR, J. S. 1992. [The atlas of breeding seabirds of Balearic Islands]. *Anuari Orn. Balears* 6 (1991), 17–28. [In Spanish.]

AINLEY, D. G. 1980. Geographic variation in Leach's Storm-petrel. *Auk* 97, 837–53.

AINSLIE, J. A. & ATKINSON, R. 1937. On the breeding habits of Leach's Fork-tailed Petrel. *Brit. Birds* 30, 234–48.

AKRIOTIS T. & HANDRINOS G. 1986. First breeding case of the Storm Petrel in Greece. In: MEDMARAVIS & Monbailliu, X. (eds.) *Mediterranean Marine Avifauna*. Springer Verlag, Berlin.

ALBON, S., BRAZIER, H., FROST, D., MARTIN, A. & MASON, D. 1976. *University of East Anglia Shetland Isles Expeditions 1973/74*. University of East Anglia, Norwich.

ALEXANDER, W. B. & LACK, D. 1944. Changes in status among British breeding birds. *Brit. Birds* 38, 42–5, 62–9, 82–8.

ALLEN, R. 1977. Population trends of seabirds in Scilly. Unpubl. Rep. to Nature Conservancy Council.

AMENGUAL, J. F., GARGALLO, G., SUÁREZ, M., BONNIN, J., GONZÁLEZ, J. M., REBASSA, M. & McMINN, M. 1999. The Mediterranean Storm Petrel *Hydrobates pelagicus melitensis* at Cabrera archipelago (Balearic Islands, Spain): breeding moult, biometry and evaluation of population size by mark and recapture techniques. *Ring. & Migr.* 19, 181–90.

ANDERSON, A., BAGENAL, T. B., BAIRD, D. E. & EGGELING, W. J. 1961. A description of the Flannan Isles and their birds. *Bird Study* 8, 71–88.

ANDERSON, D. R., BURNHAM, K. P. & WHITE, G. C. 1985. Problems in estimating age-specific survival rates from recovery data of birds ringed as young. *J. Anim. Ecol.* 54, 89–98.

ANDREW, D. G. 1965. Manx Shearwaters breeding in Lewis. *Scott. Birds* 3, 435–6.

ANDREWS, D. J. & DAY, K. R. 1999. Reproductive success in the Great Cormorant *Phalacrocorax carbo carbo* in relation to colony nest position and timing of nesting. *Atlantic Seabirds* 1, 107–20.

ANDREWS, J. H. & STANDRING, K. T. (eds.) 1979. *Marine Pollution and Birds*. Royal Society for the Protection of Birds, Sandy.

ANKER-NILSSEN, T. 1992. Food supply as a determinant of reproduction and population development in Norwegian Puffins *Fratercula arctica*. University of Trondheim.

ANKER-NILSSEN, T. 2000a. European Storm-petrel *Hydrobates pelagicus*. In: Anker-Nilssen, T., Bakken, V., Strøm, H., Golovkin, A. N., Bianki, V. V. & Tatarinkova, I. P. (eds.) *The Status of Marine Birds Breeding in the Barents Sea Region*. Norwegian Polar Institute, Tromsø.

ANKER-NILSSEN, T. 2000b. Leach's Storm-petrel *Oceanodroma leucorhoa*. In: Anker-Nilssen, T., Bakken, V., Strøm, H., Golovkin, A. N., Bianki, V. V. & Tatarinkova, I. P. (eds.) *The Status of Marine Birds Breeding in the Barents Sea Region*. Norwegian Polar Institute, Tromsø.

ANKER-NILSSEN, T. & ANKER-NILSSEN, P. G. 1993. Breeding of the Leach's Petrel *Oceanodroma leucorhoa* in the Røst archipelago, northern Norway. *Fauna Norvegica, Ser. C, Cinclus* 16, 19–24.

ANKER-NILSSEN, T. & AARVAK, T. 2001. [The population ecology of Puffins at Røst. Status after the breeding season 2000.] *NINA Oppdragsmelding* 684, 1–40. [In Norwegian.]

ANKER-NILSSEN, T. & AARVAK, T. 2003. The population ecology of Puffins at Røst. Status after the breeding season 2002. *NINA Oppdragsmelding* 784.

ANKER-NILSSEN, T., BAKKEN, V., STRØM, H., GOLOVKIN, A. N., BIANKI, V. V. & TATARINKOVA, I. P. (eds.) 2000. *The Status of Marine Birds Breeding in the Barents Sea Region*. Norwegian Polar Institute, Tromsø.

ANKER-NILSSEN, T., JONES, P. H. & RØSTAD, O. W. 1988. Age, sex and origin of auks (Alcidae) killed in the Skagerrak oiling incident of January 1981. *Seabird* 11, 28–46.

ANKER-NILSSEN, T. & LORENTSEN, S.-H. 1995. Size variation of Common Guillemots *Uria aalge* in the northern Skagerrak. *Seabird* 17, 64–73.

ANKER-NILSSEN, T. & RØSTAD, O. W. 1993. Census and monitoring of Puffins *Fratercula arctica* on Røst, N. Norway, 1979–1988. *Ornis Scand.* 24, 1–9.

ANKER-NILSSEN, T. & TATARINKOVA, I. P. 2000. Atlantic Puffin *Fratercula arctica*. In: Anker-Nilssen, T., Bakken, V., Strøm, H., Golovkin, A. N., Bianki, V. V. & Tatarinkova, I. P. (eds.) *The Status of Marine Birds Breeding in the Barents Sea Region*. Norwegian Polar Institute, Tromsø.

ANNETT, C. A. & PIEROTTI, R. 1999. Long-term reproductive output in Western Gulls: consequences of alternate tactics in diet choice. *Ecology* 80, 288–97.

ANON. 1999. [*The Chronicle of Nature in Kandalaksha Reserve for 1998*]. Kandalaksha. [In Russian.]

ANTAS P. T. Z. 1991. Status and conservation of seabirds breeding in Brazilian waters. In: Croxall, J. P. (ed.) *Seabird Status and Conservation: A Supplement*. International Council for Bird Preservation Tech. Publ. 11, Cambridge.

APPLETON, D., BOOKER, H., BULLOCK, D., SAMPSON B. & COLE, L. 2002. Lundy seabird recovery project. Unpubl. English Nature Report, Exeter.

ARDAMATSKAYA, T. B. 1999. Breeding sites of Mediterranean Gull *Larus melanocephalus* in the countries of the former Soviet Union. In: Meininger, P. L., Hoogendoorn, W., Flamant, R. & Raevel, P. (eds.) *Proc. First Intern. Mediterranean Gull Meeting, Le Portel, Pas-de-Calais, France, 4–7 September 1998*.

ARMSTRONG, I. H., COULSON, J. C., HAWKEY, P. & HUDSON, M. J. 1978. Further mass seabird deaths from paralytic shellfish poisoning. *Brit. Birds* 71, 58–68.

ARNOTT, S. A. & RUXTON, G. D. 2002. Sandeel recruitment in the North Sea: demographic, climatic and trophic effects. *Mar. Ecol. Prog. Ser.* 238, 199–210.

ASBIRK, S. 1979. The adaptive significance of the reproductive patterns in the Black Guillemot, *Cepphus grylle*. *Vidensk. Medd. Dansk Naturhist. Fore.* 141, 29–80.

ASBIRK, S. 1988. The breeding population of the Black Guillemot *Cepphus grylle* in Denmark 1978–87. *Dansk Orn. Fore. Tidsskr.* 82, 131–4.

ASH, J. S. & KARANI, A. A. 1981. Roseate and Sooty Terns *Sterna dougallii* and *fuscata* breeding on islets in southern Somalia. *Scopus* 5, 22–7.

ASHMOLE, N. P. 1963. The regulation of numbers of tropical oceanic birds. *Ibis* 103, 458–73.

ASHMOLE, N. P., ASHMOLE, M. J. & SIMMONS, K. E. L. 1994. Seabird conservation and feral cats on Ascension Island, South Atlantic. In: Nettleship, D. N., Burger, J. & Gochfeld, M. (eds.) *Seabirds on Islands: Threats, Case Studies and Action Plans*. BirdLife International Conserv. Ser. 1, Cambridge.

ASPINALL, S. J., TAVERNER, J. H. & WISEMAN, E. J. 1993. History of Black-headed Gull colonies in Hampshire and neighbouring counties. *Brit. Birds* 86, 103–14.

ATKINSON, I. A. E. 1985. The spread of commensal species of *Rattus* to oceanic islands and their effects on island avifaunas. In: Moors, P. J. (ed.) International Council for Bird Preservation Tech. Publ. 3, Cambridge.

ATKINSON, R. 1948. Leach's Petrel. *New Naturalist* 1, 110–4.

ATKINSON, R. & AINSLIE, J. A. 1940. The British breeding status of Leach's Fork-tailed Petrel. *Brit. Birds* 34, 50–5.

ATKINSON, R. & ROBERTS, B. 1955. Leach's Fork-tailed Petrel (*Oceanodroma leucorhoa*) in the Flannan Isles and Loch Roag. *Scott. Nat.* 67, 109–10.

AVERY, M. I. 1991. A re-examination of the Operation Seafarer estimates for Arctic Tern numbers on Orkney and Shetland. *Scott. Birds* 16, 113–7.

AVERY, M. I., BURGESS, D., DYMOND, N. J., MELLOR, M. & ELLIS, P. M. 1993. The status of Arctic Terns *Sterna paradisaea* in Orkney and Shetland in 1989. *Seabird* 15, 17–23.

AVERY, M. I., COULTHARD, N. D., DEL NEVO, A. J., LEROUX, A., MEDEIROS, F., MERNE, O., MONTEIRO, L., MORALEE, A., NTIAMOA-BAIDU, Y., O'BRIAN, M. & WALLACE, E. 1995. A recovery plan for Roseate Terns in the East Atlantic: an international programme. *Bird Conserv. Intern.* 5, 441–53.

AVERY, M. I. & NEVO, A. del. 1991. Action for Roseate Terns. *RSPB Conserv. Rev.* 5, 54–59.

AVERY, M. I., SUDDABY, D., ELLIS, P. M. & SIM, I. M. W. 1992. Exceptionally low body-weights of Arctic Terns *Sterna paradisaea* on Shetland. *Ibis* 134, 87.

AVERY, M. I. & WINDER, F.L.R. 1990. Roseate Tern. In: Batten, L. A., Bibby, C. J., Clement, P., Elliott, G. D. and Porter, R. F. (eds.) *Red data birds in Britain*. T. & A.D. Poyser, London.

BACCETTI, N., TALAMELLI, A. and VOLPONI, S. 1999. *Colour-ringing and colour ring-reading of Mediterranean Gulls Larus melanocephalus in Italy: recent activities and present contents of the national database.* In: Meininger, P.L., Hoogendoorn, W., Flamant, R. and Raevel, P. (Eds). *Proceedings of the 1st International Mediterranean Gull Meeting, Le Portel, Pas-de-Calais, France, 4–7 September 1998.* EcoNum, Bailleul.

BAGENAL, T. B. & BAIRD, D. E. 1959. The birds of North Rona in 1958, with notes on Sula Sgeir. *Bird Study* 6, 153–74.

BAILEY, E. P. & DAVENPORT, G. H. 1972. Die-off of Common Murres on the Alaskan Peninsula and Unimak Island. *Condor* 74, 213–9.

BAILEY, R. S. 1991. *The interaction between sandeels and seabirds—a Case History at Shetland.* International Council for the Exploration of the Sea CM 1991/L:41.

BAILLIE, S. R., CRICK, H. Q. P., BALMER, D. E., BEAVEN, L. P., DOWNIE, I. S., FREEMAN, S. N., LEECH, D. I., MARCHANT, J. H., NOBLE, D. G., RAVEN, M. J., SIMPKIN, A. P., THEWLIS, R. M. & WERNHAM, C. V. 2002. *Breeding Birds in the Wider Countryside: Their Conservation Status 2001.* British Trust for Ornithology Res. Rep. 278, Thetford.

BAINES, M. E. & EARL, S. J. 1996. Breeding seabird survey of southwest Wales, 1996. Unpubl. Dyfed Wildlife Trust Report, Haverfordwest.

BAIRD, P. H. 1994. Black-legged Kittiwake (*Rissa tridactyla*). In: Poole, A. & Gill, F. (eds.) *The Birds of North America*, 92. Birds of North America Inc., Philadelphia, PA & American Ornithologists' Union, Washington DC.

BAKER, R. R. 1980. The significance of the Lesser Black-backed Gull to models of bird migration. *Bird Study* 27, 41–50.

BAKKEN, V. 2000. *Seabird Colony Databases of the Barents Sea Region and the Kara Sea.* Norsk Polarinstitutt Rapportseries 15, Tromsø.

BARRETT, R. T. 2001. Attendance patterns of Common Guillemots *Uria aalge* and Kittiwakes *Rissa tridactyla* at colonies during continuous daylight. *Atlantic Seabirds* 3, 41–8.

BARRETT, R. T. & FOLKESTAD, A. O. 1996. The status of the North Atlantic gannet *Morus bassanus* after 50 years in Norway. *Seabird* 18, 30–7.

BARRETT, R. T. & GOLOVKIN, A. N. 2000. Common Guillemot *Uria aalge*. In: Anker-Nilssen, T., Bakken, V., Strøm, H., Golovkin, A. N., Bianki, V. V. & Tatarinkova, I. P. (eds.) *The Status of Marine Birds Breeding in the Barents Sea Region.* Norwegian Polar Institute, Tromsø.

BARRETT, R. T., SKAARE, J. U., NORHEIM, G., VADER, W. & FROSLEI, A. 1985. Persistent organochlorines and mercury in eggs of Norwegian seabirds. *Environ. Pollution* 39, 79–93.

BARRETT, R. T. & STRANN, K.-B. 1987. Two new breeding records of the storm petrel *Hydrobates pelagicus* in Norway. *Fauna Norvegica Ser. C Cinclus* 10, 115–6.

BARRETT, R. T. & TERTITSKI, G. M. 2000. Black-legged Kittiwake *Rissa tridactyla*. In: Anker-Nilssen, T., Bakken, V., Strøm, H., Golovkin, A. N., Bianki, V. V. & Tatarinkova, I. P. (eds.) *The Status of Marine Birds Breeding in the Barents Sea Region.* Norwegian Polar Institute, Tromsø.

BARRETT, R. T. & VADER, W. 1984. The status and conservation of seabirds breeding in Norway. In: Croxall, J. P., Evans, P. G. H. & Schreiber, R. W. (eds.) *Status and Conservation of the World's Seabirds.* International Council for Bird Preservation Tech. Publ. 2, Cambridge.

BARRINGTON, R. M. 1888. The Manx Shearwater on Skomer. *Zoologist* (3) 12, 367–71.

BARTON, T. R. 1997. Survey strategies for a national seabird colony census in 1999/2000. Rep. to the Joint Nature Conservation Committee, Aberdeen.

BAUMANIS, J., BERGMANIS, U. & SMISLOV, V. 1997. Breeding status of the Cormorant *Phalacrocorax carbo* in Latvia. *Ekol. Pol.* 45, 11–13.

BAXTER, E. V. & RINTOUL, L. J. 1953. *The Birds of Scotland: Their History, Distribution and Migration.* Oliver & Boyd, Edinburgh.

BEARHOP, S., PHILLIPS, R. A., THOMPSON, D. R., WALDRON, S. & FURNESS, R. W. 2000. Variability in mercury concentrations of Great Skuas *Catharacta skua*: the influence of colony, diet and trophic status inferred from stable isotope signatures. *Mar. Ecol. Prog. Ser.* 195, 261–8.

BEARHOP, S., THOMPSON, D. R., PHILLIPS, R. A., WALDRON, S., HAMER, K. C., GRAY, C. M., VOTIER, S. C., ROSS, B. P. & FURNESS, R. W. 2001. Annual variation in Great Skua diets: the importance of commercial fisheries and predation on seabirds revealed by combining dietary analyses. *Condor* 103, 802–9.

BEATTY, I., BERRIDGE, D. & MCADAMS, D. 1997. Storm petrels (*Hydrobates pelagicus*) nesting above ground under Ling Heather *Calluna vulgaris* on Inis Tuaisceart. *Irish Birds* 6, 56.

BEATTY, J. 1992. *Sula: The Seabird Hunters of Lewis.* Michael Joseph, London.

BECKER, P. H. 1991. Population and contamination studies in coastal birds: the common tern *Sterna hirundo*. In: Perrins, C. M., Lebreton, J.-D. & Hirons, G. J. M. (eds.) *Bird Population Studies*. Oxford University Press.

BECKER, P. H. 1995. Effects of coloniality on gull predation of Common Tern (*Sterna hirundo*) chicks. *Colonial Waterbirds* 18, 11–22.

BECKER, P. H. 1998. Long-term trends of breeding success in Common Terns *Sterna hirundo* in the Wadden Sea. *Vogelwelt* 119, 233–4.

BEKHUIS, J., MEININGER, P. L. & RUDENKO, A. 1997. Mediterranean Gull. In: Hagemeijer, W. J. M. & Blair, M. J. (eds.) *The EBCC Atlas of European Breeding Birds: Their Distribution and Abundance*. T. & A. D. Poyser, London.

BECKER, P. H. & SUDMANN, S. 1998. *Quo vadis Sterna hirundo*? Implications for the conservation of Common Tern in Germany. *Vogelwelt* 119, 293–304.

BELANT, J. L., SEAMANS, T. W., GABREY, S. W. & ICKES, S. K. 1993. The importance of landfills to nesting Herring Gulls. *Condor* 95, 817–30.

BELAOUSSOFF, S. 1993. Northern Gannet and Common Guillemot nesting on Rockall. *Brit. Birds* 86, 16.

Bell, M., Bullock, I. & Humpridge, R. 2000. Eradication of rats from Ramsey Island, Wales. Unpubl. Rep. to Royal Society for the Protection of Birds by Wildlife Management International Ltd.

BENTON, T.G., BRYANT, D.M., COLE, L. & CRICK, H.Q.P. 2002. Linking agricultural practice to insect and bird populations: a historical study over three decades. *Journal of Applied Ecology* 39 (4): 673–687.

BERROW, S. D. 1998. The importance of discards from the Celtic Sea Herring fishery to seabirds. *Irish Birds* 6, 241–50.

BERTELLOTTI, M., YORIO, P., BLANCO, G. & GIACCARDI, M. 2001. Use of tips by nesting Kelp Gulls at a growing colony in Patagonia. *J. Field Orn.* 72, 338–48.

BIBBY, C. J. 1971. Auks drowned in fishing nets. *Seabird Rep.* 2, 48–9.

BIBBY, C. J. 1972. Net loss to auks. *Birds* 4, 248.

BIJLSMA, R. G., HUSTINGS, F. & CAMPHUYSEN, C. J. 2001. Algemene en schaarse vogels van Nederland (*Avifauna van Nederland*, vol. 2). GMB Uitgeverij & KNNV Uitgeverij, Haarlem & Utrecht.

BIRDLIFE INTERNATIONAL. 2000. The development of boundary selection criteria for the extension of breeding seabird Special Protection Areas into the marine environment. BirdLife International Report to OSPAR Commission, Cambridge.

BIRDLIFE INTERNATIONAL / EUROPEAN BIRD CENSUS COUNCIL. 2000. *European Bird Populations: Estimates and Trends*. BirdLife International Conserv. Ser. 10, Cambridge.

BIRKHEAD, T. R. 1977. The effect of habitat and density on breeding success in the common guillemot *Uria aalge*. *J. Anim. Ecol.* 46, 751–64.

BIRKHEAD, T. R. 1984. Distribution of the bridled form of the Common Guillemot *Uria aalge* in the North Atlantic. *J. Zool., Lond.* 202, 165–76.

BIRKHEAD, T. R. & FURNESS, R. W. 1985. Regulation of seabird populations. In: Sibley, R. M. & Smith, R. H. (eds.) *Behavioural Ecology: Ecological Consequences of Adaptive Behaviour*. Blackwell, London.

BIRKHEAD, T. R. & HATCHWELL, B. J. 2000. Skomer Island Razorbill Study 2000. Dept. Animal & Plant Sciences, University of Sheffield.

BIRKHEAD, T. R. & NETTLESHIP, D. N. 1988. Breeding performance of Black-legged Kittiwakes, *Rissa tridactyla*, at a small, expanding colony in Labrador. *Can. Field Nat.* 102, 20–4.

BIRKS, J. 1986. *Mink*. The Mammal Society: Anthony Nelson Ltd, Oswestry.

BJORDAL, Å. & LØKKEBORG, S. 1992. *Longlining*. Fishing News Books, Oxford.

BLOOMER J. P. & BESTER, M. N. 1992. Control of feral cats on sub-Antarctic Marion Island, Indian Ocean. *Biol. Conserv.* 60, 211–9.

BMT CORDAH. 2003. Offshore wind energy generation: phase 1 proposals and environmental report. Rep. for Department of Trade and Industry, Edinburgh.

BOEKELHEIDE, R. J. & AINLEY, D. G. 1989. Age, resource availability and breeding effort in the Brandt's Cormorant. *Auk* 106, 389–401.

BOERSMA, P. D., CLARK, J. A. & HILLGARTH, N. 2002. Seabird conservation. In: Schreiber, E. A. & Burger, J. (eds.) *Biology of Marine Birds*. CRC Press, Boca Raton.

BOERTMANN, D. 1994. An annotated checklist to the birds of Greenland. *Medd. Om Grønland Bioscience* 38, 1–63.

BOERTMANN, D. & MOSBECH, A. 1997. Breeding distribution and abundance of the great cormorant *Phalacrocorax carbo carbo* in Greenland. *Polar Res.* 16, 93–100.

BOERTMANN, D., MOSBECH, A., FALK, K. & KAMPP, K. 1996. Seabird colonies in western Greenland, (60°–79°30′N.lat.). National Environmental Research Institute Tech. Rep. 170, Roskilde.

BOGSTADT, B. & MEHL, S. 1997. Interactions between cod and its prey species in the Barents Sea. In: *Proc. Intern. Symp. Role of Forage Fishes in Marine Ecosystems*, 591–615. University of Alaska, Fairbanks.

BOLDREGHINI, P., MEININGER, P. L. & SANTOLINI, ?. 1992. Preliminary results of ringing Mediterranean Gulls *Larus melanocephalus* breeding in the Netherlands, Belgium and Italy. *Avocetta* 16, 73–4.

BOSCHERT, M. 1999. Population trends and status of Mediterranean Gull *Larus melanocephalus* as a breeding bird in Germany. In: Meininger, P. L., Hoogendoorn, W., Flamant, R. & Raevel, P. (eds.) *Proc. First Intern. Mediterranean Gull Meeting, Le Portel, Pas-de-Calais, France, 4–7 September 1998*.

BOUDEWIJN, T. J. & DIRKSEN, S. 1995. Impact of contaminants on the breeding success of the Cormorant *Phalacrocorax carbo sinensis* in the Netherlands. *Ardea* 83, 325–38.

BOUILLOT, M. 1999. Le fou de Bassan niche en Méditerranée. *L'Oiseau* 54, 17.

BOURNE, W. R. P. 1966. The plumage of Northern Fulmars of St. Kilda in July. *Bird Study* 13, 209–13.

BOURNE, W. R. P. 1976. Seabirds and pollution. In: Johnson, R. (ed.) *Marine Pollution*. Academic Press, London.

BOURNE, W. R. P. & CURRIE, A. 1983. A seabird survey of the Western Isles in 1977. *Hebridean Nat.* 7, 9–16.

BOURNE, W. R. P. & DIXON, T. J. 1974. The seabirds of the Shetlands. *Seabird* 4, 1–18.

BOURNE, W. R. P & SAUNDERS, D. 1992. Operation Seafarer and Arctic Terns. *Scott. Birds* 16, 205–10.

BOURNE, W. R. P. & SMITH, A. J. M. 1974. Threats to Scottish Sandwich Terns. *Biol. Conserv.* 6, 222–4.

BOWEY, K. 1995. European Storm-petrels without their toes. *Brit. Birds* 88, 111.

BOYD, J. 1961. The gannetry of St Kilda. *J. Anim. Ecol.* 30, 117–36.

BRADSTREET, M. S. W. 1979. Thick-billed Murres and Black Guillemots in the Barrow Strait area, N.W.T. during spring: distribution and habitat use. *Can. J. Zool.* 57, 1789–1802.

BRAZIER, H. & MERNE, O. J. 1989. Breeding seabirds on the Blasket Islands, Co. Kerry. *Irish Birds* 4, 43–64.

BREGNBALLE, T., ENGSTRÖM, KNIEF, H. VAN EERDEN, VAN RIJN, M. S., KIEKBUSCH, J. & ESKILDSEN, J. In press. Development of the breeding population of Great Cormorants (*Phalacrocorax carbo sinensis*) in The Netherlands, Germany, Denmark, and Sweden during the 1990s. *Vogelwelt* 123 (Suppl.).

BRENNINKMEIJER, A., STIENEN, E. M. W., KLASSEN, M. & KERSTEN, M. 2002. Feeding ecology of wintering terns in Guinea-Bissau. *Ibis* 144, 602–13.

BRIGGS, K. T., GERSHWIN, M. E. & ANDERSON, D. W. 1997. Consequences of petrochemical ingestion and stress on the immune system of seabirds. *ICES J. Mar. Sci.* 54, 718–25.

BRINDLEY, E. (ed.) Little Terns in 1995. Unpubl. Rep. Royal Society for the Protection of Birds, Sandy.

BRINDLEY, E. 1998. Little Terns in 1997. Unpubl. Rep. Royal Society for the Protection of Birds, Sandy.

BRINDLEY, E., MUDGE, G., DYMOND, N., LODGE, C., RIBBANDS, B., STEELE, D., ELLIS, P. M., MEEK, E. SUDDABY, D. & RATCLIFFE, N. 1999. The status of Arctic Terns *Sterna paradisaea* at Shetland and Orkney in 1994. *Atlantic Seabirds* 1, 135–143.

BRITISH ORNITHOLOGISTS' UNION. 1971. *The Status of Birds in Britain and Ireland*. Blackwell, Oxford.

BRITISH ORNITHOLOGISTS' UNION 2001. British Ornithologists' Union Records Committee: 27th report (October 2000). *Ibis* 141, 171–5.

BRITTON, D. J. 1986. Mediterranean Gull *Larus melanocephalus*. In: Lack, P. (ed.) 1986. *The Atlas of Wintering Birds in Britain and Ireland*. T. & A.D. Poyser, Calton.

BRITTON, P. L. & BROWN, L. H. 1974. The status and breeding behaviour of East African Lari. *Ostrich* 45, 63–82.

BROOKE, M. d. L. 1972. The Puffin population of the Shiant Islands. *Bird Study* 19, 1–6.

BROOKE, M. de L. 1978a. Some factors affecting the laying date incubation and breeding success of the Manx Shearwater *Puffinus puffinus*. *J. Anim. Ecol.* 47, 477–95.

BROOKE, M. de L. 1978b. Sexual differences in the voice and individual vocal recognition in the Manx Shearwater (*Puffinus puffinus*). *Anim. Behav.* 26, 622–9.

BROOKE, M. de L. 1990. *The Manx Shearwater*. T. & A. D. Poyser, Calton.

BROOKE, M. d. L., DOUSE, A., HAYSOM, S., JONES, F. C. & NICOLSON, A. 2002. The Atlantic Puffin population of the Shiant Islands, 2000. *Scott. Birds* 23, 22–6.

BROTHERS, N. P., COOPER, J. P. & LØKKEBORG, S. 1999. The incidental catch of seabirds by longline fisheries: worldwide review and technical guidelines for mitigation. FAO Fisheries Circular 937, Rome.

BROWN, J. G. 2001. The conservation management of Skomer Island. In: Zonfrillo, B., Câmara, D. B., Bolton, M. & Perrins, C. M. (eds.) *Proc. First Manx Shearwater Conf., Funchal, Madeira 2000*.

BROWN, J. G. & EASTON, J. 2000. Seabird monitoring on Skomer Island in 2000. Rep. to Joint Nature Conservation Committee by The Wildlife Trust, West Wales.

BROWN, K. M. & MORRIS, R. D. 1996. From tragedy to triumph: renesting in Ring-billed Gulls. *Auk* 113, 23–31.

BROWN, R. A. 1995. Roseate Tern in Northern Ireland—a review of known nesting sites. *Proceedings Carantec Roseate Tern Conservation Workshop 1992*, 27–36. SEPNB, Brittany, France.

BROWN, R. A. & McAVOY, W. 1985. Nesting terns in Strangford Lough, 1969–84—a review. *Irish Birds* 3, 33–47.

BROWN, R. G. B. 1970. Northern Fulmar distribution: a Canadian perspective. *Ibis* 112, 44–51.

BROWN, R. G. B. 1988. The influence of oceanographic anomalies on the distributions of storm-petrels (Hydrobatidae) in Nova Scotian waters. *Colonial Waterbirds* 11, 1–8.

State in full first. (BRSM). 1941. New facts about the Manx "Puffins". *J. Manx Mus.* 5, ??.

BUCKLAND, S. T. 1982. A mark-recapture survival analysis. *J. Anim. Ecol.* 51, 833–47.

BUCKLAND, S. T., ANDERSON, D. R., BURNHAM, K. P., LAAKE, J. L., BORCHERS, D. L. & THOMAS, L. 2001. *Introduction to Distance Sampling: Estimating Abundance of Biological Populations.* Oxford University Press.

BUCKLAND, S. T., BELL, M. V. & PICOZZI, N. 1990. *The Birds of North-East Scotland.* North-East Scotland Bird Club, Aberdeen.

BUCKLE, A. P. 1994. Rodent control methods: chemical. In: Buckle, A. P. & Smith, R. H. (eds.) *Rodent Pests and Their Control.* CAB International.

BUCKLEY, N. J. & O'HALLORAN, J. 1986. Mass mortality of gulls in west Cork attributed to botulism. *Irish Birds* 3, 283–5.

BUCKLEY, P. A. & BUCKLEY, F. G. 2000. Breeding Common Terns in the Greater West Indies: status & conservation priorities. In: Schreiber, E. A. & Lee, D. S. (eds.) *Status and Conservation of West Indian Seabirds.* Soc. Carib. Orn., Spec. Publ. 1.

BUDWORTH, D., CANHAM, M., CLARK, H., HUGHES, B. & SELLERS, R. M. 2000. Status, productivity, movements and mortality of Great Cormorants *Phalacrocorax carbo* breeding in Caithness, Scotland: a study of a declining population. *Atlantic Seabirds* 2, 165–80.

BUKACI_SKI, D. & BUKACI_SKI, M. 2003 *Larus canus* Mew Gull. *BWP Update* 5, 13–47.

BUKACI_SKI, M., BUKACI_SKI, D. & SPAANS, A. L. 1996. Attendance and diet in relation to breeding success in herring gulls (*Larus argentatus*). *Auk* 113, 300–9.

BUKACI_SKI, M., BUKACI_SKI, D. & SPAANS, A. L. 1998. Experimental evidence for the relationship between food supply, parental effort and chick survival in the Lesser Black-backed Gull *Larus fuscus. Ibis* 140, 422–30.

BULLOCK, I. D. & GOMERSALL, C. H. 1981. The breeding populations of terns in Orkney and Shetland in 1980. *Bird Study* 28, 187–200.

BUNCE, A., NORMAN, F. I., BROTHERS, N. & GALES, R. 2002. Long-term trends in the Australasian gannet (*Morus serrator*) population in Australia: the effect of climate change and commercial fisheries. *Mar. Biol.* 141, 263–9.

BURGER, J. 1997. *Oil Spills.* Rutgers University Press.

BURGER, J. & GOCHFELD. 2002. Effects of chemicals and pollution on seabirds. In: Schreiber, E. A. & Burger, J. (eds.) *Biology of Marine Birds.* CRC Press, Boca Raton.

BURGESS, N. D. & HIRONS, G. J. M. 1992. Creation and management of artificial nesting sites for wetland birds. *J. Environ. Manag.* 34, 285–95.

CABOT, D. 1996. Performance of the Roseate Tern population breeding in north-west Europe—Ireland, Britain and France, 1960–94. *Proc. Roy. Irish Acad.* 96, 55–68.

CADIOU, B. 1999. Attendance of breeders and prospectors reflects the quality of colonies in the Kittiwake *Rissa tridactyla. Ibis* 141, 321–6.

CADIOU, B. 2001. The breeding biology of the European Storm-petrel Hydrobates pelagicus in Brittany, France. *Atlantic Seabirds* 3(4): 149–164.

CADIOU, B., CHENESSEAU, D. & JOSLAIN, H. 2003. Marée noire de l'Erika—contribution a l'étude de l'impact sur l'avifaune. Bilan national des échouages et de la mortalité des oiseaux (BNEMO). Rapport Bretagne Vivante-SEPNB / LPO Loire-Atlantique / Observatoire des marées noires / DIREN Bretagne.

CADIOU, B., PONS, J.-M. & YÉSOU, P. (eds.) In press. *Oiseaux Marins Nicheurs de France Métropolitaine (1960–2000).* GISOM, Editions Biotope, Paris.

CADMAN, W. A. 1936. Manx Shearwater breeding on Pembrokeshire mainland. *Brit. Birds* 30, 175.

CAFF (Conservation of Arctic Flora and Fauna). 2001. *Arctic Flora and Fauna: Status and Conservation.* Edita, Helsinki.

CAIRNS, D. K. 1987a. The ecology and energetics of chick provisioning by Black Guillemots. *Condor* 89, 627–35.

CAIRNS, D. K. 1987b. Seabirds as indicators of marine food supplies. *Biol. Oceanogr.* 5, 261–71.

CAIRNS, D. K. & ELLIOT, R. D. 1987. Oil spill impact assessment for seabirds: the role of refugia and growth centres. *Biol. Conserv.* 40, 1–9.

CALDOW, R. W. G. & FURNESS, R. W. 2000. The effect of food availability on the foraging behaviour of breeding Great Skuas *Catharacta skua* and Arctic Skuas *Stercorarius parasiticus. J. Avian Biol.* 31, 367–75.

CALDOW, R. W. G. & FURNESS, R. W. 2001. Does Holling's disc equation explain the functional response of a kleptoparasite? *J. Anim. Ecol.* 70, 650–62.

CALLADINE, J. 1997. A comparison of Herring Gull *Larus argentatus* and Lesser Black-backed Gull *Larus fuscus* nest sites: their characteristics and relationships with breeding success. *Bird Study* 44, 318–26.

CALLADINE, J. 2002. Herring Gull *Larus argentatus*. In: Wernham, C. V., Toms, M., Marchant, J., Clark, J., SiriwardenÀ, G. & Baillie, S. (eds.) *The Migration Atlas: Movements of the Birds of Britain and Ireland*. T. & A. D. Poyser, London.

CALLADINE, J. & HARRIS, M. P. 1997. Intermittent breeding in the Herring Gull *Larus argentatus* and the Lesser Black-backed Gull *Larus fuscus. Ibis* 139, 259–63.

CALVERT, A. M. & ROBERTSON, G. J. 2002. Colony attendance and individual turnover of Atlantic Puffins in Newfoundland. *Waterbirds* 25, 382–7.

CÂMARA, D. 2001. Manx Shearwaters *Puffinus puffinus* in the Madeiran Archipelago. In: Zonfrillo, B., Câmara, D. B., Bolton, M. & Perrins, C. M. (eds.) *Proc. First Manx Shearwater Conf., Funchal, Madeira 2000.*

CAMPHUYSEN, C. J. 1994. Flatfish selection by Herring Gulls *Larus argentatus* and Lesser Black-backed Gulls *Larus fuscus* scavenging at commercial beamtrawlers in the southern North Sea. *Netherlands J. Sea Res.* 32, 91–8.

CAMPHUYSEN, C. J. 1998. Beached bird surveys indicate decline in chronic oil pollution in the North Sea. *Mar. Pollution Bull.* 36, 519–26.

CAMPHUYSEN, C. J., CALVO, B., DURINCK, J., ENSOR, K., FOLLESTAD, A., FURNESS, R. W., GARTHE, S., LEAPER, G., SKOV, H., TASKER, M. L. & WINTER, C. J. N. 1995. Consumption of discards by seabirds in the North Sea. EC DG XIV research contract BIOECO/93/10. NIOZ Rapport 1995–5. Netherlands Institute for Sea Research, Texel.

CAMPHUYSEN, C. J., ENSOR, K., FURNESS, R. W., GARTHE, S., HÜPPOP, O., LEAPER, G., OFFRINGA, H. & TASKER, M. L. 1993. Seabirds feeding on discards in winter in the North Sea. EC DG XIV research contract 92/3505. NIOZ Rapport 1993–8. Netherlands Institute for Sea Research, Texel.

CAMPHUYSEN, C. J. & GARTHE, S. 1997. An evaluation of the distribution and scavenging habits of Northern Fulmars (*Fulmarus glacialis*) in the North Sea. *ICES J. Mar. Sci.* 54, 654–83.

CAMPHUYSEN, C. J., HEUBECK, M., COX, S., BAO, R., HUMPLE, D., ABRAHAM, C. & SANDOVAL, A. 2002. The *Prestige* oil spill in Spain. *Atlantic Seabirds* 4, 127–9.

CAMPHUYSEN, C. J., WRIGHT, P. J., LEOPOLD, M., HÜPPOP, O. & REID, J. B. 1999. A review of the causes, and consequences at the population level, of mass mortalities of seabirds. In: Furness, R. W. & Tasker, M. L. (eds.) *Diets of Seabirds and Consequences of Changes in Food Supply.* ICES Cooperative Res. Rep. 232.

CARNDUFF, D. 1981. Black Guillemots breeding in the inner Clyde estuary. *Scott. Birds* 11, 195–6.

CARPEGNA, F., GRIECO, F., GRASSU, M., VERONESI, E. & VOLPONI, S. 1997. The Italian breeding population of the Cormorant (*Phalacrocorax carbo*). *Suppl. Ric. Biol. Selvaggina* 26, 81–7.

CARSS, D. N. 1994. Killing of piscivorous birds at Scottish finfish farms, 1984–1987. *Biol. Conserv.* 68, 181–8.

CARSS, D. N. & EKINS, G. R. 2002. Further European integration: mixed sub-species colonies of Great Cormorants *Phalacrocorax carbo* in Britain—colony establishment, diet, and implications for fisheries management. *Ardea* 90, 23–41.

CARTER, H. R. & SEALY, S. G. 1984. Marbled Murrelet mortality and gill net fishing in Berkeley Sound, British Colombia. In: Nettleship, D. N., Sanger, G. A. & Springer, P. F. (eds.) *Marine Birds: Their Feeding Ecology and Commercial Fishery Relationships.* Canadian Wildlife Service Spec. Publ., Ottawa.

CARTER, H. R., WILSON, U. W., LOWE, R. W., RODWAY, M. S., MANUWAL, D. A., TAKEKAWA, J. E. & YEE, J. L. 2001. Population trends of the common murre (*Uria aalge californica*). In: Orthmeyer, D. L. (ed.) *Biology and Conservation of the Common Murre in California, Oregon, Washington and British Columbia*, vol. 1. US Geological Survey, Information & Technology Rep. USGS/BRD/ITR-2000–0012, Washington DC.

CASEY, S., MOORE, N., RYAN, L., MERNE, O., COVENEY, J. A. & DEL NEVO, A. 1995. The Roseate Tern conservation project on Rockabill, Co. Dublin: a six year review 1989–1994. *Irish Birds* 5, 251–64.

CASTRO, M. 1984. Auks drown in Spanish nets. *BTO News* 132, 1.

CATCHPOLE, E. A., FREEMAN, S. N., MORGAN, B. J. T. & HARRIS, M. P. 1997. Integrated recovery / recapture data analysis. *Biometrics* 54, 33–46.

CATRY, P. & FURNESS, R. W. 1997. Partnerships and mechanisms of divorce in the Great Skua. *Anim. Behav.* 54, 1475–82.

CATRY, P., PHILLIPS, R. A., HAMER, K. C., RATCLIFFE, N. A. & FURNESS, R. W. 1998. The incidence of nonbreeding by adult Great Skuas and Parasitic Jaegers from Foula, Shetland. *Condor* 100, 448–55.

CEICO, T. & TANASE, C. 1994. [Mediterranean Gull breeding again at Murighiol.] *Romanian Orn. Soc. Bull.* 1–2, 7. [In Romanian.]

CHABRZYK, G. & COULSON, J. C. 1976. Survival and recruitment in the Herring Gull *Larus argentatus. J Anim. Ecol.* 45, 187–203.

CHAMBERLAIN, D.E., FULLER, R.J., BUNCE, R.G.H., DUCKWORTH, J.C. & SHRUBB, M. 2000. Changes in the abundance of farmland birds in relation to the timing of agricultural intensification in England and Wales. *Journal of Applied Ecology* 37 (5): 771–788.

CHAPDELAINE, G. & BROUSSEAU, P. 1989. Size and trends of Black-legged Kittiwake (*Rissa tridactyla*) populations in the Gulf of St Lawrence (Quebec) 1974–1985. *Amer. Birds* 43, 21–4.

CHAPDELAINE, G., DIAMOND, A. W., ELLIOT, R. D. & ROBERTSON, G. J. 2001. Status and population trends of the Razorbill in eastern North America. Can. Wildl. Service Occ. Paper 105.

CHAPDELAINE, G. & LAPORTE, P. 1982. Populations, reproductive success and analysis of contaminants in Razorbill *Alca torda* in the estuary and Gulf of St. Lawrence, Quebec. *Can. Wildl. Service, Progr. Notes* 129, 1–10.

CHARDINE, J. W. (ed.) 1999. Overview of seabird status and conservation in Canada. *Bird Trends* 7, 1–7.

CHARDINE, J. W. 2000. Census of Northern Gannet colonies in the Atlantic Region in 1999. *Can. Wildl. Service, Atlantic Region Tech. Rep. Ser.* 361, 1–13.

CHARDINE, J. W. 2002. Geographic variation in the wing-tip patterns of Black-legged Kittiwakes. *Condor* 104, 687–693.

CHASTEL, C. E. 1988. Tick-born virus infections of marine birds. In: Harris, K. F. (ed.) *Advances in Disease and Vector Research*, vol. 5. Springer Verlag, New York.

CHERNICHKO, I. 1993. Breeding population and distribution of seabirds (gulls and terns) of the northern coast of the Black sea and the Sea of Azov. In: Aguilar, J. S., Monbailliu, X. & Paterson, A. M. (eds.) *Status and Conservation of Seabirds.* SEO, Madrid.

CHRISTENSEN, J. H & CHRISTENSEN, O. B. 2003. Severe summer flooding in Europe. *Nature* 421: 805.

CHU, P. C. 1998. A Phylogeny of the Gulls (Aves: Larinae) Inferred from Osteological and Integomentary Characters, *Cladistics* 14, 1–43.

CHYLARECKI, P. 1993. New Herring Gull taxonomy. *Brit. Birds* 86, 316–9.

CHYTIL, J. 1999. The present status of Mediterranean Gull Larus *melanocephalus* in the Czech Republic, with notes on Slovakia. In: Meininger, P. L., Hoogendoorn, W., Flamant, R. & Raevel, P. (eds.) *Proc. First Intern. Mediterranean Gull Meeting, Le Portel, Pas-de-Calais, France, 4–7 September 1998.*

CLARK, R. B. 1984. Impact of oil pollution on seabirds. *Environ. Pollution* 33: 1–22.

CLEMENTS, J. F. 2000. *Birds of the World: a Checklist.* Ibis Publishing Company, Vista, CA.

CLOBERT, J. & LEBRETON, J.-D. 1991. Estimation of demographic parameters in bird populations. In: Perrins, C. M., Lebreton, J.-D. & Hirons, G. J. M. (eds.) *Bird Population Studies.* Oxford University Press.

CLODE, D. & MACDONALD, D. W. 2002. Invasive predators and the conservation of island birds: the case of American Mink *Mustela vison* and terns *Sterna* spp. in the Western Isles, Scotland. *Bird Study* 49: 118–23.

CLODE, D., MACDONALD, D. W. & BIRKS, J. D. S. 2000. Mobbing behaviour in terns and gulls. *J. Zool., Lond.* 252, 53–9.

COLEBROOK, J. M. 1986. Environmental influences on long-term variability in marine plankton. *Hydrobiologia* 142, 309–25.

COOKE, A. S. 1979. Egg shell characteristics of gannets *Sula bassana*, shags *Phalacrocorax aristotelis* and great black-backed gulls *Larus marinus* exposed to DDE and other environmental pollutants. *Environ. Pollution* 19, 47–65.

CORBETT, G. B. & SOUTHERN, H. N. 1977. *The Handbook of British Mammals*, second edn. Blackwell, Oxford.

CORBETT, G. B. & HARRIS, S. 1990. *The Handbook of British Mammals.* Blackwell, Oxford.

CORKHILL, P. 1973. Manx Shearwater numbers on Skomer: population and mortality due to gull predation. *British Birds* 66: 1363–143.

CORTEN, A. 1990. Long-term trends in pelagic fish stocks of the North Sea and adjacent waters and their possible connection to hydrographic changes. *Netherlands J. Sea Res.* 25, 227–35.

COULSON, J. C. 1963. The status of the Kittiwake in the British Isles. *Bird Study* 10, 147–79.

COULSON, J. C. 1983. The changing status of the Kittiwake *Rissa tridactyla* in the British Isles, 1969–1979. *Bird Study* 30, 9–16.

COULSON, J. C. 1986. Shag *Phalacrocorax aristotelis.* In: Lack, P. (ed.) 1986. *The Atlas of Wintering Birds in Britain and Ireland.* T. & A.D. Poyser, Calton.

COULSON, J. C. 1991. The population dynamics of culling Herring Gulls *Larus argentatus* and Lesser Black-backed Gulls *Larus fuscus*. In: Perrins, C. M., Lebreton, J.-D. & Hirons, G. J. M. (eds.) *Bird Population Studies*. Oxford University Press.

COULSON, J. C., DUNCAN, N. & THOMAS, C. 1982. Changes in the breeding biology of the Herring Gull *Larus argentatus* induced by a reduction in size and density of the colony. *J. Anim. Ecol.* 51, 739–56.

COULSON, J. C. & HOROBIN, J. 1976. The influence of age on the breeding biology and survival of the Arctic Tern *Sterna paradisaea*. *J. Zool., Lond.* 178, 247–60.

COULSON, J. C., POTTS, G. R., DEANS, I. R. & FRASER, S. M. 1968. Exceptional mortality of Shags and other seabirds caused by paralytic shellfish poison. *Brit. Birds* 61, 381–404.

COULSON, J. C. & STROWGER, J. 1999. The annual mortality rate of Black-legged Kittiwakes in NE England from 1954 to 1998 and a recent exceptionally high mortality. *Waterbirds* 22, 3–13.

COULSON, J. C. & THOMAS, C. S. 1985. Changes in the biology of the Kittiwake *Rissa tridactyla*: a 31-year study of a breeding colony. *J. Anim. Ecol.* 54, 9–26.

COULSON, J. C. & WOOLLER, R. D. 1976. Differential survival rates among breeding Kittiwake gulls *Rissa tridactyla* (L.). *J. Anim. Ecol.* 45, 205–13.

COUNSELL, D. 1983. A colony of Cormorants at a freshwater loch in North Uist. *Hebridean Nat.* 7, 25–6.

CRAIK, J. C. A. 1990. The price of mink. *Scott. Bird News* 18, 4–5.

CRAIK, J. C. A. 1995. Effects of North American mink on the breeding success of terns and smaller gulls in west Scotland. *Seabird* 17, 3–11.

CRAIK, J. C. A. 1997. Long-term effects of North American Mink *Mustela vison* on seabirds in western Scotland. *Bird Study* 44, 303–9.

CRAIK, J. C. A. 1998. Recent mink-related declines of gulls and terns in west Scotland and the beneficial effects of mink control. *Argyll Bird Rep.* 14, 98–110.

CRAIK, J. C. A. 2000. Results of the mink–seabird project 1999. Unpubl. Rep.

CRAIK, J. C. A. 2001. Results of the mink–seabird project 2000. Unpubl. Rep.

CRAIK, J. C. A. 2001. Results of the mink–seabird project in 2001. Unpubl. Rep.

CRAIK, J. C. A. 2002. Results of the mink–seabird project 2001. Unpubl. Rep.

CRAIK, J. C. A & CAMPBELL, B. 2000. Bruce Campbell's islands revisited: changes in the seabirds of Loch Sunart after half a century. *Atlantic Seabirds* 2, 181–94.

CRAMM, P. & MUSELET, D. In press. Sterne naine *Sterna albifrons*. In: Cadiou, B., Pons, J.-M. & Yésou, P. (eds.) *Oiseaux Marins Nicheurs de France Métropolitaine (1960–2000)*. GISOM Editions Biotope, Paris.

CRAMP, S. 1971. Gulls nesting on buildings in Britain and Ireland. *Brit. Birds* 64, 476–87.

CRAMP, S. (ed.) 1985. *The Birds of the Western Palearctic*, vol. 4. Oxford University Press.

CRAMP, S., BOURNE, W. R. P. & SAUNDERS, D. 1974. *The Seabirds of Britain & Ireland*. Collins, London.

CRAMP, S. & SIMMONS, K. E. L. (eds.) 1977. *The Birds of the Western Palearctic*, vol. 1. Oxford University Press.

CRAMP, S. & SIMMONS, K. E. L (eds). 1983. *The Birds of the Western Palearctic*, vol. 3. Oxford University Press.

CRAWFORD, R. J. M. 2003. Influence of food on numbers, breeding colony size and fidelity to localities of Swift Terns in South Africa's Western Cape, 1987–2000. *Waterbirds* 26, 44–53.

CRAWFORD, R. J. M. & DYER, B. M. 1995. Responses by four seabirds to a fluctuating availability of Cape Anchovy *Engraulis capensis* off South Africa. *Ibis* 137, 329–40.

CREME, G. A., WALSH, P. M., O'CALLAGHAN, M. & KELLY, T. C. 1997. The changing status of the Lesser Black-backed Gull *Larus fuscus* in Ireland. Biology and environment. *Proc. Roy. Irish Acad.* 97B, 149–56.

CRICK, H. Q. P. 1992. A bird–habitat coding system for use in Britain and Ireland incorporating aspects of land management and human activity. *Bird Study* 39, 1–12.

CROWE, O., MALJKOVIC, A. & NEWTON, S. F. 2000. Rockabill tern report 2000. BirdWatch Ireland Conservation Rep. 00/2, Dublin.

CROWN ESTATES 2003. Marine aggregates. http://www.crownestate.co.uk/estates/marine/marine_agg.shtml.

CROXALL, J. P. (ed.) *Seabird Status and Conservation: A Supplement*. International Council for Bird Preservation Tech. Publ. 11, Cambridge.

CROXALL, J. P., ROTHERY, P., PICKERING, S. P. C. & PRINCE, P. R. 1990. Reproductive performance recruitment and survival of Wandering Albatrosses *Diomedea exulans* at Bird Island, South Georgia. *J. Anim. Ecol.* 59, 775–9.

CROXALL, J. P., EVANS, P. G. H. & SCHREIBER, R. W. (eds.) 1984. *Status and Conservation of the World's Seabirds*. International Council for Bird Preservation Tech. Publ. 2, Cambridge.

CROXALL, J. P. & ROTHERY, P. 1991. Population regulation of seabirds: implications of their demography for conservation. In: Perrins, C. M., Lebreton, J.-D. & Hirons, G. J. M. (eds.) *Bird Population Studies*. Oxford University Press.

CROXALL, J. P., TRATHAN, P. N. & MURPHY, E. J. 2002. Environmental change and Antarctic seabird populations. *Science* 297, 1510–4.

CURY, P. & FONTANA, A. 1988. Competition et strategies demographiques comparées de deux espèces de sardinelles (*Sardinella aurita* et *Sardinella maderensis*) des côtes Ouest-Africaines. *Aquatic Living Resources* 1, 165–80.

CURY, P. & ROY, C. 1989. Optimal environmental window and pelagic fish recruitment success in upwelling areas. *Can. J. Fisheries and Aquatic Sci.* 46, 670–80.

CUSSEN, R. E., KELLY, T., HARTNETT, M. & WALSH, P. M. 1999. Counts of breeding seabirds, Clare Island, Co. Mayo, 1999. Rep. Roy. Irish Acad. for the New Survey of Clare Island.

DANCHIN, E. 1992a. The incidence of the tick parasite *Ixodes uriae* in Kittiwake *Rissa tridactyla* colonies in relation to the age of the colony, and a mechanism of infecting new colonies. *Ibis* 134, 134–41.

DANCHIN, E. 1992b. Food shortage as a factor in the 1988 Kittiwake *Rissa tridactyla* breeding failure in Shetland. *Ardea* 80, 93–8.

DANCHIN, E., BOULINGER, T. & MASSOT, M. 1998. Conspecific reproductive success and breeding habitat selection: implications for the study of coloniality. *Ecology* 79, 2415–28.

DANCHIN, E. & MONNAT, J.-Y. 1993. Population dynamics modelling of two neighbouring Kittiwake colonies: implications for management. *Ardea* 80, 171–80.

DAVIDSON, R. 1987. Breeding birds of Lough Neagh, 1987. Unpubl. Rep.

DAVIES, J. C. 2002. Forth Islands aerial gull count. *Seabird Group Newsletter* 92, 5–7.

DAVIS, P. E. 1957. The breeding of the storm petrel. *Brit. Birds* 50, 85–101, 371–84.

DAVIS, T. A. W. 1958. The breeding distribution of the Great Black-backed Gull in England and Wales in 1956. *Bird Study* 5, 191–215.

DEAN, T. 1990. *The Natural History of Walney Island.* Faust, Lancashire.

DEBOUT, G., RØV, N. & SELLERS, R. M. 1995. Status and population development of Cormorants *Phalacrocorax carbo carbo* breeding on the Atlantic coast of Europe. *Ardea* 83, 47–59.

D'ELBEE, J. & HEMERY, G. 1997. Diet and foraging behaviour of the British Storm Petrel *Hydrobates pelagicus* in the Bay of Biscay during summer. *Ardea* 86, 1–10.

DICKSON, R. C. 1998. Black Guillemot nesting on an operational car ferry. *Scott. Birds* 19, 301–2.

DICKSON, R. R. & LEE, A. 1972. Recent hydro-meteorological trends on the North Atlantic fishing grounds. *Fish Industry* 2, 4–11.

DIERSCHKE, J., DIERSCHKE, V., JACHMANN, F. and STÜHMER, F. 2000. Ornithologischer Jahresbericht 1999 für Helgoland. *Orn. Jber. Helgoland* 10, 1–68.

DIERSCHKE, J., DIERSCHKE, V., JACHMANN, F. & STÜHMER, F. 2002. Ornithologischer Jahresbericht 2001 für Helgoland. *Orn. Jber. Helgoland* 12, 1–69.

VAN DIJK, A. J. 1998. Breeding Black-headed Gulls *Larus riatibundus* along the coast of the Netherlands during the 20th century. *Sula* 4, 149–160.

VAN DIJK, A. J. and MAJOOR, F. 2002. Kokmeeuw *Larus riatibundus* in SOVON Vog.

DIXON, T. 1971. Estimates of the numbers of gannets breeding on St Kilda 1969–73. *Seabird* 3, 5–12.

DOTT, H. E. M. 1975. Northern Fulmars at colonies: time of day and weather. *Bird Study* 22: 255–9.

DUFFY, D. C. 1983. The ecology of tick parasitism on densely nesting Peruvian seabirds. *Ecology* 64, 110–119.

DUFFY, D. C. 1986. Foraging at patches: interactions between common and roseate terns. *Ornis Scand.* 17, 45–52.

DUNCAN, N. 1978. Effects of culling Herring Gulls (*Larus argentatus*) on recruitment and population dynamics. *J. Appl. Ecol.* 15, 697–713.

DUNCAN, N. 1981a. The Tarnbrook Fell and Mallowdale gull colony before control. *Bird Study* 28, 133–8.

DUNCAN, N. 1981b. The Lesser Black-backed Gull on the Isle of May. *Scott. Birds* 11, 180–8.

DUNCAN, N. & MONAGHAN, P. 1977. Infidelity to natal colony by breeding Herring Gulls. *Ring. & Migr.* 1, 166–72.

DUNN, E. 1997. Sustainable fisheries and seabirds. *RSPB Conserv. Rev.* 11, 44–50.

DUNN, E. K. 1973. Changes in fishing ability of terns associated with wind speed and sea surface conditions. *Nature* 244, 520–1.

DUNN, E. K. 1994. Interactions between fisheries and marine birds: research recommendations. Unpubl. Rep. Royal Society for the Protection of Birds, Sandy.

DUNN, E. K. & MEAD, C. J. 1982. Relationship between sardine fisheries and recovery rates of ringed terns in West Africa. *Seabird* 6, 98–104.

DUNN, E. K. & STEEL, C. 2001. The impact of long-line fishing on seabirds in the north-east Atlantic: recommendations for reducing mortality. Royal Society for the Protection of Birds / Joint Nature Conservation Committee, Sandy.

DUNNET, G. M. 1997. Fulmar. In: Hagemeijer, W. J. M. & Blair, M. J. (eds.) 1997. *The EBCC Atlas of European Breeding Birds: their distribution and abundance.* T & A. D. Poyser, London.

DUNSTONE, N. 1993. *The Mink.* T. & A. D. Poyser, London.

DURANT, J. M., ANKER-NILSSEN, T. & STENSETH, N. C. 2003. Trophic interactions and climate change: the Atlantic puffin as an example. *Proc. Roy. Soc. Lond.*, 1416–66.

DURHAM, M. 2002. Surveying the Gloucester gull colony. *Seabird Group Newsletter* 92, 3–4.

VAN EERDEN, M. R. & GREGERSEN, J. 1995. Long-term changes in the northwest European population of Cormorants *Phalacrocorax carbo sinensis. Ardea* 83, 61–79.

VAN EERDEN, M. R., KOFFIJBERG, K. & PLATTEEUW, M. 1995. Riding on the crest of the wave: possibilities and limitations for a thriving population of migratory Cormorants *Phalacrocorax carbo* in man-dominated wetlands. *Ardea* 83, 1–9.

VAN EERDEN, M. R. & ZIJLSTRA, M. 1985. Aalscholvers *Phalacrocorax carbo* in de Oostvaardersplassen 1970–85. *Limosa.* 58, 137–43.

EINARSSON, O. 2000. Iceland. In: Heath, M. F. & Evans, M. I. (eds.) *Important Bird Areas in Europe: Priority Sites for Conservation,* vol. 1. BirdLife International, Cambridge.

EKINS, G. R. 1990. The wintering of Cormorants in Essex with some reference to the Abberton colony. *Essex Bird Rep.* 1989, 115–22.

ELLIS, P., RATCLIFFE, N. & SUDDABY, D. 1998. Seasonal variation in diurnal attendance and response to playback by Leach's Petrels *Oceanodroma leucorhoa* on Gruney, Shetland. *Ibis* 140, 336–9.

ELWES, H. J. 1869. The bird stations of the Outer Hebrides. *Ibis* 5, 20–37.

ERIKSEN, J. & SARGEANT, D. E. 2000. *Oman Bird List: The Official List of the Birds of the Sultanate of Oman,* fifth edn. Oman Bird Records Committee, Muscat.

EUROPEAN COMMISSION (EC). 2001. Report on the state of resources and their expected development. In: *The Future of the Common Fisheries Policy,* vol. 2. European Communities, Luxembourg.

EVANS, P. G. H. 1973. Summary report of B.O.U. supported expedition to North Rona and Sula Sgeir, 1972. *Ibis* 115, 476–8.

EVANS, P. G. H. 1984a. Status and conservation of seabirds breeding in northwest Europe (excluding Norway and U.S.S.R.). In: Croxall, J. P., Evans, P. G. H. & Schreiber, R. W. (eds.) *Status and Conservation of the World's Seabirds.* International Council for Bird Preservation Tech. Publ. 2, Cambridge.

EVANS, P. G. H. 1984b. The seabirds of Greenland: status and conservation. In: Croxall, J. P., Evans, P. G. H. & Schreiber, R. W. (eds.) *Status and Conservation of the World's Seabirds.* International Council for Bird Preservation Tech. Publ. 2, Cambridge.

EVANS, P. G. H. & LOVEGROVE, R. R. 1974. The birds of the south west Irish islands. *Irish Bird Rep.* 1973, 33–64.

EVANS, P. G. H. and NETTLESHIP, D. N. 1985. Conservation of the Atlantic Alcidae. In: Nettleship, D. N. & Birkhead, T. R. (eds.) *The Atlantic Alcidae.* Academic Press, London.

EVERETT, M. J. 1982. Breeding Great and Arctic Skuas in Scotland in 1974–75. *Seabird* 6, 50–58.

EVERETT, M. J., HEPBURN, I. R., NTIAMOA-BAIDU, Y. & THOMAS, G. J. 1987. Roseate Terns in Britain and West Africa. *RSPB Conserv. Rev.* 1, 56–8.

EWINS, P. J. 1985a. Colony attendance and censusing of Black Guillemots *Cepphus grylle* in Shetland. *Bird Study* 32, 176–85.

EWINS P. J. 1985b. Otter predation on Black Guillemots. *Brit. Birds* 78, 663–4.

EWINS, P. J. 1986a. The ecology of Black Guillemots *Cepphus grylle* in Shetland. D.Phil. thesis. University of Oxford.

EWINS, P. J. 1986b. Black Guillemot *Cepphus grylle.* In: Lack, P. (ed.) 1986. *The Atlas of Wintering Birds in Britain and Ireland.* T. & A.D. Poyser, Calton.

EWINS, P. J. 1987. Opportunistic feeding of Black Guillemots *Cepphus grylle* at fishing vessels. *Seabird* 10, 58–9.

EWINS, P. J. 1989. The breeding biology of Black Guillemots *Cepphus grylle* in Shetland. *Ibis* 131, 507–20.

EWINS, P. J. 1990. The diet of Black Guillemots *Cepphus grylle* in Shetland. *Holarctic Ecol.* 13: 90–7.

EWINS, P. J., BIRD, D. R., ELLIS, P. M. & PRIOR, A. 1987. The distribution and status of Arctic and Great Skuas in Shetland, 1985–86. Rep. to Nature Conservancy Council, Royal Society for the Protection of Birds, Seabird Group and Shell UK.

EWINS, P. J. & KIRK, D. A. 1988. The distribution of Shetland Black Guillemots *Cepphus grylle* outside the breeding season. *Seabird* 11, 50–61.

EWINS, P. J. & TASKER, M. L. 1985. The breeding distribution of Black Guillemots *Cepphus grylle* in Orkney and Shetland. *Bird Study* 32, 186–93.

FABCZAK, J., SZAREK, J., MARKIEWICZ, K., SMOCZYNSKI, S. & SKIBNIEWSKA, K. 1997. Preliminary results of studies on pathology of the liver of Cormorants *Phalacrocorax carbo* from north-eastern Poland. *Ekol. Polska.* 45, 153–9.

FASOLA, M., SANCHEZ, J. M. & ROSELAAR, C. S. 2002. *Sterna albifrons* Little Tern. *BWP Update 4*, 89–114.

FEARE, C. J. 1976. Desertion and abnormal development in a colony of sooty terns infested by virus-infected ticks. *Ibis* 118, 112–5.

FEARE, C. J. 1991. Control of bird pest populations. In: Perrins, C. M., Lebreton, J.-D. & Hirons, G. J. M. (eds.) *Bird Population Studies.* Oxford University Press.

FELTHAM, M. J., DAVIES, J. M., WILSON, B. R., HOLDEN, T., COWX, I. G., HARVEY, J. P. & BRITTON, J. R. 1999. Case studies of the impact of fish-eating birds on inland fisheries in England and Wales. Ministry of Agriculture, Fisheries and Food, London.

FERNS, P. N. & MUDGE, G. P. 1981. Accuracy of nest counts at a mixed colony of Herring and Lesser Black-backed Gulls. *Bird Study* 28, 244–6.

FINNEY, S. K., HARRIS, M. P., KELLER, L. F., ELSTON, D. A., MONAGHAN, P. & WANLESS, S. 2003. Reducing the density of breeding gulls leads to enhanced recruitment of immature Atlantic puffins *Fratercula arctica* to a breeding colony. *J. Appl. Ecol.* 40, 545–552.

FINNEY, S. K., WANLESS, S. & HARRIS, M. P. 1999. The effect of weather conditions on the feeding behaviour of a diving bird, the Common Guillemot *Uria aalge. J. Avian Biol.* 30, 23–30.

FISHER, J. 1952. *The Northern Fulmar.* Collins, London.

FISHER, J. 1966. The Northern Fulmar population of Britain and Ireland, 1959. *Bird Study* 13, 5–76.

FISHER, J. & LOCKLEY, R. M. 1954. *Sea-Birds.* Collins, London.

FISHER, J. & VEVERS, H. G. 1944. The breeding distribution, history and population of the North Atlantic Gannet (*Sula bassana*). *J. Anim. Ecol.* 13–4, 49–62.

FISHER, J. & WATERSTON, G. 1941. Breeding distribution, history and population of the Northern Fulmar (*Fulmarus glacialis*) in the British Isles. *J. Anim. Ecol.* 10, 204–72.

FORD, R. G., WIENS, J. A., HEINEMANN, D. & HUNT, G. L. 1982. Modelling the sensitivity of colonially breeding marine birds to oil spills: guillemot and kittiwake populations in the Pribilof Islands, Bering Sea. *J. Appl. Ecol.* 19, 1–31.

FOSSI, C., FOCARDI, S. & REZONI, A. 1984. Trace-metals and chlorinated hydrocarbons in birds' eggs from the delta of the Danube. *Environ. Conserv.* 11, 345–50.

FOWLER, J. A. 2001. Ecological studies in the maritime approaches to the Shetland oil terminal. Rep. to Shetland Oil Terminal Environmental Advisory Group & Scottish National Heritage, De Montfort University.

FOWLER, J. A. 2002. European Storm-petrel (Storm Petrel) *Hydrobates pelagicus.* In: Wernham, C. V., Toms, M., Marchant, J., Clark, J., SiriwardenÀ, G. & Baillie, S. (eds.) *The Migration Atlas: Movements of the Birds of Britain and Ireland.* T. & A. D. Poyser, London.

FOWLER, J. A. & BUTLER, C. J. 1982. A new colony of Leach's Petrels. *Scott. Birds* 12, 86–87.

FOWLER, J. A. & HOUNSOME, M. V. 1998. Migration and arrival of immature Storm Petrels *Hydrobates pelagicus* in Shetland. *Ring. & Migr.* 19, 91–4.

FOWLER, J. A. & MILLER, C. J. 1984. Non-haematophagous ectoparasite populations of Procellariiform birds in Shetland, Scotland. *Seabird* 7, 23–30.

FOWLER, J. A., MILLER, C. J. & COHEN, S. 1984. Ectoparasite populations from breeding and wandering Storm Petrels. *Bird Study* 31, 126–30.

FOWLER, J. A. & OKILL, J. D. 1988. Recaptures of storm petrels tape-lured in Shetland. *Ring. & Migr.* 9, 49–50.

VAN FRANEKER, J. A., CAMPHUYSEN, C. J., MEHLUM, F. 1998. The Birds of Jan Mayen. *Circumpolar J.* 13, 28–43.

FREDRIKSEN, M. & BREGNBALLE, T. 2000a. Evidence for density-dependent survival in adult cormorants from a combined analysis of recoveries and resightings. *J. Anim. Ecol.* 69, 737–52.

FREDRIKSEN, M. & BREGNBALLE, T. 2000b. Diagnosing a decline in return rate of 1–year-old cormorants: mortality, emigration or delayed return? *J. Anim. Ecol.* 69, 753–61.

FREDRIKSEN, M., LEBRETON, J.-D. & BREGNBALLE, T. 2001. The interplay between culling and density-dependence in the great cormorant: a modelling approach. *J. Appl. Ecol.* 38, 617–27.

FREDRIKSSON, S. 1979. Skrattmåsen *Larus ridibundus* i Sverige. *Vår Fågelvärld* 38, 173–200.

FRIEND, M. & FRANSON, J. C. (eds.) 1999. *Field Manual of Wildlife Diseases. General Field Procedures and Diseases of Birds.* US Geological Survey / Biological Resources Division, National Wildlife Health Centre, Madison, Wisconsin.

FTITZE, E. 1999. Status of Mediterranean Gull *Larus melanocephalus* as a breeding bird in Denmark. In: Meininger, P. L., Hoogendoorn, W., Flamant, R. & Raevel, P. (eds.) *Proc. First Intern. Mediterranean Gull Meeting, Le Portel, Pas-de-Calais, France, 4–7 September 1998.*

FUCHS, E. 1977. Predation and anti-predator behaviour in a mixed colony of terns *Sterna* sp. and Black-headed Gulls *Larus ridibundus* with special reference to the Sandwich Tern *Sterna sandvicensis. Ornis Scand.* 8, 17–32.

FUKUDA, M. 2000. The Great Cormorant in Japan. *Cormorant Res. Group Bull.* 4, 9–13.

FURNESS, R. W. 1982. Seabird–fishery relationships in the northeast Atlantic and North Sea. In: Nettleship, D. N., Sanger, G. A. & Springer, P. F. (eds.) *Marine Birds: Their Feeding Ecology and Commercial Fishery Relationships.* Canadian Wildlife Service Spec. Publ., Ottawa.

FURNESS, R. W. 1977. Studies on the breeding biology and population dynamics of the great skua. PhD thesis, University of Durham.

FURNESS, R. W. 1984. Seabird biomass and food consumption in the North Sea. *Mar. Pollution Bull.* 15, 244–8.

FURNESS, R. W. 1986. The conservation of arctic and great skuas and their impact on agriculture. Nature Conservancy Council Rep.799, Peterborough.

FURNESS, R. W. 1987. *The Skuas.* T and A.D. Poyser, Calton, England

FURNESS, R. W. 1988. Predation on ground-nesting seabirds by island population of red deer *Cervus elaphus* and sheep *Ovis. J. Zool., Lond.* 216, 565–573.

FURNESS, R. W. 1990a. A preliminary assessment of the quantities of Shetland sandeels taken by seabirds, seals, predatory fish and the industrial fishery in 1981–83. *Ibis* 132, 205–17.

FURNESS, R. W. 1990b. Numbers and population changes of Manx Shearwaters on Rhum. Nature Conservancy Council Rep. 1168.

FURNESS, R. W. 1992. Implications of changes in net mesh size, fishing effort and minimum landing size regulations in the North Sea for seabird populations. Joint Nature Conservancy Committee Rep. 133, Peterborough.

FURNESS, R. W. 1993. An assessment of human hazards to seabirds in the North Sea. Unpublished WWF International Rep., Godalming.

FURNESS, R. W. 1996a. 1996 survey of moorland nesting birds on Hoy, Orkney. Scottish Natural Heritage Research, Survey & Monitoring Rep. 138, Edinburgh.

FURNESS, R. W. 1996b. Interactions between seabirds and aquaculture in sea lochs. In: Black, K. D. (ed.) *Aquaculture and Sea Lochs.* Scottish Association for Marine Science, Oban.

FURNESS, R. W. 1997a. A 1995 survey of the Rum Manx Shearwater population. Scottish Natural Heritage Research, Survey & Monitoring Rep. 73, Edinburgh.

FURNESS, R. W. 1997b. The impact of predation by great skuas on other species with particular reference to Special Protection Areas in Shetland. Rep. to Scottish Natural Heritage. Applied Ornithology Unit, University of Glasgow.

FURNESS, R. W. 1999a. Does harvesting a million metric tonnes of sand lance per year from the North Sea threaten seabird populations? In: *Ecosystem Approaches for Fisheries Management.* Alaska Sea Grant College Program, Fairbanks.

FURNESS, R. W. 1999b. Are industrial fisheries a threat to seabird populations? *Proc. Intern. Orn. Congr., Durban.*

FURNESS, R. W. 2000. Survey of moorland nesting seabirds on Hoy, Orkney: 1996. Scottish Natural Heritage Research, Survey & Monitoring Rep. 138, Edinburgh.

FURNESS, R. W. 2002. Management implications of interactions between fisheries and sandeel-dependent seabirds and seals in the North Sea. *ICES J. Mar. Sci.* 59, 261–269.

FURNESS, R. W. & BAILLIE, S. R. 1981. Factors affecting capture rate and biometrics of storm petrels on St Kilda. *Ring. & Migr.* 3, 137–48.

FURNESS, R. W., ENSOR, K. & HUDSON, A. V. 1992. The use of fishery waste by gull populations around the British Isles. *Ardea* 80, 105–13.

FURNESS, R. W., HUDSON, A. V. & ENSOR, K. 1988. Interactions between scavenging seabirds and commercial fisheries around the British Isles. In: Burger, J. (ed.) *Seabirds & Other Marine Vertebrates: Competition, Predation and Other Interactions.* Columbia University Press.

FURNESS, R. W. & MONAGHAN, P. 1987. *Seabird Ecology.* Blackie, Glasgow.

FURNESS, R. W. & TASKER, M. L. 2000. Seabird fishery interactions: quantifying the sensitivity of seabirds to reductions in sandeel abundance, and identification of key areas for sensitive seabirds in the North Sea. *Mar. Ecol. Progr. Ser.* 202, 253–64.

FURNESS, R. W. & TODD, C. M. 1984. Diets and feeding of Fulmars *Fulmarus glacialis* during the breeding season: a comparison between St Kilda and Shetland colonies. *Ibis* 126, 379–87.

GAARD, E., HANSEN, B., OLSEN, B. & REINERT, J. 2002. Ecological features and recent trends in the physical environment, plankton, fish stocks and seabirds in the Faeroe Shelf ecosystem. In: Sherman, K. & Skjoldal, H. R. (eds.) *Large Marine Ecosystems of the North Atlantic: Changing States and Sustainability.* Elsevier, Amsterdam.

GABRIELSEN, G. W., BREKKE, B., ALSOS, I. G. & HANSEN, J. R. (eds.) 1997. *Natur- og kulturmiljøet på Jan Mayen.* Norwegian Polar Institute, Tromsø.

GALBRAITH, H. 1983. The diet and feeding ecology of breeding Kittiwakes *Rissa tridactyla. Bird Study* 30, 109–20.

GALVIN, P., NEWTON, S. F., MADDEN, B. & MERNE, O. J. 1999. Black Guillemot National Population Census 1999: West Cork to Galway Bay. Birdwatch Ireland Conserv. Rep. 99/13, Monkstown.

GARCÍA, L., VIADA, C., MORENO-OPO, R., CARBONERAS, C., ALCALDE, A. & GONZÁLES, F. 2003. *Impacto de la marea negra del "Prestige" sobre las aves marinas.* SEO/BirdLife, Madrid. 126pp.

GARDARSSON, A. 1979. A census of Cormorants (*Phalacrocorax carbo*) and Shags (*Phalacrocorax aristotelis*) in Iceland in 1975. *Natturufraedingurinn* 49, 126–54.

GARDARSSON, A. 1995a. Numbers and distribution of Common Murre *Uria aalge*, Thick-billed Murre *U. lomvia* and Razorbill *Alca torda* in Iceland. *Bliki* 16, 47–65.

GARDARSSON, A. 1995b. Numbers of Gannets (*Sula bassana*) in Iceland 1989–94. *Natturufraedingurinn* 64, 203–8.

GARNETT, S. T. & CROWLEY, G. M. 2000. *The Action Plan for Australian Birds.* Environment Australia, Canberra.

GARTHE, S. & KUBETZKI, U. 1998. Diet of Sandwich Terns *Sterna sandvicensis* on Juist (Germany). *Sula* 12, 13–19.

GARTHE, S., BENVENUTI, S. & MONTEVECCHI, W. A. 2000. Pursuit plunging by Northern Gannets (*Sula bassana*) feeding on capelin (*Mallotus villosus*). *Proc. Roy. Soc. Lond. B* 267, 1717–22.

GARTHE, S., CAMPHUYSEN, C. J. & FURNESS, R. W. 1996. Amounts of discards in commercial fisheries and their significance as food for seabirds in the North Sea. *Mar. Ecol. Progr. Ser.* 136, 1–11.

GARTHE, S., FREYER, T., HÜPPOP, O. & WÖLKE, D. 1999. Breeding Lesser Black-backed Gulls *Larus graellsii* and Herring Gulls *Larus argentatus*: coexistence or competition? *Ardea* 87, 227–36.

GASTON, A. & JONES, I. L. 1998. *The Auks.* Oxford University Press.

GEAR, S. 2001. Petrel and shearwater survey, Foula 2001. Unpubl. Rep. Joint Nature Conservation Committee, Peterborough.

GÉROUDET, P. 1995. Analyse et commentaries sur les colonisations marginales du Goéland Cendré *Larus canus* en Europe Occidentale. *Alauda* 63, 1–14.

GIBBONS, D. W. & VAUGHAN, D. 1998. The population size of Manx Shearwater *Puffinus puffinus* on 'The Neck' of Skomer Island: a comparison of methods. *Seabird* 20, 3–11.

GIBBONS, D. W., REID J. B. & CHAPMAN, R. A. 1993. *The New Atlas of Breeding Birds in Britain & Ireland: 1988–1991.* T. & A. D. Poyser, London.

GIBSON, J. A. 1950. Methods of determining breeding-cliff populations of Guillemots and Razorbills. *Brit. Birds* 43, 329–31.

GIBSON, J. A. 1951. The breeding distribution, population and history of the birds of Ailsa Craig. *Scott. Nat.* 63, 73–100.

GILBERT, G., GIBBONS, D. W. & EVANS, J. 1998a. *Bird Monitoring Methods: A Manual of Techniques for Key U.K. Species.* Royal Society for the Protection of Birds, Sandy.

GILBERT, G., HEMSLEY, D. & SHEPHERD, M. 1998b. A survey of Storm Petrels on the Treshnish Isles in 1996. *Scott. Birds* 19, 145–53.

GJERSHAUG, J. O., THINGSTAD, P. G., ELDÖY, S. & BYRKJELAND, S. 1994. [*Norwegian Bird Atlas.*] Norwegian Ornithological Society, Klaebu. [In Norwegian.]

GLUTZ VON BLOTZHEIM, U. N. & BAUER, K.-A. 1982. *Handbuch der Vogel Mitteleuropas*, 8/1. Wiesbaden, Akademische Verlagsgesellschaft.

GOCHFELD, M. 1983. The Roseate Tern: world distribution and status of a threatened species. *Biol. Conserv.* 25, 103–25.

GOCHFELD, M., BURGER, J. & NISBET, I. C. T. 1998. Roseate Tern (*Sterna dougallii*). In: Poole, A. & Gill, F. (eds.) *The Birds of North America*, 370. Birds of North America Inc., Philadelphia, PA & American Ornithologists' Union, Washington DC.

GOLOVKIN, A. N. 1984. Seabirds nesting in the USSR: the status and protection of populations. In: Croxall, J. P., Evans, P. G. H. & Schreiber, R. W. (eds.) *Status and Conservation of the World's Seabirds.* International Council for Bird Preservation Tech. Publ. 2, Cambridge.

GOOD, T. P. 1998. Great Black-backed Gull (*Larus marinus*). In: Poole, A. & Gill, F. (eds.) *The Birds of North America*, 330. Birds of North America Inc., Philadelphia, PA & American Ornithologists' Union, Washington DC.

GOOSTREY, A. CARSS, D. N., NOBLE, L. R. & PIERTNEY, S. B. 1998. Population introgression and differentiation in the Great Cormorant *Phalacrocorax carbo* in Europe. *Mol. Ecol.* 7, 329–38.

GOUTNER, V., JERRENTRUP, H., KAZANTZIDIS, S. & POIRAZIDIS, K. 1999. Population trends, distribution, ring recoveries and conservation of Mediterranean Gull *Larus melanocephalus* in Greece. In: Meininger, P. L., Hoogendoorn, W., Flamant, R. & Raevel, P. (eds.) *Proc. First Intern. Mediterranean Gull Meeting, Le Portel, Pas-de-Calais, France, 4–7 September 1998*.

GRANADEIRO, J. P. & SILVA, M. P. 1993. Beached bird surveys in Portugal 1991–2 and relationship between weather and density of corpses. *Sula* 7, 1–8.

GRANDE, J. M. & PALACIOS, C. J. 2002. First breeding record of the Lesser Black-backed Gull in the Macaroesic archipelago, North Atlantic; a large spread in its breeding range. *Waterbirds* 25, 388–9.

GRAY, R. 1871. *Birds of the west of Scotland including the Outer Hebrides*. Thomas Murray & Son, Glasgow.

GREEN, R. & GREEN, J. 1997. *Otter Survey of Scotland, 1991–1997*. The Vincent Wildlife Trust, London.

GREEN, R. E. 1995. Diagnosing causes of bird population declines. *Ibis* 137, S47–S55.

GREEN, R. E. 2002. Diagnosing causes of population declines and selecting remedial actions. In: Norris, K. & Pain, D. J. (eds.) *Conserving Bird Biodiversity*. Cambridge University Press.

GREEN, R. E., BAILEY, S. R. & AVERY, M. I. 1990. Can ringing recoveries help to explain the population dynamics of British terns? *The Ring* 13, 133–7.

GREEN, R. E., HARLEY, M., SPALDING, M. & ZÖCKLER, C. (eds.) 2001. *Impacts of Climate Change on Wildlife*. Royal Society for the Protection of Birds, Sandy.

GREEN, R. E. & HIRONS, G. J. M. 1991. The relevance of population studies to the conservation of threatened birds. In: Perrins, C. M., Lebreton, J.-D. & Hirons, G. J. M. (eds.) *Bird Population Studies*. Oxford University Press.

GREENWOOD, J. G. 1987. Winter visits by black guillemots *Cepphus grylle* to an Irish breeding site. *Bird Study* 34, 135–6.

GREENWOOD, J. G. 1988. The Northern Ireland black guillemot survey 1987. *Irish Nat. J.* 22, 490–491.

GREENWOOD, J. G. 1991. Duration of winter visits by Black Guillemots *Cepphus grylle* to an Irish breeding site. *Seabird* 13, 67–9.

GREENWOOD, J. G. 2002. Nesting cavity choice by Black Guillemots *Cepphus grylle*. *Atlantic Seabirds* 4, 99–122.

GREGORY, R. D., WILKINSON, N. I., NOBLE, D. G., ROBINSON, J. A., BROWN, A. F., HUGHES, J., PROCTER, D., GIBBONS, D. W. & GALBRAITH, C. A. 2002. The population status of birds in the United Kingdom, Channel Islands and Isle of Man: analysis of conservation concern 2002–2007. *Brit. Birds* 95, 410–48.

GREIG, S. A, COULSON, J. C. & MONAGHAN, P. 1986. A comparison of foraging at refuse tips by 3 species of gull (Laridae). *J. Zool., Lond.* 210, 459–72.

GRELL, M. B. 1998. *Fuglenes Danmark*. Dansk Orn. Fore., Copenhagen.

GRELL, M. B. 2002. [Rare and threatened breeding birds in Denmark, 2001.] *Dansk Orn. Fore. Tidsskr.* 96, 43–66.

GRELL, M. B., JØRGSENSEN, H. E., MELTOFTE, H. & SKOV, H. 1998. [*The Birds of Denmark*.] Gad, Copenhagen. [In Danish.]

GRIBBLE, F. C. 1962. Census of Black-headed Gull colonies in England and Wales, 1958. *Bird Study* 9, 56–71.

GRIBBLE, F. C. 1976. A census of Black-headed Gull colonies. *Bird Study* 23, 135–45.

GRIFFITHS, A. M. 1981. European Storm-petrels *Hydrobates pelagicus* feeding by diving off South Africa. *Cormorant* 9, 47.

GROZ, P., MONTEIRO, L. R., PEREIRA, J. C., SILVA, A. G. & RAMOS, J. A. 2001. Conservation and management of the *Puffinus* species in the Azores. In: Zonfrillo, B., Câmara, D. B., Bolton, M. & Perrins, C. M. (eds.) *Proc. First Manx Shearwater Conf., Funchal, Madeira 2000*.

GURNEY, J. H. 1913. *The Gannet. A Bird With a History*. H. F. & G. Witherby, London.

GUTHOVÁ, Z. 1993. Variations in reproduction parameters of black-headed gulls (*Larus ridibundus*) living in different conditions in the Czech and Slovak republics. *Environ. Conserv.* 20, 347–51.

VON HAARTMANN, L. 1982. The Arctic Tern *Sterna paradisaea*—a new inhabitant of the inshore archipelago. *Ornis Fenn.* 59, 64–76.

HADDON, P. C. & KNIGHT, R. C. 1983. *A Guide to Little Tern Conservation*. Royal Society for the Protection of Birds, Sandy.

HAGEMEIJER, W. J. M. & BLAIR, M. J. (eds.) 1997. *The EBCC Atlas of European Breeding Bird: Their distribution and abundance*. T. & A. D. Poyser, London.

VAN HALEWYN, R, & NORTON, R.L. 1984. The status and conservation of seabirds in the Caribbean. In: Croxall, J.P., P.G.H. Evans & R.W. Schreiber (eds) Status and Conservation of the World's Seabirds. Pp 169–222. ICBP Technical Publication No. 2, Cambridge.

HALL, A. J., TASKER, M. L. & WEBB, A. 1987. The marine distribution of sooty shearwater, Manx shearwater, storm petrel and Leach's petrel in the North Sea. *Seabird* 10, 60–70.

HALLEY, D. J. & HARRIS, M. P. 1993. Intercolony movement and behaviour of immature guillemots *Uria aalge*. *Ibis* 135, 264–70.

HALLEY, D. J., HARRIS, M. P. & WANLESS, S. 1995. Colony attendance patterns and recruitment in immature Common Murres (*Uria aalge*). *Auk* 112, 947–57.

HÄLTERLEIN, B. P. SÜDBECK, W., KNIEF, ?. & KÖPPEN, U. 2000. Population trends of coastal breeding birds of the German North Sea and Baltic coasts. *Vogelwelt* 121, 241–67.

HAMER, K. C. & FURNESS, R. W. 1993. Brood defence by male and female Great Skuas *Catharacta skua*: the influence of food supply, laying date, clutch size and body condition. *J. Zool., Lond.* 230, 7–18.

HAMER, K. C., FURNESS, R. W. & CALDOW, R. W. G. 1991. The effects of changes in food availability on the breeding ecology of Great Skuas *Catharacta skua* in Shetland. *J. Zool., Lond.* 223, 175–88.

HAMER, K. C., MONAGHAN, P., UTTLEY, J. D., WALTON, P. & BURNS, M. D. 1993. The influence of food supply on the breeding ecology of Kittiwakes *Rissa tridactyla* in Shetland. *Ibis* 135, 255–63.

HAMER, K. C., PHILLIPS, R. A., HILL, J. K., WANLESS, S. & WOOD, A. G. 2001. Contrasting foraging strategies of Gannets *Morus bassanus* at two North Atlantic colonies. *Mar. Ecol. Progr. Ser.* 224, 283–90.

HAMER, K. C., THOMPSON, D. R. & GRAY, C. M. 1997. Spatial variation in the feeding ecology, foraging ranges, and breeding energetics of Northern Fulmars in the north-east Atlantic Ocean. *ICES J. Mar. Sci.* 54, 645–53.

HANDRINOS, G. & AKRIOTIS, T. 1997. *The Birds of Greece.* Christopher Helm, London.

HANNON, C., BERROW, S. D. & NEWTON, S. F. 1997. The status and distribution of breeding Sandwich *Sterna sandvicensis*, Roseate *S. dougallii*, Common *S. hirundo*, Arctic *S. paradisaea* and Little Terns *S. albifrons* in Ireland in 1995. *Irish Birds* 6, 1–22.

HANSEN, K. 2001. Threats to wildlife in Greenland. *Seabird Group Newsletter* 89, 1–2.

HANSEN, K. 2002. *A Farewell to Greenland's Wildlife.* (Publisher, place).

HARIO, M. & RINTALA, J. 2002. Population trends of the Common Eider and *Larus* gulls on Finnish coasts in 1986–2001. *Linnut Yearbook* 2001, 26–36.

HARRIS, M. P. 1964. Aspects of the breeding biology of the gulls *Larus argentatus, L. fuscus* and *L. marinus. Ibis* 106, 432–56.

HARRIS, M. P. 1970. Rates and causes of increase of some British gull populations. *Bird Study* 17, 325–35.

HARRIS, M. P. 1976. The seabirds of Shetland in 1974. *Scott. Birds* 9, 37–68.

HARRIS, M. P. 1980. Breeding performance of Puffins *Fratercula arctica* in relation to nest density, laying date and year. *Ibis* 122, 193–209.

HARRIS, M. P. 1984. *The Puffin.* T. & A.D. Poyser, Calton.

HARRIS, M. P. 1985. Morphology and breeding of puffins at Isle of May and St Kilda, Scotland. *Biol. Conserv.* 32, 81–97.

HARRIS, M. P. 1989. Variation in the correction factor used for converting counts of individual Guillemots *Uria aalge* into breeding pairs. *Ibis* 131, 85–93.

HARRIS, M. P. 2002. Atlantic Puffin (Puffin) *Fratercula arctica*. In: Wernham, C. V., Toms, M., Marchant, J., Clark, J., SiriwardenÀ, G. & Baillie, S. (eds.) *The Migration Atlas: Movements of the Birds of Britain and Ireland.* T. & A. D. Poyser, London.

HARRIS, M. P. 2002. Guillemot *Uria aalge*. In: Wernham, C. V., Toms, M., Marchant, J., Clark, J., SiriwardenÀ, G. & Baillie, S. (eds.) *The Migration Atlas: Movements of the Birds of Britain and Ireland.* T. & A. D. Poyser, London.

HARRIS, M. P. & BIRKHEAD, T. R. 1985. Breeding ecology of the Atlantic Alcidae. In: Nettleship, D. N. & Birkhead, T. R. (eds.) *The Atlantic Alcidae.* Academic Press, London.

HARRIS, M. P. & FORBES, R. 1987. The effect of date on counts of nests of Shags *Phalacrocorax aristotelis. Bird Study* 34, 187–90.

HARRIS, M. P., HALLEY, D. J. & SWANN, R. L. 1994. Age of first breeding in Common Murres. *Auk* 111, 207–14.

HARRIS, M. P., HEUBECK, M. & SUDDABY, D. 1991. Results of an examination of puffins *Fratercula arctica* washed ashore in Shetland in winter 1990–91. *Seabird* 13, 63–6.

HARRIS, M. P. & LLOYD, C. 1977. Variations in counts of seabirds from photographs. *Brit. Birds* 70, 200–5.

HARRIS, M. P. & MURRAY, S. 1977. *Birds of St Kilda.* Institute of Terrestrial Ecology, Banchory.

HARRIS, M. P., MURRAY, S. & WANLESS, S. 1998. Long-term changes in breeding performance of Puffins *Fratercula arctica* on St Kilda. *Bird Study* 45, 371–4.

HARRIS, M. P. & OSBORN, D. 1981. Effect of a polychlorinated biphenyl on the survival and breeding of puffins. *J. Appl. Ecol.* 18, 471–9.

HARRIS, M. P. & RIDDIFORD, N. J. 1989. The food of some seabirds on Fair Isle in 1986–88. *Scott. Birds* 15, 119–25.

HARRIS, M. P. & SWANN, R. L. 2002a. European Shag (Shag) *Phalacrocorax aristotelis*. In: Wernham, C. V., Toms, M., Marchant, J., Clark, J., SiriwardenÀ, G. & Baillie, S. (eds.) *The Migration Atlas: Movements of the Birds of Britain and Ireland*. T. & A. D. Poyser, London.

HARRIS, M. P. & SWANN, R. L. 2002b. Common Guillemot (Guillemot) *Uria aalge*. In: Wernham, C. V., Toms, M., Marchant, J., Clark, J., SiriwardenÀ, G. & Baillie, S. (eds.) *The Migration Atlas: Movements of the Birds of Britain and Ireland*. T. & A. D. Poyser, London.

HARRIS, M. P., TOWLL, H., RUSSELL, A. F. & WANLESS, S. 1990. Maximum dive depths attained by auks feeding young on the Isle of May, Scotland. *Scott. Birds* 16, 25–8.

HARRIS, M. P. & WANLESS, S. 1990a. Breeding status and sex of common murres (*Uria aalge*) at a colony in autumn. *Auk* 107, 603–5.

HARRIS, M. P. & WANLESS, S. 1990b. Breeding success of British Kittiwakes *Rissa tridactyla* in 1986–88: evidence for changing conditions in the northern North Sea. *J. Appl. Ecol.* 27, 172–87.

HARRIS, M. P. & WANLESS, S. 1991. The importance of the lesser sandeel *Ammodytes marinus* in the diet of the shag *Phalacrocorax aristotelis*. *Ornis Scand.* 22, 375–82.

HARRIS, M. P. & WANLESS, S. 1994. Ingested elastic and other artefacts found in Puffins in Britain over a 24-year period. *Mar. Pollution Bull.* 28, 54–5.

HARRIS, M. P. & WANLESS, S. 1995. Survival and non-breeding of adult Common Guillemots *Uria aalge*. *Ibis* 137, 192–7.

HARRIS, M. P. & WANLESS, S. 1996. Differential responses of guillemot *Uria aalge* and shag *Phalacrocorax aristotelis* to a late winter wreck. *Bird Study* 43, 220–30.

HARRIS, M. P. & WANLESS, S. 1997a. Breeding success, diet and brood neglect in the kittiwake (*Rissa tridactyla*) over an 11-year period. *ICES J. Mar. Sci.* 54, 615–23.

HARRIS, M. P. & WANLESS, S. 1997b. Inland nesting by Razorbills. *Scott. Birds* 19, 121–2.

HARRIS, M. P. & WANLESS, S. 1997c. *Phalacrocorax aristotelis* Shag. *BWP Update* 1, 3–13.

HARRIS, M. P. & WANLESS, S. 1998. The status of the Puffin *Fratercula arctica* on the Isle of May National Nature Reserve. Rep. to Scottish Natural Heritage, Cupar.

HARRIS, M. P. & WANLESS, S. 1999. Transatlantic Gannets. *BTO News* 225, 5.

HARRIS, M. P., WANLESS, S., BARTON, T. R. & ELSTON, D. A. 1997. Nest site characteristics, duration of use and breeding success in the Guillemot *Uria aalge*. *Ibis* 139, 468–76.

HARRIS, M. P., WANLESS, S., DARLING, I. & GALLACHER, C. 2000a. Breeding birds of the Isle of May, Firth of Forth, 1972–99. *Scott. Birds* 21, 6–14.

HARRIS, M. P., WANLESS, S. & ELSTON, D. A. 1998. Age-related effects of a non-breeding event and a winter wreck on the survival of Shags *Phalacrocorax aristotelis*. *Ibis* 140, 310–4.

HARRIS, M. P., WANLESS, S. & ROTHERY, P. 1983. Assessing changes in the numbers of guillemots *Uria aalge* at breeding colonies. *Bird Study* 30, 57–66.

HARRIS, M. P., WANLESS, S. & ROTHERY, P. 1986. Counts of breeding and non-breeding guillemots *Uria aalge* at a colony during the chick rearing period. *Seabird* 9, 43–6.

HARRIS, M. P., WANLESS, S. & ROTHERY, P. 2000b. Adult survival rates of Shag (*Phalacrocorax aristotelis*), Common Guillemot (*Uria aalge*), Razorbill (*Alca torda*), Puffin (*Fratercula arctica*) and Kittiwake (*Rissa tridactyla*) on the Isle of May 1986–96. *Atlantic Seabirds* 2, 133–50.

HARRIS, M. P. & YULE, R. F. 1977. The moult of the Puffin *Fratercula arctica*. *Ibis* 119, 535–40.

HARRISON, N. & ROBINS, M. 1992. The threat from nets to seabirds. *RSPB Conserv. Rev.* 6, 51–6.

HARRISON, J. M. 1953. *The Birds of Kent*. H. F & G. Witherby, London.

HARRISON, T. H. & HURRELL, H. G. 1933. Numerical fluctuations of the Great Black-backed Gull (*Larus marinus* Linn.) in England and Wales. *Proc. Zool. Soc. Lond.* 103, 191–209.

HARVEY, P. 1983. Breeding seabird population, Isles of Scilly, vol. 1. Unpubl. Nature Conservancy Council Rep., Peterborough.

HARVEY, P. V., SWALE, J., UPTON, A. J., GEAR, J., GEAR, S., ADAM, M., CHURCHILL, G., GILLHAM, K. & SKENE, A. 2000. A census of the seabirds of Foula—June 2000. Scottish Natural Heritage, Lerwick.

HARVIE-BROWN, J. A. 1912. The Northern Fulmar: its past and present distribution as a breeding species in the British Isles. *Scott. Nat.* 1912, 97–102, 121–32.

HASHMI, D. & FLIEGE, G. 1994. Herbstzug der Sturmschwalbe (*Hydrobates pelagicus*) in der meerenge von Gibraltar. *J. Orn.* 135, 203–7.

HATCH, J. J. 2002. Arctic Tern (*Sterna paradisaea*). In: Poole, A. & Gill, F. (eds.) *The Birds of North America*, 707. Birds of North America Inc., Philadelphia, PA & American Ornithologists' Union, Washington DC.

HATCH, J. J. 1996. Threats to public health from gulls (Laridae). *Intern. J. Environ. Health Res.* 6, 5–16.

HATCH, P. 1976. Threats to public health from gulls (Laridae). *Intern. J. Environ. Health Res.* 6, 5–16.

HATCH, S. A., BYRD, G. V., IRONS, D. B. & HUNT, G. L. 1993. Status and ecology of kittiwakes (*Rissa tridactyla* and *Rissa brevirostris*) in the North Pacific. In: Vermeer, K., Briggs, K. T., Morgan, K. H. & Siegel-Causey, D. (eds.) *The Status, Ecology and Conservation of Marine Birds of the North Pacific*. Can. Wildl. Serv. Spec. Publ., Ottawa.

HAYDEN, T. & HARRINGTON, R. 2000. *Exploring Irish Mammals*. Town House, Dublin.

HAYS, H. 1984. Common Tern raise young from successive broods. *Auk* 101, 274–80.

HAYS, H., NEVES, V. & LIMA, P. 2002. Banded Roseate Terns from different continents trapped in the Azores. *J. Field Orn.* 73, 180–4.

HAYS, H., NEWTON, S., LIMA, P. & CROWE, O. 2000. Rockabill Roseate Tern recaptured in Brazil. *Irish Birds* 6, 585–602.

HEANEY, V., RATCLIFFE, N., BROWN, A., ROBINSON, P. J. & LOCK, L. 2002. The status and distribution of European storm petrels *Hydrobates pelagicus* and Manx Shearwaters *Puffinus puffinus* on the Isles of Scilly. *Atlantic Seabirds* 4, 1–16.

HEATH, M. F., BORGGREVE, C. & PEET, N. 2000. *European Bird Populations—Estimates and Trends*. BirdLife International Conserv. Ser. 10, Cambridge.

HEATH, M. R., BEARE, D. J., DUNN, J., FRASER, J. G., HAY, S. J. & TURRELL, W. R. 1999. Monitoring the effects of climate change—overwintering abundance of *Calanus finmarchicus* in the Faeroe–Shetland Channel. Fisheries Res. Services Rep. 14/99, Aberdeen.

HEUBECK, M. 1989. Breeding success of Shetland seabirds: Arctic Skua, Kittiwake, Guillemot, Razorbill and Puffin. In: Heubeck, M. (ed.) *Seabirds and Sandeels: Proc. of a Seminar held in Lerwick, Shetland, 15–16 October 1988*. Shetland Bird Club, Lerwick.

HEUBECK, M. 1997. The direct effect of the *Braer* oil spill on seabird populations and an assessment of the role of the wildlife response centre. In: Davies, J. M. & Topping, G. (eds.) *The Impact of an Oil Spill in Turbulent Waters: The Braer*. The Stationary Office, Edinburgh.

HEUBECK, M. 1999. The effect of a spring gale and a freak wave on a breeding group of Common Guillemots *Uria aalge*. *Atlantic Seabirds* 1, 43–7.

HEUBECK, M. 2000. Population trends of Kittiwake *Rissa tridactyla*, Black Guillemot *Cepphus grylle* and Common Guillemot *Uria aalge* in Shetland, 1978–98. *Atlantic Seabirds* 2, 227–44.

HEUBECK, M. 2003. SOTEAG Ornithological Monitoring Programme. 2002 Summary Report. Shetland Oil Terminal Environmental Advisory Group, Aberdeen.

HEUBECK, M. In press. The impact of oil pollution on seabird populations of the United Kingdom during the past 25 years. *Proc. Conf. Oil Pollution and Conserv. Biodiv., Sardinia, October 2002*.

HEUBECK, M., BIRD, D. R., HARROP, H. R., HARVEY, P. V., MELLOR, R. M., SUDDABY, D., TASKER, M. L. & UTTLEY, J. D. 1993. An assessment of the impact of the *Braer* oil spill on the Shetland breeding population of Tysties *Cepphus grylle*. Rep. to Ecological Steering Group on the Shetland oil spill by Shetland Oil Terminal Environmental Advisory Group / Joint Nature Conservation Committee / Royal Society for the Protection of Birds / Scottish National Heritage.

HEUBECK, M., HARVEY, P. V. & OKILL, J. D. 1991. Changes in the Shetland Guillemot *Uria aalge* population and the pattern of recoveries of ringed birds, 1959–1990. *Seabird* 21, 3–21.

HEUBECK, M., MEEK, E. & SUDDABY, D. 1992. The occurrence of dead auks (Alcidae) on beaches in Orkney and Shetland. *Sula*, 1–18.

HEUBECK, M., MELLOR, R. M. & HARVEY, P. V. 1997. Changes in the breeding distribution and numbers of Kittiwakes *Rissa tridactyla* around Unst, Shetland, and the presumed role of predation by Great Skuas *Stercorarius skua*. *Seabird* 19, 12–21.

HEUBECK, M., MELLOR, R. M., HARVEY, P. V., MAINWOOD, A. R. & RIDDINGTON, R. 1999. Estimating the population size and rate of decline of Kittiwakes *Rissa tridactyla* breeding in Shetland, 1981–97. *Bird Study* 46, 48–61.

HEUBECK, M. & RICHARDSON, M. G. 1980. Bird mortality following the Esso *Bernica* oil spill, December 1978. *Scott. Birds* 11, 97–108.

HICKLING, R. A. O. 1986. Lesser Black-backed Gull *Larus fuscus*. In: Lack, P. (ed.) 1986. *The Atlas of Wintering Birds in Britain and Ireland*. T. & A.D. Poyser, Calton.

HIGGINS, P. J. & DAVIES, S. J. J. F. (eds.) 1996. *The Handbook of Australian, New Zealand and Antarctic Birds*. Oxford University Press.

HILDEN, O. 1978. Recent changes in the seabird populations in Finland. *Baltic Birds* 5, 151–3.

HILL, M. G. 1994. Manx Shearwaters *Puffinus puffinus* breeding in the Bailiwick of Guernsey, Channel Islands. *Seabird* 16, 41–5.

HIPFNER, J. M. & CHAPDELAINE, G. 2002. Razorbill (*Alca torda*). In: Poole, A. & Gill, F. (eds.) *The Birds of North America*, 635. Birds of North America Inc., Philadelphia, PA & American Ornithologists' Union, Washington DC.

HOLDGATE, M. E. 1971. The seabird wreck of 1969 in the Irish Sea. The Natural Environment Research Council, London.

HOLLOM, P. A. D. 1940. Report on the 1938 survey of Black-headed Gull colonies. *Brit. Birds* 33, 202–21, 230–44.

HOLLOWAY, S. 1996. *The Historical Atlas of Breeding Birds in Britain and Ireland 1875–1900.* T. & A.D. Poyser, London.

HORTON, N., BROUGH, T. & ROCHARD, J. B. A. 1983. The importance of refuse tips to gulls wintering in an inland area in S.E. England. *J. Appl. Ecol.* 20, 751–65.

HOSEY, G. R. & GOODRIDGE, F. 1980. Establishment of territories in two species of gull on Walney Island, Cumbria. *Bird Study* 27, 73–80.

DEL HOYO, J. ELLIOTT, A. & SARGATAL, J. (eds.) 1992. *The Handbook of the Birds of the World*, vol. 1. Lynx Edicions, Barcelona.

DEL HOYO, J., ELLIOTT, A. & SARGATAL, J. (eds.) 1996. *The Handbook of the Birds of the World*, vol. 3. Lynx Edicions, Barcelona.

HUDSON, A. V. 1982. Great Black-backed Gulls on Great Saltee Island, 1981. *Irish Birds* 2, 167–75.

HUDSON, A. V. & FURNESS, R. W. 1988. Utilization of discarded fish by scavenging seabirds behind whitefish trawlers in Shetland. *J. Zool., Lond.* 215, 151–66.

HUDSON, A. V. & FURNESS, R.W. 1989. The behaviour of seabirds foraging at fishing boats around Shetland. *Ibis* 131, 225–37.

HUDSON, P. J. 1985. Population parameters of the Atlantic Alcidae. In: Nettleship, D. N. & Birkhead, T. R. (eds.) *The Atlantic Alcidae*. Academic Press, London.

HUGHES, B. & SELLERS, R. M. 1998. Inventory of Cormorant roosts and inland breeding sites in Britain. Wildfowl & Wetlands Trust Rep., Slimbridge.

HUGHES, B., BEVAN, R. M., BOWLER, J. M., STILL, L., CARSS, D. N., MARQUISS, M., HEARN, R. D. & BRUCE, J. H. 1999. Feeding behaviour of fish-eating birds in Great Britain. Department of the Environment, Transport & Regions Rep., London.

HUNT, G. L. & McLOON, S. C. 1975. Activity patterns of gull chicks in relation to feeding by parents and their significance for density dependant mortality. *Auk* 92, 503–27.

HUNT, W. G., JACKMAN, R. E., HUNT, T. L., DRISCOLL, D. E. & CULP, L. 1999. A population study of Golden Eagles in the Altamont Pass wind resource area 1994–1997. Rep. to National Renewable Energy Lab. by the Predatory Bird Res. Group, University of California, Santa Cruz.

HUNTINGTON, C. E., BUTLER, R. G. & MAUCK, R. A. 1996. Leach's Storm-petrel (*Oceanodroma leucorhoa*). In: Poole, A. & Gill, F. (eds.) *The Birds of North America*, 233. Birds of North America Inc., Philadelphia, PA & American Ornithologists' Union, Washington DC.

HÜPPOP, O. & WURM, S. 2000. Effects of winter fishery activities on resting numbers, food and body condition of large gulls *Larus argentatus* and *L. marinus* in the south-eastern North Sea. *Mar. Ecol. Progr. Ser.* 194, 341–7.

HURRELL, J. W., KUSHNIR, Y., OTTERSEN, G. & VISBECK, M. (eds.) 2003. *The North Atlantic Oscillation: Climate Significance and Environmental Impact.* Geophysical Monograph Ser. 134.

HUTCHINSON, C. D. 1989. *Birds in Ireland.* T. & A. D. Poyser, Calton.

ICELANDIC INSTITUTE OF NATURAL HISTORY. 2000. *Red List of Threatened Species in Iceland*, vol. 2. Náttúrufræ_istofnun Islands, Reykjavik.

INTERGOVERNMENTAL PANEL ON CLIMATE CHANGE. 2001. *Climate Change.* Cambridge University Press.

INTERNATIONAL COUNCIL FOR THE EXPLORATION OF THE SEA (ICES). 1997. Report of the working group on the assessment of the demersal stocks in the North Sean and Skagerrak. ICES CM/197, Copenhagen.

INTERNATIONAL COUNCIL FOR THE EXPLORATION OF THE SEA (ICES). 2000. Working group on the effects of extraction of marine sediments on the marine ecosystem. ICES, Copenhagen.

INTERNATIONAL COUNCIL FOR THE EXPLORATION OF THE SEA (ICES). 2001. Review of the interaction between aquaculture and birds in the ICES area. In: *Report of the Working Group on Seabird Ecology*. ICES, Copenhagen.

INTERNATIONAL COUNCIL FOR THE EXPLORATION OF THE SEA (ICES). 2002a. Deep-water fisheries resources south of 63°N. In: *Report of the ICES Advisory Committee on Fishery Management*. ICES, Copenhagen.

INTERNATIONAL COUNCIL FOR THE EXPLORATION OF THE SEA (ICES). 2002b. Effects of marine wind farms on birds. In: *Report of the Working Group on Seabird Ecology*. ICES, Copenhagen.

INTERNATIONAL COUNCIL FOR THE EXPLORATION OF THE SEA (ICES). 2003. Report of the working group on seabird ecology, March 2003. ICES CM 2003/C:03, Copenhagen.

ISENMANN, P., LEBRETON, J. D. & BRANDL, R. 1991. The Black-headed Gull in Europe. *Acta XX Congressus Internationalis Ornithologici*. Ornithological Congress Trust Board, Christchurch. New Zealand.

ISENMANN, P., SADOUL, N. & YÉSOU, P. In press. Mouette mélanocéphale. In: Cadiou, B., Pons, J.-M. & Yésou, P. (eds.) *Oiseaux Marins Nicheurs de France Métropolitaine (1960–2000)*. GISOM Editions Biotope, Paris.

JACOB, J.-P. & JACOB, A. 1980. [New data upon. . . . . . avifauna of Boughzoul Lake (Algeria).] *Alauda* 48, 209–18. [In French.]

JAMES, P. C. 1984. Sexual dimorphism in the voice of the British storm petrel *Hydrobates pelagicus*. *Ibis* 126, 89–92.

JAMES, P. C. 1985. Geographical and temporal variation in calls of Manx shearwaters *Puffinus puffinus* and British storm petrels *Hydrobates pelagicus*. *J. Zool., Lond*. 201, 331–44.

JAMES, P. C. & ROBERTSON, H. A. 1985. The use of playback recordings to detect and census nocturnal burrowing seabirds. *Seabird* 8, 18–20.

JARDINE, D. C., HOW, J., CLARKE, J. & CLARKE P. M. 2002. Seabirds on Colonsay and Oronsay, Inner Hebrides. *Scott. Birds* 23, 1–9.

JENSEN, J. K. 1993. Sub-surface night-foraging of storm petrels *Hydrobates pelagicus*. *Dansk Orn. Fore. Tidsskr*. 87, 3–4.

JOHNSON, G. D., YOUNG, D. P., ERICKSON, W. P., STRICKLAND, M. D., GOOD, R. E. & BECKER, P. 2001. Avian and bat mortality associated with the initial phase of the Foote Creek Rim windpower project, Carbon County, Wyoming: November 3 1998–October 21 2000. Tech. Rep. to Sea West Energy Corporation and Bureau of Land Management by WEST Inc.

JONES, P. H. 2001. Night-time attractions of Manx Shearwaters to the lighthouse at Bardsey, Gwynedd, U.K. In: Zonfrillo, B., Câmara, D. B., Bolton, M. & Perrins, C. M. (eds.) *Proc. First Manx Shearwater Conf., Funchal, Madeira 2000*.

JONES, P. H., BARRETT, C. F., MUDGE, G. P. & HARRIS, M. P. 1985. Examination of corpses of auks beached on east British coasts in February 1983. *Seabird* 8, 9–14.

DE JUANA, E. 1984. The status and conservation of seabirds in the Spanish Mediterranean. In: Croxall, J. P., Evans, P. G. H. & Schreiber, R. W. (eds.) *Status and Conservation of the World's Seabirds*. International Council for Bird Preservation Tech. Publ. 2, Cambridge.

KARAUZ, S. & KIRAÇ, C. 1999. Breeding, wintering and migration of Mediterranean Gull *Larus melanocephalus* in Turkey. In: Meininger, P. L., Hoogendoorn, W., Flamant, R. & Raevel, P. (eds.) *Proc. First Intern. Mediterranean Gull Meeting, Le Portel, Pas-de-Calais, France, 4–7 September 1998*.

KARNOVSKY, N. J., KWASNIEWSKI, S., WESLAWSKI, J. M., WALKUSZ, W. & BESZCZYNSKA-MÖLLER, A. 2003. Foraging behavior of Little Auks in a heterogeneous environment. *Mar. Ecol. Progr. Ser*. 253, 289–303.

KASEMIR, G. & LUTTEROP, D. 2002. Noordse Stern *Sterna paradisaea*. In: SOVON Vogelonderzoek Nederland (ed.) *Atlas van de Nederlandse Broedvogels 1998–2000*. Nationaal Natuurhistorisch Museum Naturalis, KNNV Uitgeverij & European Invertebrate Survey, Leiden.

KEIJL, G. O. & ARTS, F. A. 1998. Breeding Mew Gulls *Larus canus* in The Netherlands, 1990–96. *Sula* 12, 161–74.

KEIJL, G. O., BRENNINKMEIJER, A., SCHEPERS, F. J., STIENEN, E. W. M., VEEN, J. & NDIAYE, A. 2001. Breeding gulls and terns in Senegal in 1998, and proposal for new population estimates for gulls and terns in north-west Africa. *Atlantic Seabirds* 3, 59–74.

KEITT, B. S., WILCOX, C., TERSHY, B. R., CROLL, D. A. & DONLAN, C. J. 2002. The effect of feral cats on the population viability of black-vented Shearwaters (*Puffinus opisthomelas*) on Natividad Island, Mexico. *Anim. Conserv*. 5, 217–23.

KIHLMAN, J. & LARSSON, L. 1974. On the importance of refuse dumps as a food source of wintering Herring Gulls *Larus argentatus* Pont. *Ornis Scand*. 5, 63–70.

KILPI, M. 1995. Breeding success, predation and local dynamics of colonial Mew Gulls *Larus canus*. *Ann. Zool. Fenn*. 32, 175–82.

KIRBY, J. S. HOLMES, J. S. & SELLERS, R. M. 1996. Cormorants *Phalacrocorax carbo* as fish predators: an appraisal of their conservation and management in Great Britain. *Biol. Conserv*. 75, 191–9.

KITAYSKY, A. S. & GOLUBOVA, E. G. 2000. Climate change causes contrasting trends in reproductive performance of planktivorous and piscivorous alcids. *J. Anim. Ecol.* 69, 248–62.

KLAASSEN, K. & LEMMETYINEN, R. 1998. Arctic Tern. In: Hagemeijer, W. J. M. & Blair, M. J. (eds.) *The EBCC Atlas of European Breeding Birds: Their Distribution and Abundance.* T. & A. D. Poyser, London.

KLOMP, N. I. & FURNESS, R. W. 1992. Nonbreeders as a buffer against environmental stress: declines in numbers of great skuas on Foula Shetland and prediction of future recruitment. *J. Appl. Ecol.* 29, 341–8.

KNIEF, W., OTTO, M. & BERNDT, R. K. 2001. Ergebnisse der Brutbestandserfassung in den Naturschutzgebieten an der Schleswig-holsteinischen Ostseeküste 1999. *Seevögel* 22, 39–40.

KOERTS, J. 1992. [Feeding storm petrels at the Ijmuiden breakwaters, 22 September 1990]. *Sula* 6, 19–20. [In Dutch.]

KONDRATYEV, A. Y., LITVINENKO, N. M., SHIBAEV, Y. V., VYATKIN, P. S. & KONDRATYEVA, L. F. 2000. The breeding seabirds of the Russian Far East. In: Kondratyev, A. Y., Litvinenko, N. M. & Kaiser, G. W. (eds.) *Seabirds of the Russian Far East.* Spec. Publ. Can. Wildl. Service, Ottawa.

KÖPPEN, U. 2001. Brutbestände der Küstenvögel in Schutzgebieten Mecklenburg-Vorpommerns in den Jahren 1999 und 2000. *Seevögel* 22, 104–5.

KRASNOV, J. V. & BARRETT, R. T. 1995. Large-scale interactions among seabirds, their prey and humans in the southern Barents Sea. In: Skjoldal, H. R., Hopkins, C., Erikstad, K. E. & Leinaas, H. P. (eds.) *Ecology of Fjords and Coastal Waters.* Elsevier, Amsterdam.

KRASNOV, J. V. & BARRETT, R. T. 1997. The first record of North Atlantic gannets *Morus bassanus* breeding in Russia. *Seabird* 19, 54–7.

KRASNOV, Y. V., MATISHOV, G. G., GALAKTIONOV, K. V. & SAVINOVA, T. N. 1995. [The colonial seabirds of Murman.] Nauka, St Petersburg. [In Russian.]

KRASNOV J. V. & NIKOLAEVA, N. G. 1998. [Ecology and morphology of black-backed and herring gulls in the Barents Sea]. In: [*Biology and Oceanography of the Kara and Barents Seas (Along the Northern Marina Route)*]. Apatity. [In Russian.]

KRESS, S. W. 1997. Using animal behaviour for conservation: case studies in seabird restoration from the Maine coast, USA. *J. Yamashina Inst. Orn.* 29, 1–26.

KRESS, S. W., WIENSTEIN, E. H. & NISBET, I. C. T. 1983. The status of tern populations in northeastern United States and adjacent Canada. *Colonial Waterbirds* 6, 84–106.

KUBETZKI, U. 2001. Zum Bestandsrückgang der Sturmmöwe (*Larus canus*) an der Schleswig-holsteinischen Ostseeküste—Aumaß, Ursachen und Schutzkonzepte. *Corax* 18, 301–23.

KÜRGER, T. & GARTHE, S. 2001. Flight altitudes of coastal birds in relation to wind direction and windspeed. *Atlantic Seabirds* 3, 203–16.

KWEI, E. A. 1964. Migration of *Sardinella aurita* (Val. et Cuv.). *Ghana J. Sci.* 4, 34–43.

LACK, P. (ed.) 1986. *The Atlas of Wintering Birds in Britain and Ireland.* T. & A. D. Poyser, Calton.

LACK. D. 1966. *Population Studies of Birds.* Oxford University Press.

LAMBERT, R. A. 2003. Seabird control and fishery protection in Cornwall, 1900–50. *Brit. Birds* 96, 30–4.

LANGHAM, N. E. P. 1974. Comparative breeding biology of the Sandwich Tern. *Auk* 91, 255–77.

LARNER, J. & DOUGLAS J. 2002. *Special Protection Areas for Birds in Ireland.* The Heritage Service, Dept. of Environment and Local Government, Dublin.

LAW, R. J., ALLEN, C. R., BENNETT, M. E., MORRIS, S. & ROGAN, E. 2002. Polybrominated diphenyl ethers in two species of marine top predators from England and Wales. *Chemosphere* 46, 673–81.

LE NEVÉ, A. 2003. *Sternes de Bretagne.* Bretagne Vivante–SEPNB Report, Brest.

LEAPER, G., STANSFIELD, S. & MITCHELL, P. I. in prep. Census of the breeding population of Manx Shearwaters *Puffinus p. puffinus* on Ynys Enlli (Bardsey Island), Wales, 2001. Rep. Joint Nature Conservation Committee, Peterborough.

LEBRETON, J. D., HINES, J. E., PRADEL, R., NICHOLS, J. D. & SPENDELOW, J. A. 2003. Estimation by recapture of recruitment and dispersal over several sites. *Oikos* 101, 253–64.

LEIGHTON, F. A. 1991. The toxicity of petroleum oils to birds: an overview. In: White, J. & Frink, L. (eds.) *The Effects of Oil on Wildlife: Research, Rehabilitation and General Concerns.* Sheridan Press, Hanover, PA.

LENSINK, C. J. 1984. The status and conservation of seabirds in Alaska. In: Croxall, J. P., Evans, P. G. H. & Schreiber, R. W. (eds.) *Status and Conservation of the World's Seabirds.* International Council for Bird Preservation Tech. Publ. 2, Cambridge.

LESTER, F. R. & KAVAUGH, B. P. 1982. An analysis of the ringing and recovery data of razorbills and guillemots from Great Saltee Island, Co. Wexford. *Irish Birds* 4, 653–4.

LEWIS, S., SHERRATT, T. N., HAMER, K. C. & WANLESS, S. 2001a. Evidence of intra-specific competition for food in a pelagic seabird. *Nature* 412, 816–9.

LEWIS, S., WANLESS, S., WRIGHT, P. J., HARRIS, M. P., BULL, J. & ELSTON, D. A. 2001b. Diet and breeding performance of black-legged kittiwakes *Rissa tridactyla* at a North Sea colony. *Mar. Ecol. Progr. Ser.* 221, 277–84.

LITVINENKO, N. & SHIBAEV, Y. 1991. Status and conservation of the seabirds nesting in southeast USSR. In: Croxall, J. P. (ed.) *Seabird Status and Conservation: A Supplement*. International Council for Bird Preservation Tech. Publ. 11, Cambridge.

LLOYD, C. 1973. Attendance at auk colonies during the breeding season. *Skokholm Bird Observ. Rep.* 1972, 15–23.

LLOYD, C. S. 1974. Movement and survival of British Razorbills. *Bird Study* 21, 102–16.

LLOYD, C. S. 1975. Timing and frequency of census counts of cliff-nesting auks. *Brit. Birds* 68, 507–13.

LLOYD, C. S. 1979. Factors affecting breeding of Razorbills *Alca torda* on Skokholm. *Ibis* 121, 165–76.

LLOYD, C. S., BIBBY, C. J. & EVERETT, M. J. 1974. Roseate Terns in trouble. *BTO News* 63, 8–9.

LLOYD , C. S., BIBBY, C. J. & EVERETT, M. J. 1975. Breeding terns in Britain and Ireland in 1969–74. *Brit. Birds* 68, 221–37.

LLOYD, C. S. & PERRINS, C. M. 1977. Survival and age at first breeding in the Razorbill (*Alca torda*). *Bird Banding* 48, 239–52.

LLOYD, C. S., TASKER, M. L. & PARTRIDGE, K. 1991. *The Status of Seabirds in Britain and Ireland*. T. & A. D. Poyser, Calton.

LLOYD, C. S., THOMAS, G. J., MacDONALD, J. W., BORLAND, E. D., STANDRING, K. & SMART, J. L. 1976. Wild bird mortality caused by botulism in Britain, 1975. *Biol. Conserv.* 10, 119–29.

LOCK, A. R. 1987. Increases in the breeding population of Black-legged Kittiwakes, *Rissa tridactyla*, in Nova Scotia. *Can. Field Nat.* 101, 331–4.

LOCK, A. R. BROWN, R. G. B. & GERRIETS, S. H. 1994, *Gazetteer of Marine Birds in Atlantic Canada, an Atlas of Sea Bird Vulnerability to Oil Pollution*. Can. Wildl. Service, Ottawa.

LØKKEBORG, S. 1998. Seabird by-catch and bait loss in long-lining using different of various mitigation measures. *ICES J. Mar. Sci.* 54, 145–9.

LØKKEBORG, S. 2000. Review and evaluation of three mitigation measures—bird scaring line, under-water setter and line shooter—to reduce bycatch in the Norwegian long-line fishery. ICES 88th Statutory Meeting, Brugges.

LORENTSEN, S.-H. 1994. Svartbak *Larus marinus*. In: Gjershaug, J. O., Thingstad, P. G., Eldøy, S. & Byrkjeland, S. (eds.) *Norsk Fugleatlas*. Norsk Orn. Fore., Klæbu.

LORENTSEN, S.-H. 2001. The national monitoring programme for seabirds. Results including the breeding season of 2001. Norwegian Institute for Nature Research, Tromsø.

LOVE, J. A. 1978. Leach's and Storm-petrels on North Rona: 1971–1974. *Ring. & Migr.* 2, 15–9.

LOVE, J. A. 2001. *Rum: A Landscape Without Figures*. Birlinn, Edinburgh.

LOVRIC, A. Z. & OBRADOVIC, J. 1988. Nesting areas and synecology of seabirds in Adriatic islets. Rapport de la Commission Internationale pour l'Exploration Scientifique de la Méditerranée, Monaco.

LOWTHER, P. E., DIAMOND, A. W., KRESS, S. W., ROBERTSON, G. J. & RUSSELL, K. 2002. Atlantic Puffin (*Fratercula arctica*). In: Poole, A. & Gill, F. (eds.) *The Birds of North America*, 709. Birds of North America Inc., Philadelphia, PA & American Ornithologists' Union, Washington DC.

LUDWIG, J. P., AUMAN, H. J., WESELOH, D. V., FOX, G. A., GIESY, J. P. & LUDWIG, M. E. 1995. Evaluation of the effects of toxic chemicals in Great Lakes Cormorants: has causality been established? *Colonial Waterbirds* 18 (Spec. Publ. 1), 60–9.

LUDWIGS, J.-D. & STÖBER, N. 2001. [Roseate Tern *Sterna dougallii* hybridising with Common Tern *S. hirundo* in Germany.] *Limicola* 15, 249–58. [In German.]

LUND-HANSEN, L. C. & LANGE, P. 1991. The numbers and distribution of the Great Skua *Stercorarius skua* breeding in Iceland 1984–1985. *Acta Nat. Islandica* 34, 1–16.

MACDONALD, R. A. 1987. The breeding population and distribution of the Cormorant in Ireland. *Irish Birds* 3, 405–16.

MACDONALD, R. & GOODWILLIE, R. 1984. Gull management in the Dublin area. An Foras Forbartha, Dublin.

MacKENZIE, D. 2002. African fisheries on brink of collapse. *New Scientist* 175, 5.

MADDEN, B. 2001. Roof nesting gulls in Dublin City (south of River Liffey). Unpubl. Rep. BirdWatch Ireland, Dublin.

MADDEN, B. & NEWTON, S. 2002. Lambay Ornithological Survey. Unpubl. Rep. BirdWatch Ireland, Dublin.

MADROÑO, A. & GONZÁLEZ, C. (eds.) *Libro Rojo de las Aves España*. SEO/BirdLife & Ministerio de Medio Ambiente, Madrid.

MAINWOOD, A. R. 1975. Leach's petrel breeding on Foula. *Scott. Birds* 8, 321–3.

MAINWOOD, A. R., RATCLIFFE, N., MURRAY, S. & MUDGE, G. 1996. The status of Storm Petrels *Hydrobates pelagicus* on selected islands in north-west Scotland. Rep. to Scottish Natural Heritage.

MALLING OLSEN, K. & LARSSON, H. 2003. *Gulls of Europe, Asia and North America*. Christopher Helm, London.

MARTÍ, R. & DEL MORAL, J. C. (eds) 2003. *Atlas de las Aves Reproductoras de España*. Sociedad Española de Ornitología (SEO/BirdLife). Madrid.

MARTIN, A. R. 1989. The diet of Atlantic puffin *Fratercula arctica* and Northern gannet *Sula bassana* chicks at a Shetland colony during a period of changing prey availability. *Bird Study* 36, 170–80.

MARTIN, A. R. 2002. Ornithological fieldwork on Hermaness NNR, Shetland conducted by the Cambridge group, June/July 2002. Rep. to Scottish Natural Heritage and Shetland Oil Terminal Environmental Advisory Group.

MARTIN, T. E. 1987. Food as a limit on breeding birds, a life history perspective. *Ann. Rev. Ecol. Syst.* 18, 453–87.

MASSA, B. & SULTANA, J. 1990–1. Status and conservation of the storm petrel *Hydrobates pelagicus* in the Mediterranean. *Il-Merrill* 27, 1–5.

MASSEY, B. W., BRADLEY, D. W. & ATWOOD, J. L. 1992. Demography of a California Least Tern colony, including effects of the 1982–1983 El Niño. *Condor* 94, 976–83.

MAVOR, R. A., PARSONS, M., HEUBECK, M., PICKERELL, G. & SCHMITT, S. 2003. *Seabird Numbers and Breeding Success in Britain and Ireland, 2002*. Joint Nature Conservation Committee, Peterborough.

MAVOR, R. A., PICKERELL, G., HEUBECK, M. & MITCHELL, P. I. 2002. *Seabird Numbers and Breeding Success in Britain and Ireland, 2001*. Joint Nature Conservation Committee, Peterborough.

MAVOR, R. A., PICKERELL, G., HEUBECK, M. & THOMPSON, K. R. 2001. *Seabird Numbers and Breeding Success in Britain and Ireland 2000*. Joint Nature Conservation Committee, Peterborough.

MAYHEW, P., CHISHOLM, K., INSLEY, H. & RATCLIFFE, N. 2000. A survey of storm petrels on Priest Island in 1999. *Scott. Birds* 21, 78–84.

MCCARTAN, L. 1958. Mortality of Kittiwakes during the breeding season. *British Birds* 57: 267–268.

MCPHERSON, H. A. *c.*1898. *British Birds—Their Nests and Eggs*, vol. 6. Brumby & Clarke, London.

MCSORLEY, C., DEAN, B., WEBB, A. & REID, J. 2002. Seabird use of waters adjacent to colonies. Implications for seaward extensions to existing breeding colony special protection areas. Joint Nature Conservation Committee, Peterborough.

MEAD, C. J. 1978. Tern mortality in West Africa as shown by British and Dutch ringing results. *Ibis* 120, 110.

MEAD, C. J. 1989. Mono-kill and auk netfax. *BTO News* 163, 1–8.

MEEK, E. R., BOOTH, C. J., REYNOLDS, P. & RIBBANDS, B. 1985. Breeding skuas in Orkney. *Seabird* 8, 21–33.

MEEK, E. R., SIM, I. M. W. & RIBBANDS, B. 1994. Breeding skuas in Orkney: the results of the 1992 census. *Seabird* 16, 34–40.

MEHLUM, F. & BAKKEN, V. 1994. Seabirds in Svalbard (Norway): status, recent changes and management. In: Nettleship, D. N., Burger, J. & Gochfeld, M. (eds.) *Seabirds on Islands: Threats, Case Studies and Action Plans*. BirdLife International Conserv. Ser. 1, Cambridge.

MEININGER, P. L. 2002. Mediterranean Gull *Larus melanocephalus*. In: SOVON Vogelonderzoek Nederland (ed.) *Atlas van de Nederlandse Broedvogels 1998–2000*. Nationaal Natuurhistorisch Museum Naturalis, KNNV Uitgeverij & European Invertebrate Survey, Leiden.

MEININGER, P. L. 2002. Dwergstern *Sterna albifrons*. In: SOVON Vogelonderzoek Nederland (ed.) *Atlas van de Nederlandse Broedvogels 1998–2000*. Nationaal Natuurhistorisch Museum Naturalis, KNNV Uitgeverij & European Invertebrate Survey, Leiden.

MEININGER, P. L. & BEKHUIS, J. P. 1990. The Mediterranean Gull *Larus melanocephalus* as a breeding bird in the Netherlands and Europe. *Limosa* 63, 121–34.

MEININGER, P. L., BERREVOETS, C. M., SCHEKKERMAN, H., STRUCKER, R. C. W. & WOLF, P. A. 1991. Food and feeding areas of breeding Mediterranean Gulls in the SW-Netherlands. *Sula* 5, 138–45.

MEININGER, P. L., RAEVEL, P. & HOOGENDOORN, W. 1993. Occurrence of Mediterranean Gull at Le Portel in north-western France. *Dutch Birding* 15, 45–54.

MELVILLE, D. 1973. Birds and salmon nets. *Seabird Rep.* 1971, 47–50.

MENDELSSOHN, R. & CURY, P. 1987. Fluctuations of a fortnightly abundance index of the Ivorian coastal pelagic species and associated environmental conditions. *Can. J. Fisheries & Aquatic Sci.* 44, 408–21.

MERIKALLIO, E. 1958. Finnish birds: their distribution and numbers. *Fauna och Flora Fenn.* 5, 1–181.

MERINO, S., MÍNGUEZ, E. & BELLIURE, B. 1999. Ectoparasite effects on nestling European Storm-Petrels. *Waterbirds* 22, 297–301.

MERNE, O. J. 1997a. Herring Gull. In: Hagemeijer, W. J. M. & Blair, M. J. (eds.) *The EBCC Atlas of European Breeding Birds: Their Distribution and Abundance.* T. & A. D. Poyser, London.

MERNE, O. 1997b. Sandwich Tern. In: Hagemeijer, W. J. M. & Blair, M. J. (eds.) *The EBCC Atlas of European Breeding Birds: Their Distribution and Abundance.* T. & A. D. Poyser, London.

MERNE, O. J. 2002. Razorbill *Alca torda.* In: Wernham, C. V., Toms, M., Marchant, J., Clark, J., SiriwardenÀ, G. & Baillie, S. (eds.) *The Migration Atlas: Movements of the Birds of Britain and Ireland.* T. & A. D. Poyser, London.

MERNE, O. J. & MADDEN, B. 1999. Breeding seabirds of Lambay, County Dublin. *Irish Birds* 6, 345–59.

MERNE, O. J., NEWTON, S. & CROWE, O. 2001. Lady's Island Lake tern report 2001. BirdWatch Ireland Conserv. Rep. 01/8, Dublin.

MIGOT, P. 1992. Demographic changes in a French Herring Gull population: a modelling approach and a hypothesis regarding the regulation of numbers. *Ardea* 80, 161–9.

MÍNGUEZ, E. 1994. [Census, laying chronology and breeding success of the European Storm-petrel in Benidorm Island.] *Ardeola* 41, 3–11. [In Spanish.]

MÍNGUEZ, E. 1997. Evidence of occasional relaying in British Storm Petrel. *Colonial Waterbirds* 20, 102–4.

MÍNGUEZ, E., ELIZONDO, R. S., BALERDI, M. & SABAN, P. 1992. Statut, distribution, taille de la population et phenologie de la reproduction du petrel tempête *Hydrobates pelagicus* dans la communauté autonome basque (Espagne). *L'Oiseau et R.F.O.* 62, 234–46.

MITCHELL, J. K & ERICKSEN, N. J. 1992. Effects of climate change on weather-related disasters. In: Mintzer, I. M. (ed.) *Confronting Climate Change: Risks, Implications and Responses.* Cambridge University Press.

MITCHELL, P. I. & THOMPSON, K. R. 1998. Survey of breeding Mew Gulls *Larus canus* in the Mortlach and Correen Hills, Grampian, 1998. Joint Nature Conservation Committee rep. to Scottish Natural Heritage, Aberdeen.

MITCHELL, P. I., WEBB, A., POLLOCK, C., REID, A., MAVOR, R. & DUNN, T. In prep. *The Status of Breeding Seabirds on St Kilda in 1999 and 2000.* Joint Nature Conservation Committee, Aberdeen.

MOEN, S. M. 1991. Morphological and genetic variation among breeding colonies of the Atlantic Puffin (*Fratercula arctica*). *Auk* 108, 755–63.

MOLLER, A. P. 1978. [Distribution, population size and changes in gulls Larinae breeding in Denmark, with a review of the situation in other parts of Europe]. *Dansk Orn. Fore. Tidsskr.* 72, 15–39. [In Danish.]

MONAGHAN, P. 1979. Aspects of the breeding biology of Herring Gulls *Larus argentatus* in urban colonies. *Ibis* 121, 475–81.

MONAGHAN, P. 1992. Seabirds and sandeels: the conflict between exploitation and conservation in the northern North Sea. *Biodiv. & Conserv.* 1, 98–111.

MONAGHAN, P. 2002. Arctic Tern *Sterna paradisaea.* In: Wernham, C. V., Toms, M., Marchant, J., Clark, J., SiriwardenÀ, G. & Baillie, S. (eds.) *The Migration Atlas: Movements of the Birds of Britain and Ireland.* T. & A. D. Poyser, London.

MONAGHAN, P. & COULSON, J. C. 1977. The status of large gulls nesting on buildings. *Bird Study* 24, 89–104.

MONAGHAN, P., UTTLEY, J. D. & BURNS, M. D. 1992. Effects of changes in food availability on reproductive effort in Arctic Terns. *Ardea* 80, 71–81.

MONAGHAN, P., UTTLEY, J. D., BURNS, M. D., THAINE, C. & BLACKWOOD, J. 1989a. The relationship between food supply, reproductive effort and breeding success in Arctic Terns *Sterna paradisaea. J. Anim. Ecol.* 58, 261–74.

MONAGHAN, P., UTTLEY, J. D. & OKILL, J. D. 1989b. Terns and sandeels: seabirds as indicators of changes in marine fish populations. *J. Fish Biol.* 35, 339–40.

MONAGHAN, P., WALTON, P., AUSTIN, G., BURNS, M. D., TURNER, C. M. & WRIGHT, P. J. 1997. Sub-lethal effects of the *Braer* oil spill on seabirds. In: Davies, J. M. & Topping, G. (eds.) *The Impact of an Oil Spill in Turbulent Waters: the Braer.* The Stationery Office, Edinburgh.

MONAGHAN, P., WALTON, P., WANLESS, S., UTTLEY, J. D. & BURNS, M. D. 1994. Effects of prey abundance on the foraging behaviour, diving efficiency and time allocation of breeding Guillemots *Uria aalge. Ibis* 136, 214–22.

MONNAT, J.-Y. & CADIOU, B. In press. Guillemot de Troil. In: Cadiou, B., Pons, J.-M. & Yésou, P. (eds.) *Oiseaux Marins Nicheurs de France Métropolitaine (1960–2000).* GISOM Editions Biotope, Paris.

MONNAT, J.-Y. & PASQUET, E. In press. Cormoran huppé. In: Cadiou, B., Pons, J.-M. & Yésou, P. (eds.) *Oiseaux Marins Nicheurs de France Métropolitaine (1960–2000).* GISOM Editions Biotope, Paris.

MONNAT, J.-Y. and CADIOU, B. In press. Goéland marin. In: Cadiou, B., Pons, J.-M. & Yésou, P. (eds.) *Oiseaux Marins Nicheurs de France Métropolitaine (1960–2000).* GISOM Editions Biotope, Paris.

MONTEIRO, L. R., J. A. RAMOS & R. W. FURNESS 1996. Past and present status and conservation of the seabirds breeding in the Azores archipelago. *Biological Conservation* 78: 319–328.

MONTEVECCHI, W. A. 1991. Incidence and types of plastic in gannet nests in the northwest Atlantic. *Can. J. Zool.* 69, 295–7.

MONTEVECCHI, W. A. 2002. Interactions between fisheries and seabirds. In: Schreiber, E. A. & Burger, J. (eds.) *Biology of Marine Birds*. CRC Press, Boca Raton.

MONTEVECCHI, W. A., BIRT-FRIESEN, V. L. & CAIRNS, D. K. 1992. Reproductive energetics and prey harvest of Leach's Storm-Petrels in the northwest Atlantic. *Ecology* 73, 823–32.

MONTEVECCHI, W. A., CAIRNS, D. K., BURGER, R. E., ELLIOT, R. D. & WELLS J. 1987. The status of the Common Black-headed Gull in Newfoundland and Labrador. *Amer. Birds* 41, 197–204.

MONTEVECCHI, W. A. & MYERS, R. A. 1997. Centurial and decadal oceanographic influences on changes in Northern Gannet populations and diets in the north-west Atlantic: implications for climate change. *ICES J. Mar. Sci.* 54, 608–14.

MOORS, P. J. & ATKINSON, I. A. E. 1984. Predation on seabirds by introduced mammals and factors affecting its severity. In: Croxall, J. P., Evans, P. G. H. & Schreiber, R. W. (eds.) *Status and Conservation of the World's Seabirds*. International Council for Bird Preservation Tech. Publ. 2, Cambridge.

MORRISON, P. G., FLETCHER, D. & WIFFEN, T. 2002. Coquet Island nature reserve annual report 2001/02. Unpubl. Rep. Royal Society for the Protection of Birds, Sandy.

MOSS, R., WANLESS, S. & HARRIS, M. P. 2002. How small Northern Gannet colonies grow faster than big ones. *Waterbirds* 25, 442–8.

MOURIÑO, J., ARCOS, F. & ALCALDE, A. In press. El Arao Común (*Uria aalge*). In: Madroño, A. & González, C. (eds.) *Libro Rojo de las Aves España*. SEO/BirdLife & Ministerio de Medio Ambiente, Madrid.

MUDGE, G. P. 1978. The gull increase, as illustrated by studies in the Bristol Channel. *Ibis* 120 115–6.

MUDGE, G. P., CROOKE, C. H. & ASPINALL, S. J. 1992. Non-oiling Guillemot mortality incidents in the Moray Firth 1983–86. *Seabird* 14, 48–54.

MUDGE, G. P. & FERNS, P. N. 1982. The feeding ecology of five species of gulls (Aves: Larini) in the inner Bristol Channel. *J. Zool. Soc. Lond.* 197, 497–510.

MURRAY, S. 1984. Abnormalities and diseases of the feet of Storm Petrels. *Seabird* 7, 74.

MURRAY, S. 1993. *Marine Wildlife and Net Fisheries Around Scotland and Northern Ireland in 1992*. Royal Society for the Protection of Birds, Sandy.

MURRAY, S. 2002. Birds of St Kilda. *Scott. Birds* 23 (Suppl.), 1–64.

MURRAY, S., MONEY, S., GRIFFIN, A. & MITCHELL, P. I. In press. A survey of Leach's and European Storm-petrel populations on North Rona and Sula Sgeir, Western Isles. *Atlantic seabirds*.

MURRAY, S. & SHEWRY, M. C. 2002. A survey of Manx Shearwaters on Rum NNR in 2000 and 2001. Rep. to Scottish Natural Heritage, Edinburgh.

MURRAY, S. & WANLESS, S. 1986. The status of the Gannet in Scotland in 1984–85. *Scott. Birds* 14: 74–85.

MURRAY, S. & WANLESS, S. 1997. The status of the Gannet in Scotland in 1994–95. *Scott. Birds* 19, 10–27.

MURRAY, S., WANLESS, S. & HARRIS, M. P. 1994. The effects of fixed salmon *Salmo* salar nets on guillemot *Uria aalge* and razorbill *Alca torda* in northeast Scotland in 1992. *Biol. Conserv.* 70, 251–6.

MUSIL, P., FORMÁNEK, J. & SKOPEK, J. 1997. Numbers and movements of Cormorants *Phalacrocorax carbo sinensis* in the Czech Republic and Slovakia. *Suppl. Ric. Biol. Selvaggina*, 26, 61–72.

NELSON, J. B. 1978. *The Sulidae: Gannets and Boobies*. Oxford University Press.

NELSON, J. B. 2002. *The Atlantic Gannet*. Fenix Books, Norfolk.

NETTLESHIP, D. N. & BIRKHEAD, T. R. (eds.) 1985. *The Atlantic Alcidae*. Academic Press, London.

NETTLESHIP, D. N. & EVANS, P. G. H. 1985. Distribution and status of the Atlantic Alcidae. In: Nettleship, D. N. & Birkhead, T. R. (eds.) *The Atlantic Alcidae*. Academic Press, London.

NEUBAUER, W. 1998. Habitat choice of the Common Tern *Sterna hirundo* in eastern Germany. *Vogelwelt* 169, 293–304.

DEL NEVO, A. J., E. K. DUNN, F. M. MEDEIROS, G. LE GRAND, P. AKERS, M. I. AVERY & L. R. MONTEIRO 1993. The status of roseate terns *Sterna dougallii* and common terns *S. hirundo* in the Azores. *Seabird* 25: 30–37.

NEWSON, S. E. 2000. Colonisation and range expansion of inland breeding Great Cormorants *Phalacrocorax carbo* in England. Ph.D. thesis. University of Bristol.

NEWSON, S., HUGHES, B. & SELLERS, R. M. 1997. Status and breeding success of Cormorants *Phalacrocorax carbo* in Wales in 1997. Wildfowl & Wetlands Trust Res. Rep., Slimbridge.

NEWTON, I. 1972. *Population Ecology of Raptors*. T. & A. D. Poyser, Calton.

NEWTON, I. (ed.) 1989. *Lifetime Reproduction in Birds*. Academic Press, London.

NEWTON, I. 1998. *Population Limitation in Birds*. Academic Press, London.

NEWTON, I., DALE, L., FINNIE, J. K., FREESTONE, P., WRIGHT, J., WYATT, C. & WYLLIE, I. 1998. *Wildlife and Pollution: 1997/98*. Joint Nature Conservation Committee Rep. 285, Peterborough.

NEWTON, I., HAAS, M. B. & FREESTONE, P. 1990. Trends in organochlorine and mercury levels in gannet eggs. *Environ. Pollution* 63, 1–12.

NEWTON. S. F. 2002. Manx Shearwaters *Puffinus puffinus* proved breeding on Lambay, Co. Dublin. *Irish Birds* 7, 140–1.

NEWTON, S. F. (ed.) 2003. *Abstracts from the 9th International Roseate Tern Workshop, Wexford, April 2003.* BirdWatch Ireland, Dublin.

NEWTON, S. F. & CROWE, O. 2000. Roseate Terns—the natural connection. Maritime (Ireland/Wales) INTERREG Rep. 2, Marine Institute, Dublin.

NEWTON, S. F., DONAGHY, A., ALLEN, D. & GIBBONS, D. 1999. Birds of conservation concern in Ireland. *Irish Birds* 6, 333–44.

NEWTON, S. F. & MITCHELL, P. I. 2001. The last frontier: a survey of nocturnal seabirds in western Ireland and north Scotland—final report. BirdWatch Ireland Conserv. Rep. 01/9, Dublin.

NISBET, I. C. T. 1973. Terns in Massachusetts: present numbers & historical changes. *Bird Banding* 44, 27–55.

NISBET, I. C. T. 1978. Recent changes in gull populations in the western North Atlantic. *Ibis* 120, 129–30.

NISBET, I. C. T. 1980. Status and trends of the Roseate Tern in North America and the Caribbean. Unpubl. Rep. US Fish & Wildlife Service, Office of Endangered Species.

NISBET, I. C. T. 1992. Predation by a Peregrine Falcon on Common and Roseate Terns at Bird Island. Bird *Observer* 20, 137–9.

NISBET, I. C. T. 2000. Disturbance, habituation, and management of waterbird colonies. *Waterbirds* 23, 312–32.

NISBET, I. C. T. 2002. Common Tern (*Sterna hirundo*). In: Poole, A. & Gill, F. (eds.) *The Birds of North America*, 618. Birds of North America Inc., Philadelphia, PA & American Ornithologists' Union, Washington DC.

NISBET, I. C. T. & SPENDELOW, J. A. 1999. Contribution of research to management and recovery of the Roseate Tern: review of a twelve-year project. *Waterbirds* 22, 239–52.

NOBLE-ROLLIN, D. & REDFERN, C. 2002. Sandwich Tern *Sterna sandvicensis*. In: Wernham, C. V., Toms, M., Marchant, J., Clark, J., SiriwardenÀ, G. & Baillie, S. (eds.) *The Migration Atlas: Movements of the Birds of Britain and Ireland*. T. & A. D. Poyser, London.

NOORDHUIS, R. & SPAANS, A. L. 1992. Interspecific competition for food between Herring *Larus argentatus* and Lesser Black-backed Gulls *L. fuscus* in the Dutch Wadden Sea area. *Ardea* 80, 115–32.

NORDSTRÖM, M., HÖGMANDER, J., LAINE, J., NUMMELIN, J., LAANETU, N. & KORPIMÄKI, E. 2003. Effects of feral mink removal on seabirds, waders and passerines on small islands in the Baltic Sea. *Biol. Conserv.* 109, 359–68.

NORMAN, D. 2002. Common Tern *Sterna hirundo*. In: Wernham, C. V., Toms, M., Marchant, J., Clark, J., SiriwardenÀ, G. & Baillie, S. (eds.) *The Migration Atlas: Movements of the Birds of Britain and Ireland*. T. & A. D. Poyser, London.

NORMAN, R. K. & SAUNDERS, D. R. 1969. Status of Little Terns in Great Britain and Ireland in 1967. *Brit. Birds* 62, 4–13.

NORRIS, K. J. & BUISSON, R. 1994. Sea-level rise and its impact upon coastal breeding birds in the UK. *RSPB Conserv. Rev.* 8, 63–71.

(NASCO). 2003. Report of the ICES Advisory Council of Fisheries Management. NASCO Report CNL(03)8, Edinburgh.

NORTHRIDGE, S. 1988. Marine mammals and fisheries: a study of conflicts with fishing gear in British waters. Wildlife Links Seals Group, International Institute for Environment and Development, & Marine Resources Group Assessment, London.

NORTHRIDGE, S., Di NATALE, A., KINZE, C., LANKESTER, K., DE ZARATE, V. O. & SEQUERIA, M. 1991. Gillnet fisheries in the European Community and their impacts on the marine environment. Rep. to the EC's Directorate General Environment, Nuclear Safety & Civil Protection.

NORTON, R. L. 2000. Sandwich and Cayenne Terns. In: Schreiber, E. A. & Lee, D. S. (eds.) *Status and Conservation of West Indian Seabirds*. Soc. Carib. Orn., Spec. Publ. 1.

NTIAMOA-BAIDU, Y. 1991. Species protection as a strategy for conservation action in Africa: the case of the Roseate Tern in Ghana. In: Salathé, T. (ed.) *Conserving Migratory Birds*. International Council for Bird Preservation Tech. Publ. 12, Cambridge.

NTIAMOA-BAIDU, Y. 1995. Conservation education in threatened species management in Africa. *Bird Conserv. Intern.* 5, 455–62.

NTIAMOA-BAIDU, Y., NYAME, S. K. & NUOH, A. A. 1992. Preliminary report on tern trapping in coastal Ghana. In: Rolland, G. (ed.) *Proc. Roseate Tern Workshop*. SEPNB, Brest.

NUR, N. & SYDEMAN, W. J. 1999. Survival, breeding probability and reproductive success in relation to population dynamics of Brandt's Cormorant *Phalacrocorax pencillatus*. *Bird Study* 46, S92–S103.

NUTTALL, P. A. & HARRAP, K. A. 1982. Isolation of a corona virus during studies on Puffinosis, a disease of the Manx Shearwater (*Puffinus puffinus*). *Arch. Virology* 73, 1–13.

NYGÅRD, T. & EINVIK, K. 1991. Radio-tracking of a British storm petrel *Hydrobates pelagicus* proves a probable new breeding-site in Norway. *Seabird* 13, 59–62.

O'CONNELL, M. J., COULSON, J. C., RAVEN, S. & JOYCE, S. 1997. Non-breeding and nests without eggs in the Lesser Black-backed Gull *Larus fuscus*. *Ibis* 139, 252–8.

O'DONALD, P. 1983. Th*e Arctic Skua*. Cambridge University Press.

OEDEKOVEN, C. S., AINLEY, D. G. & SPEAR, L. B. 2001. Variable responses of seabirds to change in marine climate: California Current, 1985–1994. *Mar. Ecol. Progr. Ser.* 212, 265–81.

OFFER, D. 2000. Manx Shearwater survey 2000. Unpubl. Rep. by Treshnish Isles Auk Ringing Group to the Joint Nature Conservation Committee.

OKILL, J. D. 2002. Black Guillemot *Cepphus grylle*. In: Wernham, C. V., Toms, M., Marchant, J., Clark, J., SiriwardenÀ, G. & Baillie, S. (eds.) *The Migration Atlas: Movements of the Birds of Britain and Ireland*. T. & A. D. Poyser, London.

OKILL, J. D. FOWLER, J. A. ELLIS, P. M. & PETRIE, G. W. 1992. The diet of Cormorant *Phalacrocorax carbo* chicks in Shetland in 1989. *Seabird* 14, 21–6.

OKILL, J. D. FOWLER, J. A. ELLIS, P. M. & PETRIE, G. W. 1993. The effect of the *Braer* on the diet of the Cormorant in Shetland. Rep. to ESGOSS, Lerwick.

OLDÉN, B., PETERZ, M. & KOLLBERG, E. 1985. Seabird mortality in gill-net fishing in southeast Kattegat, south Sweden. *Anser* 24, 159–80.

OLLASON, J. & DUNNET, G. M. 1978. Age, experience and other factors affecting the breeding success of the fulmar, *Fulmarus glacialis* in Orkney. *J. Anim. Ecol.* 47, 961–76.

OLSEN, I. 2003. [Population development of breeding birds on Skúvoy, Faeroe Islands, 1961–2001.] *Dansk Orn. Fore. Tidsskr.* 97, 199–209. [In Danish]

OLSSON, O., NILSSON, T. & FRANSSON, T. 2000. Long-term study of mortality in the Common Guillemot in the Baltic Sea. Swedish Environmental Protection Agency, Stockholm.

OLSSON, V. 1974. Razorbill *Alca torda* and Black Guillemot *Cepphus grylle* on the Swedish east coast 1954–73. Changes in a population. *Vår Fågelvärld* 33, 3–14.

ORLOFF, S. & FLANNERY, A. 1992. Wind turbine effects on avian activity, habitat use and mortality in Altamount Pass and Solano County Wind Resource Areas, 1989–1991. Final report to Alameda, Contra Costa and Solano Counties & the California Energy Commission by Biosystems Analysis Inc., Tiburon.

ORO, D. 1996. Effects of trawler discard availability on egg laying and breeding success in the Lesser Black-backed Gull *Larus fuscus* in the western Mediterranean. *Mar. Ecol. Progr. Ser.* 132, 43–6.

ORO, D. & FURNESS, R. W. 2002. Influences of food availability and predation on survival of kittiwakes. *Ecology* 83, 2516–28.

ORO, D., JOVER, L. & RUIZ, X. 1996. The effects of a trawling moratorium on the breeding ecology of a threatened seabird, Audouin's Gull *Larus audouinii*. *Mar. Ecol. Progr. Ser.* 139, 19–29.

ORO, D., JOVER, L. & RUIZ, X. 1995. The effect of a trawling moratorium on the breeding success of the yellow-legged gull *Larus cachinnans*. *Ibis* 137, 547–9.

OSBORN, T. 2001. Changing intensity of rainfall over Britain. Climatic Research Unit, East Anglia University, http://www.cru.uea.ac.uk/cru/info/ukrainfall/.

OVERPECK, J. T., RIND, D. & GOLDBERG, R. 1987. Climate induced changes in forest disturbance vegetation. *Nature* 343, 51–3.

PAINE, R. T., WOOTTON, J. T. & BOERSMA, P. D. 1990. Direct and indirect effects of Peregrine Falcon predation on seabird abundance. *Auk* 107, 1–9.

PALMER, P. 2001. Northern Gannet 'nesting' on roof-top. *Brit. Birds* 94, 203.

PARSLOW, J. L. F. 1967. Changes in the status of the breeding birds in Britain and Ireland. *Brit. Birds* 60, 2–47.

PARSLOW, J. L. F. 1973. *Breeding Birds of Britain and Ireland*. T. & A. D. Poyser, Berkhamsted.

PARSLOW, J. L. F. & JEFFERIES, D. J. 1973. Relationships between organochlorine residues in livers and whole bodies of guillemots. *Environ. Pollution* 5, 87–101.

PARSONS, J. & DUNCAN, N. 1978. Recoveries and dispersal of Herring Gulls from the Isle of May. *J. Anim. Ecol.* 47, 993–1005.

PATTERSON, A. 2001. Manx Shearwater conservation and proposed rat eradication project on the Hebridean Islands of Canna and Sanday, west Scotland. In: Zonfrillo, B., Câmara, D. B., Bolton, M. & Perrins, C. M. (eds.) *Proc. First Manx Shearwater Conf., Funchal, Madeira 2000*.

PATTERSON, I. J. 1967. The control of fox movement by electric fencing. *Biol. Conserv.* 11, 267–78.

PEARSON, T. H. 1968. The feeding biology of sea-bird species breeding on the Farne Islands, Northumberland. *J. Anim. Ecol.* 37, 521–52.

PERDECK, A. C. 1960. Observations on the reproductive behaviour of the Great Skua or Bonxie, *Stercorarius skua skua* (Brunn.), in Shetland. *Ardea* 48, 111–36.

PERRINS, C. M. 1997. The shearwaters and storm petrels of the Welsh islands. In: Rhind, P. M., Blackstock, T. H. & Parr, J. (eds.) 1997. *Welsh Islands: Ecology, Conservation and Land Use.* Countryside Council for Wales, Bangor.

PERRINS, C. M. 2002. Skomer Island 2002—seabird survival studies. Rep. to Joint Nature Conservation Committee, Peterborough.

PERRINS, C. M. & SMITH, S. B. 2000. The breeding *Larus* gulls on Skomer Island National Nature Reserve, Pembrokeshire. *Atlantic Seabirds* 2, 195–210.

PETERZ, M. & OLDÉN, B. 1987. Origin and mortality of Guillemots *Uria aalge* on the Swedish coast. *Seabird* 10, 22–7.

PETERSEN, A. 1998. *Islenskir Fuglar.* Vaka-Helgafell, Reykjavik.

PETERSEN, Æ. 2000. Vöktun sjófuglastofna. *Náttúrufræ_ingurinn* 69, 189–200.

PHILIPS, B. N. 1982. The status of the Manx Shearwater *Puffinus puffinus* on the Isle of Rhum. MSc thesis. University College, London.

PHILLIPS, R. A. 2001. *Stercorarius parasiticus* Arctic Skua. *BWP Update* 3, 25–41.

PHILLIPS, R. A., BEARHOP, S., THOMPSON, D. R. & HAMER, K. C. 1999a. Rapid population growth of Great Skuas at St Kilda: implications for management and conservation. *Bird Study* 46, 174–83.

PHILLIPS, R. A, CALDOW, R. W. G. & FURNESS, R. W. 1996a. The influence of food availability on the breeding performance and reproductive success of Arctic Skuas. *Ibis* 138, 410–20.

PHILLIPS, R. A., CATRY, P., THOMPSON, D. R., HAMER, K. C. & FURNESS, R. W. 1997. Inter-colony variation in diet and reproductive performance of great skuas *Catharacta skua*. *Mar. Ecol. Prog. Ser.* 152, 285–93.

PHILLIPS, R. A., FURNESS, R. W. & CALDOW, R. W. G. 1996b. Behavioural responses of Arctic Skuas *Stercorarius parasiticus* to changes in sandeel availability. In: Greenstreet, S. P. R. & Tasker, M. L. (eds.) *Aquatic Predators and Their Prey.* Blackwell, Oxford.

PHILLIPS, R. A., FURNESS, R. W. & STEWART, F. M. 1998. The influence of territory density on the vulnerability of Arctic Skuas *Stercorarius parasiticus* to predation. *Biol. Conserv.* 86, 21–31.

PHILLIPS, R. A., PETERSEN, M. K., LILLIENDHAL, K., SOLMUNDSSON, J., HAMER, K. C., CAMPHUYSEN, C. J. & ZONFRILLO, B. 1999b. Diet of the northern fulmar *Fulmarus glacialis*: reliance on commercial fisheries? *Mar. Biol.* 135, 159–170.

PHILLIPS, R. A., THOMPSON, D. R. & HAMER, K. C. 1999c. The impact of great skua predation on seabird populations at St Kilda: a bioenergetic model. *J. Appl. Ecol.* 36, 218–32.

PIATT, J. F., NETTLESHIP, D. N. & THRELFALL, W. 1984. Net mortality of common murres *Uria aalge* and Atlantic puffins *Fratercula arctica* in Newfoundland, 1951–1981. In: Nettleship, D. N., Sanger, G. A. & Springer, P. F. (eds.) *Marine Birds: Their Feeding Ecology and Commercial Fishery Relationships.* Canadian Wildlife Service Spec. Publ., Ottawa.

PIATT, J. F. & GOULD, P. F. 1994. Endangered Japanese Murrelets: incidental catch in high seas drift nets and post-breeding dispersal. *Auk* 111, 953–61.

PICKERELL, G. (ed.) Little Terns in 1998: UK and Ireland. Unpubl. Rep. Royal Society for the Protection of Birds, Sandy.

PICKERELL, G. (ed.) 2002. Little Terns in Britain and Ireland, 2001. Unpubl. Rep. Royal Society for the Protection of Birds, Sandy.

PLANQUE, B. & TAYLOR, A. H. 1998. Long-term changes in zooplankton and the climate of the North Atlantic. *ICES J. Mar. Sci.* 55, 644–54.

POLLOCK, C. M., MAVOR, R., WEIR, C. R., REID, A., WHITE, R. W., TASKER, M. L., WEBB, A. & REID, J. B. 2000a. *The Distribution of Seabirds and Marine Mammals in the Atlantic Frontier, North and West of Scotland.* Joint Nature Conservation Committee, Peterborough.

POLLOCK, C. M., REID, J. B., WEBB, A. & TASKER, M. L. 2000b. *The Distribution of Seabirds and Cetaceans in the Atlantic Waters Around Ireland.* Joint Nature Conservation Committee Rep. 267, Peterborough.

PONS, J.-M. 1992. Effects of changes in the availability of human refuse on breeding parameters in a Herring Gull *Larus argentatus* population in Brittany, France. *Ardea* 80, 143–50.

PONS, J.-M. & MIGOT, P. 1995. Life-history strategy of the herring gull, changes in survival and fecundity in a population subjected to various feeding conditions. *J. Anim. Ecol.* 64, 592–9.

PONS, J.-M. & YÉSOU, P. 1997. Lesser Black-backed Gull. In: Hagemeijer, W. J. M. & Blair, M. J. (eds.) *The EBCC Atlas of European Breeding Birds: Their Distribution and Abundance*. T. & A. D. Poyser, London.

POOLE, J. 1995. Changes in the diet of Great Black-backed Gulls *Larus marinus* on Skomer Island 1958–1992. *Seabird* 17, 50–5.

POOLE, J., SMITH, S., PERRINS, C. M., BIRKHEAD, T. R. & THOMPSON K. R. 2001. *Seabird monitoring on Skomer Island in 1997 and 1998*. Joint Nature Conservation Committee Rep. 318, Peterborough.

PORTER, J. M. & COULSON, J. C. 1987. Long-term changes in recruitment to the breeding group, and the quality of recruits at a kittiwake *Rissa tridactyla* colony. *J. Anim. Ecol.* 56, 675–89.

POST, P. W. & LEWIS, R. H. 1995. Lesser Black-backed Gull in the Americas: occurrence and subspecific identity. *Birding* 27, 370–81.

POTTER, E. C. E. & PAWSON, M. G. 1991. *Gill Netting*. MAFF Directorate of Fisheries Res. Lab. Leaflet 69, Lowestoft.

POTTS, G. R. 1969. The influence of eruptive movements, age, population size and other factors on the survival of the shag (*Phalacrocorax aristotelis* (L.)). *J. Anim. Ecol.* 38, 53–102.

POTTS, G. R., COULSON, J. C. & DEANS, I. R. 1980. Population dynamics and breeding success of the shag, *Phalacrocorax aristotelis*, on the Farne Islands, Northumberland. *J. Anim. Ecol.* 49, 465–84.

POWER, D. M. & AINLEY, D. G. 1986. Seabird geographic variability: similarity among populations of Leach's Storm-petrel. *Auk* 103, 575–85.

PRACH, R. W. & SMITH, A. R. 1992. Breeding distribution and numbers of Black Guillemots in Jones Sound, N.W.T. *Arctic* 45, 111–4.

PRÉVOT-JULLIARD, A.-C., LEBRETON, J.-D. & PRADEL, R. 1998. Re-evaluation of adult survival of Black-headed Gulls (*Larus ridibundus*) in presence of recapture heterogeneity. *Auk* 115, 85–95.

PRICE, D. & BOOKER, H. 2001. Lundy Island Manx Shearwaters breeding population and distribution survey May 2001. Unpubl. Rep.

PRZYBYSZ, J., MELLIN, M., MIROWSKA-IBRON, I., PRZYBYSZ, A. & GROMADZKA, J. 1997. Recent development of the Cormorant *Phalacrocorax carbo sinensis* population in Poland. *Ekol. Pol.*, 45, 111–5.

PUGESEK, B. H. & DIEM, K. L. 1990. The relationships between reproduction and survival in known age California gulls. *Ecology* 71, 811–7.

QUINTANA, F. & YORIO, P. 1998. Competition for nest sites between Kelp Gulls (*Larus dominicanus*) and terns (*Sterna maxima* and *S. eurygnatha*) in Patagonia. *Auk* 115, 1068–71.

RAE, S. 1999. The effect of predation by mink on ground-nesting birds in the Outer Hebrides. *Outer Hebrides (The Western Isles) Bird Rep.* 1999, 105–13.

RAMOS, J. A., BOWLER, J., DAVIS, L., VENIS, S., QUINN, J. & MIDDLETON, C. 2001. Activity patterns and effects of ticks on growth and survival of tropical Roseate Tern nestlings. *Auk* 118, 709–16.

RANDALL, R. M., RANDALL, B. M. & RALFE, M. 1991. Roseate terns in South Africa: population size, revision of previous estimate and conservation. *Bontebok* 7, 1–6.

RASMUSSEN, L. M., D. M. FLEET, B. H. ITERLEIN, B. J. KOKS, P. POTEL & P. S. DBECK. 2000. Breeding Birds in the Wadden Sea in 1996—Results of a total survey in 1996 and of numbers of colony breeding species between 1991 and 1996. Wadden Sea Ecosystem No. 10. Common Wadden Sea Secretariat, Trilateral Monitoring and Assessment Group, Joint Monitoring Group of Breeding Birds in the Wadden Sea. Wilhelmshaven, Germany.

RATCLIFFE, J. & SANDISON, W. 2001. Puffin Island—will removing rats bring back the puffins? *Natur Cymru* 1, 23–6.

RATCLIFFE, N. 2003. Little Terns in Britain and Ireland: estimation and diagnosis of population trends. In: Schmitt, S. (ed.) *Abstracts Proc. 2003 Little Tern Symp*. Royal Society for the Protection of Birds, Sandy.

RATCLIFFE, N., CATRY, P., HAMER, K. C., KLOMP, N. I. & FURNESS, R. W. 2002. The effect of age and year on the survival of breeding adult Great Skuas *Catharacta skua* in Shetland. *Ibis* 144, 384–92.

RATCLIFFE, N., FURNESS, R. W. & KLOMP, N. I. 1998a. Influences of breeding experience on the reproductive performance of Great Skuas. *J. Avian Biol.* 29, 293–8.

RATCLIFFE, N., FURNESS, R. W. & HAMER, K. C. 1998b. The interactive effects of age and food supply on the breeding ecology of great skuas. *J. Anim. Ecol.* 67, 853–62.

RATCLIFFE, N. & MERNE, O. 2002. Roseate Tern *Sterna dougallii*. In: Wernham, C. V., Toms, M., Marchant, J., Clark, J., SiriwardenÀ, G. & Baillie, S. (eds.) *The Migration Atlas: Movements of the Birds of Britain and Ireland*. T. & A. D. Poyser, London.

RATCLIFFE, N., NEWTON, S. & GREEN, R. E. 1998c. Survival rates, inter-colony movements and viability of the north west European Roseate Tern population. *Proc. Colonial Waterbirds Conf., Florida, 1998*.

RATCLIFFE, N., PICKERELL, G. & BRINDLEY, E. 2000. Population trends of Little and Sandwich Terns *Sterna albifrons* and *S. sandvicensis* in Britain and Ireland from 1969 to 1998. *Atlantic Seabirds* 2, 211–26.

RATCLIFFE, N., RICHARDSON, D., LIDSTONE SCOTT, R., BOND, P. J., WESTLAKE, C. & SENNETT, S. 1997. Host selection, attack rates and success rates for Black-headed Gull kleptoparasitism of terns. *Colonial Waterbirds* 20, 19–31.

RATCLIFFE, N., SUDDABY, D. & BETTS, M. 1996. An examination of the methods used to census Storm Petrels *Hydrobates pelagicus* on Mousa and Skokholm. Rep. Royal Society for the Protection of Birds / BirdLife International, Sandy.

RATCLIFFE, N., VAUGHAN, D., WHYTE, C. & SHEPHERD, M. 1998d. The status of Storm Petrels on Mousa, Shetland. *Scott. Birds* 19, 154–9.

RATCLIFFE, N., VAUGHAN, D., WHYTE, C. & SHEPHERD, M. 1998e. Development of playback census methods for Storm-petrels *Hydrobates pelagicus*. *Bird Study* 45, 302–12.

RAVEN, S. J. & COULSON, J. C. 1997. The distribution and abundance of *Larus* gulls nesting on buildings in Britain and Ireland. *Bird Study* 44, 13–34.

RAVEN, S. J. & COULSON, J. C. 2001. Effects of cleaning a tidal river of sewage on gull numbers: a before-and-after-study of the River Tyne, northeast England. *Bird Study* 48, 48–58.

REED, T. M., LANGSLOW, D. R. & SYMONDS, F. L. 1983. Arctic Skuas in Caithness 1979 and 1980. *Bird Study* 30, 24–6.

REEVES, S. A. & FURNESS, R. W. 2002. Net loss–seabirds gain? Implications of fisheries management for seabirds scavenging discards in the northern North Sea. Unpubl. Rep. Royal Society for the Protection of Birds, Sandy.

REGEHR, H. M. & MONTEVECCHI, W. A. 1997. Interactive effects of food shortage and predation on breeding failure of black-legged kittiwakes: indirect effects of fisheries activities and implications for indicator species. *Mar. Ecol. Progr. Ser.* 155, 249–60.

REID, J. B., EVANS, P. G. H. & NORTHRIDGE, S. P. 2003. *Atlas of Cetacean Distribution in North-west European Waters*. Joint Nature Conservation Committee, Peterborough.

REID, W. V. 1987. Costs of reproduction in the glaucous-winged gull. *Oecologica* 74, 458–67.

RICHARDSON, M. G., DUNNET, G. & KINNEAR, P. K. 1981. Monitoring seabirds in Shetland. *Proc. Roy. Soc. Edinburgh* 80B, 157–79.

RIDDIFORD, N. 1988. Fair Isle Bird Observatory. Report No. 40. 1987. Fair Isle Bird Observatory Trust, Edinburgh.

RIDDIFORD, N. & RIDDIFORD, E. 1984. Feeding behaviour of storm petrels. *Brit. Birds* 77, 153.

RINDORF, A., WANLESS, S. & HARRIS, M. P. 2000. Effects of changes in sandeel availability on the reproductive output of seabirds. *Mar. Ecol. Progr. Ser.* 202, 241–52.

RISBERG, L., AULÉN, G., BYLIN, K. & TYRBERG, T. 1990. *Sverigeså fåglar*. Sveriges Orn. Fore., Stockholm.

ROBARDS, M., GILCHRIST, H. G. & ALLARD, K. 2000. Breeding Atlantic Puffins, *Fratercula arctica*, and other bird species of Coburg Island, Nunavut. *Can. Field Nat.* 114, 72–7.

ROBERTSON, C.J.R. & BELL, B.D. 1984. Seabird status and conservation in the New Zealand region. In: Croxall, J.P., P.G.H. Evans & R.W. Schreiber (eds) Status and Conservation of the World's Seabirds. Pp 573–586. ICBP Technical Publication No. 2, Cambridge.

ROBERTSON, G. J. 2002. Current status of the Manx Shearwater (*Puffinus puffinus*) colony on Middle Lawn Island, Newfoundland. *Northeastern Nat.* 9, 317–24.

ROBINS, M. 1991. Synthetic gill nets and seabirds. Unpubl. Rep. Royal Society for the Protection of Birds, Sandy.

ROBINSON, H. W. 1934. First nesting by Leach's Fork-tailed Petrel in Orkney. *Scott. Nat.* 1934, 93.

ROBINSON, J. A., HAMER, K. C. & CHIVERS, L. S. 2002. Developmental plasticity in Arctic Terns *Sterna paradisaea* and Common Terns *S. hirundo* in response to a period of extremely bad weather. *Ibis* 144, 344–6.

ROBINSON, P. 1999. Distribution of European Storm Petrel *Hydrobates pelagicus* in the Isles of Scilly with probable abundance. Rep. to English Nature, Peterborough.

ROBSON, M. J. H. 1968. The breeding birds of North Rona. *Scott. Birds* 5, 126–56.

ROBSON, M. & WILLS, P. 1963. Notes of the birds of Bearasay, Lewis. *Scott. Birds* 2, 410–4.

ROCK, P. 2002. Lesser Black-backed Gull *Larus fuscus*. In: Wernham, C. V., Toms, M., Marchant, J., Clark, J., SiriwardenÀ, G. & Baillie, S. (eds.) *The Migration Atlas: Movements of the Birds of Britain and Ireland*. T. & A. D. Poyser, London.

ROCK, P. 2003. Birds of a feather flock together. *Environ. Health J.* May 2003, 132–5.

RODWAY, M. S. 1991. Status and conservation of breeding seabirds in British Columbia. In: Croxall, J. P. (ed.) *Seabird Status and Conservation: A Supplement*. International Council of Bird Preservation Tech. Publ. 11, Cambridge.

ROSENEAU, D. G., KETTLE, A. B. & BYRD, G. V. 1998. Common Murre population monitoring at the Barren Islands, Alaska, 1997. Exxon Valdez Oil Spill Restoration Ann. Rep., US Fish and Wildlife Service, Alaska Maritime NWR, Homer.

ROTHERY, P., HARRIS, M. P. & SHAW, D. N. 2002. Colony size, adult survival rates, productivity and population projections of Black-legged Kittiwakes *Rissa tridactyla* on Fair Isle. *Atlantic Seabirds* 4, 17–28.

ROTHERY, P., WANLESS, S. & HARRIS, M. P. 1988. Analysis of counts from monitoring guillemots in Britain and Ireland. *J. Anim. Ecol.* 57, 1–19.

RØV, N. 1994. Breeding distribution, population status and regulation of breeding numbers in the northeast-Atlantic Great Cormorant *Phalacrocorax carbo carbo*. Ph.D. thesis. University of Trondheim.

RØV, N. & PANEVA, T. 2000. Great Cormorant *Phalacrocorax carbo*. In: Anker-Nilssen, T., Bakken, V., Strøm, H., Golovkin, A. N., Bianki, V. V. & Tatarinkova, I. P. (eds.) *The Status of Marine Birds Breeding in the Barents Sea Region*. Norwegian Polar Institute, Tromsø.

RØV, N., TATARINKOVA, I. P. & PANEVA, T. D. 2000. European Shag *Phalacrocorax aristotelis*. In: Anker-Nilssen, T., Bakken, V., Strøm, H., Golovkin, A. N., Bianki, V. V. & Tatarinkova, I. P. (eds.) *The Status of Marine Birds Breeding in the Barents Sea Region*. Norwegian Polar Institute, Tromsø.

RØV, N., LORENTSEN, S.-H. & NYGÅRD, T. In press. Status and trends in the Great Cormorant (*Phalacrocorax carbo carbo*) populations in Norway and the Barents Sea Region). *Vogelwelt* 123 (Suppl.).

RUSSELL, I. C., DARE, P. J., EATON, D. R. & ARMSTRONG, J. D. 1996. Assessment of the problem of fish-eating birds at inland fisheries in England and Wales. Directorate of Fisheries Res. Rep., Lowestoft.

RUSSELL, J. O. & MONTEVECCHI, W. A. 1996. Predation on adult Puffins *Fratercula arctica* by Great Black-backed Gulls at a Newfoundland colony. *Ibis* 138, 791–4.

RUTTLEDGE, R. F. 1950. A list of the birds of the counties of Galway and Mayo showing their status and distribution. *Proc. Roy. Irish Acad.* 52B, 315–81.

RUTTLEDGE, R. F. 1966. *Ireland's Birds*. H. F. & G. Witherby, London.

RUTTLEDGE, R. F. 1994. *Birds in Counties Galway and Mayo—An Account of Their Status and Distribution*. Irish Wild Bird Conservancy, Dublin.

DE RUWE, F. & DE SMET, G. 1997. [Hybrid Roseate × Common Tern breeding with Common Tern at Zeebrugge in 1995.] *Dutch Birding* 19, 60–4. [In Dutch.]

SALIVA, J. 2000. Conservation priorities for Roseate Terns in the West Indies. In: Schreiber, E. A. & Lee, D. S. (eds.) *Status and Conservation of West Indian Seabirds*. Soc. Carib. Orn., Spec. Publ. 1.

SALOMONSEN, F. 1965. Geographic variation of the Northern Fulmar (*Fulmarus glacialis*) and zones of the marine environment in the North Atlantic. *Auk* 85, 327–55.

SALOMONSEN, F. 1979. Marine birds in the Danish Monarchy and their conservation. In: Bartonek, J. C. & Nettleship, D. N. (eds.) *Conservation of Marine Birds of Northern North America*. US Dept. of Interior Fish & Wildlife Service, Res. Rep. 11. Washington DC.

SANGSTER, G., COLLINSON, J. M., HELBIG, A. J., KNOX, A. G. & PARKIN, D. T. 2002. The specific status of Balearic and Yelkouan Shearwaters. *Brit. Birds* 95, 636–9.

SCHAFFNER, F. C. 1986. Trends in Elegant Tern and Northern Anchovy populations in California. *Condor* 88, 347–54.

SCHARENBERG, W. & SCHULZ, W. 1992. Kormorane (*Phalacrocorax carbo sinensis*) und Chlorkohlenwasserstoffe—eine Untersuchung zur Ökotoxikologie und Bioindikation. *Seevögel* 13, 47–53.

SCHNEIDER, U. 2002. Baßtolpel auf Helgoland ein Hochssevogel auf dem Vormarsch. *Seevögel* 23, 35.

SCHREIBER, E. A. 2003. Climate and weather effects on seabirds. In: Schreiber, E. A. & Burger, J. (eds.) *Biology of Marine Birds*. CRC Press, Boca Raton.

SCOTT, D. A. 1970. The breeding biology of the storm petrel *Hydrobates pelagicus*. Ph.D. thesis. University of Oxford.

SCOTTISH NATIONAL HERITAGE (SNH). 2001. Hebridean mink project gets go-ahead. SNH news release, Inverness.

SEARS, J. 1993. Common Tern *Sterna hirundo*. In: Gibbons, D. W., Reid J. B. & Chapman, R. A. (eds.) *The New Atlas of Breeding Birds in Britain & Ireland: 1988–1991*. T. & A. D. Poyser, London.

SEARS, J. & AVERY, M. I. 1993. Population and productivity trends of Little Terns *Sterna albifrons* in Britain 1969–89. *Seabird* 15, 3–16.

SEARS, J., ELLIS, P. M., SUDDABY, D. & HARROP, H. R. 1995. The status of breeding Arctic skuas *Stercorarius parasiticus* and Great Skuas *S. skua* in Shetland in 1992. *Seabird* 17, 21–31.

SELLERS, R. M. 1994. The 1994 survey of Cormorant colonies in Wales. Wildfowl & Wetlands Trust Rep., Slimbridge.

SELLERS, R. M. EKINS, G. R. HUGHES, B. & KIRBY, J. S. 1997. Population development of inland breeding Cormorants in Great Britain. *Suppl. Ric. Biol. Selvaggina* 26, 11–21.

SELLERS, R. M. & HUGHES, B. 1996. Status and breeding success of Cormorants *Phalacrocorax carbo* in Wales in 1996: the effect of the *Sea Empress* oil spill. CCW Sea Empress Contract Sci. Rep. 231.

SELLERS. R. M. & HUGHES, B. 1997. *Inventory of inland cormorant roosts and breeding sites in Great Britain.* Report to the Joint Nature Conservation Committee, No. F76-01-98.

SEMASHKO, V. Y. & CHERENKOV, A. E. In press. [Recent numbers and trends of the breeding populations of marine birds and waterfowl on the islands of Onega Bay, White Sea]. [In Russian.]

SERJEANTSON, D. 1988. Archaeological and ethnographic evidence for seabird exploitation in Scotland. *Archaeozoologia* 2, 209–24.

SEYS, J., WAEYENBERGE, J. van, DEVOS, K., MEIRE, P. & KUIJKEN, E. 1998. The recent expansion of breeding gulls along the Belgian North sea coast. *Sula* 12, 209–16.

SHARP, B. E. 1996. Post-release survival of oiled cleaned birds in North America. *Ibis* 138, 222–8.

SHARPE, C. M. & SAPSFORD, A. M. 1999. Report on a survey of breeding seabirds of the Isle of Man 1999. Manx Bird Atlas, Laxey.

SHARROCK, J. T. R. 1976. *The Atlas of Breeding Birds in Britain and Ireland.* T. & A. D. Poyser, Berkhamsted.

SHAW, D. N., HOLT, C. A., MAGGS, H. E. & DE PALACIO, D. 2002. *Fair Isle Seabird Studies 2000.* Joint Nature Conservation Committee Rep. 332, Peterborough.

SHEALER, D. 1999. Sandwich Tern (*Sterna sandvicensis*). In: Poole, A. & Gill, F. (eds.) *The Birds of North America,* 92. Birds of North America Inc., Philadelphia, PA & American Ornithologists' Union, Washington DC.

SHEALER, D. A. & BURGER, J. 1993. Effects of interference competition on the foraging activity of tropical Roseate Terns. *Condor* 95, 322–9.

SIBLET, J.-P. In press. Sterne pierregarin. In: Cadiou, B., Pons, J.-M. & Yésou, P. (eds.) *Oiseaux Marins Nicheurs de France Métropolitaine (1960–2000).* GISOM Editions Biotope, Paris.

SIM, I., SUDDABY, D. & AVERY, M. I. 1993. Body weights of incubating Arctic Terns *Sterna paradisaea* on Orkney & Shetland in 1990 & 1991. *Seabird* 15, 24–9.

SIOKHIN, V. D. 2000. *Numbers and Distribution of Breeding Waterbirds in the Wetlands of Azov-Black sea Region of Ukraine.* Wetlands International. Kiev.

SIORAT, F. In press a. Fou de Bassan. In: Cadiou, B., Pons, J.-M. & Yésou, P. (eds.) *Oiseaux Marins Nicheurs de France Métropolitaine (1960–2000).* GISOM Editions Biotope, Paris.

SIORAT, F. In press b. Macareux moine. In: Cadiou, B., Pons, J.-M. & Yésou, P. (eds.) *Oiseaux Marins Nicheurs de France Métropolitaine (1960–2000).* GISOM Editions Biotope, Paris.

SKLEPKOVYCH, B. O. & MONTEVECCHI, W. A. 1989. The world's largest known nesting colony of Leach's Storm-Petrel, on Baccalieu Island, Newfoundland. *Amer. Birds* 43, 38–42.

SKOV, H., DURINK, J., LEOPOLD, M. F. & TASKER, M. L. 1995. *Important Bird Areas for Seabirds in the North Sea, including the Channel and Kattegat.* BirdLife International, Cambridge.

SKOV, H., UPTON, A. J., REID, J. B., WEBB, A., TAYLOR, S. J. & DURINCK, J. 1999. *Dispersion and Vulnerability of Marine Birds and Cetaceans in Faeroese Waters.* Joint Nature Conservation Committee, Aberdeen.

SKOV, H., VAITKUS, G., FLENSTED, K. N., GRISHANOV, G., KALAMEES, A., KONDRATYEV, A., LEIVO, M., LUIGUJOE, L., MAYER, C., RASMUSSEN, J. F., RAUDONIKIS, L., SCHELLER, W., SIDLO, P. O., STIPNIECE, A., STRUWE JUHL, B. & WELANDER, B. 2000. *Inventory of Coastal and Marine Important Bird Areas in the Baltic Sea.* BirdLife International, Cambridge.

SLINN, D. J. 1971. The numbers of seabirds breeding in the Isle of Man during 1969–70. *Proc. Isle of Man Nat. Hist. & Antiquarian Soc.* 7, 419–39.

SMART, J. & RATCLIFFE, N. 2000. Monitoring the effectiveness of supplementary feeding as a means of reducing Kestrel predation on Little Tern chicks at the Great Yarmouth colony. Royal Society for the Protection of Birds, Sandy.

SMIDDY, P. 1987. Northern Razorbills on the south Irish coast. *Irish Birds* 3, 455–90.

SMIDDY, P. 1998. Cormorant *Phalacrocorax carbo* breeding numbers in Waterford, east Cork and mid Cork. *Irish Birds* 6, 213–26.

SMITH, A. J. M. 1974. Studies of breeding Sandwich Terns. *Brit. Birds* 68, 142–56.

SMITH, S. B. 2001. Breeding seabirds on the Outer Trial Bank, Norfolk, UK—an island in the Wash. Unpubl. Rep. English Nature, Peterborough.

SMITH, S., THOMPSON, G. & PERRINS, C. M. 2001. A census of the Manx Shearwater *Puffinus puffinus* on Skomer, Skokholm and Middleholm, west Wales. *Bird Study* 48, 330–40.

SNOW, D. W. & PERRINS, C.M. 1998. *The Birds of the Western Palearctic, Concise Edition.* Oxford University Press.

SOUTHERN, H. N. & TUCKER, B. W. 1944. The Manx Shearwater on Lundy. *Brit. Birds* 38, 122–9.

SOWLS, A. L., DEGANGE, A. R., NELSON, J. W. & LESTER, G. S. 1980. Catalog of Alaskan seabird colonies. US Fish & Wildlife Service Rep. FWS/OBS78/78.

SOWTER, D. J. 2002. The Tarnbrook Fell gullery: 2002 report. Unpubl. Rep.

SPAANS, A. L. 1971. On the feeding ecology of the Herring Gull *Larus argentatus* Pont. in the northern part of the Netherlands. *Ardea* 59, 73–188.

SPAANS, A. L. 1998. The Herring Gull *Larus argentatus* as a breeding bird in The Netherlands during the 20th century. *Sula* 12, 185–98.

SPAANS, A. L., DE WIT, A. A. N. & VLAARDINGEN, M. A. VAN. 1987. Effects of increased population size in herring gulls on breeding success and other parameters. *Stud. Avian Biol.* 10, 57–65.

SPEAR, L. B. 1993. Dynamics and effects of western gulls feeding in a colony of guillemots and Brandt's Cormorants. *J. Anim. Ecol.* 62, 399–414.

SPENDELOW, J. A., NICHOLS, J. D., NISBET, I. C. T., HAYS, H., CORMONS, G. D., BURGER, J., SAFINA, C., HINES, J. E. & GOCHFELD, M. 1995. Estimating annual survival and movement rates of adults within a metapopulation of Roseate Terns. *Ecology* 76, 2415–28.

STAPP, P. 2002. Stable isotopes reveal evidence of predation by ship rats on seabirds on the Shiant Islands, Scotland. *J. Appl. Ecol.* 39, 831–40.

STEARNS, S.C. 1992. *The Evolution of Life Histories.* Oxford University Press.

STEELE, D. H. & MONTEVECCHI, W. A. 1994 Leach's storm-petrels prey on lower mesopelagic (*Mysidacea* and *Decapoda*) crustaceans: possible implications for crustacean and avian distributions. *Crustaceana* 66, 212–8.

STEGEMAN, L. 1990. Stormvogeltjes *Hydrobates pelagicus* fouragerend in een haven. *Sula* 4, 99–100.

STENHOUSE, I. J. & MONTEVECCHI, W. A. 1999a. Indirect effects of the availability of capelin and fishery discards: gull predation on breeding storm-petrels. *Mar. Ecol. Progr. Ser.* 184, 303–7.

STENHOUSE, I. J. & MONTEVECCHI, W. A. 1999b. Increasing and expanding populations of breeding Northern Fulmars in Atlantic Canada. *Waterbirds* 22, 382–91.

STENHOUSE, I. J., ROBERTSON, G. J. & MONTEVECCHI, W. A. 2000. Herring Gull *Larus argentatus* predation on Leach's Storm-Petrels *Oceanodroma leucorhoa* breeding on Great Island, Newfoundland. *Atlantic Seabirds* 2, 35–44.

STEPHENS, J. A., JORDAN, M. B., TAYLOR, A. H. & PROCTER, R. 1998. The effects of fluctuations in North Sea flows on zooplankton abundance. *J. Plankton Res.* 20, 943–56.

STEWART, B. 1986. Expansion of roof nesting by Mew Gulls in Aberdeen. *Scott. Bird News* 4, 9.

STEWART, J. 1991. Report on the 1990 gull study project. Copeland Bird Observ. Ann. Rep. 1990, Belfast.

STIENEN, E. W. M. 2002a. Grote Stern *Sterna sandvicensis*. In: SOVON Vogelonderzoek Nederland (ed.) *Atlas van de Nederlandse Broedvogels 1998–2000.* Nationaal Natuurhistorisch Museum Naturalis, KNNV Uitgeverij & European Invertebrate Survey, Leiden.

STIENEN, E. W. M. 2002b. Visdief *Sterna hirundo*. In: SOVON Vogelonderzoek Nederland (ed.) *Atlas van de Nederlandse Broedvogels 1998–2000.* Nationaal Natuurhistorisch Museum Naturalis, KNNV Uitgeverij & European Invertebrate Survey, Leiden.

STIENEN, E. M. W., VAN BEERS, P. W. M., BRENNINKMEIJER, A., HABRAKEN, J. M. P. M., RAAIJMAKERS, M. H. J. E. & VAN TIENEN, P. G. M. 2000. Reflections of a specialist: patterns in food provisioning and foraging conditions in Sandwich Terns *Sterna sandvicensis*. *Ardea* 88, 33–49.

STIENEN, E. M. W & BRENNINKMEIJER, A. 1998a. Effects of changing food availability on population dynamics of the Sandwich Tern *Sterna sandvicensis*. Beon Rep. 98–3, Inst. Forestry & Nature Res., Wageningen.

STIENEN, E. M. W & BRENNINKMEIJER, A. 1998b. Population trends in Common Terns *Sterna hirundo* along the Dutch coast. *Vogelwelt* 119, 165–8.

STIENEN, E. M. W & BRENNINKMEIJER, A. 2002a. Variation in growth in Sandwich Tern chicks Sterna sandvicensis and the consequences for pre- and post-fledging mortality. *Ibis* 144, 567–76.

STIENEN, E. M. W & BRENNINKMEIJER, A. 2002b. Foraging decisions of Sandwich Terns in the presence of kleptoparasitising gulls. *Auk* 119, 473–486.

STIENEN, E. M. W., BRENNINKMEIJER, A. & GESCHIERE, C. E. 2001. Living with gulls: the consequences for Sandwich Terns of breeding in association with Black-headed Gulls. *Waterbirds* 24, 68–82.

STIENEN, E. M. W., JONARD, A. & BRENNINKMEIJER, A. 1998. Tern trapping along the Senegalese coast. *Sula* 12, 19–26.

STONE, B. H., SEARS, J., CRANSWICK, P., GREGORY, R. D., GIBBONS, D. W., REHFISCH, M. M., AEBISCHER, N. J. & REID, J. B. 1997. Population estimates of birds in Britain and in the United Kingdom. *Brit. Birds* 90, 1–21.

STONEHOUSE, J. 1996. European Storm-petrels and other seabirds without their toes. *Brit. Birds* 89, 185.

STONEMAN, U. 2000. Handa Island summer warden's report 2000. Scottish Wildlife Trust, Edinburgh.

STOWE, T. J. & HARRIS, M. P. 1984. Status of guillemots and razorbills in Britain and Ireland. *Seabird* 7, 5–18.

STRAAN, K. B. & VADER, W. 1992. The nominate Lesser Black-backed Gull *Larus fuscus fuscus*, a gull with tern-like feeding biology, and its recent decreases in northern Norway. *Ardea* 80, 133–42.

STRAAN, K. B., VADER, W. & BARRETT, R. 1991. Auk mortality in fishing nets in north Norway. *Seabird* 13, 22–9.

STROUD, D. A., CHAMBERS, D., COOK, S., BUXTON, N., FRASER, B., CLEMENT, P., LEWIS, P., MCLEAN, I., BAKER, H. & WHITEHEAD, S. 2001. *The UK SPA Network: Its Scope and Content*. Joint Nature Conservation Committee, Peterborough.

STUART, D. 1948. Vital statistics of the Mochrum Cormorant colony. *Brit. Birds* 41, 194–9.

SÜDBECK, P. & HÄLTERLEIN, B. 1997. Brutvogelbestände an der deutschen Nordseeküste im Jahre 1995— Neunte Erfassung durch die Arbeitsgemeinschaft "Seevogelschutz". *Seevögel* 18, 11–19.

SÜDBECK, P. & HÄLTERLEIN, B. 2001. Brutvogelbestände an der deutschen Nordseeküste 1998 und 1999: 12. und 13. Erfassung durch die Arbeitsgemeinschaft "Seevogelschutz". *Seevögel* 22, 41–8.

SÜDBECK, P., HÄLTERLEIN, B., KNIEF, W. & KÖPPEN, U. 1998. Population development of Common Tern *Sterna hirundo* and Arctic Tern *S. paradisaea* along the North Sea & Baltic coasts of Germany. *Vogelwelt* 119, 147–63.

SUDDABY, D. 1992. Storm petrel monitoring on Mousa, Shetland. Unpubl. Rep. Royal Society for the Protection of Birds, Sandy.

SUDDABY, D. & RATCLIFFE, N. 1997. The effects of fluctuating food availability on breeding Arctic Terns *Sterna paradisaea*. *Auk* 114, 524–30.

SULLIVAN, M. A. 1982. Mew Gulls successfully nesting on a roof in Aberdeen. *Scott. Birds* 13, 229.

SULTANA, J. & BORG, J. 1996. European Storm-petrels and other seabirds without their toes. *Brit. Birds* 89, 185–6.

SURYAN, R. M. & IRONS, D. B. 2001. Colony and population dynamics of Black-legged Kittiwakes in a heterogeneous environment. *Auk* 118, 636–49.

SUTCLIFFE, S. J. 1986. Changes in the gull populations of SW Wales. *Bird Study* 33, 91–7.

SUTCLIFFE, S. J. 1997. Populations of breeding *Larus* gulls on Welsh islands. In: Rhind, P. M., Blackstock, T. H. & Parr, S. J. (eds.) *Welsh Islands: Ecology, Conservation and Land Use*. Countryside Commission for Wales, Bangor.

SVERIGES ORNITOLOGISK FORENING (SOF). 2002. *Sveriges fåglar*. 3:e uppl. Stockholm.

SWANN, B. 2003. What is happening to Canna seabirds? *Scott. Bird News* 67, 14–15.

SWANN, R. L. 1995. Numbers and breeding success of Manx Shearwaters on the Isle of Canna, 1973–94. *Scott. Birds* 18, 56–7.

SWANN, R. L. 1997. *Canna Seabird Studies 1997*. Joint Nature Conservation Commission Rep. 268, Peterborough.

SWANN, R. L. 2000. Integrated seabird monitoring studies on the Isle of Canna, Scotland 1969–99. *Atlantic Seabirds* 2, 151–64.

SWANN, R. L. 2002. *Easter Ross seabird monitoring* 2002. Unpublished report, Highland Ringing Group.

SWANN, R. L. In press. *Canna Seabird Studies 2002*. Joint Nature Conservation Committee Rep., Peterborough.

TAOKA, M., SATO, T., KAMADA, T. & OKUMURA, H. 1989a. Heterosexual response to playback calls of the Leach's Storm-petrel *Oceanodroma leucorhoa*. *J. Yamashina Inst. Orn.* 21, 84–9.

TAOKA, M., SATO, T., KAMADA, T. & OKUMURA, H. 1989b. Sexual dimorphism of chatter-calls and vocal sex recognition in Leach's Storm-petrels (*Oceanodroma leucorhoa*). *Auk* 106, 498–500.

TAPPER, S. C. 1992. *Game Heritage: An Ecological Review From Shooting & Gamekeeping Records*. The Game Conservancy, Fordingbridge.

TASKER, M. L. & WALSH, P. M. 1993. Mew Gull *Larus canus*. In: Gibbons, D. W., Reid J. B. & Chapman, R. A. 1991. *The New Atlas of Breeding Birds in Britain & Ireland: 1988–1991*. T. & A. D. Poyser, London.

TASKER, M. L., CAMPHUYSEN, C. J., COOPER, J., GARTHE, S., LEOPOLD, M., MONTEVECCHI, W. A. & BLABER, S. 2000. The impact of fisheries on marine birds. *ICES J. Mar. Sci.* 57, 531–47.

TASKER, M. L., WEBB, A. & MATTHEWS, J. M. 1991. A census of the large inland Mew Gull colonies of Grampian. *Scott. Birds* 16, 106–12.

TAVERNER, J. H. 1970. Mediterranean Gulls nesting in Hampshire. *Brit. Birds* 65, 67–79.

TAYLOR, A. M. 1985. Manx Shearwaters on Lundy: ringing studies and other observations. *Lundy Field Soc. Ann. Rep.* 36, 23–4.

TAYLOR, I. R. 1983. Effect of wind on the foraging behaviour of Common & Sandwich Terns. *Ornis Scand.* 14, 90–6.

TEIXEIRA, A M. 1986. Razorbill losses in Portuguese nets. *Seabird* 9, 11–14.

TEKKE, M. J. 1976. Ringed Mediterranean Gulls *Larus melanocephalus* from the Black Sea area, recovered in the Netherlands. *Limosa* 49, 217.

THÉVENOT, M., VERNON, J. D. R. & BERGIER, P. 2003. *The Birds of Morocco: An Annotated Checklist.* British Ornithologists' Union, Tring.

THOM, V. 1986. *Birds in Scotland.* T. & A. D. Poyser, Calton.

THOMAS, D. H. 1981. The size of the colony of Manx Shearwaters (*Puffinus puffinus*) on Lundy. *Lundy Field Soc. Ann. Rep.* 32, 16–20.

THOMAS, D. H. 1992. Marine wildlife and net fisheries around Wales. Unpubl. Rep. Royal Society for the Protection of Birds & Countryside Commission for Wales, Sandy.

THOMAS, G. J. 1972. Review of gull damage and management methods at nature reserves. *Biol. Conserv.* 4, 117–27.

THOMAS, G. J. 1982. Breeding terns in Britain and Ireland, 1975–1979. *Seabird* 6, 59–69.

THOMAS, G. J., UNDERWOOD, L. A. & PARTRIDGE, K. J. 1989. Breeding terns in Britain and Ireland 1980–1984. *Seabird* 12, 20–31.

THOMPSON, D. R. & FURNESS, R. W. 1995. Stable-isotope rations of carbon and nitrogen in feathers indicate seasonal dietary shifts in Northern Fulmars. *Auk* 112, 493–8.

THOMPSON, D. R., FURNESS, R. W. & LEWIS, S. A. 1995. Diets and long-term changes in $-^{15}$N and $-^{13}$C values in Northern Fulmars *Fulmarus glacialis* from two northeast Atlantic colonies. *Mar. Ecol. Progr. Ser.* 125, 3–11.

THOMPSON, D. R., FURNESS, R. W. & WALSH, P. M. 1992. Historical changes in mercury concentrations in the marine ecosystem of the north and north-east Atlantic ocean as indicated by seabird feathers. *J. Appl. Ecol.* 29, 79–84.

THOMPSON, K. R. 1987. The ecology of the Manx Shearwater *Puffinus puffinus* on Rhum, West Scotland. Ph.D. thesis. University of Glasgow.

THOMPSON, K. R., BRINDLEY, E. & HEUBECK M. 1997. *Seabird Numbers and Breeding Success in Britain and Ireland, 1996.* Joint Nature Conservation Committee (UK Nature Conserv. Rep. 21.), Peterborough.

THOMPSON, K. R., BRINDLEY, E. & HEUBECK M. 1998. *Seabird Numbers and Breeding Success in Britain and Ireland, 1997.* Joint Nature Conservation Committee (UK Nature Conserv. Rep. 22.), Peterborough.

THOMPSON, K. R. & FURNESS, R. W. 1991. The influence of rainfall and nest-site quality on the population dynamics of the Manx Shearwater *Puffinus puffinus* on Rhum. *J. Zool., Lond.* 225, 427–37.

THOMPSON, K. R., PICKERELL, G. & HEUBECK, M. 1999. *Seabird Numbers and Breeding Success in Britain and Ireland, 1998.* Joint Nature Conservation Committee (UK Nature Conserv. Rep. 23.), Peterborough.

THOMPSON, P. & OLLASON, J. C. 2001. Lagged effects of ocean climate change on fulmar population dynamics. *Nature* 413, 417–20.

TOMS, M. 2002. Mediterranean Gull *Larus melanocephalus*. In: Wernham, C. V., Toms, M. P., Marchant, J. H., Clark, J. A., SiriwardenÀ, G. M. & Baillie, S. R. (eds.) *The Migration Atlas: Movements of the Birds of Britain and Ireland.* T. & A.D. Poyser, London.

TREE, A. J. & KLAGES, N. T. W. 2003. Status, biometrics, moult, and possible relationships of the South African population of Roseate Tern. *Ostrich* 74, 74–80.

TUCKER, G. M. & HEATH, M. F. 1994. *Birds in Europe: Their Conservation Status.* BirdLife International Conserv. Ser. 3, Cambridge.

ULENAERS, P., DEVOS, K. & JACOB, J.-P. 1997. Population development of wintering and breeding Cormorants (*Phalacrocorax carbo sinensis*) in Belgium. *Suppl. Ric. Biol. Selvaggina*, 26, 55–60.

UPTON, A. J., PICKERELL, G. & HEUBECK M. 2000. *Seabird Numbers and Breeding Success in Britain and Ireland, 1999.* Joint Nature Conservation Committee (UK Nature Conserv. Rep. 24.), Peterborough.

URBAN, E. K, FRY, C. H. & KEITH, S. K. (eds.) 1986. *The Birds of Africa*, vol. 2. Academic Press, London.

UTTLEY, J., MONAGHAN, P. & WHITE, S. 1989. Differential effects of reduced sandeel availability on two sympatrically breeding species of tern. *Ornis Scand.* 20, 273–7.

VADER, W. 1994. Storjø *Stercorarius skua*. In: Gjershaug, J. O., Thingstad, P. G., Eldøy, S. & Byrkjeland, S. (eds.) *Norsk Fugleatlas.* Norsk Orn. Fore., Klæbu.

VADER, W., BARRETT, R. T., ERIKSTAD, K. E. & STRANN, K. B. 1990. Differential responses of common and thick-billed murres to a crash in the capelin stock in the southern Barents Sea. *Stud. Avian Biol.* 14, 175–80.

VAL HALEWYN, R. & NORTON, R. L. 1984. The status and conservation of seabirds in the Caribbean. In: Croxall, J. P., Evans, P. G. H. & Schreiber, R. W. (eds.) *Status and Conservation of the World's Seabirds.* International Council for Bird Preservation Tech. Publ. 2, Cambridge.

VARGA, L., VEPRIK, R., SZÉLL, A. & BAKACSI, G. 1999. Colour ringing of Mediterranean Gulls *Larus melanocephalus* in Hungary in 1994–1998. In: Meininger, P. L., Hoogendoorn, W., Flamant, R. & Raevel, P. (eds.) *Proc. First Intern. Mediterranean Gull Meeting, Le Portel, Pas-de-Calais, France, 4–7 September 1998.*

VAUGHAN D. 2001. Storm petrel census of Skokholm Island, Pembrokeshire, 2001. Rep. to Joint Nature Conservation Committee, Wildlife Trust West Wales.

VAUGHAN, D. & GIBBONS, D. 1996. Storm petrels on Skokholm Island, 1995. Rep. to Countryside Commission for Wales, Royal Society for the Protection of Birds & Dyfed Wildlife Trust.

VEEN, J. 1977. Functional and causal aspects of nest distribution in the Sandwich Tern. *Behav.* (Suppl.) 20, 1–193.

VEITCH, C. R. & BELL, B. D. 1990. Eradication of introduced animals from the islands of New Zealand. In: Towns, D. R., Daugherty, C. H. & Atkinson, I. A. E. (eds.) *Ecological Restoration of New Zealand islands.* Conserv. Sci. Publ. 2, Dept. Conservation, Wellington.

VELANDO, A. & ALVAREZ, D. In press. El Cormoran Moñudo (*Phalacrocorax aristotelis aristotelis*). In: Madroño, A. & González, C. (eds.) *Libro Rojo de las Aves España.* SEO/Birdlife & Ministerio de Medio Ambiente,, Madrid.

VELANDO, A. & FREIRE, J. 2002. Population modeling of European shags (*Phalacrocorax aristotelis*) at their southern limit: conservation implications. *Biol. Conserv.* 107, 59–69.

VERBEEK, N. A. M. 1977. Comparative feeding ecology of Herring Gulls *Larus argentatus* and Lesser Black-backed Gulls *Larus fuscus. Ardea* 65, 25–42.

VERMEERSCH, G., FLAMANT, R. & ANSELIN, A. 2002. Kokmeeuw *Larus ridibundus*, Zwartkopmeeuw *Larus melanocephalus* en Stormmeeuw *Larus canus* als broedvogels in Vlaanderen. *Natuur. Oriolus* 68, 111–9.

VINCENT, T. 1990. Les noyades d'oiseaux marins plongeurs dans les filets de pêche: l'example des guillemots de troil en Baie de Seine. *Le Cormoran* 34, 289–91.

VINE, A. E. & SARGEANT, D. E. 1948. Arboreal nesting of Black-headed Gull colony. *Br. Birds* 41, 158–9.

VISSER, J. M. & PETERSON, G. W. 1994. Breeding populations & colony site dynamics of seabirds nesting in Louisiana. *Colonial Waterbirds* 17, 146–52.

VOTIER, S. C. 2001. Conservation implications of variation in diet and dietary specialisation in great skuas. Ph.D. thesis. University of Glasgow.

VOTIER, S. C., BEARHOP, S., MACCORMICK, A., RATCLIFFE, N. & FURNESS, R. W. In press. Assessing the diet of Great Skuas *Catharacta skua* using five different techniques. *Polar Biol.*

WALLACE, D. I. M. 1972. Seabirds at Lagos and in the Gulf of Guinea. *Ibis* 115, 559–71.

WALSH, P. M., BRINDLEY, E. & HEUBECK M. 1995. *Seabird Numbers and Breeding Success in Britain and Ireland, 1994.* Joint Nature Conservation Committee (UK Nature Conserv. Rep. 18), Peterborough.

WALSH, P. M., HALLEY, D. J., HARRIS, M. P., DEL NEVO, A., SIM, I. M. W. & TASKER, M. L. 1995. *Seabird Monitoring Handbook for Britain and Ireland.* Joint Nature Conservation Committee / Royal Society for the Protection of Birds / Seabird Group, Peterborough.

WALSH, P. M., SIM, I. & HEUBECK M. 1993. *Seabird Numbers and Breeding Success in Britain and Ireland, 1992.* Joint Nature Conservation Committee, Peterborough.

WALTER, U. & BECKER, P. H. 1997. Occurrence and consumption of seabirds scavenging on shrimp trawler discards in the Wadden Sea. *ICES J. Mar. Sci.* 54, 684–94.

WANLESS, S. 1987. A survey of the numbers and breeding distribution of the North Atlantic Gannet *Sula bassana* and an assessment of the changes that have occurred since Operation Seafarer 1969/70. *Res. & Survey in Nature Conserv.* 4, 1–100.

WANLESS, S. 1988. The recolonisation of the Isle of May by Common and Arctic Terns. *Scott. Birds* 15, 1–8.

WANLESS, S. 2002. Northern Gannet (Gannet) *Morus bassanus.* In: Wernham, C. V., Toms, M., Marchant, J., Clark, J., Siriwardene, G. & Baillie, S. (eds.) *The Migration Atlas: Movements of the Birds of Britain and Ireland.* T. & A. D. Poyser, London.

WANLESS, S. & HARRIS, M. P. 1984. Effect of date on counts of Herring Gulls and Lesser Black-backed Gulls. *Ornis Scand.* 15, 89–94.

WANLESS, S. & HARRIS, M. P. 1992. Activity budgets, diet and breeding success of Kittiwakes *Rissa tridactyla* on the Isle of May. *Bird Study* 39, 145–54.

WANLESS, S. & HARRIS, M. P. 1997. *Phalacrocorax aristotelis* Shag. BWP update 1 (1): 3–13.

WANLESS, S. & HARRIS, M. P. 1997. Successful double-brooding in European Shags. *Colonial Waterbirds* 20, 291–4.

WANLESS, S., HARRIS, M. P., CALLADINE, J. & ROTHERY, P. 1996. Modelling responses of Herring Gull and Lesser Black-backed Gull populations to reduction of reproductive output: implications for control measures. *J. Appl. Ecol.* 33, 1420–32.

WANLESS, S., HARRIS, M. P., MURRAY, S. & WILSON, L. J. 2003. Status of the Atlantic Puffin *Fratercula arctica* on the Isle of May National Nature Reserve, Craigleith and Fidra, Forth Islands Special Protection Area. Rep. to Scottish Natural Heritage, Cupar.

WANLESS, S. & LANGSLOW, D. R. 1983. The effects of culling on the Abbeystead and Mallowdale gullery. *Bird Study* 30, 17–23.

WANLESS, S., MATTHEWS, J. & BOURNE, W. R. P. 1996. The Troup Head gannetry. *Scott. Birds* 18, 214–21.

WARING, M. & DAVIS, S. 1983. Rediscovery of Leach's Petrels breeding in Ireland. *Irish Birds* 2, 360–4.

WATANUKI, Y. 1986. Moonlight avoidance behaviour in Leach's Storm-petrels as a defense against Slaty-backed Gulls. *Auk* 103, 14–22.

WATANUKI, Y., KONDO, N. & NAKAGAWA, H. 1988. Status of seabirds breeding in Hokkaido. *Japan J. Orn.* 37, 17–32.

WATSON, P. S. & RADFORD, D. J. 1982. Census of breeding seabirds at Horn Head, County Donegal in June 1980. *Seabird Rep.* 6, 26–34.

WEBB, A., CLAIRE A., McSORLEY, C. A., DEAN, B. J. & REID, J. B. 2002. Modelling the distribution and abundance of black scoter *Melanitta nigra* in Carmarthen Bay in winter 2001/02: a method for identifying potential boundaries for a marine Special Protection Area. Joint Nature Conservation Committee, Peterborough.

VAN DER WEIDE, M. 2002. Grote Mantelmeeuw *Larus marinus*. In: SOVON Vogelonderzoek Nederland (ed.) *Atlas van de Nederlandse Broedvogels 1998–2000*. Nationaal Natuurhistorisch Museum Naturalis, KNNV Uitgeverij & European Invertebrate Survey, Leiden.

WEIMERSKIRCH, H. 2002. Seabird demography and its relationship with the marine environment. In: Schreiber, E. A. & Burger, J. (eds.) *Biology of Marine Birds*. CRC Press, Boca Raton.

WEIMERSKIRCH, H., BROTHERS, N. & JOUVENTIN, P. 1997. Population dynamics of wandering albatross *Diomedea exulans* and Amsterdam albatross *D. amsterdamensis* in the Indian Ocean and their relationships with long-line fisheries: conservation implications. *Biol. Conserv.* 79, 257–70.

WEIMERSKIRCH, H., INCHAUSTI, P., GUINET, C. & BARBRAUD, C. 2003. Trends in bird and seal populations as indicators of a system shift in the Southern Ocean. *Antarctic Sci.* 15, 249–56.

WEIMERSKIRCH, H. & JOUVENTIN, P. 1987. Population dynamics of the Wandering Albatross, *Diomedea exulans*, of the Crozet Islands: causes and consequences of the population decline. *Oikos* 49, 315–22.

WEIR, D. N., KITCHENER, A. C. & McGOWAN, R. Y. 1996. Biometrics of Kittiwakes *Rissa tridactyla* wrecked in Shetland in 1993. *Seabird* 18, 5–9.

WENDELN, H. & BECKER, P. H. 1999. Significance of ring removal in Africa for a Common Tern *Sterna hirundo* colony. *Ring. & Migr.* 19, 210–2.

WENDELN, H. & BECKER, P. H. 2000. Parental care of replacement clutches in Common Terns *Sterna hirundo*. *Behav. Ecol. & Sociobiol.* 47, 382–92.

WERNHAM, C. V. ARMITAGE, M., HOLLOWAY, S. J., HUGHES, B., HUGHES, R., KERSHAW, M., MADDEN, J. R., MARCHANT, J. H., PEACH, W. J. & REHFISCH, M. M. 1999. *Population, Distribution, Movements and Survival of Fish-eating Birds in Great Britain*. Dept. Environment, Transport & the Regions, London.

WERNHAM, C. V., PEACH, W. J. & BROWNE, S. J. 1997. *Survival Rates of Rehabilitated Guillemots*. BTO Res. Rep. 186, Thetford.

WERNHAM, C. V., TOMS, M., MARCHANT, J., CLARK, J., SIRIWARDENA, G. & BAILLIE, S. (eds.) 2002. *The Migration Atlas: Movements of the Birds of Britain and Ireland*. T. & A. D. Poyser, London.

WETLANDS INTERNATIONAL. 2002. *Waterbird Population Estimates*, third edn. Wetlands International Global Ser. 12, Wageningen.

WHILDE, A. 1978. A survey of gulls breeding inland in the West of Ireland in 1977 and 1978 and a review of the inland breeding habit in Ireland and Britain. *Irish Birds* 1, 134–60.

WHILDE, A. 1979. Auks trapped in salmon drift-nets. *Irish Birds* 1, 370–6.

WHILDE, A. 1985. The 1984 All Ireland Tern Survey. *Irish Birds* 3, 1–32.

WHILDE, A., COTTON, D. C. F. & SHEPPARD, J. R. 1993. A repeat survey of gulls breeding inland in counties Donegal, Sligo, Mayo and Galway, with recent counts from Leitrim and Fermanagh. *Irish Birds* 5, 67–72.

WHITE, R.W., GILLON, K.W., BLACK, A.D. & REID J.B. 2001. *The distribution of seabirds and marine mammals in Falkland Islands waters*. JNCC, Peterborough.

WHITE, R., WALSH, P. M., BARTON, C. & THOMPSON, K. R. 1996. *Survey of Breeding Mew Gulls in the Correen Hills and Mortlach Hills, Grampian, 1995: Summary Report.* Joint Nature Conservation Committee Rep. 224, Aberdeen.

WHITTINGTON, P. A., DYER, B. M., CRAWFORD, R. J. M. & WILLIAMS, A. J. 1999. First recorded breeding of Leach's Storm-petrel *Oceanodroma leucorhoa* in the southern hemisphere, at Dyer Island, South Africa. *Ibis* 141, 327–30.

WILLCOX, N. 2001. Life after rats. *Scott. Wildlife Trust* 42, 28–30.

WILLIAMSON, K. 1940. The puffins of the Calf Isle—the history of the Manx Shearwater. *J. Manx Mus.* 4, 178–180, 203–5.

WILLIAMSON, K. 1973. The antiquity of the Calf of Man Manx Shearwater colony. *Bird Study* 20, 310–11.

WILSON, D. R. 1959. The storm petrel colony on Roaninish. *Bird Study* 6, 73–6.

WILSON, J. G. & EARLY, J. J. 1986. Pesticide and PCB levels in the eggs of the Shag *Phalacrocorax aristotelis* and Cormorant *Phalacrocorax carbo* from Ireland. *Environ. Pollution Ser. B* 12, 15–26.

WILSON, J. G. M. and VAN ZEGEREN, K. 1996. White-breasted Cormorants *Phalacrocorax carbo lucidus* more abundant in Southern Africa than previously thought. *Cormorant Res. Group Bull.* 2, 42–3.

WILSON, L. J., WANLESS S., HARRIS, M. P. & RUSSELL, D. 2003. Isle of May seabird studies in 2002. Joint Nature Conservation Committee Rep., Aberdeen.

WILSON P. R., AINLEY D. G., NUR N., JACOBS, S. S., BARTON, K. J., BALLARD, G. & COMISO, J. C. 2001. Adélie Penguin population change in the Pacific sector of Antarctica: relation to sea-ice extent and the Antarctic Circumpolar Current. *Mar. Ecol. Progr. Ser.* 213, 301–9.

WINKLEMAN, J. E. 1985. Impact of medium sized wind turbines on birds: a survey on flight behaviour, victims and disturbance. *Netherlands J. Agricultural Sci.* 33, 75–7.

WINNEY, B. J. LITTON, C. D. PARKIN, D. T. & FEARE, C. J. 2001. The subspecific origin of the inland breeding colonies of the Cormorant *Phalacrocorax carbo* in Britain. *Heredity* 86, 45–83.

WOLF, S. 2002. The relative status and conservation of island breeding seabirds in California and northwest Mexico. M.Sc. thesis. University of California, Santa Cruz.

WOOD, D. 1995. An aerial survey of Great Cormorants *Phalacrocorax carbo* nesting in Orkney during 1995. *Orkney Bird Rep.* 1995: 63–6.

WOOD, D. 1997. An estimate of the numbers of Storm petrels *Hydrobates pelagicus* breeding on Auskerry, Orkney. *Seabird* 19, 40–6.

WOODLEY, T. H. & EARLE, M. 1991. Observations on the French Albacore driftnet fishery of the northeast Atlantic. Prelim. Rep. to Greenpeace International.

WOODROW, L. 2003. Hamford Water NNR: sand and gravel recharge. In: Schmitt, S. (ed.) Little Terns in Britain and Ireland, 2002. Unpubl. Rep. Royal Society for the Protection of Birds, Sandy.

WORMELL, P. 1976. The Manx Shearwaters of Rhum. *Scott. Birds* 9, 103–8.

WRIGHT, P. J. 1996. Is there a conflict between sandeel fisheries and seabirds? A case study at Shetland. In: Greenstreet, S. P. R. & Tasker, M. L. (eds.) *Aquatic Predators and Their Prey.* Fishing News Books, Oxford.

WRIGHT, P. J. & BAILEY, M. C. 1993. Biology of sandeels in the vicinity of seabird colonies at Shetland. Fisheries Res. Rep. 15/93. SOAFD Marine Laboratory, Aberdeen.

WRIGHT, P. J. & BEGG, G. S. 1997. A spatial comparison of guillemots and sandeels in Scottish waters. *ICES J. Mar. Sci.* 54, 578–92.

WYNNE-EDWARDS, V. C. 1962. *Animal Dispersion in Relation to Social Behaviour.* Oliver & Boyd, Edinburgh.

YEATMAN, L. 1976. *Atlas des Oiseaux Nicheurs de France de 1970 a 1975.* Soc. Orn. France, Ministère de la Qualité de la Vie Environnement, Direction de la Protection de la Nature, Paris.

YÉSOU, P. 1997. Mediterranean Gull breeding in France. *Ornithos* 4, 54–62.

YÉSOU, P., FILCHAGOV, A. V. & DUBOIS, P. J. 1994. An answer to Chylarecki's comments on the 'new Herring Gull taxonomy'. *Brit. Birds* 87, 73–8.

YÉSOU, P. & SADOUL, N. In press. In: Cadiou, B., Pons, J.-M. & Yésou, P. (eds.) *Oiseaux Marins Nicheurs de France Métropolitaine (1960–2000).* GISOM Editions Biotope, Paris.

YORIO, P. & QUINTANA, F. 1997. Predation by Kelp Gulls *Larus dominicanus* at a mixed-species colony of Royal Terns *Sterna maxima* & Cayenne Terns *Sterna eurygnatha* in Patagonia. *Ibis* 139, 536–41.

YORIO, P., FRERE, E., GANDINI, P. & CONWAY, W. 1999. Status and conservation of seabirds breeding in Argentina. *Bird Conserv. Intern.* 9, 299–314.

YOUNG, E. C. 1963. Feeding habits of the South Polar Skua *Catharacta maccormicki*. *Ibis* 105, 301–18.

YOUNG, E. C. 1978. Behavioural ecology of *lonnbergi* skuas in relation to environment on the Chatham Islands, New Zealand. *New Zealand J. Zool.* 5, 401–16.

ZONFRILLO, B. 1996. European Storm-petrels and other seabirds without their toes. *Brit. Birds* 89, 186–7.

ZONFRILLO, B. 2001. Ailsa Craig—before and after the eradication of rats in 1991. *Ayrshire Bird Rep.* 2000, 5–10.

ZONFRILLO, B. 2002. Puffins return to Ailsa Craig. *Scott. Bird News* 66, 1–2.

ZONFRILLO, B. & MONAGHAN, P. 1995. Rat eradication on Ailsa Craig. In: Tasker, M. L. (ed.) *Threats to Seabirds: Proc. Fifth Intern. Seabird Group Conf.* Seabird Group.

ZONFRILLO, B. & NOGALES M. 1992. First breeding records of Shelduck & Black Guillemot on Ailsa Craig. *Glasgow Nat.* 22, 197–8.

ZOTIER, R., THIBAULT, J. C. & GUYOT, I. 1992. Known population and distribution of cormorants, shearwaters and storm petrels in the Mediterranean. *Avocetta* 16, 118–26.

Appendix I: Seabird 2000 Census Instructions and Recording Forms

Census Instructions
(Revised March 2000)

Introduction

Seabird 2000 is the third census of all breeding seabirds in Britain and Ireland, following on from Operation Seafarer in 1969/70 and the Seabird Colony Register (SCR) census in 1985-87. JNCC and the Seabird Group jointly own the SCR database, to which information on existing and new colonies is constantly added. JNCC also co-ordinates the Seabird Monitoring Programme (SMP) which through contributions from other bodies and dedicated individuals, regularly monitors population size and productivity at a number of sites in Britain and Ireland. The two main aims of Seabird 2000 are:

1. To determine whether population trends recorded at local levels by the SMP are representative of national trends.

2. To identify long-term (last 30 years) national trends by comparison with the previous two censuses.

IMPORTANT

PLEASE READ THESE INSTRUCTIONS CAREFULLY AND KEEP THEM AVAILABLE FOR REFERENCE DURING FIELD WORK. IF YOU HAVE ANY QUERIES, CONTACT YOUR REGIONAL CO-ORDINATOR.

PLEASE FOLLOW THE SAFETY GUIDELINES DETAILED IN THE SEABIRD 2000 SAFETY BOOKLET.

PLEASE OBTAIN PERMISSION BEFORE VENTURING ONTO PRIVATE LAND; SEABIRD 2000 DOES NOT GIVE YOU THE RIGHT TO ENTER ONTO PRIVATE PROPERTY.

Recording Forms & Maps

Coastal sites (example on page 3): you should also have been provided with a 1:10,000 scale (1:50,000 or 6 inch for Ireland) map of the stretch of coast you need to survey. The section of coastline required for counting will be clearly marked on the map. Within each section, legislative boundaries (eg. Sites of Special Scientific Interest SSSI, Special Protection Areas SPA, National Nature Reserves NNR), and/or boundaries of independent nature reserves (eg. RSPB, local wildlife trusts etc) will also be marked.

If your survey section is over 1km in length, then you should divide it into easily defined sub-sections no longer than 1km and provide separate counts for each sub-section (see recording instructions below). No sub-section should cross one of the existing boundaries (eg. SPA or RSPB reserve) and each sub-section should be chosen so that a different observer, visiting the area in the future, may identify the section exactly using a 1:10,000 map.

This mapping approach will ensure that counts can be ascribed to a specific area along a stretch of coastline. This will be extremely useful to the end users of the Seabird 2000 database, who may only wish to obtain data for stretches of coastline that fall within legislative boundaries, such as SPAs. Likewise, local Wildlife Trusts may want information relating solely to one of their nature reserves that might lie within a larger seabird colony.

Black Guillemots: You should only divide sections of coastline into sub-sections of 1km or less where black guillemots are actually present. Do not sub-divide other sections which do not contain any black guillemots. 1:50,000 or 1:25,000 scale maps should suffice for Black guillemot surveys along large stretches of coastline.

Inland gull, tern and cormorant colonies: You will not need to map these colonies. A single grid ref. for the centre of the colony will suffice. Please enter this on sheet A under the column marked '*Grid Start*'.

You should have been provided with <u>three</u> separate recording forms for Seabird 2000:

<u>SHEET A:</u>   Colony / site data

<u>SHEET B:</u>   Site visit details

<u>SHEET C:</u>   Count data

IMPORTANT

Please refer to the instructions below and the examples on pages 4, 5 & 7 before completing the forms

Counts for Seabird 2000 should only be entered on the dedicated recording forms and should NOT be submitted on Seabird Colony Register recording sheets or in any other form.

<u>SHEET A:</u>   Colony / site data (example on page 4)

In the top half of the sheet you should enter: i) the county or unitary authority which covers the site(s) you have counted ; ii) your name and address, together with those of anyone else conducting the counts.

Inland sites and coastal sites (less than 1km in length):
In the table (at the bottom of the sheet), you should enter information for each site on a separate row. Each site should be given a unique code consisting of up to 4 characters of your choosing. The site code will be used to cross-referencing the three separate recording sheets. For each sub-section you should indicate the habitat types present using up to four numeric codes which are listed on the reverse of sheet A.

For sub-sections of coastal sites (greater than 1km in length): assign each sub-section a unique name and code (eg. for Fowlsheugh RSPB Reserve: Fowlsheugh 1 = FH1, Fowlsheugh 2 = FH2 etc) and enter the information for each subsection on a separate row in geographical order (eg. from north to south or east to west etc). Then give the six-figure OS grid reference of the start and end points of each sub-section. In the 'Site Rel' column describe the relationship of a site/sub-section to the others listed, using one of the four codes (i.e. ADJ or GAP or OVL or CON) defined at the bottom of sheet A. For each sub-section, indicate the habitat types present using up to four numeric codes which are listed on the reverse of sheet A.

Example of Coastal Site Mapping (not applicable to Black Guillemots):

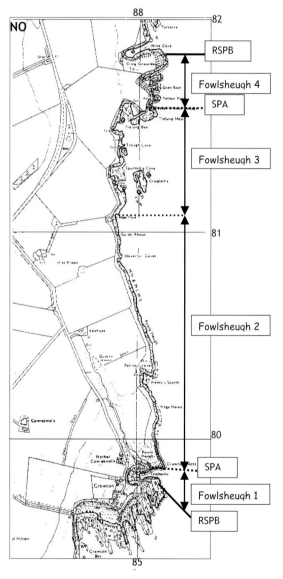

Opposite is a copy of a 1:10,000 scale map of a stretch of coastline to be counted. Boundaries of the designated Special Protection Area (SPA) and the RSPB reserve are marked on the map.

The arrows inidicate the separate count sub-sections that the observer has divided this section of coast into and labelled 'Fowlsheugh 1, 2, 3, 4'.

Note how the sub-sections have been chosen so that: i) no sub-section is more than 1km in length; ii) each sub-section is demarcated by a distinct geographical feature; iii) no sub-section crosses the desinated boundaries (i.e. RSPB, SPA) and thus, total counts can be obtained for both the SPA and the RSPB reserve, if counts from the relevant sub-sections are added together.

The grid references for each sub-section and the habitat present within each of them is entered in the example of Sheet A on page 5.

Use the column labelled 'Pred' to indicate the presence of predators at the site/subsection, using the categories given at the bottom of sheet A. NB If you found evidence of predator presence during at least one of your repeated visits, then enter '1' for all other visits, regardless of whether or not you checked for predators at the other visits. Please give details on the reverse of sheet A of the species of predator present and the nature of the evidence of their presence (eg. sightings, prey remains, tracks, scats etc.).

EXAMPLE - SHEET A

Below is an example of how to fill in the three data sheets. The example data is based on the mapped sections given overleaf. **NB. The details given in the examples are there to illustrate certain points and do not equate to actual data gathered at Fowlsheugh.**

Site Data

Site/sub-section Name	*Site Code*	Grid Start	Grid End	#Site Rel	‡Pred Key	†Habitat Code			
						1	2	3	4
Fowlsheugh 1	FH1	NO881798	NO881799	ADJ	1	H2	I1		
Fowlsheugh 2	FH2	NO881799	NO871811	ADJ	1	H1	I1		
Fowlsheugh 3	FH3	NO871811	NO881816	ADJ	1	H1	I1	H6	
Fowlsheugh 4	FH4	NO881816	NO880817	ADJ	1	H1	I2	I1	

Predators

What measures did you take to assess the presence or absence of predators at each site or sub-section you visited?

During each visit, as I walked between each counting point along the top of the cliffs, I checked for any predator signs eg. scats or prey remains. I wasn't able to check for ground predators at FH3 as this was surveyed purely from a boat, though did note aerial predators

Site/sub-section code	Species Present	Evidence
FH1	cat	Seen around the cliff-top
FH2	fox	3 separate pellets
	Great black-backed gull	Flying past the colony
FH3	Peregrine	Flying past the colony
FH4	rat	Droppings found on cliff-top

SHEET B: Site Visit Information (example on page 5)

These sheet is used to enter information about the date, time, weather conditions and count methods used during each visit to a site or sub-section previously defined on sheet A. The time of day as well as the time of year, in addition to weather conditions and count methods, can all affect the accuracy of the counts (see below), so it is important that you record this information every time you visit a colony.

Each visit to a site or sub-section should be entered on a separate row and defined uniquely by a 'Sample Code'. The sample code should be composed of the site/sub-section code defined in sheet A, followed by a '/' and a letter corresponding to each visit (eg. Fowlsheugh may have 4 subsections called FH1...FH4. So if 2 visits where made to each subsection, the sample codes would be FH1/A, FH1/B ....FH4/A, FH4/B).

The 'VISIT REL' column denotes the relationship between duplicate visits to the same site or sub-section (i.e. + or REC: see sheet B for definitions).

Numeric codes for count method, visibility, sea state, rainfall and wind speed are all given on sheet B.

EXAMPLE - SHEET B

At each section fulmars, guillemots, razorbills, puffins, kittiwakes and shags were counted. Subsection 'FH1' was counted once from land and sub-section FH3 once from a boat. Some parts of sub-section FH2 were counted initially from land, but other areas were counted on separate days by boat.

SAMPLE CODE[#]	Date	Time start	Time End	VISIT REL*	METH[†]	Weather[‡]			
						Visibility	Sea State	Rain	Wind
FH1/A	6/6/99	09.30	11.30		1.1	1	2	0	2
FH2/A	6/6/99	12.00	16.00	+	1.1	1	2	0	2
FH2/B	8/6/99	10.00	13.00	+	1.2	1	1	0	1
FH3/A	7/6/96	09.00	12.00		1.2	1	1	0	1
FH4/A	9/6/99	16.00	18.00		1.1	2	2	2	2
FH4/B	15/6/99	12.00	14.00	REC	1.1	1	1	0	1

The first visit to sub-section FH4 was made too late in the day to make a reliable count of guillemots and razorbills (i.e. later than 16.00 BST). Never the less, a count of both species was made, but the observer was able to revisit the site during the prescribed period at a later date and recounted them. These latter counts are therefore, considered the most reliable and should supercede the previous counts. The species for which a recount was made should be noted by filling in the table on the reverse of sheet B, as follows:

Sample code	Species	Sample code	Species
FH4/B	guillemot		
FH4/B	razorbill		

Appendix I

SHEET C: Count Data (example on page 7)

On this sheet you should enter counts for each species present at each site/sub-section during each visit. Counts for each species are listed on separate rows and each visit denoted by a different sample code (see sheet B) are listed in separate columns. For each species count in each sample code column, you should also note the accuracy code of the count and the unit code used.

Accuracy Code:

ACC = **accurate count**; applies to counts of sections where all birds are visible
EST = **estimated count;** an estimated count of all visible birds or an estimate of the whole colony derived from accurate counts of samples of the colony
HID = **estimated count of hidden birds**; applies to estimated numbers of birds on sections of cliff which are hidden from view.
UCL = **95% Upper confidence limit;**
LCL = **95% Lower confidence limit;** both UCL and LCL should be attached to estimated counts that have been determined by counting sample plots within the colony.

The unit code used varies with the species being counted and also on the situation. Details of what codes to use on which species are given in the Recommended Counting Techniques section below and summarised in Appendix 1.

EXAMPLE: SHEET C

Below is an example of how to enter count data, based on the example of Fowlsheugh, given above for sheets A & B. Each bold column represents a single visit to a particular sub-section. Note that two rows of counts for guillemots are given: one is for accurate counts (ACC) of individuals and the other is for estimates of the number of birds hidden from view (HID). Note also that counts were made of guillemots and razorbills during each visit to subsection FH4. As shown in example sheet B above, the second visit (FH4/B) was made to recount the auks at a more reliable time of day than was originally achieved on the first visit (FH4/A).

SPECIES CODE	Sample Code:FH1/A			Sample Code:FH2/A			Sample Code:FH2/B			Sample Code:FH3/A			Sample Code:FH4/B			Sample Code:FH4/B		
	Acc	COUNT	Unit	Acc	COUNT	Unit	Acc	COUNT	Unit	Acc	COUNT	Unit	Acc	COUNT	Unit	Acc	COUNT	Unit
FUL	ACC	200	AOS	ACC	300	AOS	ACC	730	AOS	ACC	60	AOS	ACC	45	AOS			
GUI	ACC	450	IND	ACC	2200	IND	ACC	6,500	IND	ACC	1200	IND	ACC	230	IND	ACC	420	IND
GUI	HID	20	IND	HID	50	IND												
RAZ	ACC	10	IND	ACC	200	IND	ACC	1500	IND				ACC	20	IND	ACC	35	IND
PUFF				ACC	300	IND	ACC	700	IND									
SH	ACC	30	AON							ACC	40	AON	ACC	57	AON			
KIT	ACC	50	AON	ACC	2500	AON	ACC	12,500	AON	ACC	830	AON	ACC	30	AON			

Recommended Counting Techniques

This section summarises species by species, how to undertake counts for Seabird 2000. These methods are taken from Walsh et al. 1995: *Seabird Monitoring Handbook*. Your local regional co-ordinator will have a copy of the handbook, so any queries concerning any of these methods should be directed to him/her. **No other methods should be implemented (apart from those in Gilbert, Gibbons & Evans 1998: *Bird Monitoring Methods*).**

The main points to note about counting each species are i) the recommended timing of counts, and ii) the recommended count unit; these are summarised in Appendix 1. The timings of the counts are crucial, since they take into account the breeding behaviour of each particular species and thus maximise the accuracy of estimating breeding numbers.

Hidden Sections of Cliff-nesting Colonies
It is likely that if you are conducting counts of cliff-nesting colonies from land, some sections of the cliff will be hidden from view. If this occurs, please do the following:
i)   Keep a note of (and map) any parts of a colony that might not be visible from land.
ii)   Try to estimate the number of AONs, AOSs or INDs likely to be hidden, based on numbers on visible sections (although these may not necessarily show similar densities to hidden sections) or on previous sea-based v. land-based counts. However, in reporting these estimates be very clear that they are of unknown reliability, and may not be directly comparable with other counts.
iii)   If at all possible, check and count hidden sections from a boat on a calm day (especially if you estimate that hidden sections are likely to total more than *c*10% of the population).

Weather
Please ensure that on every visit you make to a site or sub-section, you note down the prevailing weather conditions on Sheet B. Weather conditions can greatly affect the attendance of cliff-nesting birds at colonies, so counts should be conducted within the conditions specified below to ensure comparability of counts made in different years and at different colonies.

IMPORTANT

NEVER CONDUCT COUNTS OF ANY BREEDING SEABIRDS DURING WINDS STRONGER THAN BEAUFORT FORCE 4 OR DURING HEAVY OR CONTINUOUS RAIN.

AVOID FLUSH COUNTS OR ANY OTHER DISTURBANCE OF GULL OR TERN COLONIES DURING WET WEATHER, OTHERWISE EGGS & CHICKS MAY BECOME IRREVERSIBLY CHILLED.

FULMAR

Census units

Apparently occupied site (AOS) = A site is counted as occupied only when a bird appears to be sitting tightly on a reasonably horizontal area judged large enough to hold an egg.

NB. Two birds on such a site, apparently paired, count as one site. (This should exclude birds which are sitting on / hanging on to sloping sections of cliff.)

Timing
June: 0900 - 1730 BST (Counts in late May and early July are better than nothing).

STORM PETREL & LEACH'S PETREL

A major objective of Seabird 2000 is to improve our knowledge of how many petrels breed in these islands. It is clear that Britain and Ireland hold internationally important numbers of both species, but currently, we have a poor understanding of exactly how many storm and Leach's petrels breed around Britain and Ireland (current estimates range 70,000 – 250,000 and 10,000 – 100,000 respectively). Furthermore, we have only an incomplete understanding of their distribution. The main potential threat to petrel numbers is the introduction of mammalian predators to the islands where they breed. Thus, in addition to determining the location and size of petrel colonies, it is also important to ascertain the presence or absence of mammalian predators at each colony.

What to do if petrels are likely to be present at your site...

⑦ **Firstly, consult with your regional co-ordinator:** he/she will provide you with precise instructions on what to do and supply you with recordings of petrel calls.

⑦ **Your primary aim should be to ascertain presence of breeding birds i.e. an *Apparently occupied site* (AOS) = a nest cavity containing a brooding adult i.e. an adult that responds to an appropriate play-back call during day-light hours.**
Visit the site at night to determine which areas the petrels are returning to and then revisit these areas during the day and play the taped calls in suitable nesting habitat.

NB. The presence of an AOS **CANNOT** be confirmed by any of the following:
a) birds present at the site at night.
b) birds caught (either with or without the use of tape-lures) and found to possess brood patches.

⑦ **If possible, ascertain the presence or absence of mammalian predators (eg. rats, mink, stoats, weasels).** Again consult with your regional co-ordinator on how best to do this.

Timing

Peak incubation periods:
Storm Petrels: early to mid- July
Leach's Petrels: mid to late June

The shortfall in our knowledge of petrel numbers has been due mainly to the absence of a reliable and accurate technique for counting them. **However, the RSPB has recently developed such a technique. This involves playing recordings of calls of either species during the day in suitable nesting habitat in order to elicit calls from brooding adults within the nest cavities.** By doing so the number of apparently occupied sites (AOS's) can be estimated. However, the technique can be time consuming, since not all incubating birds respond to the play-back. A correction for this has to be made for each colony. This entails repeatedly surveying a sample patch of habitat in order to find the proportion of birds present that responded to the first play-back. Thus, a complete survey of a colony, could take 7-10 days. This calibration procedure must be repeated every time a colony is surveyed, as response rates vary significantly within a colony between years, as well as between different colonies.

MANX SHEARWATER

If shearwaters are present at your site, try and establish the presence of breeding (i.e. apparently occupied sites AOSs). You should do this in a similar manner as described above for petrels and you should consult with your regional co-ordinator before doing so.

Timing

Peak incubation period: late May – early June

Breeding colonies can be surveyed using two methods:
a) counting burrows which show evidence of use (see puffin section below)

b) counting incubating adults by eliciting calls using taped calls during day-light hours (see petrel section above).

Your regional co-ordinator should be consulted before embarking on such a survey.

GANNET

A census of gannets will not take place as part of Seabird 2000. A regular census of all British and Irish gannet colonies takes place every 10 years and the last one being in 19994/95, with the next one planned for 2004/5. Hence, priority has been given to all other species during Seabird 2000.

CORMORANT

Census units

Apparently occupied nest (**AON**) = Birds apparently incubating or brooding; unattended broods of young; or other attended well-built nests including empty ones capable of holding eggs.

NB. Nests at a lesser stage of construction should not be included in the standard AON figures, but should be noted separately.

Timing

Early May – late June. This is the period of maximum occupancy of nests, though the exact timing varies depending on location. Thus, if possible, repeated counts should be made of each colony.

SHAG

Census units

Apparently occupied nest (**AON**) = Birds apparently incubating or brooding; unattended broods of young; or other attended well-built nests including empty ones capable of holding eggs.

NB. Nests at a lesser stage of construction should not be included in the standard AON figures, but should be noted separately.

Timing

Late May – late June. This is the period of maximum occupancy of nests, though the exact timing varies depending on location: peak laying occurs generally earlier in south & west Britain than in the north & east. You should consult with your regional co-ordinator on the best timing for the survey in your area. If possible, repeated counts should be made of each colony.

ARCTIC SKUA, GREAT SKUA

Census units

Apparently occupied territory (**AOT**) = a) nest, eggs or chicks;
b) apparently incubating or brooding adult;
c) adults distracting or alarm-calling;
d) pair or single bird in potential breeding habitat, apparently attached to area.

NB. The following should not be scored as AOTs:
e) bird(s) flying past, *en route* to somewhere else;
f) feeding individual(s);
g) single bird (or pair) flushed from an area, which flies completely out of sight;
h) three or more skuas of same species regularly together but not showing any signs of territoriality.

Counts of nests are thus not recommended for general census purposes. Attempts to count actual occupied nests are likely to underestimate numbers of breeding pairs to a much greater degree, unless observations are very intensive.

Timing

Late May to mid-July, preferably in June.

The best way to survey large areas of moorland is to walk rough transects at up to 500 m intervals, stopping at regular intervals (e.g. every 200-300 m) and thoroughly scanning all around. In areas of high skua density, closer transects will be needed, and it is important to sit or stand still to allow birds to re-settle. If the ground is undulating, or any areas are not visible during the main transect surveys, transect walks may need to be more closely spaced. Alternatively, scan breeding areas from suitable vantage points using binoculars and telescope.

Record all evidence of territorial skuas (e.g. using different code for nest, eggs, alarming adults etc.), and plot sightings on a 1:10,000 scale map. Territorial birds may utilise prominent mounds in their territory and these may be useful indicators of an AOT (though territorial birds may use more than one mound). Take care to avoid assigning members of the same pair, standing apart, to different territories. If there is uncertainty about the status of birds in any parts of the colony, check again on a different date in June.

For arctic skuas, if possible record the colour-phase of territorial adults: broadly, pale phase (light-coloured underparts) and 'dark' phase (including typical intermediates, dark apart from pale neck or ear-covert feathers). Where possible, record phases for each member of individual pairs.

GULLS (except kittiwakes)

There are five possible methods for censusing gulls, which depend on species, size of colony, location and man-power available:

1. Counts from vantage points
2. Sample quadrat counts
3. Transect counts
4. Flush-counts of adults
5. Aerial counts

Please consult with your regional co-ordinator on the most appropriate method to use and for further details on the implementation of each of these techniques. The following table should serve as a guide on which method is most appropriate for your colony.

Attributes of colony		Method
Location:	Cliff-tops or rocky islets visible from cliff-top	1
	Roof-top	1 or 5
	Ground-nesting or islets not visible from a cliff-top	1, 2, 3 or 4
Size	Small (<500 AONs)	1 or 4
	Large (>500 AONs)	2, 3 or 5
Terrain	Easily walked, level	2 or 3
	Difficult by foot, uneven	4
	Inaccessible by foot	1 or 5
Labour required	1 – 2 people	1 or 4
	2 – 4 people	2 or 4
	4 or more people	3

Census units

Apparently occupied nest (**AON**) = a well-constructed nest, attended by an adult and capable of holding eggs; or an adult apparently incubating if, e.g., actual nests are obscured by vegetation (methods 1 & 5); or a well-constructed nest, either containing eggs or young, or capable of holding eggs (methods 2 & 3).

Apparently occupied territory (**AOT**) = estimate based on the spacing of birds or pairs viewed from a vantage point, if actual nests or incubation cannot be discerned (methods 1 & 5).

Individual adult bird (**IND**) = method 4 only.

NB. Method 4 should be avoided if possible as it does not provide an accurate estimate of breeding numbers and creates considerable disturbance.

Timing

late May - early June (mid-incubation period),

09:00 – 16:00 BST (for methods 1 &4 only)

Mixed – species colonies

The most common species associations are lesser black-backed with herring gulls and black-headed gulls with common gulls. With the former pairing, it is not possible to separate nests of these species with any accuracy. However, with experience the eggs of black-headed and common gulls are somewhat easier to distinguish from each other, although there is some overlap in colour, weights and measurements. For methods based on direct observation (especially *Method 1*), separating the two species is generally not difficult. For *Methods 2 & 3*, the number of active nests belonging to each species is estimated by finding the ratio of one species to the other and partitioning the nest count in proportion. Species ratio should be determined by either walking through all parts of the colony (as breeding pairs of the two species may be clumped) or by inspecting the colony from a distance *provided* most of the colony is visible from suitable vantage points.

KITTIWAKE

Census units

Apparently occupied nest (**AON**) = a well-built nest capable of containing eggs with at least one adult present.

Timing

Preferably repeated counts in late May - mid-June; or a single count in early to mid - June

If the season appears to be unusually late (indicated by a high proportion of 'trace' nests or unoccupied well-built nests in June), a count in late June is a useful further check.

TERNS

IMPORTANT

ALL TERN COLONIES IN BRITAIN SHOULD BE SURVEYED IN 2000
Populations of breeding terns can be very mobile in comparison to other seabirds. In some cases, whole colonies may shift location from year to year or a large proportion of one colony may move to a different colony (not always nearby) in a different year. Pairs that fail at one colony early in the breeding season may even move to a different colony later in the same season. Thus, trends or fluctuations in counts of single colonies may in some cases simply reflect movements to or from other colonies. Hence the need to simultaneously count all British tern colonies within the same season.

There are three possible methods for censusing terns:

1. **Counts of apparently incubating adults from vantage points:** recommended for any colony that can be suitably viewed from a vantage point; avoids any disturbance.
2. **Foot-counts of occupied nests, with eggs or nest material:** recommended for any colony that <u>cannot</u> be suitably viewed from a vantage point. Visits should be no more than 20 minutes to avoid undue disturbance.
3. **Flush-counts of adults:** for use in colonies where counts of apparently incubating adults or active clutches are generally difficult. It is also useful where large numbers of colonies need to be covered rapidly.

Census units

Apparently occupied nest (**AON**) = either apparently incubating adults (Method 1), or active clutches plus empty nests with material (Method 2).
Inidvidual adult bird (**IND**) = total numbers of adults visible or, preferably, flushed from the colony (Method 3). (Distinguish between adults visible in or flushed from the nesting area and those loafing outside the nesting area. Loafing areas are usually adjacent to the colony and below high water mark.)

Timing

Methods 1 & 2: preferably repeated counts in mid May - late June or single count in mid June (or c. 3.5 weeks after first incubating birds are seen, i.e. late incubation period)**.**

Method 3: preferably three repeat counts in mid May – early June (i.e. last 2 weeks incubation & first week of after hatching) **or a single count in early June; 10:00 – 12:00 BST.**

GUILLEMOT & RAZORBILL

Census units

Individual adults on land at colony (**IND**) = all visible birds on the cliff, except for those only loosely associated with the colony (i.e. on intertidal rocks, or on the sea). On parts of the cliff higher than the intertidal areas, do not attempt to judge breeding status of individual birds which appear to be 'unattached' - even if they are not obviously associated with a potential breeding site, they should be counted.

Where birds are nesting among boulders, divide the occupied area into discrete sub-colonies, and count visible birds from suitable vantage points. Select *c*5 of the accessible sub-colonies *randomly* (**Please consult first with your regional co-ordinator**). Then, move carefully into and through each sub-colony, counting the actual number of individuals by direct observation and by flushing from crevices, etc. Try to minimise the time spent in each sub-colony, especially when many eggs or small chicks are present. Calculate the ratio of birds visible from the vantage point to the total birds for each group. Use the average factor derived in order to estimate 'hidden' numbers of individuals at other boulder sub-colonies.

Timing

1 – 21 June (incubation/early nestling period)**: 0800 - 1600 BST**

BLACK GUILLEMOT / TYSTIE

Census units

Individual adults associated with a colony (**IND**) = counting all birds in adult summer plumage seen on the sea within *c*300 m of the shore and any on land (Birds ashore are often difficult to see but can be flushed onto the water by clapping, shouting, etc. from a cliff-top observer).

Also, record separately:

 a) birds in other plumages (largely or partly grey, or with dark bars visible in white wing-patch);

 b) any birds seen >300 m offshore (thus less obviously associated with potential breeding habitat).

 c) any birds seen feeding, as these should not be considered 'associated' with the colony.

Timing

Ideally 1 -21 April (starting 25 March in Shetland).
From first light to *c*2 hours later (*c*0600-0800 BST in the north, but as late as 0900 further south).Counts in late April or early May are acceptable, although these tend to underestimate the population slightly. (By early May, birds are less easily disturbed into flying onto the sea, and more birds are missed, especially during counts from the cliff-top).

PUFFIN

There are four possible methods for censusing puffins:
1. Whole colony count of apparently occupied burrows (AOBs)
2. Sample quadrat counts of AOBs
3. Sample transect counts of AOBs
4. Counts of individuals

Methods 1, 2 & 3 should be used where the puffins are nesting in burrows accessible to the observer.
Please consult with your regional co-ordinator before implementing either technique. Method 4 is

the most widely applicable, being used for cliff-top nesting birds where burrows are inaccessible or where birds are nesting under boulders.

Census units

Methods 1, 2 & 3: *Apparently occupied burrow* **(AOB) =** a burrow with signs of regular use, e.g. fresh digging, hatched eggshells, broken vegetation or fish in the entrance. Rabbit burrows are usually larger, usually have much soil outside, and often have droppings at the entrance and conspicuous runs through the vegetation leading away. There is no simple way to separate Manx shearwater and puffin burrows, although mixed colonies are relatively uncommon.

Method 4: *Individual adults on land at colony* **(IND)** = the number of individuals present above ground Please, provide separate counts for (a) birds flying over the colony or nearby sea, and (b) birds on the sea within 200 m of shore.

Timing

Methods 1&2: Late April (SE Scotland) or early to mid-May (NW Scotland): i.e. before or during the laying period, when birds are digging or cleaning burrows and when ground vegetation is short;. However, acceptable counts can be made at any time from late April to early August, although assessments of population change should be based counts made at approximately the same time of year.

Method 3: Ideally repeated counts before mid April on North Sea coasts, or before late April off NW Scotland: i.e. in the pre-laying period. **Otherwise, make counts before June**, when substantial numbers of immatures begin to attend the colony. Numbers visible on land or close inshore are usually highest in the evenings or during foggy conditions, so try to make some counts at these times.

Appendix 1: Summary of prescribed counting periods and units

Species	Time of year	Time of day (BST)	Count Unit
Fulmar	Late May – early July (ideally June)	0900 – 1730	AOS
Manx Shearwater	Late May – early June	Day light	AOS
British Storm Petrel	Early July	Day light	AOS
Leach's Storm Petrel	Late June	Day light	AOS
Cormorant	Normally early May – late June (peak nesting period, repeated counts if possible)	Day light	AON
Shag	Normally late May – late June (peak nesting period, repeated counts if possible)	Day light	AON
Arctic & Great Skuas	Late May – mid July (preferably June)	Day light	AOT
Gulls (*Larus spp.*)	Late May – early June	Day light or 0900 – 1600 for vantage point counts and flush counts	AOT, AON or individuals (flush counts)
Kittiwake	Late May – mid June (repeated counts if possible)	Day light	AON
Terns	mid May – late June if repeated counts are possible, otherwise early – mid June	0800-1600 or preferably 1000-1200 if flush counts are used	AON or individuals (flush counts)
Guillemot & Razorbill	1st – 21st June	0800 - 1600	Individuals on suitable breeding ledges
Black guillemot	Late March – early May	first light - 0900	Individuals on sea and/or land
Puffin	Late April –mid May optimal (late April – early August is acceptable)	Day light	AOB or individuals on land & adjacent sea for cliff-nesters

AON = Apparently occupied nest; AOT = Apparently occupied territory; AOS = Apparently occupied site (includes burrows), AOB = Apparently occupied burrow.

Survey Sheet A

(Please refer to instructions and the example on page 4
before completing this form)

Site Name(s):	For office use only

County / Region etc:...

Principal Recorder's Name and Address:
....
....
....

Other Recorders Names & Addresses:
....
....
....
....
(continue on a separate sheet if necessary)

Site Data

COASTAL SITES: Please enter a row of information for every site or sub-section you have defined on your map. The grid references must match those of the boundaries on the map.

INLAND SITES: Please enter a row of information for every site. Give a single grid reference for the centre of each colony, under column: *'Grid Start'*. Ignore column: *'Site Rel'*.

Site/sub-section Name	*Site Code*	Grid Start	Grid End	#Site Rel	‡Pred Key	†Habitat Code			
						1	2	3	4

*Site Code:
Enter a code of your choosing for each site (no more than 4 characters) and use these site codes to form the basis of the sample codes on Sheets B & C; eg. Fowlsheugh (see mapping example) may have 4 subsections called FH1....FH4.

†Habitat Codes: please enter up to four of the habitat codes listed on the back of this sheet. Please only enter codes for habitats that are actually occupied by breeding seabirds. Enter each relevant code in a separate column in order of importance to the birds.

#Site Rel = the relationship between each site/sub-section and the previous one listed on the table, described by the codes below: **NB. for coastal sections only.**
ADJ = Adjacent sites
GAP = Gap between this and previous site
OVL = Overlapping with previous site
CON = Contained by previous site

‡Pred Key = Predators: 0 = absent, 1 = present, 2 = don't know, 3 = not checked.
If you entered either 0, 1 or 2, please enter details on the back of this form of how you checked for predators and what evidence of presence (if any) you found

Please now use SHEET B to enter details of each visit you made to each site/sub-section you have described above.

Habitat Codes

Please choose upto four categories (denoted by a letter) and corresponding sub-categories (denoted by a number) to describe the habitat of each site/sub-section listed overleaf. Please note that for rocky coastlines, a 'coastal' (i.e. H) category should be entered in the first habitat column overleaf and 'rock type' (category I) should be entered in second the column eg. an open cliff site would be denoted as **H1, I1.**

C – Semi-natural grassland & marsh: 1. Chalk downland; **2.** Grass moor; **3.** Grass moor mixed with heather; **4.** Machair; **5.** Other dry grassland; **6.** Water-meadow/grazing marsh; **7.** Reed swamp; **8.** Other open marsh; **9.** Saltmarsh.

D – Heathland & bogs: 1. Dry heath; **2.** Wet heath; **3.** Mixed wet/dry heath; **4.** Bog; **5.** Breckland; **6.** Drained bog.

E – Farmland: 1. Apparently improved grassland; **2.** Apparently unimproved grassland; **3.** Mixed grass/tilled land; **4.** Tilled land; **5.** Orchard; **6.** Other farming.

F. – Human Sites: 1. Urban: **a)** building, **b)** other structure; **2.** Suburban: **a)** building, **b)** other structure; **3.** Rural: **a)** building, **b)** other structure.

G – Water Bodies (freshwater): 1. Pond (less than 50m_); **2.** Small water body (50 – 450m_); **3.** Lake/unlined reservoir; **4.** Lined reservoir; **5.** Gravel pit, sand pit etc.; **6.** Stream (less than 3m wide); **7.** River (more than 3m wide); **8.** Ditch with water (less than 2m wide); **9.** Small canal (2-5m wide); **10.**large canal (more than 5m wide); **11.** Island (also give the type of water body)

H – Coastal: 1. Marine – open shore; **2.** marine – inlet/cove/loch; **3.** Estuarine; **4.** Brackish lagoon; **5.** Sand dune. **6.** Offshore island.

I – Rock type: 1. Open cliff; **2.** Geo; **3.** Cave; **4.** Boulder Beach; **5.** Scree/boulder slope; **6.** Quarry; **7.** Other rock outcrop; **8.** Mine/spoil/slag heap; **9.** Coastal sloping rock platform.

Predators

What measures did you take to assess the presence or absence of predators at each site or sub-section you visited?...
....
....

Please enter in the table below the species of predator found to be present and the evidence you used to ascertain presence (e.g. you saw it, scats, footprints, prey remains etc.).

Site/sub-section code	Species Present	Evidence

Survey Sheet B

(Please refer to instructions and the example on page 5 before completing this form)

Enter a row of information for every separate occasion you visit each site/sub-section during your survey.

SAMPLE CODE#	Date	Time start	Time End	VISIT REL*	METH†	Weather‡			
						Visib-ility	Sea State	Rain	Wind

#Sample codes = site code from sheet A plus a forward slash (/) and a letter corresponding to each separate visit. Eg. two visits to each of four sub-sections of Fowlsheugh (see sheet A) would use sample codes of FH1/A, FH1/B,.......FH4/A, FH4/B.

†Method Codes:
please see overleaf for key.
NB. Do not enter more than one method code per visit. If more than one method was used, enter a separate visit for each method used.

‡Weather Codes:
Visibility: 1 = good, 2 = fair, 3 = poor
Sea State: 1 = flat calm, 2 = small waves, 3 = large waves, 4 = white wave crests, 5. = waves breaking high onto rocks.
Rain: 1 = none, 2 = discontinuous light, 3 = discontinuous heavy, 4. Continuous light, 5 = continuous heavy.
Wind (Beaufort scale): 0, 1, 2, 3, 4, >4

*VISIT REL = the relationship between duplicate visits to the same site/sub-section (use the codes given below):
+ = Different part of the site/sub-section counted on this visit, so these counts must be added to other visits to arrive at the correct total count for this site/sub-section.
REC = Re-count for some or all species, which should supercede those from previous visit(s). Use the back of the form to mark very clearly which species this applies to, with clear reference to the sample codes.

Please now use SHEET C to enter the counts made during each visit you have described above.

Method Codes:

Please refer to the instructions for the appropriate count units to use for each method.

1 = Fulmar, shag, cormorant, kittiwake, guillemot, razorbill and cliff- nesting puffins or gulls:
  1.1.= sea-based counts
  1.2 = land-based counts
2 = Puffins (NB. If the following methods are used to count puffins, then please also send all raw count data with your recording forms):
  2.1 = whole colony counts of AOBs
  2.2 = sample quadrats counts of AOBs
  2.3 = sample transects counts of AOBs
  2.4 = other (please provide full details of the methods used)
3 = Gulls (except cliff-nesters and kittiwakes):
  3.1 = counts from vantage point
  3.2 = sample quadrats counts of AONs
  3.3 = transect counts of AONs
  3.4 = flush counts of individuals
  3.5 = Aerial counts
4 = Terns
  4.1 = counts from a vantage point

  4.2 = foot-based counts of AONs from within colony
  4.3 = flush counts of individuals
5 = Skuas:
  5.1 = counts of AOTs from a vantage point
  5.2 = walked transect counts of AOTs
6 = Black guillemots:
  6.1 = sea-based counts of individuals
  6.2 = land-based counts of individuals
7 = Manx shearwaters (please provide full details of the methods used):
  7.1 = ascertained presence/absence of AOS
  7.2 = count of AOSs using tape-playback
  7.3 = counts occupied burrows (using visible signs of use)
8 = Storm Petrel & Leach's Petrel (please provide full details of the methods used):
  8.1 = ascertained presence/absence of AOS
  8.2 = count of AOSs using tape-playback

If you entered 'REC' in the 'Visit Rel' column overleaf, please enter in the table below the species and sample code for the count which should surpercede all previous counts for that species in that particular site/sub-section.

Sample code	Species	Sample code	Species

Survey Sheet C

(Please refer to instructions and the example on page 7 before completing this form)

Please see overleaf for key to species, Acc and Unit codes.

seabird 2000

seabird 2000

SPECIES CODE	Sample Code:			Sample Code:			Sample Code:			Sample Code:		
	Acc	COUNT	Unit	Acc	COUNT	Unit	Acc	COUNT	Unit	Acc	COUNT	Unit

SPECIES CODE	Sample Code:			Sample Code:			Sample Code:			Sample Code:		
	Acc	COUNT	Unit	Acc	COUNT	Unit	Acc	COUNT	Unit	Acc	COUNT	Unit

Species Codes:

FUL	Fulmar
MX	Manx Shearwater
SP	European Storm-petrel
LP	Leach's Storm-petrel
GAN	Northern Gannet
COR	Great Cormorant
SCR	*sinensis* Cormorant
CCR	*carbo* cormorant
SH	Shag
ASK	Arctic Skua
BX	Great Skua / Bonxie
MEG	Mediterranean Gull
BHG	Black-headed Gull
CG	Common Gull
LB	Lesser Black-backed Gull
YLG	Yellow-legged Gull
HG	Herring Gull
GB	Great Black-backed Gull
KIT	Kittiwake
SAT	Sandwich Tern
ROT	Roseate Tern
COT	Common Tern
ART	Arctic Tern
LIT	Little Tern
GUI	Common Guillemot
RAZ	Razorbill
TYS	Black Guillemot / Tystie
PUF	Atlantic Puffin

Accuracy Codes:

ACC	Accurate Count
EST	Estimated Count
HID	Estimate of hidden birds
UCL	Upper 95% confidence limit
LCL	Lower 95% confidence limit

Unit Codes:

AON	Apparently Occupied Nests
AOS	Apparently Occupied Sites
AOT	Apparently Occupied Territory
AOB	Apparently Occupied Burrow
IND	Individuals on land at colony
SEA	Inidividuals on sea adjacent to colony
AIR	Individuals flying over colony (NB. Puffins only)

Black Guillemot/Tystie Codes

PLU	Individuals with plumage other than that of a full adult (i.e. largely or partly grey, or with dark bars visible in white wing-patch).
FED	Feeding birds
FAR	Birds seen >300m offshore

Appendix II:
Techniques for estimating the response rates of storm-petrels and Manx Shearwaters to tape playback

As detailed in the chapters on European and Leach's Storm-petrels and Manx Shearwaters, the predominant method for surveying all three species during Seabird 2000 was tape playback. This involved eliciting calls from incubating adult storm-petrels or shearwaters by playing recordings of conspecific calls during the day in the vicinity of their subterranean nests. A response to playback was assumed to equate to an apparently occupied site (AOS). However, not all European and Leach's Storm-petrels and Manx Shearwaters will respond to tape playback during a single playing. Therefore it was necessary to determine what proportion of birds responded during a playback survey to ensure that the number of AOSs at a colony was not underestimated. The number of AOSs was estimated by multiplying the total number of responses to playback by the reciprocal of the response rate (equation 1).

$$\text{Number of AOSs} = \text{number of responses} * (1 / \text{response rate}) \qquad \text{Equation 1}$$

During Seabird 2000 we adopted Ratcliffe *et al.*'s (1998e) method for determining response rate in European Storm-petrels, which is equally applicable to Leach's Storm-petrels and Manx Shearwaters (see Gilbert *et al.*, 1998a). This involves establishing a calibration plot within the colony. European Storm-petrels nesting in different habitats (e.g. boulder beaches, cracks in peat) can respond at differing rates (Ratcliffe *et al.*, 1998e), making it advisable to set up plots in habitat typical of the rest of the colony. During a survey of European Storm-petrels on Priest Island, Mayhew *et al.* (2000) set up separate calibration plots for the four different habitat types in which storm-petrels were nesting, i.e. boulder beach, stone walls and heath/grassland. It is unknown if Leach's Storm-petrels and Manx Shearwaters show differing response rates in different habitats.

In order to measure response rate within the calibration plot, repeated tape playback surveys were conducted on successive days. Each day, the positions of newly responding birds (i.e. = 1 AOS) were marked. The size of the plot was determined by the density of nesting petrels or shearwaters, in that it was large enough for 20–30 response to be elicited on the first visit. Thus, the size of plots varied between species and between colonies. Playback was conducted in the plot on subsequent consecutive days until no new AOSs were found. Thus, if a total of 60 AOSs was found after repeated visits to the plot and 20 birds responded on the first visit, the response rate on the first day would equate to 20/60 = 0.33 (or 33%). The number of responses obtained from a survey of the whole colony would therefore need to be multiplied by 1/0.33 = 3, in order to estimate the number of AOSs in the colony. The calibration plot more realistically represents the overall playback survey where the number of burrows and attendance rate are both unknown at the start of the survey.

Unfortunately, finding all the occupied burrows in a calibration plot can take more than five days and visits of such duration are impractical on some islands. An insufficient number of visits to a study plot will produce an overestimate of response rate, which will lead to an underestimate, of an unknown quantity, in the number of AOS in the whole colony. In cases where an insufficient number of visits were made to a calibration plot a curve was fitted to a plot of the cumulative number of burrows found on each visit (Fig. 1). The curve reaches an asymptote at the total number of burrows in the plot and has a slope equal to the response rate. This technique allows 95% confidence limits to be attached to the estimate of response rate (Mayhew *et al.*, 2000).

For each calibration plot, an asymptotic regression model was fitted to the cumulative number of responses on each visit. The model took the form of equation 2 and the parameters *a* and *b* were predicted using the iterative regression function of S-Plus(r) 2000 (Mathsoft Inc., Seattle, Washington).

$$y = a(1 - e^{-b})$$ Equation 2

where *y* = number of AOSs detected on a given visit (x); *b* = the exponential (e) proportional rate of increase to the asymptote (*a*).

Thus, the coefficient *a* is an estimate of the total number of AOSs present in the study plot. The coefficient *a* is either equal to or greater than the number of AOSs actually found during the calibration sampling, depending on how many visits were made to the calibration plot (i.e. the more visits, the more likely that all AOSs will be detected). The response rate (i.e. the proportion of the total population detected on the first visit) was calculated by substituting the values of the coefficients for *b* into equation 3:

$$1 - e^{-b}$$ Equation 3

The upper and lower 95% confidence intervals of the response rate were determined from the equations 4 and 5 respectively:

$$1 - e^{-b-(se*1.96)}$$ Equation 4

$$1 - e^{-b+(se*1.96)}$$ Equation 5

where *se* is the standard error of the estimate of the coefficient *b*.

Alternatively, the curve can be easily straightened using a reciprocal transformation of both axes (i.e. y axis = 1/number of responses; x axis = 1/visit number) and the reciprocal of the intercept on the y axis is the estimate of the asymptote (Fowler, 2001).

Counting the number of responses in a colony can also be prone to error in terms of making sure that all birds likely to respond to the tape within the survey area actually hear the tape and that the surveyor hears the response. Gilbert *et al.* (1998a) recommended playing the tape within 1 m of potential burrows for 30 seconds. However, experience suggests, if a bird hears the tape and is going to respond, it will do so immediately. It is much more crucial to ensure the bird hears the tape and that the surveyor hears the response. Detection rate by the bird and, in turn, the surveyor, are both likely to vary in different habitats based upon depth of burrow, thickness of vegetation, depth of boulder beach etc. Distance sampling techniques (Buckland *et al.*, 2001) would be a useful tool in determining the optimum distance from potential burrows that taped calls should be played in different habitats.

Appendix III:
Common and scientific names of organisms referred to in the text

Birds

Carrion Crow *Corvus corone*
Common Raven *Corvus corax*
Golden Eagle *Aquila chrysaetos*
Kelp Gull *Larus dominicanus*
Kestrel *Falco tinnunculus*
Little Owl *Athene noctua*
Oystercatcher *Haematopus ostralegus*
Slaty-backed Gull *Larus schistisagus*

Mammals

American Mink *Mustela vison*
Arctic Fox *Alopex lagopus*
Badger *Meles meles*
Black Rat *Rattus rattus*
Brown Rat *Rattus norvegicus*
European Rabbit *Oryctolagus cuniculus*
Feral Dog *Canis lupus familiaris*
Feral/Domestic Cat *Felis catus*
Ferret *Mustela furo*
Polecat *Mustela putorius*
Red Deer *Cervus elaphus*
Red Fox *Vulpes vulpes*
Sable *Martes zibellina*
Sheep *Ovis aries*
Skunk *Mephitis* sp.
Stoat *Mustela erminea*

Fish

Butterfish *Pholis gunnellus*
Capelin *Mallotus villosus*
Cod *Gadus morhua*
Haddock *Melanogrammus aeglefinus*
Herring *Clupea harengus*
Lesser Sandeel *Ammodytes marinus*
Saithe/Coley *Pollachius virens*
Sprat *Sprattus sprattus*
Whiting *Merlangius merlangus*

Crustaceans

Goose-barnacle *Lepas anatifera*

Molluscs

Common Squid *Loligo vulgaris*

Plants

Bracken *Pteridium aquilinum*
Gorse *Ulex* sp.
Heather *Calluna vulgaris*
Nettle *Urtica dioica*
Ragwort *Senecio spp*
Rock Sea Spurrey *Spergularia rupicola*
Sea Campion *Silene maritima*
Tree-mallow *Lavatera arborea*

Appendix IV:
Numbers of seabirds breeding in Britain and Ireland in 1998–2002

N.B. Figures refer to pairs of all species except for Razorbills, Common Guillemots and Black Guillemots, where numbers of individuals birds are given

Species	Scotland	England	Isle of Man	Channel Islands	Wales	Northern Ireland	Republic of Ireland	Great Britain, Isle of Man and Channel Islands total	All-Ireland total
Northern Fulmar	485,852	6,291	3,147	317	3,474	5,992	32,918	499,081	38,910
Manx Shearwater	126,545	367	34	10	168,133	4,633	32,545	295,089	37,178
European Storm-petrel	21,370	1,475	0	60	2,805	0	99,065	25,710	99,065
Leach's Storm-petrel	48,047	0	0	0	0	0	310	48,047	310
Northern Gannet	187,363	2,552	0	5,950	30,688	0	32,758	226,553	32,758
Great Cormorant	3,626	2,896	134	115	1,699	663	4,548	8,470	5,211
European Shag	21,487	3,863	912	1,403	914	301	3,426	28,579	3,727
Arctic Skua	2,136	0	0	0	0	0	0	2,136	0
Great Skua	9,634	0	0	0	0	0	1	9,634	1
Mediterranean Gull	0	108	0	0	0	2	3	108	5
Black-headed Gull	43,191	82,728	2	0	1,986	10,107	3,876	127,907	13,983
Common Gull	48,113	44	6	0	0	557	1,060	48,163	1,617
Lesser Black-backed Gull	25,057	64,208	114	1,734	20,722	1,973	2,876	111,835	4,849
Herring Gull	72,130	45,365	7,126	4,347	13,974	714	5,521	142,942	6,235
Great Black-backed Gull	14,776	1,476	405	310	427	76	2,243	17,394	2,319
Black-legged Kittiwake	282,213	76,281	1,045	3	7,293	13,060	36,100	366,835	49,160
Sandwich Tern	1,068	9,018	0	0	450	1,954	1,762	10,536	3,716
Roseate Tern	14	36	0	0	2	4	734	52	738
Common Tern	4,784	4,676	0	174	674	1,704	2,485	10,308	4,189
Arctic Tern	47,306	3,602	8	0	1,705	767	2,735	52,621	3,502
Little Tern	331	1,521	20	0	75	0	206	1,947	206
Common Guillemot	1,167,841	91,986	4,566	476	57,961	98,546	138,108	1,322,830	236,654
Razorbill	139,186	11,144	1,524	65	12,638	27,446	25,980	164,557	51,530
Black Guillemot	37,505	7	602	0	28	1,174	3,367	38,142	4,541
Atlantic Puffin	493,042	75,734	85	311	10,328	1,610	19,641	579,500	21,251

Index of species

Alca torda 351, 364–376, 393, 404, 408, 415
Auk, Great 413
Auk, Little 433

Badger 323

Cat, Domestic 32, 74, 78, 79, 97, 109–110, 113, 351, 388, 403, 419
Cattle, Domestic 338
Cepphus grille 375, 393, 408, 417
Cod 257
Cormorant, Great 24, 29, 32–34, 36, 43, 128–145, 148, 155, 414
  Introduction 128
  Census methods 129
  Current status and trends 131
  Causes of change 140
  International context 143
Crow, Carrion 345

Deer, Red 77
Dog, Domestic 113, 338, 345

Eagle, Golden 77
Eagle, White-tailed Sea 420

Ferret 77, 403
Fox, Red 61, 113, 210, 257, 258, 297, 316, 323, 324, 336, 345, 346, 351, 419
Fratercula arctica 374, 392–406, 417, 420, 428
Fulmarus glacialis 49–62, 351, 373, 416, 420
Fulmar, Northern 29, 34, 37, 49–62, 108, 125, 185, 351, 373, 416, 420
  Introduction 49
  Census Methods 52
  Current status and trends 52
  Causes of change 57
  International context 61

Gannet, Northern 32, 115–127, 183–184, 239, 257, 357, 414, 416
  Introduction 115
  Census methods 116
  Current status and trends 120
  Causes of change 124
  International context 126

Guillemot, Black 23, 28–29, 33–34, 36–37, 40–42, 47, 375, 393, 408, 417
  Introduction 377
  Census methods 378
  Current status and trends 381
  Causes of change 386
  International context 389
Guillemot, Common 23, 29, 34, 37, 116, 125, 171, 350–363, 365, 373, 375, 404
  Introduction 350
  Census methods 351
  Current status and trends 352
  Causes of change 359
  International context 362
Gull, Black-headed 189, 196–213, 224, 248, 255, 298, 414, 417, 420, 427, 429
  Introduction 196
  Census methods 197
  Current status and trends 199
  Causes of change 210
  International context 212
Gull, Common 214–225, 248, 417, 429
  Introduction 214
  Census methods 215
  Current status and trends 216
  Causes of change 223
  International context 224
Gull, Great Black-backed 29, 77, 110, 185, 239, 263–276, 248, 255, 257, 404, 414, 419, 420
  Introduction 263
  Census methods 265
  Current status and trends 265
  Causes of change 273
  International context 276
Gull, Herring 25, 110, 113, 235, 237, 239–240, 242–262, 265, 273, 311, 324, 357, 375, 404, 414, 420, 421, 426, 429
  Introduction 242
  Census methods 243
  Current status and trends 248
  Causes of change 255
  International context 260
Gull, Lesser Black-backed 110, 226–241, 243, 248, 255, 258, 265, 273, 404, 414, 420, 425
  Introduction 226
  Census methods 227

Gull, Lesser Black-backed—*cont'd*
  Current status and trends 228
  Causes of change 237
  International context 240
Gull, Mediterranean 25, 187–195, 414
  Introduction 187
  Census methods 188
  Current status and trends 189
  Causes of change 192
  International context 193
Gull, Slaty-backed 109
Gull, Yellow-legged 25,97, 254, 255, 260, 261, 42 5

Hedgehog 345
Hydrobates pelagicus 417, 420

Kestrel 345, 346, 420
Kittiwake, Black-legged 29, 34, 160, 171, 185,
    277–290, 351, 357, 361, 365, 373, 374, 400,
    419, 422, 423
  Introduction 277
  Census methods 278
  Current status and trends 279
  Causes of change 285
  International context 289

Larus argentatus 262, 265, 273, 311, 324, 357, 375,
    404, 414, 420, 421, 426, 429
Larus canus 248, 417, 429
Larus fuscus 243, 248, 255, 258, 265, 273, 404, 414,
    420, 425
Larus marinus 263–276, 248, 255, 257, 404, 414, 419,
    420
Larus melanocephalus 414
Larus ridibundus 248, 255, 298, 414, 417, 420, 427, 429

Magpie 345
Mink, American 61, 109, 157, 210–211, 224, 238,
    257, 273, 297, 316, 323, 324, 326, 329, 336,
    338, 351, 375, 388, 389, 405, 417, 441
Morus bassanus 257, 357, 414, 416

Oceanodroma leucorhoa 417, 419
Otter 210, 323
Owl, Barn 314
Owl, Little 97, 420

Peregrine 311
Pig, Domestic 260, 428
Phalacrocorax aristotelis 257, 373, 374
Phalacrocorax carbo 414
Puffin, Atlantic 23, 28–29, 32, 34, 37, 43, 49, 64, 66,
    78, 83, 95, 96, 102, 104, 125, 171, 185, 274,
    374, 392–406, 417, 419, 420, 428
  Introduction 392
  Census methods 393
  Current status and trends 395

Causes of change 400
International context 405
Puffinus puffinus 63–80, 274, 394, 417, 421

Rabbit 64, 66, 86, 94, 96, 184, 257, 274, 394, 400
Rat, Black 77, 404
Rat, Brown 74, 76–77, 109, 113, 297, 311, 323, 336,
    375, 403, 404, 417, 441
Raven, Common 351
Razorbill 23, 29, 34, 37, 171, 351,364–376, 393, 404,
    408, 415
  Introduction 364
  Census methods 365
  Current status and trends 367
  Causes of change 373
  International context 375
Rissa tridactyla 277–290, 351, 357, 361, 365, 373, 374,
    400

Sable 113
Sandeel 157, 169, 171, 184–185, 277, 287, 288, 298,
    310, 329, 334, 335, 350, 373, 374, 386, 400,
    423, 424, 425, 426
Shag, European 29, 34, 43, 146–159, 257, 373, 374,
    422
  Introduction 146
  Census methods 147
  Current status and trends 148
  Causes of change 155
  International context 158
Shearwater, Manx 23–24, 29, 31–32, 34, 37, 40–42,
    63–80, 81, 83, 95, 98, 101–103, 274, 394, 417, 421
  Introduction 63
  Census methods 64
  Current status and trends 68
  Causes of change 76
  International Context 79
Sheep, Domestic 96–97, 104, 400
Skua, Arctic 40, 47, 160–172, 414, 419, 424, 428
  Introduction 160
  Census methods 161
  Causes of change 169
  International context 171
Skua, Great 40, 78, 97, 109–110, 113, 160–161,
    169–171, 173–186, 239, 257, 274, 275, 286,
    288, 325, 402, 408, 409, 413, 414, 416, 419,
    420, 424, 425, 428, 437
  Introduction 173
  Census methods 174
  Current status and trends 176
  Causes of change 181
  International context 185
Skunk 113
Stercorarius parasiticus 414, 419, 424, 428
Stercorarius skua 257, 274, 275, 286, 288, 325, 402,
    408, 409, 413, 414, 416, 419, 420, 424, 425,
    428, 437

Sterna albifrons 339–349, 414, 420, 429
Sterna dougallii 302–314, 408, 409, 414, 420, 435
Sterna hirundo 255, 304, 315–327, 329, 330, 336, 337, 417, 429
Sterna paradisaea 304, 316, 317, 320, 325, 326, 328–338, 340, 374, 400, 417, 424
Sterna sandvicensis 291–301, 304, 317, 408
Stoat 323, 375, 388
Storm-petrel, European 24, 29, 31, 34, 40, 66, 81–100, 101–104, 110,-111, 417, 420
  Introduction 81
  Census methods 82
  Factors controlling distribution and numbers 96
  International context 98
Storm-petrel, Leach's 24, 29, 34, 40, 66, 81, 84, 96–97, 101–114, 417, 419
  Introduction 101
  Census methods 102
  Current status and trends 104
  Factors controlling distribution and numbers 109
  International context 112

Tern, Arctic 47, 160, 171, 304, 316, 317, 320, 325, 326, 328–338, 340, 374, 400, 417, 424
  Introduction 328
  Census methods 329
  Current status and trends 330
  Causes of change 334

  International context 337
Tern, Common 47, 255, 304, 315–327, 329, 330, 336, 337, 417, 422, 429
  Introduction 315
  Census methods 316
  Current status and trends 320
  Causes of change 323
  International context 325
Tern, Little 339–349, 414, 420, 429
  Introduction 339
  Census methods 340
  Current status and trends 341
  Causes of change 345
  International context 347
Tern, Roseate 302–314, 408, 409, 414, 420, 435
  Introduction 302
  Census methods 303
  Current status and trends 304
  Causes of change 309
  International context 312
Tern, Sandwich 291–301, 304, 317, 408
  Introduction 291
  Census methods 292
  Current status and trends 293
  Causes of change 297
  International context 299

Uria aalge 350–363, 365, 373, 375, 404